THE BIG BOOK OF ANSWERS

EDITED BY KEVIN S. HILE

VISIBLE INK PRESS

This 2015 edition printed for Barnes & Noble, Inc. by Visible Ink Press.

Managing Editor: Kevin Hile
Indexer: Lawrence W. Baker
Typesetting: Marco Di Vita

Visible Ink Press
43311 Joy Road #414
Canton, MI 48187

ISBN: 978-1-4351-1656-6

Printed and bound in the United States of America

10 9 8 7 6 5 4

Contents

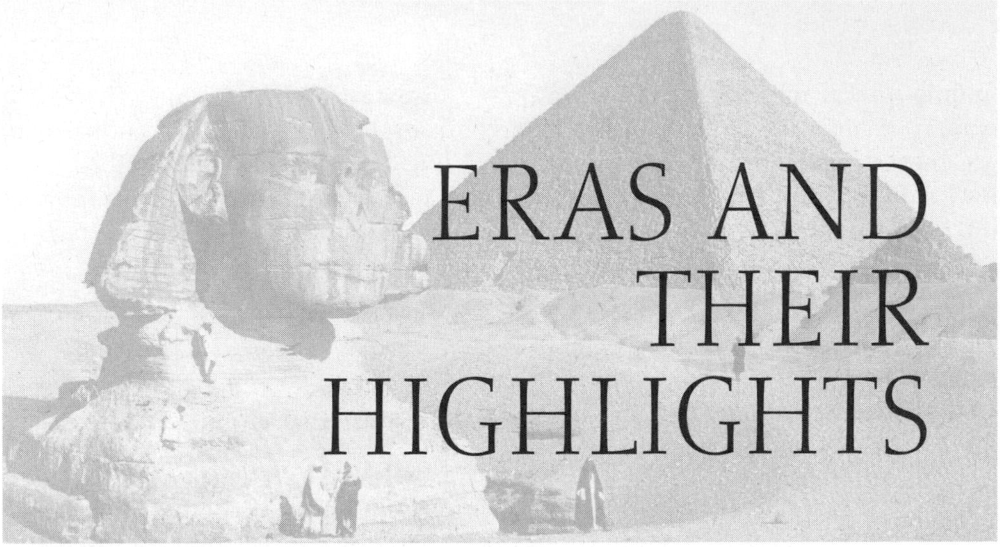

ERAS AND THEIR HIGHLIGHTS

When did **history begin**?

History began when human beings were able to document events in writing; anything prior to the advent of writing is commonly referred to as prehistoric. Humans began to write approximately 3,500 years before Christ, and the Classical Age, which began with the rise of Greek civilization (c. 2000 B.C.), is considered the beginning of history.

PREHISTORIC ERA: 2,000,000 TO 2000 B.C.

What is the **Prehistoric era**?

The term *Prehistoric era* refers to the time before written history began, so it encompasses the Stone Age (Paleolithic and Neolithic ages), the Bronze Age, and the Iron Age. The Prehistoric era spans the time from about 2,000,000 B.C. to roughly 2000 B.C., when the Classical Age began with the rise of the Greek and Roman empires.

What is **Neanderthal Man**?

The term refers to a hominid who walked the Earth in the Middle Paleolithic Age (during the Old Stone Age). The term *hominid* refers to an upright-walking primate that is an extinct ancestor to man. A hominid can be an ancestor of "true" man (modern man) or a relative, such as a modern primate. (In this context, the term *man* is used to refer to both males and females of the genus *Homo*.)

Neanderthal Man was discovered in 1856 near Düsseldorf, Germany, when workers came across the skull and skeletal remains of what appeared to be a human. The finding sparked discussion and controversy about the nature of the being. There were two arguments: the skull, markedly different from that of nineteenth-century man, was that of a pathologically deformed human being (an individual who was thought to have suffered from severe bone disease or some sort of congenital malformation); or, the skull belonged to an "early" man. This latter view was supported by the famous English naturalist Thomas Henry Huxley (1825-1895) in his book *Man's Place in Nature* (1863).

Another advocate for the argument that the skull belonged to an early man was French surgeon and anthropologist Paul Broca (1824-1880), who accepted Charles Darwin's (1809-1882) theory of evolution. In this light, Broca argued that the Neanderthal skull was a key to human evolution.

In 1886 two similar skeletons and some stone tools were found in Belgium. This discovery strengthened the argument of Huxley and Broca—that these remains actually belonged to man's early ancestors. Excavations from 1890 to 1892 on the island of Java (in Southeast Asia) furthered the argument and, for the most part, settled the controversy: A number of fossil remains were found in the banks along the Solo River. Named *Pithecanthropus erectus* by their discoverer, Dutch paleontologist Marie Eugène F. T. Dubois (1858-1940), the findings were popularly known as Java Man.

Subsequent findings, including that of the so-called Peking Man in the summer of 1923 in China, produced evidence that approximately 70,000 to 11,000 years ago there were groups of the Neanderthal race in Europe, western Asia, and northern Africa. At some point they disappeared and were replaced by another type of man; the cause of this disappearance is unknown.

When did **humankind first walk on** the face of the **Earth**?

For decades after the discovery of "Lucy" (in the 1970s), it was thought that humankind first walked the Earth about 3 million years ago. But fossil finds in the mid-1990s pushed the evolutionary start-point for humans to more than 4 million years ago. Further astonishing finds in the early 2000s led researchers to conclude that human ancestors first walked the Earth nearly 6 million years ago.

In November 1974 American Donald C. Johanson (1943-) made one of paleoanthropology's most widely publicized finds when he discovered a partial skeleton at Hadar, Ethiopia. More than 3 million years old, the female skeleton was the most complete hominid fossil ever found, but the skull was not recovered. The creature stood three and a half feet tall and, although apelike, had definitely walked upright. When Johanson officially announced his find in 1979, "Lucy" (named for the Beatles song "Lucy in the Sky with Diamonds," which was popular in the camp at the time the fossil was found) became known as the mother of all humankind. (Her sex was confirmed by the pelvic bones.) Since she was an erect-walker, the finding gave certainty to theories that hominids walked erect at 3 million years B.C.

After the discovery of Lucy, older hominid fossils were unearthed by researchers in the field. In 1994 anthropologist Meave Leakey (1942-) and her associates found fossils of a 4.1-million-year-old bipedal species near Lake Turkana, Kenya. These were designated *Australopithecus anamensis.* (Technically, the first fossils of the *Australopithecus anamensis* were discovered in 1965 by a Harvard expedition in Kenya, but they were not identified as such until later finds were made.) Also in 1994, University of California at Berkeley paleoanthropologist Tim White and an international team published their 1993 discovery of the fossils of a chimplike animal in Ethiopia; they classified it as *Ardipithecus ramidus.* These fossils were dated to nearly 4.4 million years ago. Fossils discovered between 1997 and 2001 in the Middle Awash region of Ethiopia were determined to be nearly 6 million years old. In 2001 Yohannes Haile-Selassie (Cleveland Museum) and coauthors Tim White and Gen Suwa (University of Tokyo Museum) reported the monumental findings in the journal *Nature*: The hominid named *Ardipithecus kadabba* was thought to "represent the first species on the human branch of the family tree just after the evolutionary split [from chimpanzees]."

What is the **Stone Age**?

What people commonly refer to as the Stone Age is actually two ages: The Old Stone Age (about 2,000,000 B.C. to about 10,000 B.C.) and the New Stone Age (c. 10,000 to c. 3300 B.C.). It was during these periods that humans used stone tools.

During the Old Stone Age, also called the Paleolithic Age, man was evolving from his apelike ancestors to modern-looking hunter-gatherers. Early modern man's progress continued to the end of the Old Stone Age, around 10,000 B.C. Then, as the Ice Age ended and the Earth warmed, the hunter-gatherers again revolutionized their way of life. They opted for a more settled existence in which they could exercise greater control over their food supplies. With the coming of the New Stone Age, or Neolithic Age, humans turned to agriculture.

The New Stone Age brought profound changes in the development of humans. Neolithic man learned to produce food rather than collect it. People were no longer dependent on hunting, fishing, and gathering wild fruit and nuts for subsistence. They learned to cultivate crops, domesticate animals, make pottery, weave textiles from fiber and hair, and produce more sophisticated tools and weapons by hammering, grinding, and polishing granite, jasper, and other hard stone. More substantial houses and communities, even fortified villages, came into being, laying the foundation for the great civilizations that would follow.

Near the end of the New Stone Age, craftsmen in the Middle East learned to make tools and weapons from metal. The world's earliest known manmade copper objects—beads, pins, and awls—were fabricated in Turkey and Iran around 8000 B.C. Archaeological evidence points to copper mining in the Balkans around 5000 B.C. From there the technology probably spread west, reaching the Alps about a thousand years later and marking the beginning of the Copper Age (c. 4000-2200 B.C.).

Was there really such a thing as the **Copper Age**?

Some texts do not refer to a Copper Age, moving directly from the Stone Age to the Bronze Age. In fact, the Copper Age (c. 4000-2200 B.C.) overlapped with both the end of the Old Stone Age (the Neolithic Age) and the Bronze Age and is marked by man's use of copper as a material for toolmaking.

What is the **Bronze Age**?

The Bronze Age (c. 3300-2500 B.C.) is the period of human culture when man began using bronze metal to make objects—principally, tools. The Neolithic Age slowly came to an end as various cultures in Eurasia that had depended on wood, stone, and bone for tools began to develop the techniques for metallurgy. Bronze proved to be an excellent material for making tools and weapons. People in the Middle East learned to produce bronze by mixing tin and copper (hence, the transition years between the Neolithic Age and the Bronze Age are sometimes referred to as the Copper Age). Bronze had considerable hardness, strength, and density, and it proved more reliable and durable than the stone, wood, and bone tools that had been in use. The Bronze Age lasted until the beginning of the Iron Age.

When did the **Iron Age** begin?

The real advent of the Iron Age came not with the discovery of metal (in about 2500 B.C.), but with the invention of the process of casing or steeling it, probably about 1500 B.C. This happened when it was learned that by repeatedly reheating wrought iron in a charcoal fire and then hammering it, it not only became harder than bronze but kept its hardness after long use. (Wrought iron was discovered accidentally when smiths found that by hammering the small beadlike pieces of iron left as a residue after smelting copper they could form the iron particles into a mass. This kind of wrought iron, however, was good only for decorative purposes, and for more than a thousand years after 2500 B.C., iron remained a precious ornamental metal. Bronze, which was harder and capable of being sharpened to a fine cutting edge, continued to be the metal for tools and weapons.)

The next technological improvement, which again meant a further hardening of the metal, was the process of quenching it, which involved repeatedly plunging the hot iron into cold water. It was only after this series of discoveries and inventions that the significant impact of iron on culture and civilization was appreciably felt.

Because bronze was scarce, it was also costly. Consequently, it was not until iron came into use that humans extended their control over nature. For this reason, iron has been called the "democratic metal." Widespread use of iron tools meant a general increase in living standards. For example, the use of iron axes brought about the clearing of forests, and therefore new land came under cultivation. Other significant devel-

During the Old Kingdom of ancient Egypt commerce prospered and the arts flourished, as evidenced by the Great Pyramids at Giza and the Great Sphinx.

opments included the application of iron tools to sheep shearing and cloth cutting, and the invention of the lathe, the most fundamental machine tool.

The Iron Age lasted until the beginning of the Classical Age (c. 2000 B.C.).

What were the **hallmarks of ancient Egypt**?

One of the world's oldest civilizations, ancient Egypt developed about 3000 B.C., or 5,000 years ago, in the Nile River valley; it lasted until 332 B.C., when it was conquered by Alexander the Great (356-323 B.C.). In that time, Egypt was ruled by 30 dynasties. Most of those dynasties fall into three kingdoms: Old Kingdom (during the third millennium B.C.), Middle Kingdom (early second millennium B.C.), and New Kingdom (mid-second millennium B.C.); the kingdoms were followed by intermediate periods, which were times of weakened government or foreign domination.

The First Dynasty was founded by Menes in 3110 B.C. after he united rival kingdoms of Upper and Lower Egypt under his rule and established the capital at Memphis (the present-day village of Mit Rahina, 14 miles south of Cairo, in northern Egypt). During the Old Kingdom commerce prospered and the arts flourished, as evidenced by the Great Pyramids at Giza (including the Great Sphinx), which were begun during the Fourth Dynasty (c. 2500 B.C.). The Old Kingdom was followed by a 258-year (intermediate) period of weak rulers and anarchy, which was ended when Amenemhet I rose to power in 1991 B.C., reunifying Egypt and beginning the Middle Kingdom. During the Middle Kingdom, Egypt launched imperialistic campaigns, expanding its territory and conquering Palestine and Syria in the east. About 1720 B.C., Semitic nomads entered Egypt and wrested power from the pharaohs, establishing the fifteenth through the seventeenth dynasties—a peaceful and prosperous period. But the Egyptians expelled this foreign influence (c. 1570) to establish the New Kingdom: the 200 years that followed were the height of Egyptian civilization, with the cities of Thebes and Memphis regarded as the political, commercial, and cultural centers of the known world.

Ancient Egyptians invented a calendar, created a form of hieroglyphic writing, and developed papyrus (paper made from the papyrus plant). Situated along the Nile and south of the Mediterranean Sea, Egyptians also produced early seagoing vessels. But it is their buildings for which this ancient group is renowned: In addition to the Great Pyramids at Giza, the impressive relics that have been discovered include those at Abu Simbel, where King Ramses II (c. 1250-? B.C.) had two temples built out of rock during his reign (1304-1237 B.C.); numerous ruins and tombs at Abydos; a complex of temples and shrines at Karnak (part of the site of ancient Thebes); and temples and other buildings at Luxor (also part of ancient Thebes).

During the last 700 years of ancient Egypt (c. 1085-332 B.C.), the kingdom increasingly came under foreign domination, which weakened it to the point that Alexander the Great (356-323 B.C.) was able to claim it without struggle in 332 B.C.

THE CLASSICAL AGE: 2000 B.C. TO A.D. 500

What is the **Classical Age**?

The Classical Age refers to the ancient Roman and Greek worlds, roughly 2000 B.C. to A.D. 500. The Classical Age followed the Prehistoric era and preceded the Middle Ages. During this period, the ancient Greeks and Romans made contributions to literature, philosophy, science, the arts, and letters that are still relevant today.

How did **Greek civilization** begin?

Ancient Greek civilization began with the Minoans. Europe's first advanced civilization, the Minoans were a prosperous and peaceful people who flourished on the Mediterranean island of Crete from about 3000 to 1450 B.C. The Minoans built structures from stone, plaster, and timbers; painted walls with brilliant frescoes; made pottery; wove and dyed cloth; cultivated the land (they are believed to be the first people to produce an agricultural surplus, which they exported); constructed stone roads and bridges; and built highly advanced drainage systems and aqueducts. (At Knossos, the royal family had a system for showers and even had toilets that could be flushed.) Minoans were a sophisticated people who loved music and dance, games and entertainment.

What is the **Mycenaean Age**?

The Minoans were either conquered by or succeeded by the Mycenaeans, who were mainland Greeks: In about 1450 B.C., Crete was struck by a 200-foot tsunami (or seismic wave), which is thought to either have completely destroyed the island or to have weakened it to a point that it could be overtaken. The Mycenaeans flourished from about 1650 B.C. to 1200 B.C., a time known as the Mycenaean Age, carrying forth the culture and skills they had learned from the Minoans (who had been their neighbors). The Mycenaeans were skilled horsemen, charioteers, and accomplished sailors who ruled the Aegean. Mycenaean culture revolved around its fortified palaces, called *acropolises* (top cities). Its cities included Argos, Corinth, Sparta, and the then-small cities of Athens and Thebes.

In about 1200 B.C. the Mycenaeans attacked the city of Troy, which was considered the key to the profitable Black Sea trade, thus launching the Trojan War. After 10 years of fighting (a period that is recounted by Greek poet Homer [c. 850-? B.C.] in the *Iliad*), the Mycenaeans were victorious. But soon their period of triumph ended as the Dorian peoples (from the northwestern part of the Greek mainland) overran most of the Peloponnesus (the southern peninsula of Greece). The Dorians, aided by the superiority of the iron sword, flooded southward, where they sacked and burned the great Mycenaean cities and conquered the wealthy sea traders, throwing Greece into the period known as the Dark Ages, or Archaic Period, which lasted from 1100 to about 800 B.C.

What were the **Dark Ages** of ancient Greece?

After the Dorians conquered the Mycenaeans in 1100 B.C., these nomadic peoples thrust Greece into a period of decline that lasted more than 300 years. The Dorians rejected the life of the great Mycenaean cities in favor of their nomadic shepherding and hunting life. A tribal people, they possessed a harsh sense of justice, and the period was marked by feuds between clans. Men typically carried weapons—now made of iron (it was the Dorians who brought the new, more durable metal from the north, ending the Bronze Age in Greece).

During this Dark Age, there is little evidence of Greek civilization; the script used by the Mycenaeans disappeared, and art, which had prospered during the Mycenaean Age, declined. Under Dorian rule numerous Mycenaean cities were abandoned, and many regions and islands seem to have been depopulated. There is no evidence of trade with other countries. Poverty had overtaken the Greeks.

As the Dorians took possession of the Greek mainland, a few Mycenaean communities survived in remote areas. Many Mycenaeans fled eastward to Athens, which became a haven for those who hoped for a return to the former civilization. Other Mycenaeans crossed the Aegean and settled on the coast of Asia Minor. Most of these refugees spoke Ionian Greek.

A lasting legacy of the Dark Ages of Greece is its mythology. As Ionian Greeks attempted to hold on to the refined civilization of the Bronze Age, they commemorated the greatness of the past in song and verse, including Greek poet Homer's (c. 850-? B.C.) *Iliad* and *Odyssey*. These epics were combined with eighth-century poet Hesiod's *Theogony*, an account of the creation of the universe and the generations of the gods, to give rise to a new Greek religion based on the god Zeus and 11 other gods who were believed to reside on Mount Olympus in northeastern Greece. The Greek gods were later adopted by the Romans and given different names.

What was the **golden age** of ancient Greece?

It is the period of classical Greek civilization that followed the so-called Dark Ages of Greece, which came to an end about 800 B.C. Over time the Dorians had become more settled, and they gradually revived trade and culture on mainland Greece. The self-governing city-state (*polis*) evolved, including the military center of Sparta and Athens, which became a center for the arts, education, and democracy. This was the beginning of the great Hellenic period of classical Greek civilization. Greek civilization reached its height in Athens during the mid-400s B.C., a period of outstanding achievement known as the Golden Age.

What are the hallmarks of **classical Greek civilization**?

The classical Greeks, who called themselves the Hellenes and their land Hellas, influenced western civilization more than any other people. Their contributions to every field of endeavor remain with us today, more than 2,000 years later.

Greek thought shaped science, medicine, philosophy, art, literature, architecture and engineering, mathematics, music, drama, language, and politics. The classical Greeks believed in individual freedom, reasoning, and truth, and that everything should be done in moderation. They also held that people should find time for both work and play and should balance the life of the mind with the exercise of the body.

The knowledge that became the Greek legacy had its beginnings in the settlements established in Asia Minor (the peninsula between the Black Sea and the Mediterranean, and which today is occupied by Turkey) after the Dorians invaded the Greek mainland. The Phoenician alphabet, an early alphabet developed by Semitic

The Parthenon, seen at the top of the Acropolis, in Athens, Greece, was constructed between 447 and 432 B.C.

peoples in the ancient maritime country of Phoenicia (present-day western Syria and Lebanon), was acquired by the Greeks, who adapted it to their language. They began using it to record Greek poet Homer's (c. 850-? B.C.) oral epics (*Iliad* and *Odyssey*) and the works of other Greek poets and historians.

Among the great Greek philosophers are Socrates, Plato, and Aristotle. Greek literature includes the epic poetry of Homer as well as the passionate love poems of Sappho. The Greeks gave humankind the tragedies of Aeschylus, Sophocles, and Euripides, which continue to be studied by students today, along with the comedies of Aristophanes and Menander. The classical Greeks loved to speak, and oratory is considered by some to be their highest form of prose. Orators known to the modern world are Antiphon, Lysias, Isocrates, and Demosthenes.

Herodotus, called the "father of history," left the modern world with an account of the Persian Wars (500-449 B.C.), a conflict between the Greek city-states and the Persian Empire. The Greeks also gave humankind the "father of medicine" in physician Hippocrates, who taught that doctors should use reason to determine the cause of illness and should study the patient's appearance, behavior, and lifestyle to diagnose and treat. (The "Hippocratic Oath," versions of which are still sworn by medical students graduating today, is attributed to Hippocrates.) Greek scientists include Thales and

Pythagoras; scientist-philosophers include Leucippus and Democritus. And of course, the Greeks gave modern culture the Olympic Games.

Did the **Roman Republic** precede the Roman Empire?

Yes, the Roman Republic, which for centuries afterward was considered the model form of a balanced government, was established in 509 B.C. The Roman Empire was not established until 27 B.C. when Augustus (also known as Octavian; 63 B.C.-A.D. 14) became its first ruler. In brief, the development of ancient Rome is as follows.

In 753 B.C. the city of Rome was established. (Legend has it, the city was founded by brothers Romulus and Remus.) Situated on wooded hills above the Tiber River, about 15 miles from the sea, Rome enjoyed the advantages of access to trade routes while having natural protection from aggressors. The city was defensible. Agriculture prospered in the area, as did other economic endeavors including manufacturing and mining.

In 509 B.C. the Republic was established by noblemen. The government was headed by two elected officials who were called consuls. Since they shared power, a certain measure of balance was ensured in that either one could veto the actions of the other. And the posts were brief: each elected official served for only one year. These heads of state were guided by the Roman Senate, which was made up of senior statesmen. There were also assemblies in which the people had a voice.

In 390 B.C. Rome was captured and sacked by the Gauls (a Celtic people from western Europe), who were able to hold it for a short time. About 300 B.C. the Romans came into contact with the Greeks, adopting not only some of their ideas, but their mythology as well. The Greek gods and goddesses were soon given Roman names.

By 275 B.C. Rome controlled most of the Italian peninsula. Their homeland stable, the Romans set their sights on overseas expansion, and between 264 and 146 B.C. fought the Punic Wars in order to gain territory. They conquered the Mediterranean islands of Sicily, Sardinia, and Corsica; part of Gaul; much of Spain; and Carthage (in northern Africa).

In the last century B.C. Rome entered a period that is considered the height of their civilization. But about the middle of that century, the Republic was torn by civil wars. After 20 years of fighting, the Roman Empire was formed in 27 B.C. when Augustus (Octavian) became the first emperor. While vestiges of the Republic were maintained, the emperor held supreme authority, nominating the consuls and appointing senators, controlling the provinces, and heading the army. The civilian assemblies were still in place, but had for the most part lost their voice in government.

The Roman Empire lasted nearly 500 years. By the third century A.D. Roman armies had conquered so many peoples that the empire stretched across Europe and included the entire Mediterranean coast of Africa as well as parts of the Middle East. During this time of power and expansion, trade thrived over a vast network of roads and sea routes, which extended to China, India, and Africa. Coins, made of gold, silver, copper, and bronze, were issued and controlled by the Roman government.

In 395, upon the death of emperor Theodosius the Great (347-395), the Roman Empire was divided into two: East and West. In 476, after suffering a series of attacks from nomadic Germanic tribes, Rome fell.

What was the **Pax Romana**?

The Pax Romana was the height of the Roman Empire, a period of peace that lasted from 27 B.C. to A.D. 180, roughly two centuries. During this time, no other country or force was strong enough to challenge the Roman Empire, so citizens turned their attention to commerce, learning, the arts, and literature, all of which flourished.

What is the legacy of **ancient Rome**?

Since the Romans borrowed and adapted the ideas of the Greeks, with whom they had come into contact about 300 B.C. and later conquered in 146 B.C., the culture of ancient Rome is sometimes called Greco-Roman. Over the course of centuries, Romans spread their ideas throughout their vast empire.

They also developed a legal code, which outlined basic principles while remaining flexible enough that lawyers and judges could interpret the laws, taking into consideration local customs and practices. The code later became the model for legal systems in Europe and in Latin America. Further, Roman armies built a network of roads, aqueducts, and tunnels, putting in place an infrastructure that outlasted the empire itself. Latin, the Roman language, remained the language of educated Europeans for more than 1,000 years, while the Latin-based (or Romance) languages of Italian, French, and Spanish took over everyday communication. The economic system put in place during the height of the Roman Empire, with a centrally controlled money supply, also had lasting effect.

Though the empire crumbled by A.D. 476, its cultural, social, and economic establishments continued to have validity well into the Middle Ages (500-1350).

What is the difference between the **Roman Empire** and the Holy Roman Empire?

Roughly four and a half centuries separated the two empires, both of which were comprised of vast regions of western and central Europe. The Roman Empire was established in 27 B.C., when Augustus (also known as Octavian; 63 B.C.-A.D. 14), the grandnephew, adopted son, and chosen heir of Julius Caesar (100-44 B.C.), became emperor. His reign lasted until A.D. 476, when Rome fell to Germanic tribes.

The Holy Roman Empire (H.R.E.) began in the mid-900s A.D., when Otto I (912-973) of Germany gained control of most of northern and central Italy. Pope John XII (c. 937-964) crowned Otto emperor in 962. In the 1200s the area of power officially became known as the Holy Roman Empire. The H.R.E. was dismantled July 12, 1806, in the Confederation of the Rhine, which brought most of the German states under French domination—the result of the Napoleonic wars. But even after Napoleon Bonaparte (1769-1821) was permanently ousted as head of France in 1815, there were no attempts to reinstate the Holy Roman Empire.

What happened to **the Celts** during the Roman Empire?

The Celts were an Indo-European people who by 500 B.C. had spread across what is now France, Italy, Portugal, Spain, and the British Isles, and by 200 B.C. they had expanded as far as present-day Bulgaria and Greece. When the Romans conquered much of Europe (about 300 B.C.), many Celts were absorbed into the Roman Empire. However, those Celts living in Ireland, Scotland, Wales, southwest England, and Brittany (in northwestern France) were able to maintain their cultures, and it is in these regions that people of Celtic origin still live today.

What is known about the **Celts prior to the Roman Empire**?

Before Europe was conquered by Rome, Celts, who were themselves divided into smaller tribes, had become rather advanced in many ways. Their society was divided among three classes: commoners, the educated, and aristocrats. They formed loose federations of tribes, raised crops and livestock, used the Greek alphabet to write their own language, and were among the first peoples in northern Europe to make iron. They also developed a form of metalwork that most people today recognize as Celtic, called *La Tène*. They never formed one united nation, however, so that when Roman armies swept across Europe, the Celtic tribes were overrun.

THE MIDDLE AGES: 500 TO 1350

What are the characteristics of **medieval times**?

Although the Middle Ages were shadowed by poverty, ignorance, economic chaos, bad government, and the plague, it was also a period of cultural and artistic achievement. For example, the university originated in medieval Europe (the first university was established in 1158 in Bologna, Italy). The period was marked by the belief, based on the Christian faith, that the universe is an ordered world, ruled by an infinite and all-

What are the Dark Ages and how did they get that name?

The Dark Ages usually refer to the historical period in Europe from about A.D. 500 to 1350, also known as the Middle Ages, or medieval period (medieval is from the Latin *medium aevum,* meaning "middle age"). The Middle Ages followed the collapse of the Roman Empire (in A.D. 476, which signaled the end of the Classical Age) and preceded the Renaissance.

The term *Dark Ages* is the legacy of seventeenth-century historians who considered the period a barbaric interruption of a tradition that began in ancient Greece and continued through the European Renaissance. Modern scholars have tried to correct this view, but the popular perception of the medieval period as "dark" still remains. (The term *Dark Ages* is also used to refer to a Greek historical period, from about 1100 B.C. to about 700 B.C., which was considered to be a period of decline.)

knowing God. This belief persisted even through the turmoil of wars and social upheavals, and it is evident in the soaring Gothic architecture (such as the Cathedral of Chartres, France), the poetry of Dante Alighieri (1265-1321), the philosophy of St. Thomas Aquinas (1225-1274), the Gregorian chant, and the music of such composers as Guillaume de Machaut (c. 1300-1377).

Who were **the Huns**?

The Huns were a nomadic central Asian people who, in the middle of the fourth century A.D., moved westward. They first defeated the Alani (a group in the Caucasus Mountain region, between the Black and the Caspian Seas), and then conquered and drove out the Goths. Unified by the ruler Attila in 434, the Huns gained control of a large part of central and eastern Europe by about 450. The Italian countryside was ravaged in the process, and many people sought refuge on the numerous islands in the Lagoon of Venice; the settlement later became the city of Venice.

With the death of Attila in 453, the subjects of the Huns revolted and defeated them. The Huns were later absorbed into the various peoples of Europe.

Who were **the barbarians**?

The term is used to refer to any of the Germanic tribes that, during the middle of the first millennium A.D. (beginning about 400), repeatedly attacked Rome, eventually conquering it and dividing the territories of the West Roman Empire into many kingdoms (while what was the East Roman Empire survived as the Byzantine Empire). The Germanic tribes included the Goths, the Vandals, the Franks, and the Lombards.

A powerful ruler of the Huns, Attila led his people to gain control of a large part of Central and Eastern Europe.

Who were **the Goths**?

The Goths were a group of Germanic tribes who originated in what is now Scandinavia. As early as the third century A.D., the Goths invaded the eastern provinces of the Roman Empire. During the following century, they divided into two groups: a western group known as the Visigoths, who predominated north of the lower Danube River, in central Europe; and an eastern group known as the Ostrogoths, who were situated north of the Black Sea, between Europe and Asia. Along with other tribal Germanic peoples, the Goths brought the downfall of the Roman Empire.

What happened to **the Ostrogoths**?

The eastern division of the Goths, the Ostrogoths were overrun and absorbed by the Huns in 370. When the powerful Hun leader, Attila, died in 453, subjects of the Huns revolted and the Ostrogoths regained their freedom. Theodoric (c. 454-526) became the ruler of the Ostrogoths in 493, and it was under his leadership that the group invaded northern Italy, where they remained. In the middle of the following century, they were overthrown by the armies of the Byzantine Empire. Like other Germanic tribes, the Ostrogoths were absorbed into the various groups of Europe.

What happened to **the Visigoths**?

When both the Visigoths and Ostrogoths were attacked by the Huns in 370, the Visigoths fared better, many of them fleeing into a Roman province. In 378 the Visigoths rebelled against the Roman authorities. On horseback, they fought the battle of Adrianople (in present-day Turkey), destroying a Roman army and killing Rome's eastern emperor, Valens (c. 328-378). The Visigoths' introduction of the cavalry (troops trained to fight on horseback) as part of warfare determined European military, social, and political development for the next thousand years.

After the battle of Adrianople, the Visigoths moved into Italy, and under the leadership of their ruler, Alaric (c. 370-410), sacked Rome in 410, an event that signaled the beginning of the decline of the Roman Empire. After the success of the Visigoths, one tribe after another invaded the empire.

The Visigoths continued westward into Gaul, and there set up a monarchy that consisted of much of France and Spain and was centered in Toulouse. But in 507 they were driven out by the Franks, and the Visigoths withdrew into the Iberian Peninsula (present-day Spain and Portugal). Toledo was established as the capital of the Visigoth kingdom in 534. Roderick (or Rodrigo), the last of the Visigoth kings in Spain, was defeated and killed in 711 during a battle with the Muslims (Moors), who invaded from northern Africa. The Muslims went on to rule most of the Iberian Peninsula until the mid-1400s.

Who were **the Vandals**?

Like the Goths, the Vandals were a Germanic people who originated in an area south of the Baltic Sea in what is now Scandinavia. By A.D. 100 they had moved into the southern region of (present-day) Poland. But there they eventually found themselves threatened by the Huns, and so they began moving westward late in the fourth century. Early in the fifth century, the Vandals overran Gaul (in western Europe), Spain, and northern Africa, where they eventually settled. Between 428 and 477 the Vandals were ruled by the powerful King Genseric. Under his reign, they ravaged Rome (in 455). Their pillage was so thorough that the word *vandal* is used to describe anyone who willfully destroys property that is not theirs. In 533 and 534, like the Ostrogoths, the Vandals were defeated by armies of the Byzantine Empire.

Who were **the Franks**?

The Franks were another Germanic people who divided into two branches: the Salians, who settled near the lower Rhine River, near the North Sea; and the Ripuarians, who moved into what is now Germany, along the middle Rhine River.

In 359 the Franks entered into the Roman Empire as allies, but in 481 Clovis (c. 466-511) gained the Salerian Frank kingship. By 486 he had begun a campaign of aggression, conquering Romans, Gauls, Visigoths, and other groups. Under this cruel and cunning king, the Franks soon controlled all of Europe—from the Mediterranean to the English Channel, and from the Pyrenees Mountains to the Rhine River. Even after Clovis's death, the Franks maintained their stronghold in the region, which is how France eventually got its name.

Though Clovis was a powerful ruler, he was succeeded as king of the Franks by the even more powerful Charlemagne (also called Charles the Great; 742-814), who ruled from 771 to 814, creating a vast empire. In 800 Pope Leo III (c. 750-816) crowned him Emperor of the West, thus initiating the Holy Roman Empire. It was after Charlemagne that the empire of the Franks began to break up, becoming the kingdoms of France, Germany, and Italy.

How were **the Gauls** related to the Celts?

The ancient Gauls were a Celtic people who spoke forms of the Celtic language. They occupied the ancient country of Gaul, a region west of the Rhine River and north of the

Pyrenees Mountains (an area that today consists of France, Belgium, Luxembourg, part of Germany, and part of the Netherlands). The Gauls were led by priests, who were called Druids. By 390 B.C. the Gauls had moved southward, across the Alps and into Italy. In the third century B.C., they battled the powerful Romans and were briefly successful. Ultimately, however, they were defeated, becoming subjects of Rome. Later, under Julius Caesar, the Romans conquered all of Gaul, so that by 50 B.C. the region became part of the Roman Empire. Five centuries later, Gaul was overrun by the Franks, for whom the region was named. Thus, French people today are descendants of the Gauls. Also, the Galatians (one of the Christian peoples to whom the Apostle Paul wrote while he was in jail) were descendants of the Gauls who settled in Macedonia and Asia Minor (the peninsula between the Black Sea and the Mediterranean, which today is occupied by Turkey).

Who were **the Lombards**?

The Lombards, too, were a Germanic tribe; they are believed to have originated on an island in the Baltic Sea. In the last century B.C., the Lombards moved into Germany and gradually continued southward so that by A.D. 500, they were settled in present-day Austria. From 568 to the mid-700s, they controlled much of Italy, posing a serious threat to the papal supremacy so that in 754, Pope Stephen II (d. 757) appealed to the powerful Franks for help. By this time the Franks were ruled by Pepin III (called Pepin the Short; c. 714-768), who was able to defeat the Lombards. The northern region of Italy, Lombardy, is named for them.

Who were **the Saxons**?

Saxons were a Germanic people who in the second century lived in southern Jutland, in the area of present-day Denmark and northwestern Germany. During the next two centuries the Saxons raided the coastal areas of the North Sea. By about 400, they had reached northern Gaul, the ancient country that occupied the area west and south of the Rhine River, west of the Alps, and north of the Pyrenees Mountains (roughly modern-day France, Belgium, Luxembourg, part of Germany, and part of the Netherlands). By about 450, as Roman rule was declining, the Saxons had reached England, where they merged with the Angles and began setting up Anglo-Saxon kingdoms. The Anglo-Saxons dominated England until it was conquered by Danish Vikings (under the leadership of Canute) in 1016.

Who were **the Angles**?

The Angles were yet another Germanic tribe; they originated in Schleswig in northwestern Germany. Like other Germanic peoples, they were on the move by the fifth century. Arriving in England, the Angles joined the Saxons (also a Germanic-speaking people), after which time they together became known as Anglo-Saxons, a term referring to any non-Celtic settler of Britain.

Who were **the Vikings**?

The Vikings, also called Norsemen, were fierce, seafaring warriors who originated in Scandinavia. Beginning in the late 700s they raided England, France, Germany, Ireland, Scotland, Italy, Russia, and Spain. Great shipbuilders, the Vikings also reached Greenland, Iceland, and probably even North America long before the Europeans. (Ruins of a Norse settlement were found on the northeastern coast of Newfoundland, Canada.) The Vikings were converted to Christianity during the tenth and eleventh centuries, about the same time that the kingdoms of Norway, Denmark, and Sweden were established. Under the Danish leader Canute, Vikings conquered England in 1016 and ruled it as part of Denmark until 1042.

Who were **the Danes**?

The Danes are the Scandinavian people of Denmark. Their origins date as far back as 100,000 years. Beginning at about the time of Christ (c. 30 A.D.), the Danes were organized into communities that were governed by local chieftains. During the sixth and seventh centuries they participated in the Viking (pirate) raids of England, France, the Netherlands, Belgium, and Luxembourg (these last three are sometimes referred to as the Low Countries). In about 950 Denmark was united by King Harold II (also called Harald Bluetooth; c. 910-c. 985), who 10 years later was converted to Christianity and thereafter fostered its spread. The Vikings gained control of England in 1016, and the Dane warrior Canute became king of England (and of Denmark). The Danes ruled England until 1042.

Who were **the Normans**?

The Normans, like the Danes, originated in Scandinavia and were Vikings. In the mid-800s they invaded northern France, ousting the Franks who had conquered the region 400 years earlier. There they stayed, in the region that came to be known as Normandy (or Normandie). In 1066 the Norman duke William (the Conqueror; 1027-1087) sailed across the channel and claimed the English throne, uniting Normandy with the English kingdom. This arrangement lasted until 1204 when French King Philip Augustus (1165-1223) reclaimed the territory. England took it back during the fifteenth century, but in 1450 Normandy was permanently restored to France, becoming a province. Norman descendants still live there today, and their influence is also evident across the English Channel, where the Norman nobility intermixed with the Anglo-Saxons.

What were **lords**?

Lords (or seigniors) were wealthy landowners during the Middle Ages (500-1350). By about the ninth century, much of western Europe was divided into huge estates, called

William the Conqueror in battle. In 1066 the Norman duke sailed across the English Channel and claimed the throne of England.

manors. These were self-sufficient estates that were held by a lord (members of the clergy could also be lords). The lord would lease land to peasants who would farm it; in return, the peasants would pay the lord in taxes, in services, or in kind (with crops or goods). In addition to farmland, a manor would typically have meadow, woodland, and a small village. The lord presided over the entire manor and all the people living there. As the administrator of the land, he collected taxes and presided over legal matters. But the manors were not military entities; in other words, the lord did not promise protection to the peasants living on his land. As such, the manors were purely socioeconomic (as opposed to fiefs, which were social, economical, and political units).

What were **fiefs**?

A fief was an estate that was owned, governed, and protected by a lord. A fief consisted of several manors (each of which might have had its own lord) and their villages, along with all buildings on the land as well as the peasants (serfs) who worked the land, served at court, or took up arms on behalf of the lord. The lord of the fief, called a feudal lord, would secure the allegiance of the manorial lords (sometimes called seigniors), who would in turn secure the allegiance of the peasants. In short, land was exchanged for loyalty; this was feudalism, the political and economic system of the Middle Ages (500-1350). The word *feud* is of Germanic origin and means "fee"; in repayment for the land they lived on and for the protection they received from the lord, serfs were expected to pay the lord fees—in the form of money (taxes), services, or goods.

The feudal system arose in the seventh century. It was suspended during the Carolingian Empire, which began in 751 when a series of powerful kings (including Charlemagne, or Charles the Great, 742-814) united much of western Europe. But after Charlemagne died in 814, his grandsons fought each other and later divided the vast kingdom among themselves. Each of their territories later came under attack, dissolving Carolingian rule. By the ninth century feudalism had replaced the Carolingian Empire as the political and economic entity governing medieval life. Feudalism lasted into the fifteenth century.

What were **serfs**?

Serfs were the peasants who lived on either a manor or a fief, the two organizing entities of the Middle Ages (500-1350). They performed labor and were bound to the lord of the property where they lived and worked. A serf was somewhere between a free person and a slave: Though the word serf is derived from the Latin word *servus,* meaning "slave," the serfs had certain rights, which were governed not by law but by custom. One such custom was that a serf who could escape his lord for one year and a day was then considered free. A free peasant was called a *villein,* a village commoner.

What were **vassals**?

In the Middle Ages (500-1350) a vassal was anyone who was under the protection of another and therefore owed and avowed not only allegiance but a payment of some sort to their protector. Peasants (serfs and village commoners) were always vassals to a lord—whether it was the lord of the manor or the lord of the fief. But the lord of the manor was himself a vassal—to the lord of the fief. As kingdoms were created, with many fiefs within their jurisdiction, the feudal lords became the vassals of the kings.

What were **knights**?

In the Middle Ages (500-1350) knights were armed and mounted warriors who were also landholders; in other words, they were noblemen who took up arms. A knight might have been the lord of a manor who vowed to fight for the feudal lord (the lord of the fief where the manor was situated). During the Carolingian Age (during the eighth and ninth centuries), when a monarchy was established in western Europe, a feudal lord might also have been a knight in service to the king. In times of war, any man who pledged loyalty to his lord and took up arms on his behalf would become a knight, who later might receive lands from the lord or king as repayment. During the Crusades

(1096-1291) knights were made of men who were not landowners—they were instead designated by primogeniture (the eldest son would bear the honor of becoming a knight). Knighthood was traditionally conferred by a blow on the shoulder with the flat side of a sword. Feudal knighthood ended by the sixteenth century. Today, the only vestige of this tradition is found in Britain, where knighthood is an honorific designation conferred by the king or queen on a noble or commoner for extraordinary achievement.

What was a **papal state**?

A papal state was a manor or fief where the lord was a member of the clergy. In 754 Carolingian king Pepin the Short (c. 714-768) granted extensive lands to the pope. These territories, which included much of what is now the Mediterranean coast of France as well as most of central Italy, were organized by the Roman Catholic Church into states. These states played an important role in medieval life. Like the fiefs, the papal states collected taxes and maintained courts of law. Also, like their secular counterparts, they were prone to war and invasion. Thus members of the Roman Catholic Church were temporal as well as spiritual leaders during the Middle Ages (500-1350). The last of the territories held by the church was in central Italy and included Rome. After 1871 these lands were claimed by Italy. The resulting land dispute (sometimes referred to as the Roman Question) was settled by the Lateran Treaty (1929), which created the sovereign state known as Vatican City.

What was the **church's role during the Middle Ages**?

Though the Roman Catholic Church became increasingly involved in secular concerns during the Middle Ages (500-1350), it played a much larger part in medieval European life. Missionaries converted many of the Germanic tribes; thus, the church was influential in civilizing these so-called barbarians. Further, churches throughout Europe housed travelers and served as hospitals for the sick. Monasteries and cathedrals became centers of learning.

What was the **Investiture Struggle**?

Also called the Investiture Controversy, it is the name for the power struggle between kings and popes during the Middle Ages (500-1350). Since the papal states played the same role in medieval society as the other states (fiefs and manors, which were held by kings), their lords, who were members of the clergy, eventually became subject to the same human weaknesses that guided the feudal lords and kings—namely, corruption and greed. Popes became powerful and worldly leaders. The struggle for supremacy peaked in 1075 when Pope Gregory VII (c. 1020-1085), who was trying to protect the church from the influence of Europe's powerful leaders, issued a decree against lay investitures, meaning that no one except the pope could name bishops or heads of monasteries. German King Henry IV (1050-1106), who was engaged in a power struggle with Saxon nobles at the time, took exception to Gregory's decree and challenged it, asserting that the kings should have the right to name the bishops. (This was an important point of disagreement, since kings wanted to be in the favor of the pope, and popes were selected from among the bishops. So, it was not purely a religious issue; political power was also at stake.) Henry was excommunicated by the pope. Though he later sought—and was granted—forgiveness by Gregory, the struggle did not end there. Henry soon regained political support, deposed Gregory (in 1084), and set up an antipope (Clement III), who, in turn, crowned him Holy Roman Emperor. The debate over whose right it was to invest clergymen with the symbol of office continued through much of the Middle Ages.

What was the **Holy Roman Empire**?

The Holy Roman Empire (sometimes abbreviated H.R.E.) was a loose federation of German and Italian states, originally formed on Christmas of A.D. 800, when Charlemagne, or Charles the Great (742-814), was crowned emperor of the Romans by Pope Leo III (c. 750-816). But after Charlemagne's death, the empire lapsed and was not fully reinstated until Otto I (912-973) was crowned emperor. Though the empire was strongly associated with the Roman Catholic Church, disputes between emperors and popes began in the mid-1100s. In 1250 Pope Innocent IV (d. 1254) was successful in gaining independence from the empire for the Italian city-states.

Later in the history of the Holy Roman Empire, the House of Habsburg rose to power. But after the 1648 signing of the Peace of Westphalia, which recognized the sovereignty of all the states of the empire, the title of Holy Roman Emperor was for the most part an honorific one. With the exception of a five-year period (1740-45), the family continued to hold power until 1806, when Emperor Francis II (1768-1835) declared the end of the Holy Roman Empire.

THE RENAISSANCE: 1350 TO c. 1600

Why is **the Renaissance** considered **a time of rebirth**?

The term *renaissance* is from the French word for "rebirth," and the period from A.D. 1350 to 1600 in Europe was marked by the resurrection of classical Greek and Roman ideals; the flourishing of art, literature, and philosophy; and the beginning of modern science.

Italians in particular believed themselves to be the true heirs to Roman achievement. For this reason, it was natural that the Renaissance began in Italy, where the ruins of ancient civilization provided a constant reminder of their classical past and where subsequent artistic movements (such as Gothic) had never taken firm hold.

How did the **Renaissance begin**?

Social and political developments in the late Middle Ages gave rise to the spirit of the Renaissance. The Crusades (1096-1291)—the military expeditions undertaken by Christian powers to win the holy land from the Muslims—brought Europeans into contact with other cultures and most importantly with Byzantine civilization. The remnant of the East Roman Empire, Byzantium had preserved the knowledge of ancient times. In addition, many texts thought to have been destroyed during the tribal ransacking of the West Roman Empire (in the fifth century A.D.) remained preserved in various translations throughout the Middle East. So it was during the Crusades that some of these were brought back to Europe, where classical scholars undertook the task of deciphering the West's cultural past.

In northern Italy, a series of city-states developed independent of the larger empires to the north and south of them. These small states—Florence, Rome, Venice, and Milan, among others—gained prosperity through trade and banking, and as a result, a wealthy class of businessmen emerged. These community leaders admired and encouraged creativity, patronizing artists who might glorify their commercial achievement with great buildings, paintings, and sculptures. The most influential patrons of the arts were the Medicis, a wealthy banking family in Florence. Members of the Medici family supported many important artists, including Botticelli and Michelangelo. Guided by the Medici patronage, Florence became the most magnificent city of the period.

One way patrons encouraged art was to sponsor competitions in order to spur artists to more significant achievement. In many cases, the losers of these contests went on to greater fame than the winners. After his defeat in the competition to create the bronze doors of the Baptistery of Florence Cathedral, architect Filippo Brunelleschi (1377-1446) made several trips to take measurements of the ruined buildings of ancient Rome. When he returned to Florence, he created the immense *il duomo* (dome) of the Santa Maria del Fiore Cathedral, a classically influenced structure that became the first great monument of the Renaissance.

How is **the attitude of the Renaissance** characterized?

The artists and thinkers of the Renaissance, like the ancient Greeks and Romans, valued earthly life, glorified man's nature, and celebrated individual achievement. These new attitudes combined to form a new spirit of optimism, the belief that man was capable of accomplishing great things.

This outlook was the result of the activities of the wealthy mercantile class in northern Italy, who, aside from supporting the arts and letters, also began collecting the classical texts that had been forgotten during the Middle Ages (500-1350). Ancient manuscripts were taken to libraries, where scholars from around Europe could study them. The rediscovery of classical texts prompted a new way of looking at the world.

During the Middle Ages, scholars argued that the meaning of life on Earth lay primarily in its relation to an afterlife. Therefore, they believed that art for its own sake had no value, and they even frowned on the recognition of individual talent. (For this reason, many of the great works of the Middle Ages were created anonymously or were hidden from public view.)

In contrast, Renaissance artists and thinkers studied classical works for the purpose of imitating them. As an expression of their new optimism, Renaissance scholars embraced the study of classical subjects that addressed human, rather than scientific, concerns. These "humanities," as they came to be called, included language and literature, art, history, rhetoric, and philosophy. Above all, humanists, those who espoused the values of this type of education, believed in man's potential to become well versed in many areas. Thus, a "Renaissance man" is anyone whose talents span a variety of disciplines. During the Renaissance, people in all disciplines began using critical skills as a means of understanding everything from nature to politics.

Which artists and thinkers are considered **the greatest minds of the Renaissance**?

The great writers of the Renaissance include the Italian poet Petrarch (1304-1374), who became the first great writer of the Renaissance and was one of the first proponents of the concept that a "rebirth" was in progress; Florentine historian Niccolò Machiavelli (1469-1527), who wrote the highly influential work *The Prince* (1513); English dramatist and poet William Shakespeare (1564-1616), whose works many view as the culmination of Renaissance writing; Spain's Miguel de Cervantes (1547-1616), who penned *Don Quixote* (1605), the epic masterpiece that gave birth to the modern novel; and Frenchman François Rabelais (c. 1483-1553), who is best known for writing the five-volume novel *Gargantua and Pantagruel.*

The great artists of the Renaissance include the Italian painters/sculptors Sandro Botticelli (1445-1510), whose works include *The Birth of Venus*; Leonardo da Vinci (1452-1519), whose *Mona Lisa* and *The Last Supper* are among the most widely studied works of art; Michelangelo Buonarroti (1475-1564), whose sculpture *David* became the symbol of the new Florence; and Raphael Sanzio (1483-1520), whose *School of Athens* is considered by art historians to be the complete statement of the High Renaissance.

When did **European colonialism** begin?

Seeking out colonies for economic benefit dates back to ancient times: Even the Romans ruled colonies in Europe, the Middle East, and Africa. But colonialism took hold during the Renaissance, between 1400 and 1600, when powerful European countries sent explorers to find new lands and forge new trade routes.

Portugal and Spain sought sea routes to India and the Far East. In the process, the Portuguese gained control of what is now Brazil; they also established trading posts in West Africa, India, and Southeast Asia. Spain gained control of most of Latin America and vast regions of what is now the United States. However, the Dutch, English, and French also had influence in these areas. And of course, the English eventually established thirteen colonies in North America. The English also became a strong influence in India and Africa, while the Dutch gained control of the Indonesian islands (which became the Dutch East Indies).

The results of colonialism were many. While trade was expanded and there was an enormous exchange of raw goods, the colonies were also rife with conflict: Indigenous peoples were killed or forcibly displaced from their lands, and foreign powers fought with each other for control of the same areas (the British and French fought four wars in North America between 1689 and 1763 alone). Further, Europeans brought to these new lands their own languages, religions, and systems of government, imposing their culture, beliefs, and ideologies on native peoples.

THE ENLIGHTENMENT AND THE SCIENTIFIC REVOLUTION: 1600s TO 1700s

What was **the Enlightenment**?

The Enlightenment, which is also referred to as the Age of Reason (or alternately as the Age of Rationalism), was a period when European philosophers emphasized the use of reason as the best method for learning the truth. Beginning in the 1600s and lasting through the 1700s, philosophers such as Jean-Jacques Rousseau (1712-1778), Voltaire (1694-1778), and John Locke (1632-1704) explored issues in education, law, and politics. They published their thoughts, issuing attacks on social injustice, religious superstition, and ignorance. Their ideas fanned the fires of the American and French revolutions in the late 1700s.

Hallmarks of the Age of Reason include the idea of the universal truth (two plus two always equals four, for example); the belief that nature is vast and complex but well ordered; the belief that humankind possesses the ability to understand the universe; the philosophy of Deism, which holds that God created the world and then left it alone; and the concept of the rational will, which posits that humans make their own choices and plans, and therefore, do not have a fate thrust upon them.

While the Age of Reason proved to be a flurry of intellectual activity that resulted in the publication of several encyclopedias of knowledge, toward the end of the eighteenth

How did the Renaissance spread from Italy to the rest of Europe?

Eventually the ideas born in Italy during the 1300s spread northward, which is at least in part attributable to German inventor Johannes Gutenberg's printing press (c. 1440-1450). Before long, the spirit and ideas that were taking hold in Italy reached France, Germany, England, and the Netherlands, where the Renaissance continued into the 1600s.

One of the most important figures of the northern Renaissance was the Dutch humanist Desiderius Erasmus (c. 1466-1536), whose book *In Praise of Folly* (1509) is a blistering criticism of the clergy, scholars, and philosophers of his day.

Another notable figure of the northern Renaissance was Englishman Sir Thomas More (1478-1535), who was a statesman and adviser to the king. More's *Utopia,* published in 1516, criticizes the times by envisioning an ideal society in which land is communally held, men and women alike are educated, police are unnecessary, politicians are honest, and where there is religious tolerance.

The works of Flemish artist Jan van Eyck (1395-1441), including his groundbreaking portrait *Man in a Red Turban* (1433), demonstrate that the principles of the Renaissance were felt as strongly in northern Europe as they were in Italy.

century a shift occurred. During this time Europeans began to value passion over reason, giving rise to the romantic movement and ending the Age of Reason. (This change in outlook is evident in English novelist Jane Austen's *Sense and Sensibility.*)

Nevertheless, the philosophies put forth during the Age of Reason were critical to the development of Western thought. The celebration of individual reason during this era was perhaps best expressed by René Descartes (1596-1650), who refused to believe anything unless it could be proved. His statement, "I think, therefore I am," sums up the feelings of skeptical and rational inquiry that characterized intellectual thought during the era.

Are the Enlightenment and **the scientific revolution** the same?

The two terms describe interrelated and sequential European intellectual movements that took place from the 1500s to the 1800s. Together, the movements shaped an era that would lay the foundations of modern western civilization, foundations that required the use of reason, or rational thought, to understand the universe, nature, and human relations. During this period, many of the greatest minds in Europe developed new scientific, mathematical, philosophical, and social theories.

Scientists came to believe that observation and experimentation would allow them to discover the laws of nature. Thus, the scientific method emerged, which required tools. Soon the microscope, thermometer, sextant, slide rule, and other instruments were invented. Scientists working during this time included Sir Isaac Newton (1642-1727), Joseph Priestley (1733-1804), and René Descartes (1596-1650). The era witnessed key discoveries and saw rapid advances in astronomy, anatomy, mathematics, and physics. The advances had an impact on education: universities introduced science courses to the curricula, and elementary and secondary schools followed suit. As people became trained in science, new technologies emerged: complicated farm machinery and new equipment for textile manufacturing and transportation was developed, paving the way for the Industrial Revolution.

THE INDUSTRIAL REVOLUTION: 1700s TO 1800s

When did the **Industrial Revolution** begin?

The Industrial Revolution began in Great Britain during the 1700s, and by the early 1800s it had spread to western Europe and the United States. It was brought about by the introduction of steam-power-driven machinery to manufacturing. By the close of the 1800s most finished goods, which had once been made by hand or by simple machines, were produced in quantity by technologically advanced machinery.

What were the **effects of the Industrial Revolution**?

The dawn of the Industrial Revolution spelled the end of home- or workshop-based production. Factories were built to house the new machines, causing a population shift from rural to developing urban areas by the mid-1800s, as people went where the work was. Factory owners turned to child labor, and in the United States, to the steady influx of immigrants to run the machinery in their plants. As industry grew, it required financial institutions that could provide money for expansion, thus giving birth to a new breed of wealthy business leaders— including the extraordinarily prosperous "robber barons," the industrial and financial tycoons of the late nineteenth century.

But as industry evolved, government and policy changes did not keep pace: Serious social, political, and economic problems resulted, including poor and often dangerous working conditions, exploitation of workers (including child laborers), overcrowded housing, pollution, corruption, industry monopolies, and a widening gap between the rich and the poor. Change was slow to come, but social activism and government reforms in the late 1800s and during the Progressive Era of the early 1900s, much of which centered around trade unions, alleviated these problems. The rapid development of industry caused sweeping social changes: The Western world, which

During the Industrial Revolution factory owners commonly hired child laborers to work long hours for little pay.

had long been agriculturally based, became an industrial society, where goods and services are the primary focus.

THE TWENTIETH CENTURY

What was the world like **between the World Wars**?

Before World War II began in 1939, World War I (1914-18) was referred to as the Great War, and understandably so given its enormous impact. The price of the conflict was paid in human casualties: more than 10 million soldiers died and another 20 million were wounded. Civilian deaths were equally devastating, resulting from widespread hunger and flu epidemics (this was in the days preceding the advent of penicillin to treat complications from influenza).

During the 1920s, with the death toll of the Great War a recent memory, the civilized world enjoyed a period of relative peace. In the United States, the decade was known as the Roaring Twenties—ten years of prosperity and even frivolity, despite rat-

Relief programs helped ease hunger during the Great Depression: Here, a long line of people wait for their ration of a sandwich and cup of coffee in Times Square, New York City.

ification of the Eighteenth Amendment to the U.S. Constitution (1919), which prohibited the sale and consumption of "intoxicating liquors."

At the close of the Great War, the League of Nations had been established to handle disputes among countries and avoid another major conflict. This was followed in 1928 by the Kellogg-Briand Pact (also called the Pact of Paris), in which 15 nations agreed to settle conflicts by diplomacy rather than military might; eventually 62 nations ratified the agreement.

Meanwhile, in Germany an extreme sense of nationalism was taking hold: The Treaty of Versailles, which had ended the Great War, seriously weakened the nation, allowing the rise of the Nazi Party, led by Adolf Hitler (1889-1945). Nazis were determined to see their beloved homeland rise to power once again, and they found a ready following among the German people.

In 1929 a general downturn began in the world economy, triggered by the U.S. stock market crash of late October. As the United States fell into the severe and sustained economic crisis known as the Great Depression, other industrialized nations—including Germany—also felt the impact. Unemployment jumped to record levels in many countries, and a lack of social welfare programs resulted in the destitution of numerous families. Politicians and economists alike searched for solutions to the crisis, many turning to anti-free trade or isolationist policies to "protect their own."

Meanwhile, postwar efforts to keep peace were proving ineffective: Japan invaded Manchuria (China) in 1931; Italy conquered Ethiopia in 1936; civil war raged in Spain (1936-39); India became the site of a bitter struggle between British rulers and Indian nationalists; and the Sino-Japanese War (which began in 1937 and would be absorbed by the outbreak of World War II) was fought in Asia. A dangerous alliance was forged when Germany, Italy, and Japan formed the Axis powers in 1936. Also, by 1933, Germany had become a totalitarian state known as the Third Reich. In 1938 Nazi armies took their first steps toward gaining supremacy when they marched into Austria and claimed it, setting the stage for World War II (1939-45).

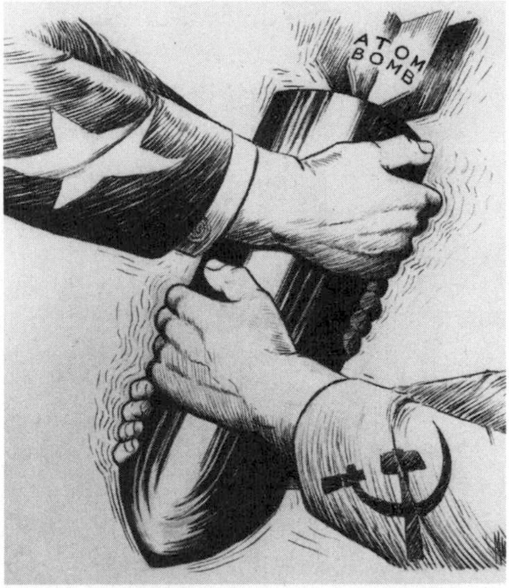

A Cold War-era cartoon, "Handle with Care," illustrating the opposing superpowers of the United States and Soviet Union, each grasping for an atomic bomb.

When did the **Cold War** begin?

In the years following the conclusion of World War II (1939-45), the nations of Western Europe and the United States became alarmed by Soviet advances into Eastern Europe, and many Europeans and Americans voiced concerns that Communists, led by the Soviet Union, were plotting to take over the world. Political leaders in England, the United States, and elsewhere referred to this new menace in grim terms. In March 1946 former British prime minister Winston Churchill (1874-1965) warned of an "Iron Curtain" of Soviet totalitarianism that had divided the European continent, and in 1947 U.S. president Harry S. Truman (1884-1972) announced a policy of containment of Communist incursion into other countries. This policy came to be known as the Truman Doctrine, and it remained an integral part of American foreign policy for the next 40 years, ultimately leading to the nation's involvement in the Korean War (1950-53) and the Vietnam War (1954-75).

The eroding relationship between the Western powers and the Soviet-led countries of Eastern Europe was largely brought on by disagreements over Germany. At the close of World War II, marked differences of opinion on what to do with Germany had resulted in a plan for joint government of the nation by the Allies—the Soviet Union, the United States, Britain, and France. But the arrangement quickly proved unworkable. By 1948 Germany was in serious economic straits, and the United States, Britain, and France began to discuss uniting their zones. The Soviets responded by ordering a blockade of land and water traffic into Berlin, control of which had been divided between the Allies after the war (the Soviets controlled East Berlin, while the other Allies controlled West Berlin). To counter the blockade, Great Britain and the United States ordered an airlift operation to provide food and other supplies to the people of West Berlin, alleviating the effects of the 11-month Soviet blockade. In 1949 the East-West differences resulted in the formal division of Germany into two countries: West Germany, formed by the zones occupied by the United States, Great Britain, and France, was allowed to form a democratic government, and it became officially known as the Federal Republic of Germany. The same year, East Germany (also known as the German Democratic Republic) was formed out of the Soviet zones and was folded into the "Eastern bloc" countries.

By 1949, the year that the Soviet Union exploded its first nuclear bomb, the world had been roughly divided into two camps: the United States and its democratic allies, which included the nations of Western Europe and other anticommunist governments; and the Eastern bloc, the Soviet Union and its satellite countries. These camps were soon girded by formal political alliances. In 1949 a military alliance known as the North Atlantic Treaty Organization (NATO) was formed by 12 nations (the United States, Great Britain, France, Italy, Norway, Portugal, Iceland, Denmark, Canada, Belgium, Luxembourg, and the Netherlands). By 1955 three more countries—Greece, Turkey, and West Germany—joined the alliance. The Soviet Union responded by creating the Council for Mutual Economic Assistance (COMECON) in 1949 and the Warsaw Pact in 1955. COMECON was an effort to coordinate economic and industrial activities among Communist nations, while the Warsaw Pact was a military agreement between the Soviets and the Communist governments of Eastern Europe. The Cold War was on.

What were the **hallmarks of the Cold War era**?

At home, the hysteria of the Cold War era reached its height with the so-called McCarthyism of the 1950s; historian Doris Kearns Goodwin described it as "one of the most destructive chapters in American political history." In early 1950 Republican senator Joseph McCarthy (1908-1957) of Wisconsin claimed to possess a list of more than two hundred known communists in the U.S. State Department. The startling accusation launched congressional inquiries conducted by the senator's subcommittee and the House Committee to Investigate Un-American Activities. Suspicions of communist subversion ran high—even in Hollywood, where a "blacklist" named those who were believed to have been involved in the Communist Party. McCarthy never produced his laundry list of offenders in the State Department, and the sorry chapter was closed when, on live television, the senator's bitter attacks went too far: In televised hearings in 1954, the senator took on the U.S. Army, determined to ferret out what he believed was a conspiracy to cover up a known communist in the ranks. Faced with McCarthy's slanderous line of questioning, Army counsel Joseph Welch (1890-1960) delivered a reply that finally disarmed McCarthy, saying "Have you no sense of decency, sir? If there is a God in heaven, your attacks will do neither you nor your cause any good." The retort was met with applause in the courtroom, heralding the end of the Communist-in-our-midst hysteria.

In the 1950s the hysteria of the Cold War reached its height when Wisconsin senator Joseph McCarthy (foreground) made aggressive accusations of communist infiltration of the U.S. government.

But the Cold War deepened during the course of the 1950s, as distrust on both sides was increased by the shadow of possible nuclear destruction. Both the United States and the Soviet Union funneled vast resources into the development of weapons systems, as each side believed deterrence would determine the victor in the Cold War: It would be won by the nation able to create weapons so powerful that the other nation would be deterred from attacking. The military build-up became an all-out arms race.

Competition between the Eastern bloc and the West spilled over into athletics, the arts, and the sciences. In 1957 the Soviets beat the West into space with the launch of the first artificial satellite, Sputnik, which they followed in 1961 by completing the first successful manned space launch. The United States responded by stepping up its space program and vowing to put a man on the moon.

Events in the early 1960s heightened tensions between the two sides, causing many to fear the war would turn hot: When an American U-2 spy plane was shot down over the Soviet Union and its pilot was captured in 1960, the United States was forced to admit to conducting a program of aerial reconnaissance; in 1961, the U.S.-backed invasion of Cuba, known as the Bay of Pigs, failed, revealing American involvement in the plot; also that year, the Berlin Wall was built to stop the flow of emigrants out of East Germany, and becoming a visible symbol of the division between East and West; and in 1962 U.S. president John Kennedy (1917-1963) and Soviet premier Nikita Khrushchev (1894-1971) squared off in the Cuban Missile Crisis—a full-scale conflict was averted through diplomacy.

Later in the decade and into the 1970s, tensions relaxed and both sides began agreeing to limit the arms race, signing the Nuclear Non-Proliferation Treaty in 1968 and the Strategic Arms Limitation Treaty (SALT I) in 1972, and agreeing to the Helsinki Accords in 1975. But East and West remained suspicious and watchful of each other into the 1980s. Most observers agree the Cold War did not come to an end until the fall of communism in Eastern Europe (c. 1990).

What led to **the decline of communism** in Eastern Europe?

Anticommunist sentiment among Eastern Europeans was bolstered by the actions and policies of Soviet leader Mikhail Gorbachev (1931-). When Gorbachev took office in 1985, the Soviet economy was in decline. In order to reverse the trend, he advocated dramatic reforms to move the economy away from the government-controlled (communist) system and toward a decentralized system, similar to those of Western democracies. Gorbachev's efforts to modernize the Soviet Union were not limited to the economy; he further proposed a reduction in the power of the Communist Party, which had controlled the country since 1917. Gorbachev's programs for reform were termed *perestroika* (meaning "restructuring"). In the meantime, Gorbachev opened up relations with the West, which included visits with U.S. president Ronald Reagan (1911-2004), who strongly supported the Soviet leader's programs. Gorbachev referred to his policy of openness as *glasnost.* Both Russian terms quickly caught on around the world. While the economic reforms produced a slow and painful change for the Soviet people and Gorbachev had many detractors (including government officials), he also had many supporters—both inside and outside the Soviet Union.

People in other Eastern European countries watched with interest the Soviet move toward a more democratic system. Strikes in Poland had begun as early as 1980, where workers formed a free labor union called Solidarity. But the following year, the Communist leaders of the Soviet Union pressured the Polish government to put an end to the movement—which it did. After Gorbachev became head of the Soviet Union and initiated sweeping changes, the reform movements in other countries soon realized that the Soviets under Gorbachev would no longer take hard-handed tactics toward anticommunist efforts in other countries. In 1989 the Polish government ceased to prohibit Solidarity, and the Communist party there lost influence. The same was true in Hungary, East Germany, and Czechoslovakia. By the end of the decade, most of the Eastern European Communist governments were overthrown in favor of democratic-oriented governments. The transition was effected differently in each country: the "overthrow" in Czechoslovakia was so peaceful that it was called the Velvet Revolution; while in Romania, a bloody revolt ensued, and hard-line communist dictator Nicolae Ceausescu (1918-1989) was executed.

In 1990 multiparty elections were held in Romania, Czechoslovakia, Hungary, East Germany, and Bulgaria. The noncommunist party that was put in power in East Germany agreed to unification with West Germany, again creating one Germany on October 3, 1990. That same year Gorbachev received the Nobel peace prize for his contributions to world peace.

When was the **Berlin Wall dismantled**?

The barrier wall surrounding West Berlin began coming down in November 1989, as a wave of democratization swept Europe.

East German border guards watch as demonstrators pull down a segment of the Berlin Wall. The wall was removed in 1990, and East Germany reunited with West Germany.

The concrete, electrically fortified wall was first built in 1961 as a barbed wire and cinder block structure. Communist East German leader Walter Ulbricht (1893-1973) convinced Soviet premier Nikita Khrushchev (1894-1971) that the wall was needed to prevent people from fleeing communist Eastern Europe. (Before the wall was erected, an estimated 2.5 million people had fled to the free world through West Berlin; after its completion, perhaps 5,000 managed to escape. Hundreds died trying.) When the wall was complete, it had an average height of 12 feet and ran more than 100 miles, along which there were posts where armed East German guards stood sentinel, preventing their countrymen from escaping to the West. The wall completely surrounded West Berlin and divided the German capital between East and West, communism and the free world.

The wall was a symbol of communism's oppression and of the Cold War. On June 26, 1963, President John F. Kennedy delivered his memorable "I am a Berliner" speech in its shadows, saying, "There are some who say communism is the wave of the future...Let them come to Berlin." He went on to say that the wall was "a vivid demonstration of the failure of the communist system," and that though democracy is not perfect, democratic nations had "never had to put up a wall to keep our people in." On June 12, 1987, President Ronald Reagan (1911-2004) addressed West Berliners at the wall's Brandenburg Gate; his now-famous speech was audible on the East Berlin side of the wall as well. There, Reagan issued a challenge to Soviet leader Mikhail Gorbachev (1931-), saying "if you seek peace, if you seek prosperity for the Soviet Union and Eastern Europe, if you seek liberalization...[c]ome here to this wall...Mr. Gorbachev, tear down this wall!"

East Germany's communist government was finally toppled in October 1989. On November 9 restrictions between the two Berlins were lifted, and the wall was opened. The resulting celebration brought the wall down, with gleeful Berliners chipping away at the barrier; it was gradually dismantled. By 2005 only a few sections of the wall and some watch towers still existed—the capital no longer divided, the country a unified, democratic Germany.

How did the **Soviet Union** fall apart?

Soviet leader Mikhail Gorbachev's (1931-) liberal reforms met with the opposition of conservative communist officials who were angered by the hardships produced by the transition to a free market economy and dissatisfied with the Soviet Union's loss of influence over neighboring countries, where communism had fallen by 1990. On August 19, 1991, communists attempted to overthrow Gorbachev as president of the Soviet Union. Though the effort failed in the face of widespread public opposition, it nevertheless weakened Gorbachev's leadership. Soon the 15 Soviet republics declared independence but indicated their willingness to become part of a loose confederation of former Soviet republics. Though Gorbachev tried to prevent the complete dissolution of the Soviet Union, on December 8, 1991, the republics of Russia, Ukraine, and Belorussia (Belarus) broke away completely from the Soviet Union and formed the Commonwealth of Independent States. All the remaining republics, except Georgia, followed suit. On December 25, Gorbachev resigned as president, and the Soviet Union ceased to exist.

With continuing reforms in Eastern Europe and the end of the Soviet Union, by 1992 the only communist-dominated countries that remained were, with the exception of Cuba, Asian nations: China, Laos, North Korea, and Vietnam.

EARLY TWENTY-FIRST CENTURY

How is the **current era characterized**?

Ask the question of most any observer, and the answer would include catchphrases like "global marketplace," "global village," or "globalization." Modern communications and transportation connect people as never before—businesses enjoy broader markets for their goods and services, manufacturing facilities and jobs are located far from the offices of the companies that market them, and people of many nationalities, races, and religions have more and more contact with one another every day, for business and pleasure. Some observers worry that this contact will blur rich cultural differences, diluting diversity; others say that globalization will bring tolerance and increase understanding. Whatever the case, we are living our lives on a global stage: The things we buy and use are as likely to carry "Made in China" or "Made in Mexico" labels as they are any other; people continents away talk to each other not just over the telephone, but via cell phones, instant messages, e-mail, and Internet chat rooms; we have an international forum—the Internet—for buying, selling, and publishing; and we can get almost anywhere in the world with all due haste. Everything travels faster today, including ideas.

The upsides are many. Modern communications and transportation made it possible, for example, for the world to mobilize aid to victims of the Southeast Asian tsunami of December 2004. But there are downsides as well. Critics say globalization is fueling the exploitation of workers in developing nations, contributing to a modern slave trade, rapidly depleting resources, and wiping out environmental diversity. These are some of the reasons protesters have demonstrated outside meetings of the World Trade Organization, why some people opposed the North American Free Trade Agreement (NAFTA) and oppose the pending CAFTA (Central American Free Trade Agreement), and why many people dislike that American popular culture is marketed around the world. The problem could be distilled to this: diversity versus homogeneity. And the resulting culture clashes are not restricted to the realm of scholarly thought; they are making headline news. The enemy is no longer the strong-armed, nuclear-fortified, absolutist government of the Cold War era (though, as of mid-2005, North Korea remained a serious concern); the enemy, as the U.S. State Department reminds us, is any group of individuals with extreme views.

Who is the enemy of the day? Terrorists. News stories reinforce that this catch-all term does not only include the 9/11 hijackers and their al Qaeda associates, the Madrid and London train bombers, and suicide bombers in Gaza, but antigovernment extremists who blew up a federal building in Oklahoma City, a still-unknown distributor of deadly anthrax, and animal rights activists who routinely damage property to make a point. Terrorism is a decades- (some might argue, centuries-) old problem. Remember Birmingham, Alabama's Sixteenth Street Baptist Church, bombed in 1963 by white supremacists during Sunday services. Remember the 1972 summer Olympics in Munich, when the Arab terrorist group Black September killed 11 Israeli athletes held captive in the Olympic village. Remember the October 1985 hijacking of the *Achille Lauro* cruise ship by members of the Palestinian Liberation Front, who killed a wheelchair-bound American Jew. Remember the December 1988 bombing of Pan Am Flight 103, which came down in Lockerbie, Scotland, claiming 270 lives. The list is long and growing.

The shocking events of September 11, 2001, centered the world's attention on the problem of well-financed terrorist networks that can turn the freedoms of democracy against civilians—and who are feared to have in their possession or access to powerful weapons of mass destruction (WMD). The events of that day launched what the U.S. government calls the Global War on Terrorism, a long battle that even the president acknowledged may not be winnable in a traditional sense. This is a new kind of war, fought not against a nation, but against anarchists halfway around the world, and in our midst. Globalization and terrorism are the twin concerns of the modern era.

GOVERNMENT AND POLITICS

What was the **first national government**?

It is believed to have been that of the first Egyptian king, Menes, who united Upper and Lower Egypt in 3110 B.C. and founded a central government at Memphis (near present-day Cairo). Ruling for 62 years, Menes established the first of what would eventually number 30 dynasties that ruled ancient Egypt for nearly 3,000 years—until 332 B.C.

By the time the Third Dynasty began around 2700 B.C., the central government was well established and strong—subjects believed their kings and queens to be half-human and half-god. The pharaohs lived in magnificent luxury: Palaces and temples were built for them and were filled with exotic goods from other lands. These treasures were even buried with the pharaohs in order to be enjoyed in the afterworld. It was during the Third Dynasty that the 500-year period known as the Old Kingdom or the Pyramid Age began; it would become the period that saw the building of gigantic pyramids for Egypt's kings.

EMPIRES, ROYALTY, AND DYNASTIES

Was **King Tut** the greatest ruler of ancient Egypt?

No, in fact, King Tut's reign was relatively unimportant in the vast history of ancient Egypt. A ruler of the Eighteenth Dynasty, Tutankhamen (c. 1370-1352 B.C.) was in power from age nine (1361 B.C.) until his death at the age of 18—a nine-year period that would be of little significance were it not for the November 1922 discovery of his tomb in the Valley of the Kings near ancient Thebes (present-day Luxor). Of the 27 pharaohs buried near Thebes, only the tomb of the minor king, Tutankhamen, was spared looting through the ages. Having not been opened since ancient times, the tomb still contained its treasures.

In the antechamber English archeologist Howard Carter (1873-1939) found more than 600 artifacts, including funerary bouquets, sandals, robes, cups and jars, a painted casket, life-size wooden statues of Tutankhamen, animal-sided couches, remnants of chariots, and a golden throne. In the burial chambers a team of archaeologists discovered four golden shrines and the golden coffin containing the royal mummy of Tutankhamen—complete with a golden mask covering his head and shoulders.

Earlier in his career, Carter had discovered the tombs of King Tut's predecessors, Queen Hatshepsut (c. 1520-c. 1468 B.C.) and King Thutmose IV (d. 1417 B.C.), both of whom were also rulers during Egypt's Eighteenth Dynasty.

Was the **Mayan Empire** the most advanced early civilization?

In some regards, the Mayas were more advanced than other civilizations. Their development preceded that of the other agrarian civilizations in North and South America, principally the Aztec and the Inca.

The Mayas were an agricultural people who in about 1000 B.C. settled in southern Mexico and Central America. Their territory covered Mexico's Yucatan Peninsula, Belize, much of Guatemala, and parts of Honduras and El Salvador. They developed a civilization that was highly advanced: Not only did the Mayas produce remarkable architecture (including flat-topped pyramids, temples, and towers that are still visited by tourists today) and art (including sculpture, painting, and murals), but they developed their own writing system—probably the first in the Western Hemisphere. They used this system to record time, astronomical events, their history, and religion (they believed in more than 160 gods). They also developed an advanced mathematics as well as a 365-day calendar believed by some to be even more accurate than the Gregorian calendar in use today.

At its peak, the Mayan population numbered some 14 million. Their history is divided into three periods. The Pre-Classic period began about the time they originated (roughly 1000 B.C.) and extended into A.D. 300; this was the group's formative period. During the Classic period, 300 to 900, Mayan culture spread throughout the area and city-centers were developed at Copán (Honduras), Palenque, Uxmal, and Chichén Itzá (Mexico), and Piedras Negras, Uaxactún, and Tikal (Guatemala). Scholars believe that Tikal was home to some 50,000 people and was not only a center for government, education, economics, and science, but was also a spiritual mecca for the Maya.

It was in the second half of the Classic period that the Maya made their greatest accomplishments in art and science: Europe would not produce a superior system of mathematics for centuries to come. During the Post-Classic period (900-1546), they were invaded by the Toltecs. However, the Maya absorbed these people rather than being conquered by them. Nevertheless, by the time the Spaniards arrived in the mid-

1500s, the Mayan civilization was in decline. Some historians attribute this to widespread famine or disease while others believe the decline was due to a rebellion of the people against the harsh government. Though they were conquered by the Spaniards and became assimilated into the larger culture that developed in the region, Maya Indians still survive in Mexico and Central America today.

How did the **Aztec and Inca Empires** compare with the Mayan?

While all were advanced civilizations that were eventually conquered by Spaniards, the Inca and Aztec cultures reached their peaks in the fifteenth century—just before the arrival of the Europeans in the New World. The Mayan civilization reached its zenith about 500 years earlier and was already in decline by the time of European incursion. Each group also occupied a different region of the Americas, where each carved out its own stronghold and flourished: The Aztecs settled in central Mexico, the Incas in western South America (primarily Peru), and the Mayas in the Yucatan Peninsula and Central America. There is evidence that they traded with each other as well as with American Indians to the north.

The Aztecs founded their central city of Tenochtitlán (the site of Mexico City) about 1325. A poor nomadic people before their arrival in Mexico's central region, the Aztecs believed the Lake Texcoco marsh was a prophetic place to settle. Before they built it into a great city, they first had to fill in the swampy area, which they did by creating artificial islands. In the 1500s, when the Spanish first saw the remarkable city—with its system of causeways, canals, bridges, and aqueducts—they called it the Venice of the New World. In addition to constructing the impressive trade and cultural center of Tenochtitán, the Aztecs were farmers, astronomers, mathematicians, and historians who recorded the events of their civilization. Their religion was pantheistic, meaning they worshiped many gods. Given that, it's not surprising that when the Spanish conquistadors arrived, at first the Maya believed they were gods (or at least, the heavenly hosts of their long-awaited god Quetzalcoatl), and even welcomed them with gifts. Later, the Aztec rose up against the Europeans, but under the leadership of Hernán Cortés (1485-1547), the Spaniards conquered the group, claiming Mexico in August 1521.

The Incas developed one of the most extensive empires in all the Americas. During the hundred years before the arrival of the Europeans, the Incas expanded their territory along the western coast of South America to include parts of present-day Peru, Ecuador, Colombia, Bolivia, Chile, and Argentina. Though it was a vast region, it was nevertheless a closely knit state ruled by a powerful emperor. The government was subdivided down to the local level, but because the emperor required total obedience from his subjects, local rulers were kept in check.

Like the Aztecs in Mexico, the Inca developed an infrastructure that included a network of roads, bridges, and ferries as well as irrigation systems. They, too, built impressive edifices, demonstrating their abilities as engineers. The magnificent city of

Machu Picchu was modeled in clay before construction began. The Inca were also skilled craftspeople, working with gold, silver, and textiles. Like the Aztecs, the Incas worshiped many gods. And when the Spanish explorer Francisco Pizarro (c. 1475-1541) arrived in the region in 1532, he was welcomed as a god at first. However, by 1537 the Inca were brought under Spanish control.

Why was **Julius Caesar** murdered?

The Roman general and statesman Julius Caesar (100-44 B.C.) was stabbed to death in the senate house by a group of men, including some of his former friends, who viewed him as an ambitious tyrant and a threat to the Roman Republic. The date of the assassination, March 15, fell into relatively common usage thanks to William Shakespeare's tragedy, *Julius Caesar* (written in the late 1590s), which has a soothsayer warning the Roman general to "Beware the ides of March." After Caesar's death in 44 B.C., a triumvirate was formed to rule Rome, with Lepidus, Octavian (who would in 27 B.C. become Augustus, the Roman Empire's first ruler), and Marc Antony sharing power. It was Marc Antony (c. 83-30 B.C.), of "Antony and Cleopatra" fame, who aroused the mobs against Caesar's conspirators, driving them out of Rome.

The events illustrate the controversy about Julius Caesar: While some clearly viewed him as a demagogue who forced his way into power, others considered the patrician-born Caesar a man of noble character who defended the rights of the people in an oligarchic state—where the government was controlled by a few people who had only their own interests in mind. This divided opinion has followed Caesar throughout history.

While opinion is still divided on what kind of a ruler Caesar was, there can be no denying his contributions—both to Rome (which would soon emerge as the Roman Empire) and to modern civilization. In his battles, Caesar brought the provinces of Italy under control and defeated his former co-ruler, Pompey the Great (who had, along with Caesar and Crassus, formed the first triumvirate), effectively ending the oligarchy that had ruled Rome. In so doing, he had succeeded in ending the disorder that had plagued Rome for decades and laid the groundwork for the formation of the empire under his grandnephew Augustus in 27 B.C. While Caesar was in office, he planned and carried out several reforms, not the least of which was the implementation of the Julian calendar, which he introduced in 46 B.C. The Gregorian calendar we use today evolved from it.

Caesar also left a legacy of literature: He penned a total of 10 books on his battles in Gaul (c. 58-50 B.C.) and on the civil war, which he had more or less started in 49 B.C. These clear commentaries are still considered masterpieces of military history.

Who were the most important rulers of the **Roman Empire**?

The 500 years of the Roman Empire (27 B.C. to A.D. 476) gave history some of its most noteworthy—and most diabolical—leaders. The major emperors are names that are familiar to most every student of Western civilization: Augustus, Tiberius, Caligula, Claudius, Nero, Trajan, Marcus Aurelius, Diocletian, and Constantine I (called "the Great").

Augustus, Tiberius, Caligula, Claudius, and Nero were the first five emperors, a succession covering 75 years of Roman rule. Octavian (63 B.C.-A.D. 14), later known as Augustus, became Roman emperor when, after the assassination of his great-uncle, Julius Caesar, a power struggle ensued and he defeated Mark Antony and Cleopatra to take the throne. Under Augustus's rule from 27 B.C. to A.D. 14 began the 200 years of the Pax Romana, a period of relative peace. During this time no power emerged that was strong enough to sustain conflict with the Roman army. Consequently, Rome was able to turn its attention to the arts, literature, education, and trade.

As second emperor of Rome, Tiberius (42 B.C.-A.D. 37) came under the influence of Roman politician and conspirator Sejanus (d. A.D. 31). Tiberius was the adopted son of Emperor Augustus, and though he had been carefully schooled and groomed to take on the leadership role, ultimately he became a tyrannical ruler; the final years of his reign were marked by viciousness and cruelty. Upon Tiberius's death, his nephew Caligula (A.D. 12-41) ascended the throne. Born Gaius Caesar, he was nicknamed Caligula, meaning "Little Boots," since he was brought up in military camps and at an early age had been dressed as a soldier. For a short time Caligula ruled with moderation. But not long after he came to power, he fell ill and thereafter exhibited the erratic behavior for which he is well known. Most scholars agree that Caligula must have been crazy. He was murdered in A.D. 41, and Claudius, also nephew to Tiberius, was then proclaimed emperor.

Claudius (10 B.C.-A.D. 54) renewed the expansion of Rome, waging battle with Germany, Syria, and Mauritania (present-day Algeria and Morocco), and conquering half of Britain. Though his administration was reportedly well run, he had his enemies; among them was his niece, Agrippina the Younger (A.D. 15?-59), who is believed to have murdered him in 54, after securing her son, Nero, as successor to the throne.

In Nero (A.D. 37-68) the early Roman Empire had perhaps its most despotic ruler: Though his early years in power were marked by the efficient conduct of public affairs, in 59 he had his mother assassinated (she reportedly had tried to rule through her son), and Nero's legacy from that point forward is one of ruthless behavior. He was involved in murder plots, ordered the deaths of many Romans, instituted the persecution of Christians, and led an extravagant lifestyle that emptied the public coffers. He was declared a public enemy by the Roman Senate and in the year 68 took his own life.

With the exception of Augustus, the first century A.D. of the Roman Empire was marked by extreme rulers. The second century A.D. was marked by the leadership of soldiers and statesmen. Trajan (53-117), who ruled from the year 98 until his death 19 years later, is best known for his military campaigns, which expanded Rome's territory. He was also a builder—constructing bridges, roads, and many buildings. When Marcus Aurelius (121-80) ascended to emperor in 161, he had already been in public office for more than 20 years. A man of great experience, he was reportedly both learned and of gentle character. His generals put down revolting tribes, and, in addition to winning victories along the Danube River, his troops also fought barbarians in the north. Diocletian (245?-313?) had served as an army commander before becoming emperor in 284. In an effort to effectively rule the expansive territory, he divided it into four regions, each with its own ruler, though he himself remained the acknowledged chief. Two years before he abdicated the throne (305), he began the persecution of Christians—a surprising move since he had long been friendly toward them. Unlike his predecessors who died in office, Diocletian had a retirement, which he reportedly spent gardening.

Constantine the Great (who ruled from 306 until his death in 337) is notable for reuniting the regions that Diocletian had created, bringing them all under his rule by 324. He was also the first Roman emperor to convert to Christianity. Theodosius I (347-395), also called "the Great," is known to many since he was the last to rule the united Roman Empire (379-95).

Why was **Constantine I** called "the Great"?

Roman emperor Constantine the Great (c. 275-337) is credited with no less than beginning a new era in history. His father, Constantius, was ruler of the Roman Empire when he died in 306. Though Constantine was named emperor by Roman soldiers, a power struggle ensued. During a battle near Rome in 312, Constantine, who had always been sympathetic toward Christians, reportedly saw a vision of a flaming cross. He emerged from the conflict both converted and victorious. For the next 12 years, Constantine ruled the West Roman Empire while Licinius (also tolerant to Christians) ruled the East. But a struggle between the two emperors ended in death for Licinius and, beginning in 325, Constantine ruled as sole emperor.

During Constantine's reign, Christians regained freedom of worship and the Christian Church became legal. In 325 he convened the Council of Nicaea (from whence came the Nicene Creed so familiar to Christians today). In moving the capital of the Roman Empire to Byzantium (in 330), Constantine shifted the empire's focus from west to east and in so doing laid the foundation for the Byzantine Empire. The Eastern Orthodox Church regards Constantine as a saint.

How was the **Byzantine Empire formed**?

The Byzantine Empire was a continuation of the Roman Empire—its citizens even called themselves Romans. Two dates are given for the formation of the Byzantine Empire, which, though boundaries shifted constantly, was centered in Asia Minor and the Balkan Peninsula: In A.D. 395, upon the death of emperor Theodosius the Great, the Roman Empire was divided into two: East and West. In the years that followed, the West Roman Empire was subject to repeated attacks from nomadic barbarian groups, and Rome finally fell in 476. The East Roman Empire survived as the Byzantine Empire, which, after the fall of Rome, laid claim to much of the lands in the west.

However, many historians date the beginning of the Byzantine Empire earlier—at A.D. 330, when Roman emperor Constantine the Great moved the capital of the then united Roman Empire from Rome to Byzantium (present-day Istanbul, Turkey—subsequently known as Constantinople). By this definition of the empire, Constantine the Great was its first ruler. He was succeeded by nearly 100 rulers over the course of more than 1,000 years of Byzantine rule. At its height, during the sixth century reign of Justinian I from 483 to 565, the empire included parts of southern and eastern Europe, northern Africa, and the Middle East. The Byzantine Empire ended when the Ottoman Turks conquered Constantinople in 1453.

What is the **Byzantine Empire's role** in history?

The Byzantine Empire (330 or 395-1453) is considered a link between ancient and modern civilizations. Though the empire was constantly fighting off invaders, plagued by religious controversies, and marred by political strife, as the heir of the Roman world it allowed for the customs of Greco-Roman civilization to mix with those of the East and with Christianity. The fall of the Byzantine Empire in 1453 typically marks the beginning of the modern era.

What was the **Tang dynasty**?

The Tang (617-907) was the sixth-to-last Chinese dynasty. It's well known since the period saw great achievements not only in government and business, but in letters and the arts—principally lyrical poetry, formal prose, painting, sculpture, and porcelain pottery. The first published book, the *Diamond Sutra,* was produced during this time (in 868). Considered a golden age of Chinese civilization, the Tang was also an age of great expansion. At its height, the empire stretched from Turkmenistan in the west to Korea (which was a vassal state) in the east, and from Manchuria to northern India. As a result, trade prospered, with Chinese jade, porcelain, silk, rice, spices, and teas exported to India, the Middle East, and Europe. One historian called the Tang "the consummate Chinese dynasty...formidable, influential, and innovative."

One of the Tang's innovations was the balance of administrative power: government was separated into three main branches: the Imperial Secretariat (which organized the emperor's directives into policies), the Imperial Chancellery (which reviewed the policies and monitored bureaucracy), and the Department of States Affairs (which carried out the policies through the administration of six ministries). Add to this triumvirate a Board of Censors, which ensured that corruption was kept to a minimum. This form of government outlasted the Tang dynasty: Subsequent monarchies perpetuated the system into the twentieth century.

Yet another example of the forward thinking of the Tang dynasty was a civil service. Candidates for public service were trained in the Confucian principles before they took an exam that would qualify them for official duty.

What were the highlights of the **Ming dynasty**?

The focus on Chinese culture that was the hallmark of the Ming dynasty (1368-1644) was both its strength and its weakness. After the foreign Mongols (whose dynasty had been established by Kublai Khan in 1260) were overthrown as rulers of China in 1368, the Ming emperors returned their—and their subjects'—attention to those things that are distinctively Chinese. The focus on Chinese culture produced a flowering in the arts, evidenced by the name *Ming* itself, meaning "bright" or "brilliant." Architects working during this period produced the splendor of Beijing's Forbidden City. Ming porcelain, bronze, and lacquerware are coveted collectors' items today. Additionally, the novel and drama flourished.

And though the Ming rulers promoted this artistic renaissance and reinstated Confucianism and the program of civil service suspended by the Mongols, the rulers' myopia prevented them from seeing the threat of the nomadic Manchu people on the horizon. In 1644 the Manchus invaded from the north and conquered China, setting up the last dynastic period in Chinese history (it lasted until 1912). Nevertheless, it was the Ming, and not the Manchu, who formed the last great and truly Chinese dynasty.

What was the **Carolingian Empire**?

The empire, which united most of western Europe under a single leader from about 734 until 987, was named for the Carolingians, a family of Frankish kings.

After the decline of the Roman Empire (in 476), various Germanic tribes (including the Goths, the Vandals, the Franks, and the Anglo-Saxons) dominated western Europe—fighting each other as well as the advancing Muslims to protect and expand their territories. In 719 Charles Martel (c. 688-741) united the lands of all the Franks under his rule. (The Franks were the descendants of Germanic tribes who settled in the Rhine River region of western Europe.) He then went on to protect France from Arab incursion and campaigned against the Burgundians and the Frisians, eventually bringing them under his control. Upon his death in 741, Charles Martel was succeeded by his son, Pepin III (known better perhaps as Pepin the Short; c. 714-768). It was Pepin who established the Carolingian Empire and brought the Lombards into the empire. Upon his death, he was succeeded by his son Charlemagne, or Charles the Great (742-814).

Why is **Charlemagne** so well known?

Charlemagne's popularity with history students is due not only to the ruler's great accomplishments during his lifetime, but also to the fact that these accomplishments were documented: His biography, titled *Vita Caroli Magni* (*The Life of Charlemagne*) was written by a fellow named Einhard (c. 770-840), who was his adviser.

Charlemagne (742-814), or Charles the Great, became king of the western Franks when his father, Pepin the Short (c. 714-768) died in 768. Upon the death of his brother, Carloman, in 771, Charles became king of all the Franks. He then went on to conquer much of western Europe, including Saxony, Lombardy, northeastern Spain, and Bavaria. He sometimes employed brutal tactics in bringing people and regions under control: During the last two decades of the eighth century, he used mass executions to subdue Saxon rebellions. Charlemagne succeeded in uniting all of these areas under one empire, and on Christmas Day 800, he had Pope Leo III (c. 750-816) crown him Emperor of the West, thus initiating the Holy Roman Empire. As a patron of the arts, literature, and science, Charlemagne revived western Europe, which had been in decline since the fall of the West Roman Empire (in 476). He is credited with laying the foundation for the Holy Roman Empire and the European civilization that developed later in the Middle Ages. He ruled until his death in 814.

What was the **Ottoman Empire**?

It was a vast Turkish state founded in the thirteenth century by the Osmani Turks, Turks who were led by descendants of Osman I (1258-c. 1326). By the middle of the next century, the Ottoman Empire consisted roughly of modern-day Turkey (the terms "Turkey" and "Ottoman Empire" are used interchangeably). The empire was expanded further by conquests during the 1400s, including the conquest of the Byzantine Empire in 1453. At its height, the Byzantine Empire extended over an area that included the Balkan Peninsula (present-day Slovenia, Croatia, Bosnia and Herzegovina, Macedonia, Yugoslavia, Romania, Bulgaria, Albania, Greece, and Turkey), Syria, Egypt, Iraq, the northern coast of Africa, Palestine, and parts of Arabia, Russia, and Hungary. The capital was placed at Constantinople (present-day Istanbul, Turkey). Thus the Turks established a Muslim empire that would remain a formidable force and influence in the region and in Europe for the next three centuries.

During the 1500s and 1600s the Ottoman Empire was the most powerful in the world. It reached its most glorious heights during the reign of Süleyman the Magnificent (1494-1566), who ruled from 1520 to 1566: It was he who added parts of Hungary to the Ottoman territory. He also tried to take Vienna, but failed. He did succeed in strengthening the Ottoman navy, which dominated the Mediterranean Sea. Süleyman was not only an expansionist, but a patron of the arts and a builder. He ordered the construction of mosques (to spread the Islamic religion throughout the empire), bridges, and other public works.

But by the time World War I began in 1914, the Ottoman Empire had been in decline for some 300 years and only consisted of Asia Minor, parts of southwestern Asia, and part of the Balkan Peninsula. As one of the losing Central powers, the Ottoman Empire was dissolved in 1922 by the peace treaties that ended the war.

Who were the **Habsburgs**?

The Habsburgs were Europe's most powerful royal family. Even if one chose to argue the point of power, there can be no arguing the longevity of the house of Habsburg: They supplied Europe with a nearly uninterrupted stream of rulers for more than 600 years.

Also spelled Hapsburg (which is closer to the pronunciation, HAPS-berg), the name came from the castle of Habichtsburg (meaning "Hawk's Castle"), built during the early eleventh century in Switzerland. The first member of the family to bear the name was Count Werner I (who died in 1096). It was Werner's descendant, Rudolf I (1218-1291), who was elected king of Germany and the Holy Roman Empire in 1273. When Rudolf conquered Austria three years later, he established that country as the family's new home. Austria, Bohemia, Germany, Hungary, and Spain were among the European states ruled by the house of Habsburg. With only one exception, the Habsburg family also ruled the Holy Roman Empire from 1438 (when Albert II was elected) until 1806.

It was the reign of Emperor Charles V during the sixteenth century that the Habsburg influence reached its high-water mark. When in 1496 Spain's Philip I (called Philip the Handsome; 1478-1506) married Joan of Castile (1479-1555), it assured that their son Charles V (1500-1558) would inherit the crown of Spain, which he did in 1516. (Charles was grandson to Spain's King Ferdinand and Queen Isabella.) He also inherited the rest of what by then was a vast empire, and he ruled as Holy Roman Emperor from 1519 until 1556.

Charles V is considered the greatest of all the Habsburgs, though he did face problems. Chief among these were the Protestant Reformation; opposition from his lifelong rival, Francis I (1494-1547), king of France; and the Ottoman Turks, who were at the height of their power during his reign. Nevertheless, he was a successful ruler and his accomplishments included Spain's conquest of lands in the New World—Mexico (at the hands of Hernán Cortés, 1485-1547) and Peru (by Francisco Pizarro, c. 1475-1541).

In 1867 the Habsburg empire was reorganized as the Austro-Hungarian monarchy. That monarchy was dissolved in 1918, after World War I, with the Treaty of Versailles establishing new boundaries for the successor states.

Who were the **Romanovs**?

The Romanov family ruled Russia from 1613 until 1917, when Nicholas II (1868-1918) was overthrown by the Russian Revolution (1905-17). The dynasty was established by Michael Romanov, grandnephew to Ivan the Terrible, who ruled from 1533 to 1584. There were 18 Romanov rulers, including the much-studied Peter the Great, who ruled from 1682 to 1725, and Catherine the Great, who ruled from 1762 to 1796.

As the last tsar of Russia, Nicholas II, who ruled from 1894 to 1917, likely suffered not only the recrimination that was due him, but the public hostility that had accumulated over centuries of ruthless Romanov leadership. Nicholas's difficulties came to a head when he got Russia involved in World War I (1914-18), which produced serious hardships for the Russian people and for which there was little public support. Once Tsar Nicholas was overthrown (and later killed) in the Russian Revolution (1905-17), Bolshevik leader Vladimir Lenin (1870-1924) set about extracting Russia from the conflict by agreeing to sever concessions to Germany. Oddly enough, the Romanov family had, in the fourteenth century, originated with a German nobleman, Andrew Kobyla, who had emigrated to Russia.

Why were **tsars Peter and Catherine** known as "the Great"?

The epithet "the Great" can be misleading: While Romanov tsars Peter the Great, who ruled from 1682 to 1725, and Catherine the Great, who ruled from 1762 to 1796, are among the best-known of the Romanov dynasty and both had many accomplishments during their reigns, they are also known for having increased their power at the expense of others.

Peter is recognized for introducing western European civilization to Russia and for elevating Russia to the status of a great European power. But he also relied on the serfs (the peasants who were little more than indentured servants to the lords) not only to provide the bulk of the funding he needed to fight almost continuous wars, but for the manpower as well: most soldiers were serfs. The man responsible for establishing schools (including the Academy of Sciences), reforming the calendar, and simplifying the alphabet also carried out ruthless reforms. Peter's most vain-glorious act was, perhaps, to move the capital from Moscow to the city he had built for himself on the swampy lands ceded by Sweden: St. Petersburg (known as Petrograd 1914-24, as Leningrad 1924-91). As his "window on Europe," Peter succeeded in making the city into a brilliant cultural center.

For her part, Catherine the Great may well be acknowledged as a patron of the arts and literature (one who corresponded with the likes of French writer Voltaire, 1694-1778), but she, too, increased the privileges of the nobility while making the lives of the serfs even more miserable. Her true colors were shown by how she ascended to power in the first place. In 1744 she married Peter (III), who became tsar of Russia in 1762. That same year, Catherine conspired with her husband's enemies to depose him. He was later killed. And so Catherine came to power, proclaiming herself tsarina. She began her reign by attempting reforms, but a peasant uprising (1773-74) and the French Revolution (which began in 1789) prompted her only to strengthen and protect her absolute authority. Like Peter the Great, she, too, extended the frontiers of the empire through a series of conquests. By the end of her reign, in 1796, Catherine had reduced even the free peasants to the level of serfdom.

What are **England's royal "houses"**?

England's royal houses are simply families, including ancestors, descendants, and kin. Since 1066 England's rulers have come from a series of 10 royal houses: Normandy (ruled 1066-1135), Blois (1135-54), Plantagenet (1154-1399), Lancaster (1399-1471),

York (1471-85), Tudor (1485-1603), Stuart (1603-49, restored 1660-1714), Hanover (1714-1901), Saxe-Coborg (1901-10), and Windsor (1910 to present).

Prior to the establishment of the House of Normandy, England had been ruled by Saxons and Danes since 802. The first king of the House of Normandy was William I (also known as William the Conqueror [c. 1028-1087]), who was the son of the French Duke of Normandy. William invaded England in 1066 on the death of Edward the Confessor and the ascension of Harold II (c. 1022-1066). Ousting Harold, William was coronated at Westminster Abbey on Christmas Day. William's grandson, Stephen, was all that consisted of the short-lived reign of the House of Blois (named such since Stephen was the Count of Blois and Chartres, though he was raised in the court of his uncle, King Henry I, whom he succeeded).

The House of Plantagenet, also called the House of Anjou, included the 10-year reign (1189-99) of Richard I, or Richard the Lionhearted (1157-1099), who fought his father, Henry II (1068-1135), and his brothers for control of the throne. Richard's military prowess made him the hero of romantic legends. Thereafter, two contending branches of the House of Plantagenet—the houses of Lancaster and York—vied for the crown in the infamous War of the Roses (1455-85). The struggle finally ended when Henry VII (a Lancaster) ascended the throne and married into the House of York, reuniting the two sides of the family under the newly minted House of Tudor.

The Tudors were a famous lot, remembered for the reigns of Henry VIII (1509-47) and his daughters, Mary I (1553 to 1558) and Elizabeth I (1558-1603). The Tudors were followed by the Stuarts, whose reign was interrupted by the establishment of the Commonwealth and Protectorate under Oliver Cromwell (1599-1658). The house was restored to power, giving history the eight-year period known as the Restoration, in 1660. It was King William III (1650-1702), a Stuart, and Queen Mary II (1662-1694), who began in 1689 to rule England in a more modern fashion—through Parliament.

A Stuart descendant, George I (1660-1727), established the House of Hanover, which originated in Germany. Queen Victoria (1819-1901), who presided over the Victorian Age (1837-1901), was of the House of Hanover. She was succeeded by her son, Edward VII (1841-1910), who established the House of Saxe-Coburg. Technically, this is the royal house still at the helm today—the name was changed to Windsor during World War I (1914-18).

Why is **Henry VIII** so famous?

The reign of Henry VIII, from 1509 to 1547, is perhaps the most well-known Tudor monarchy. It was marked by papal conflicts and England's subsequent break with the Roman Catholic Church. When Henry's wife, Catherine of Aragon (1485-1536), failed to produce a male heir, he appealed to the pope to grant him a divorce. The request was of course denied. Though Henry went on to have his marriage to Catherine declared invalid (on the grounds that she was his brother's widow) and he secretly married Anne

Boleyn (c. 1507-1536) in 1533, his troubles with the church continued. In 1534 he set up the Church of England, declaring the monarch as its head. He went to extreme measures to ensure the act was upheld—even executing his appointed chancellor, Sir Thomas More (1478-1535), for his refusal to acknowledge royal supremacy.

Because of papal conflicts and England's break with the Roman Catholic Church, the reign of Henry VIII is perhaps the most well-known Tudor monarchy. (Original painting by Hans Holbein II.)

Henry VIII was eventually successful in procuring a male heir to the throne—but it required a third marriage, to Jane Seymour (c. 1509-1537): His son, Edward VI (1537-53), succeeded him in 1547. Nevertheless, it was Henry VIII's daughters who went on to make history. Mary I, who ruled England and Ireland from 1553 to 1558, was the daughter of Henry and his first wife, Catherine of Aragon. In 1554 Mary wed Spain's Philip II (1527-1598), forming a temporary alliance between the two powers. The following year she realigned England with the Catholic Church, undertaking the persecution of Protestants and earning herself the name "Bloody Mary."

Why did **Queen Elizabeth I** have an entire age named after her?

Ascending the throne in 1558, Queen Elizabeth (1533-1603) remained in power until 1603, a 45-year period during which England dominated the seas to become a European power; colonization began, with Sir Walter Raleigh (1554-1618) and others establishing British settlements in North America; culture flourished, with the likes of William Shakespeare (1564-1616), Christopher Marlowe (1564-1593), and Sir

Edmund Spenser (1552-1599) producing literary masterpieces; and industry and commerce boomed. This was the Elizabethan Age, one of England's high-water marks.

One of the most well-known events of Elizabeth's reign was England's defeat of the Spanish Armada in July-August 1588. This event has an interesting twist. The only child of Henry VIII (1491-1547) and his second wife, Anne Boleyn (c. 1507-1536), Elizabeth had succeeded her half-sister Mary Tudor (1516-58) as queen. In the summer of 1588, the "invincible" Spanish fleet, which was headed for invasion of England, had been dispatched by none other than Spain's Philip II (1527-1598), Mary Tudor's former husband. Though the English were severely outnumbered (having only 34 ships to Spain's 132), they were aided by weather and defeated the Spanish Armada on August 8. This victory at sea opened the world to English trade and colonization.

Queen Elizabeth was the last of the Tudor rulers, who are credited with strengthening the monarchy in England. They were succeeded by the House of Stuart in 1603, when James I (1566-1625), who ruled from 1603 to 1625, ascended the throne. It is that James who gave the world the King James version of the Bible. He is also notable for having been the son of Mary, Queen of Scots (1542-1587), whom Elizabeth I had reluctantly put to death.

Who was **Mary, Queen of Scots**?

Mary Stuart was born in 1542 to James V of Scotland, who ruled from 1513 to 1542, and his wife, Mary of Guise. When Mary was just six days old, her father died, making the infant a queen. Her mother ruled the country as a regent until 1561, when Mary officially took on her duties. She was, by all reports, a beautiful and charming young woman whose courage and mettle would be tested by time. When she ascended the throne, she inherited her mother's struggle with the Protestants, who were led by John Knox (1513-1572), a former Catholic priest who was involved in the Reformation. As a Roman Catholic, Mary was subject to harsh verbal attacks issued by Knox, who denounced the pope's authority and the practices of the church. But this was not the worst of her troubles: In 1565 Mary wed her English cousin, Lord Darnley (1545-1567), in an attempt to secure her claim to the English throne as successor to Elizabeth I (1533-1603), also her cousin.

But Mary's ambitions would be her undoing. She quickly grew to dislike her husband, who became aligned with her Protestant opponents and successfully carried out a plot to murder—in her presence—Mary's adviser, David Rizzio (c. 1533-1566). Surprisingly, Mary and Darnley reconciled shortly thereafter (a politically savvy move on her part), and she conceived a child, James, who was born in 1566. Darnley had enemies of his own, and one year later he was murdered. Mary promptly married the Earl of Bothwell (1536-1578), with whom she had fallen in love well before becoming a widow. Bothwell was accused of Darnley's murder, and though he was acquitted, his marriage to the queen shocked Scotland. The people took up arms, forcing Mary to abdicate the throne in 1567. She was 25 years old.

Fleeing to England, Mary, Queen of Scots, was given refuge by Elizabeth I (1533-1603). Though she was technically a prisoner, Mary nevertheless was able to conspire with Elizabeth's enemies—including English Catholics and the Spanish—in attempts to kill her. When one such plot was discovered in 1586, Mary was charged for her involvement in it and was put on trial. Found guilty, she was put to death in 1587, though Elizabeth hesitated to take such action.

Meantime, Mary's son, James VI of Scotland (1566-1625), had taken on his responsibilities in 1583—after Scotland had been ruled on his behalf by regents since Mary's abdication some 16 years prior. He had promptly formed an alliance with Elizabeth I and, in 1587, accepted with resignation his mother's execution. In 1603 James succeeded Elizabeth, becoming James I, King of England, uniting Scotland and England under one throne. The union was made official about a century later (in 1707) when Parliament passed the Act of Union.

How did the **House of Windsor** originate?

The origins of Windsor, the family name of the royal house of Great Britain, can be traced to the 1840 marriage of Queen Victoria, who ruled from 1837 to 1901, to her first cousin Albert, the son of the Duke of Saxe-Coburg-Gotha (in present-day Germany). As a foreigner, Prince Albert had to overcome the distrust of the British public, which he did by proving himself to be a devoted husband to Queen Victoria and by demonstrating his genuine concern in Britain's national affairs. Victoria and Albert had nine children. Their oldest son, Albert Edward (1841-1910), became King Edward VII upon Victoria's death in 1901. But Edward's reign lasted only until 1910, when he died and his son, George V (1865-1936), ascended the throne. George was king during World War I (1914-18), and, in 1917, with Britain and Germany bitter enemies, he denounced his ties and claims to Germany, superseding his grandfather's (Prince Albert's) family name of Wettin and establishing the House of Windsor.

Thus, George V was the first ruling member of the House of Windsor. The others were Edward VIII (1894-1972), who abdicated the throne in 1936 so that he could marry American socialite Wallis Simpson (1896-1986); George VI (1895-1952), who became king upon his brother Edward's abdication and who would work tirelessly during World War II (1939-45) to keep up the morale of the British people; and Elizabeth II (1926-), George VI's elder daughter, who still reigns as Queen of England today. Elizabeth, who ascended the throne in 1952, proclaimed that she and all her descendants who bear the title prince or princess are to be known as Windsor.

Why is the **Magna Carta** important?

The Magna Carta, arguably the most famous document in British history, has had many interpreters since it was signed by King John (1167-1216), who was under pressure to do so, on June 15, 1215, "in the meadow which is called Runnymede, between

Windsor and Staines," in Surrey, England. Drawn up by English barons who were angered by the king's encroachment on their rights, the charter has been credited with no less than insuring personal liberty and putting forth the rights of the individual, which include the guarantee of a trial by jury: "No freeman shall be arrested and imprisoned, or dispossessed, or outlawed, or banished, or in any way molested; nor will be set forth against him, nor send against him, unless by the lawful judgment of his peers, and by the law of the land."

King John, who ruled from 1199 to 1216 and was also called John Lackland, had a long history of abuse of power. While his brother Richard I (or Richard the Lionhearted, 1157-1199) was still king, John tried to wrest the throne from him. Though he failed in his effort, when Richard died in 1199, John did ascend to king, inheriting four French duchies (which he soon lost). Upon his refusal to recognize the new archbishop of Canterbury, John was excommunicated. In order to regain favor with the pope, he was forced to give up his kingdom (1213) and receive it back as a papal fief. He was further required to pay an annual tribute to the pope. It was in raising funds that John ran into trouble with England's powerful barons, who were outraged at and tired of his interference in their affairs. The barons drafted the 63 chapters of the Magna Carta, writing it in the king's voice, and met John along the banks of the Thames River as he returned in 1215 from an unsuccessful invasion of France. The document, to which John was forced to put his seal, asserted the rights of the barons, churchmen, and townspeople, and provided for the king's assurance that he would not encroach on their privileges. In short, the Magna Carta stipulated that the king, too, was subject to the laws of the land.

In that the Magna Carta made a provision for a Great Council, to be comprised of nobles and clergy who would approve the actions of the king vis-a-vis his subjects and ensure the tenets set forth in the charter were upheld, it is credited with laying the foundation for a parliamentary government in England.

After signing it, John immediately appealed to Pope Innocent III (1160 or 1161-1216), who issued an annulment of the charter. Nevertheless, John died before he could fight it, and the Magna Carta was later upheld as the basis of English feudal justice. It is still considered by many to be the cornerstone of constitutional government.

THE BIRTH OF MODERN GOVERNMENT

How old is the **British parliament**?

The legislative assembly of Great Britain has roots dating back to the Middle Ages (500-1350) when a great council, known as the Curia Regis, advised the king. This body was made up of nobility and clergy. The body evolved over time and progressively gained more power to govern.

Today Parliament consists of the House of Commons, a democratically elected body (roughly equivalent to the U.S. House of Representatives); the House of Lords, which consists of noblemen (dukes, marquesses, earls, viscounts, and barons) as well as high-ranking Anglican clergy (bishops and abbots); and the monarch (king or queen). Since 1911 the power of the House of Lords has been negligible, with the House of Commons charged with electing the prime minister (who must be a member of Commons). The prime minister—not the monarch—is the executive head of government.

Why was **Oliver Cromwell** important to British history?

English soldier and statesman Oliver Cromwell (1599-1658) was a key player in a chain of events that shaped modern British government. The events began when Charles I (1600-1649), House of Stuart, ascended the throne in 1625 and shortly thereafter married a French Catholic princess, immediately raising the ire of his Protestant subjects. This was not the end of England's problems with King Charles: After repeated struggles with the primarily Puritan Parliament, Charles dismissed the legislative body in 1629 and went on to rule without it for 11 years. During this period, religious and civil liberties were seriously diminished, and political and religious strife prevailed. Fearing the king's growing power, Parliament moved to raise an army, and soon civil war broke out (1642-48). Like the French Revolution (1789-99), fought 150 years later, the struggle in England was largely one between a king who claimed to rule by divine right and a government body (in this case Parliament) that claimed the right to govern the nation in behalf of the people.

Enter military leader Oliver Cromwell: After two years of indecisive battles in the English civil war, Cromwell led his parliamentary army troops to victories at Marston Moor (1644) and Naseby (1645), which resulted in Charles's surrender. But when Charles escaped his captors in 1647, the fighting was briefly renewed. It was ended once and for all in 1648. When the king was tried the following year, Cromwell was among those leading the charge to have Charles executed. The king's opponents had their way and, having abolished the monarchy, soon established the Commonwealth of England, installing Oliver Cromwell as "Lord Protector."

Though Cromwell endeavored to bring religious tolerance to England and was somewhat successful in setting up a quasi-democratic government (he declined to take the title of king in 1657), his leadership was constantly challenged by those who wished to restore the Stuart monarchy. When Cromwell died in 1658, he was succeeded by his son, Richard (1626-1712), whose talents were not up to the challenges put to the Lord Protector. The movement to restore the monarchy—particularly the Stuart line—gained impetus, and Richard Cromwell was soon dismissed and went to live outside of England for the next 20 years.

Charles II (1630-1685), the son of Charles I, ascended the throne in 1660, beginning the eight-year period known as the Restoration. Both Charles and his brother, James II (1633-1701), who succeeded him in 1685, worked to reassert the absolutism of the Stuart monarchy. But both kings butted heads with Parliament, particularly when it came to financial matters. Finally in 1688, James II was deposed in the so-called Glorious Revolution. William III (1650-1702), grandson of Charles I, and his wife, Queen Mary II (1662-1694), daughter of James II, were placed on the throne the following year. Though the House of Stuart remained in power, there was an important hitch: Parliament compelled William and Mary to accept the Bill of Rights (of 1689), which asserted that the Crown no longer had absolute power in England and that it must rule responsibly through the nation's representatives sitting in Parliament. Thus, the English civil war (also called the Protestant Revolution) and the influence of Oliver Cromwell and other parliamentarians laid the foundation for England's constitutional monarchy.

What was the **Bill of Rights of 1689**?

The English bill, accepted by King William III (1650-1702), who ruled jointly with his Protestant wife Queen Mary II (1662-1694), seriously limited royal power. After a struggle between the Stuart kings and Parliament and the subsequent ousting of King James II (1633-1701), Parliament presented the Bill of Rights to King William and Queen Mary as a condition of their ascension: The document not only described certain civil and political rights and liberties as "true, ancient, and indubitable," but it also ironed out how the throne would be succeeded. This point was of critical importance to the future of England—the article stipulated that no Roman Catholic would rule the country. Since the Bill of Rights served to assert the role of Parliament in the government of England, it is considered one of the seminal documents of British constitutional law.

What were the **Rights of Man**?

In 1789 the French assembly made the Declaration of the Rights of Man and of the Citizen, meant to flesh out the revolutionary cry of "liberty, equality, and fraternity." Influenced by the U.S. Declaration of Independence (1776) as well as the ideas of the Enlightenment, the document guaranteed religious freedom, the freedom of speech and the press, and personal security. It proclaimed that man has natural and inalienable rights, which include "liberty, property, personal security, and resistance to oppression.... " The declaration further stipulated that "No one may be accused, imprisoned, or held under arrest except in such cases and in such a way as is prescribed by law" and that "Every man is presumed innocent until he is proved guilty.... " The declaration was subsequently written into the preamble of the French constitution (1791). However, the Code Napoleon superseded many of the ideas it set forth.

What were **Napoleon's Hundred Days**?

The term refers to Napoleon Bonaparte's last 100 days as ruler of France. Having been defeated by his enemies—a coalition of European powers Britain, Sweden, Austria, and Prussia, who aligned themselves against Napoleon's domination—the emperor abdicated the throne in the spring of 1814, and was exiled to the island of Elba in the Mediterranean Sea. There he heard of the confusion and discontent that came after he had descended the throne. He left Elba, and with more than 1,000 men, arrived on the French coast at Cannes and marched inland to Paris. Hearing of his arrival, the new Bourbon king, Louis XVIII (1755-1824), fled. On March 20 Napoleon began a new reign, but it was only to last until the European allies defeated him again, at the Battle of Waterloo, June 12 through 18. After that battle, the so-called Little Corporal (for his diminutive stature) was permanently exiled to the British island of St. Helena, where he remained until his death in 1821.

Why is **Napoleon still controversial**?

Even history has not been able to sort out the widely disparate opinions of the diminutive French ruler. And both the detractors and the champions (or some would say, the apologists) continue to publish their arguments and supporting research. The most obvious point on which scholars differ centers on the fact that first and foremost Napoleon Bonaparte (1769-1821) was a military man. Here opinion divides quite naturally. Not long after Napoleon assumed power (in the coup of 1799), he proceeded to keep France—and the rest of Europe—at war for more than 10 years. From the French perspective, Napoleon was a great man, a brilliant strategist who could not only muster his troops but could keep them motivated to fight one campaign after another. The targets of these campaigns—England, Russia, Austria, Germany, Spain, and Portugal among them—view Napoleon in quite a different light, as would be expected. Researchers from these countries have seen and rendered Napoleon's dark side, calling him a megalomaniac and a psychopath, and even seeing him as a forerunner of Adolf Hitler (1889-1945).

To further complicate the matter of how history views Napoleon, before he declared himself emperor for life (in 1804) and launched his military conquests throughout the continent and beyond (1805), Napoleon enjoyed a brief period in which many Europeans—not just the French —believed him to be a hero. After all, he assumed leadership of France after the hideous period of Robespierre's Terror and the ineffectual government of the Directory, and then he proceeded to make peace with the Americans, the Russians, *and* the British. Many believed Napoleon was just the man to bring order to the chaos France had known since the storming of the Bastille, and he extended an olive branch to France's longtime enemies. It looked like he would restore order at home and abroad. Of course this honeymoon did not last: By 1805 the leader many had looked to to end the turmoil only became the cause of more turmoil. His "compulsive war-making," as one writer put it, soon swept over the continent, ultimately uniting various countries in an effort to rid Europe of the scourge that was Napoleon and his Grand Army.

Thus, students and readers are left to sort through the diverging accounts of this controversial figure. Napoleon has been called the "Emperor of Kings," credited for

llustration of the 1776 signing of the Declaration of Independence, which has long been regarded as history's most eloquent statement of the rights of the people. (Original painting by Asher Durand.)

his vision, insight, courage, and even with the development of the modern liberal democracy; he has also been described as a compulsive tyrant who had an insatiable appetite for battle, a man whose own ambitions left millions dead. But on a few descriptions both sides can agree: He was a brave soldier, an inspired military leader, and, at least for a time, a charismatic ruler.

What does the **Declaration of Independence** say?

The Declaration of Independence, adopted July 4, 1776, has long been regarded as history's most eloquent statement of the rights of the people. In it, not only did the 13 American colonies declare their freedom from Britain, they also addressed the reasons for the proclamation (naming the "causes which impel them to the separation") and cited the British government's violations of individual rights, saying "the history of the present King 'George III' of Great Britain is a history of repeated injuries and usurpations," which aimed to establish "an absolute Tyranny over these States."

The opening paragraphs go on to state the American ideal of government, an ideal that is based on the theory of natural rights. The Declaration of Independence puts forth the fundamental principles that a government exists for the benefit of the people and that "all men are created equal." As the chairman of the Second Continental Congress committee that prepared the Declaration of Independence, it was Thomas Jefferson (1743-1826) who wrote and presented the first draft to the Second Continental Congress on July 2, 1776.

The passage that is most frequently quoted is this:

> We hold these truths to be self-evident, that all men are created equal, that they are endowed by their Creator with certain unalienable Rights, that among these are Life, Liberty and the pursuit of Happiness. That to secure these rights, Governments are instituted among Men, deriving their just powers from the consent of the governed, That whenever any Form of Government becomes destructive of these ends, it is the Right of the People to alter or to abolish it, and to institute new Government, laying its foundation on such principles and organizing its powers in such form, as to them shall seem most likely to effect their Safety and Happiness.

Who are considered the **Founding Fathers** of the United States?

The term is used to refer to a number of American statesmen who were influential during the revolutionary period of the late 1700s. Though definitions vary, most include the authors of the Declaration of Independence and the signers of the U.S. Constitution among the nation's Founding Fathers.

Of the 56 members of the Continental Congress who signed the Declaration of Independence (July 4, 1776), the most well-known are John Adams (1735-1826) and Samuel Adams (1722-1803) of Massachusetts, Benjamin Franklin (1706-1790) of Pennsylvania, John Hancock (1737-1793) of Massachusetts, and Thomas Jefferson (1743-1826) of Virginia.

The 39 men who signed the U.S. Constitution on September 17, 1787, include notable figures such as George Washington (1732-1799), who would go on, of course, to become the first president of the United States; Alexander Hamilton (1755-1804), who, as a former military aid to George Washington, went on to become the first U.S. secretary of the treasury; and James Madison (1751-1836), who is called the "father of the constitution" for his role as negotiator and recorder of debates between the delegates. At 81 years of age, Benjamin Franklin was the oldest signer of the Constitution and was among the six statesmen who could claim the distinction of signing both it and the Declaration of Independence; the others were George Clymer (1739-1813), Robert Morris (1734-1806), George Read (1733-1798), Roger Sherman (1721-1793), and James Wilson (1742-1798).

Patriots and politicians conspicuous by their absence from the Constitutional Convention of 1787 were John Adams and Thomas Jefferson, who were performing other government duties at the time and would each go on to become U.S. president; Samuel Adams and John Jay (1745-1829), who were not appointed as state delegates but who continued in public life, holding various federal and state government offices (including governor of their states); and Patrick Henry (1736-1799) of Virginia, who saw no need to go beyond the Articles of Confederation (1777) to grant more power to the central government. Henry's view on this issue foreshadows the discontent that crested nearly 100 years later when 12 southern states (including Virginia) seceded from the Union, causing the Civil War (1861-65) to break out.

Adams, Franklin, Hancock, Jefferson, Washington, Hamilton, Madison, Jay, and Henry: These are the names that come to mind when the words "Founding Fathers" are uttered. Each of them had a profound impact in the political life of the United States—even beyond their starring roles as patriots and leaders during the American revolutionary era. However, it's important to note that in many texts and to many Americans, the term *Founding Fathers* refers *only* to the men who drafted the U.S. Constitution since it is that document that continues—more than 200 years after its signing—to provide the solid foundation for American democratic government.

What were the **Articles of Confederation**?

This American document was the forerunner to the U.S. Constitution (1788). Drafted by the Continental Congress at York, Pennsylvania, on November 15, 1777, the Articles of Confederation went into effect on March 1, 1781, when the last state (Maryland) ratified them. The articles had shortcomings that were later corrected by the Constitution: They provided the states with more power than the central government, stipulating that Congress rely on the states both to collect taxes and to carry out the acts of Congress.

It is largely thanks to Alexander Hamilton (1755-1804) that the articles were thrown out: realizing they made for a weak national government, Hamilton led the charge to strengthen the central government—even at the expense of the states. Eventually, he won the backing of George Washington (1732-1799), James Madison (1751-1836), John Jay (1745-1829), and others, which led to the convening of the Philadelphia Constitutional Convention, where the ineffectual Articles of Confederation were thrown out and the Constitution was drafted.

One lasting provision of the Articles of Confederation was the ordinance of 1787. Signed in an era of westward expansion, the ordinance set the guidelines for how a territory could become a state: A legislature would be elected as soon as the population had reached 5,000 voting citizens (which were men only), and the territory would be eligible for statehood once its population had reached 60,000.

Which states were the **original 13**?

In order of admission they are Delaware, Pennsylvania, New Jersey, Georgia, Connecticut, Massachusetts, Maryland, South Carolina, New Hampshire, Virginia, New York, North Carolina, and Rhode Island. Vermont was fourteenth and the first free state (the first state without slavery).

Who wrote the **U.S. Constitution**?

In spirit the U.S. Constitution was created by all of the 55 delegates to the meeting that convened on May 25, 1787, in Philadelphia's Independence Hall. Thomas Jefferson (1743-1826) called the Constitutional Convention "an assembly of demi-gods," and with good cause: The delegates were the young nation's brightest and best. When the states had been called upon to send representatives to the meeting, 12 states answered by sending their most experienced, most talented, and smartest men; Rhode Island, which feared the interference of a strengthened national government in state affairs, sent no one to Philadelphia.

Even in such stellar company, the document did have to be written. While many had a hand in this process, it was New York lawyer and future American politician and diplomat Gouverneur Morris (1752-1816) who actually took on the task of penning the Constitution, putting into prose the resolutions reached by the convention. Morris had the considerable help of the records that James Madison (1751-1836) of Virginia had kept as he managed the debates among the delegates and suggested compromises. In that capacity and in that he designed the system of checks and balances among the legislative (Congress), the executive (the president of the United States), and the judicial (Supreme Court), Madison had considerable influence on the document's language, quite rightfully earning him the designation "father of the constitution."

The original document, drafted by Morris, is preserved in the National Archives Building in Washington, D.C. While the Constitution has been amended by Congress, the tenets set forth therein have remained with Americans for more than two centuries, and they have provided proof to the countries of the world that a constitution outlining the principles and purposes of its government is necessary to good government.

When was the **U.S. Constitution ratified**?

The Constitution was ratified by the required nine states by June 21, 1788. It went into effect the following year, superseding the Articles of Confederation (1781).

What rights are protected in the **Bill of Rights**?

The first 10 amendments to the U.S. Constitution are collectively called the Bill of Rights, which became law on December 15, 1791, and are meant to guarantee individual liberties.

The First Amendment, which is perhaps most often cited by Americans, guarantees freedom of religion, speech, and the press, as well as the right to assemble peaceably and the right to petition the government for a redress of grievances. The Second Amendment guarantees the right to keep and bear arms (stating that "a well regulated militia being necessary to the security of a free State"). The Third Amendment forbids peacetime quartering of soldiers in private dwellings without consent of the owner. The Fourth Amendment forbids unreasonable searches and seizures.

The Fifth through the Seventh amendments establish basic standards of jurisprudence. The Fifth (which long ago fell into common usage with the phrase, "s/he's pleading the Fifth") guarantees that a person will not be compelled to testify against himself. The amendment also ensures that a criminal indictment can only be handed down by a grand jury (12 to 23 people who determine if a trial is necessary) and prohibits double jeopardy (being prosecuted twice for the same criminal offense). The Sixth Amendment protects the rights of accused persons in criminal cases by guaranteeing a speedy and fair trial, an impartial jury, and the right to counsel. The Seventh Amendment guarantees trial by jury. The Eighth Amendment prohibits excessive bail, excessive fines, and cruel and unusual punishment.

The Ninth Amendment, which is one that many Americans are probably unable to cite, is an important one nevertheless: It states that simply because a right is not enumerated in the Constitution, it does not mean that the people do not retain that right.

The Tenth Amendment relinquishes to the state governments those powers the Constitution did not expressly grant the federal government or deny the states. In other words, it limits the power of the federal government to that which is granted in the Constitution.

Who **determines whether a law violates the liberties** guaranteed by the Bill of Rights?

It is the job of the U.S. Supreme Court to decide whether or not a law impinges upon the liberties listed in—or implied by—the Bill of Rights (1791). The difficult task before the Supreme Court justices is in determining what rights are implied. Such questions prompt months of hearings and deliberations before a decision can be reached as to the constitutionality of a contested law. The judicial body makes its determinations based on a majority vote of the nine justices (one chief justice and eight associates). Established as the highest court in the country by Article 3 of the Constitution, the Court has ultimate authority in all legal questions that arise pertaining to the Constitution. Called the "court of last resorts," the Supreme Court both interprets the acts of Congress (including laws and treaties) and determines the constitutionality of federal and state laws (under the Fourteenth Amendment, the Court has upheld that most of the Bill of Rights also applies to state governments).

How are **amendments** made to the U.S. **Constitution**?

There are two paths that proposed amendments can take to become law. The first path is this: An amendment is proposed in Congress; two-thirds of both houses must then approve it (if they do not, then the proposal ends here); if approved in both houses of the U.S. Congress, the proposed amendment is sent to the legislatures (or conventions) of each state of the union; three-fourths of all the state legislatures must then approve it (by whatever rules each state legislature uses); once three-fourths of the states approve it, the amendment is made (if three-fourths of the states do not approve it, the amendment fails to become law).

The second path is this: The legislatures of two-thirds of the states ask for an amendment to be made to the U.S. Constitution; Congress then calls a convention to propose it; then the proposed amendment becomes a law when it is ratified by the legislatures in three-fourths of the states. While this path has never been taken, it's an important provision nonetheless since it allows for a popular, state-based proposal to be considered.

How many amendments have been made to the U.S. Constitution?

There have been 27 amendments to date. The following list gives brief summaries and the year each became part of the U.S. Constitution.

First Amendment through the Tenth Amendment (1791): Comprise the Bill of Rights.

Eleventh Amendment (1798): Declares that U.S. federal courts cannot try any case brought against a state by a citizen of another state or country.

Twelfth Amendment (1804): Revised the presidential and vice presidential election rules such that members of the electoral college, called electors, vote for one person as president and for another as vice president. Prior to the passage of this amendment, the electors simply voted for two men—the one receiving more votes became president and the other became vice president.

Thirteenth Amendment (1865): Prohibits slavery. Along with Amendments 14 and 15, these are sometimes called the Civil War amendments.

Fourteenth Amendment (1868): Defines U.S. citizenship and gives all citizens equal protection under the law. (This amendment made former slaves citizens of both the United States and the state where they lived. It further forbade states to deny equal rights to any person.)

Fifteenth Amendment (1870): States that the right of U.S. citizens to vote shall not be denied or abridged by the United States or by any state on account of race, color, or previous condition of servitude. (This amendment was meant to extend suffrage to black men.)

Sixteenth Amendment (1913): Authorizes a federal income tax.

Seventeenth Amendment (1913): Provides for the direct election of senators. Before this passed, state legislatures elected senators to represent them; this amendment gave that power to the people of each state.

Eighteenth Amendment (1919): Made prohibition legal. (In other words, the manufacture and distribution of alcohol became illegal.)

Nineteenth Amendment (1920): Grants women the right to vote.

Twentieth Amendment (1933): Also called the "lame duck amendment," it changed congressional terms of office and the dates of the presidential inauguration so that newly elected officials take office closer to election time.

Twenty-first Amendment (1933): Repealed Amendment 18 to end prohibition.

Twenty-second Amendment (1951): Limits presidential tenure to two terms in office. (A president can hold office for no more than 10 years—two years as an unelected president, and two terms as an elected president.)

Twenty-third Amendment (1961): Grants residents of Washington, D.C., the right to vote in presidential elections.

Twenty-fourth Amendment (1964): Outlaws the poll tax in all federal elections and primaries. (Some states had used poll taxes as a way of keeping certain populations of voters from casting their ballots; the practice had served to disenfranchise blacks and poor people.)

Twenty-fifth Amendment (1967): Provides for procedures to fill the vice presidency and further clarifies presidential succession rules. (Upon removal, resignation, or death of the president, the vice president assumes the presidency; if a vice president is removed, resigns, or dies while in office, the president nominates a vice president who takes office upon confirmation by a majority vote of both houses of Congress.)

Twenty-sixth Amendment (1971): Lowers the voting age for federal and state elections to 18.

Twenty-seventh Amendment (1992): Prevents Congress from passing immediate salary increases for itself; it requires that salary changes passed by Congress cannot take effect until after the next congressional election. (This amendment had been passed by Congress in 1788 and was then sent to the states for ratification. Since the amendment had no time limit for ratification, it became part of the Constitution in 1992, after Michigan became the thirty-eighth state to ratify it.)

THE AMERICAN PARTY SYSTEM

Who were the **Whigs**?

They were members of political parties in Scotland, England, and the United States. The name is derived from *whiggamor* (meaning "cattle driver"), which was a derogatory term used in the seventeenth century to refer to Scottish Presbyterians who opposed King Charles I of England (1600-1649). Charles, who ruled from 1625 to 1649, was deposed in a civil war and subsequently tried in court, convicted of treason, and beheaded. The British Whigs, who were mostly merchants and landed gentry, supported a strong Parliament. They were opposed by the aristocratic Tories who upheld the power of the king. For a short period during the eighteenth century, the Whigs dominated political life in England. After 1832 they became part of the Liberal Party.

At about the same time, the Whig Party in the United States emerged as one of the two major American political parties. The other was the Democratic Party that Americans still know today, which supported President Andrew Jackson (1767-1845) for re-election in 1832. Though Jackson's first term of office had proved to be somewhat controversial, the Whigs were unable to elect their candidate (Henry Clay, 1777-1852, of the so-called Southern "Cotton" Whigs), and Jackson, called "Old Hickory," went on to a second term. In the election of 1840 the Whigs, whose leadership had succeeded in uniting the party, were finally successful in putting their candidate in the White House. But William Henry Harrison (1773-1841) died after only 32 days in office, and his successor, John Tyler (1790-1862), alienated the Whig leaders in Congress, and they ousted him from the party. In 1848 the Whigs put Zachary Taylor (nicknamed "Old Rough and Ready," 1784-1850) in the White House, but two years later he, too, died in office. His successor, Millard Fillmore (1800-1874), remained loyal to the Whigs, but there were problems within the party. The last Whig presidential candidate was General Winfield Scott ("Old Fuss and Feathers," 1786-1866) in 1852, but he was defeated by Franklin Pierce (1804-1869). Shortly thereafter the Whig party broke up over the slavery issue; most of the Northern Whigs joined the Republican Party, while most of the Southern "Cotton" Whigs joined the Democratic Party.

How did the **Republican Party** begin?

The Republican Party, one of the two principal political parties of the United States, was founded in 1854 by those opposing the extension of slavery into new territories. The party mustered enough support to elect their candidate in 1860, Abraham Lincoln (1809-1865). During the 1880s party members nicknamed themselves the Grand Old Party; the vestige of this nickname is still around today, as the GOP. There have been 17 Republican presidents.

How did the **Democratic Party** begin?

The other—and older—principal party in the United States today, the Democratic Party was founded around electing Thomas Jefferson (1743-1826) to office in 1800 (against Alexander Hamilton's Federalist Party). The party's platform favored personal liberty and the limitation of federal government. Installing Jefferson in office, the party—then called the Democratic-Republicans—went on to get its candidates into the White House for the next 25 years. In 1828 they became known simply as Democrats, dropping the suffix. Depending on how one counts, there have been either 18 or 19 Democratic presidents; Andrew Johnson (1808-1875) is problematic since he was a Democrat before joining the National Union Party ticket as the vice presidential candidate in 1864. (Some sources list both party affiliations, as in Democratic/National Union.)

How were the **Southern states brought back into the Union**?

Even before the Civil War had ended, Washington, D.C., considered the difficult problem of how to rejoin the seceding states with the North. Some lawmakers felt the Southern states should be treated as if they were territories that were gained through war. Others, including both Abraham Lincoln (1809-1865) and Andrew Johnson (1808-1875), reasoned that since secession was illegal, the South belonged—and always had—to the Union, and therefore the states ought to be brought back into their "proper relationship" with the federal government. They favored punishing the Southern leaders—but not the states themselves.

President Abraham Lincoln developed his 10 percent plan: As soon as 10 percent of a state's population had taken an oath of loyalty to the United States, the state would be allowed to set up a new government. But Congress opposed it, proclaiming the policy too mild, and responded by passing the Wade-Davis Bill (June 1864), making the requirements for statehood more rigid. Instead of Lincoln's 10 percent, Congress required that a majority of voters in each state would need to swear their loyalty, in an "ironclad oath," before statehood could be restored. Further, the bill stipulated that the constitution of each state had to abolish slavery and that Confederate military leaders were to be prohibited from holding political office and otherwise disenfranchised. Lincoln opposed the bill and neither signed nor returned it before Congress was dismissed, and so the Wade-Davis measure failed to become law.

When Lincoln was assassinated the following April, the matter remained unsettled. His successor, President Andrew Johnson, soon put forth a plan to readmit the states. He called for each state constitution to abolish slavery and repudiate the Confederate war debt; further, a majority of voters in each state needed to vow allegiance to the Union. Once a state had reorganized itself under this plan, Johnson required the state legislature to approve the Thirteenth Amendment (abolishing slavery in the United States). When Congress reconvened in December 1865 for the first time since Lincoln's assassination, all former Confederate states except Texas had complied with the president's specifications for statehood. But these new states had also set up Black Codes, severely restricting the rights of blacks. Further, there was violence against blacks who were the victims of attacks by white Southerners—including members of the newly formed Ku Klux Klan, a secret white organization that spread terror across the South.

Congress became determined to fight the readmission of the Southern states by Johnson's lenient standards, and it refused to seat any representatives from the South.

The move angered President Johnson, and political volleying between the legislature and the executive office began. Ultimately it was Congress that determined the process by which the Southern states were readmitted.

By the summer of 1868 the legislatures of 7 (of 11) Southern states had approved the Fourteenth Amendment. The remaining four states—Georgia, Mississippi, Texas, and Virginia—complied with the requirements for statehood by 1870, at which time the Union was restored and Congressional representatives from the South were again welcomed in Washington.

In the intervening period (between Congress's rejection of President Johnson's plan for statehood and the ratification of the Fourteenth and Fifteenth Amendments), the South was governed by military administrators who protected people and property and oversaw the reorganization of government in each state.

THE AMERICAN PRESIDENCY

Why does the president of the United States give a **State of the Union Address**?

The U.S. Constitution requires the president to annually present a joint session of Congress (attended by representatives and senators) with a status report on the nation. Presidents George Washington (1732-1799) and John Adams (1735-1826), the first and second presidents, delivered their messages in person. Thereafter the State of the Union was sent as a written message, which was read in Congress. But President Woodrow Wilson (1856-1924) delivered his messages in person, including that of January 1918, when he delivered the Fourteen Points—his formulation of a peace program for Europe once World War I (1914-18) had ended. Since Franklin D. Roosevelt (1882-1945) held office (beginning in 1933), all U.S. presidents have made formal addresses to Congress.

What was the **Kitchen Cabinet**?

It was the name given to President Andrew Jackson's unofficial group of advisers, who reportedly met with him in the White House kitchen. The group included the then secretary of state Martin Van Buren (1782-1862), who went on to become vice president (during Jackson's second term) and president from 1837 to 1841; F. P. Blair (1791-1876), editor of the *Washington Post,* who was active in American politics and later helped get Abraham Lincoln elected to office (1860); and Amos Kendall (1789-1869), a journalist who was also a speech writer for Jackson and went on to become U.S. postmaster general. The Kitchen Cabinet was influential in formulating policy during Jackson's first term (1829-33), many believe because the president's real cabinet, which he convened infrequently, had proved ineffective. But Jackson, the seventh president of the United States, drew harsh criticism for relying on his cronies in this way. When he reorganized the cabinet in 1831, the Kitchen Cabinet disbanded.

Jackson's favoritism to his circle of friends did not end with the Kitchen Cabinet, however. During his presidency the "spoils system" was in full force: Jackson gave public offices as rewards to many of his loyal supporters. Though the term *spoils system* was popularized during Jackson's terms in office (it was his friend, Senator William Marcy, who coined the phrase when he stated, "to the victor belong the spoils of the enemy"), Jackson was not the first president to grant political powers to his party's members. And the practice continued through the nineteenth century. However, beginning in 1883 laws were passed that gradually put an end to, or at least limited, the spoils system.

What was **Teapot Dome**?

Teapot Dome was a notorious political scandal that was on a level with Watergate (1972). While the early 1920s abuses of power affected President Warren G. Harding (1865-1923), it was not Harding who was implicated in the crimes. Albert Bacon Fall (1861-1944), Harding's secretary of the interior, secretly transferred government oil lands at Elk Hills, California, and Teapot Dome, Wyoming, to private use and he did so without a formal bidding process. Fall leased the Elk Hills naval oil reserves to American businessman Edward L. Doheny (1856-1935) in exchange for an interest-free "loan" of $100,000. Fall made a similar arrangement with another businessman, Harry F. Sinclair (1876-1956) of Sinclair Oil Corporation—leasing the Teapot Dome reserves in exchange for $300,000 in cash, bonds, and livestock.

The scandal was revealed in 1922, and committees of the U.S. Senate and a special commission spent the next six years sorting it all out. By the time the hearings and investigations were concluded in 1928, Harding had died; Fall had resigned from office and taken a job working for Sinclair; all three players—Doheny, Sinclair, and Fall—had faced charges; and the government had successfully sued the oil companies for the return of the lands. The punishments were light considering the serious nature of the charges: Fall was convicted of accepting a bribe, fined $100,000, and sentenced to a year in prison, while Doheny and Sinclair were both indicted but later acquitted of the charges against them, which included conspiracy and bribery.

How were **Theodore and Franklin Roosevelt** related?

The two men, among America's most well-known presidents, were distant cousins. Theodore Roosevelt (1858-1919) was born in New York City, and after a career in public service that included organizing the first volunteer cavalry regiment that was known as the Rough Riders, the ardent outdoors enthusiast became vice president in 1901. When President William McKinley (1843-1901) died in office later that year (on September 14), "Teddy" Roosevelt succeeded him as president. He was elected in his

Who Says a Watched Pot Never Boils?

A 1924 illustration of Teapot Dome, a notorious scandal involving the Warren Harding administration.

own right in 1904 and went on to serve until 1909, spending nearly two full terms in the White House.

Teddy Roosevelt was president of the United States when he walked his niece, Eleanor Roosevelt (1884-1962), down the aisle on March 17, 1905. The young woman was marrying her distant cousin Franklin Delano Roosevelt (1882-1945), who had been courting her since he entered college at Harvard in 1900.

Franklin D. Roosevelt was born in Hyde Park, New York. Like his fifth cousin Theodore, Franklin went on to a life of public service, which bore some remarkable similarities to that of his cousin: Both Theodore and Franklin served as assistant secretary of the U.S. Navy (1897-98 and 1913-20, respectively) and both were governors of New York (1899 to 1900 and 1929 to 1933, respectively). As presidents, both served the nation for more than one term—but Franklin Roosevelt made history for being the only president to be elected for third and fourth terms. (In 1951 the U.S. Congress voted in favor of the Twenty-second Amendment, limiting presidential tenure to just two terms.) Both served the country in times of conflict: For Theodore it was the Russo-Japanese War (1904-05)—which he was instrumental in ending with the Treaty of Portsmouth (New Hampshire) on September 5, 1905, and for which he was awarded the Nobel peace prize the following year. Franklin Roosevelt was one of the so-called Big Three leaders: Along with Britain's Sir Winston Churchill (1874-1965) and the Soviet Union's Joseph Stalin (1879-1953), he coordinated the Allied nations' effort against Nazi Germany and Japan during World War II (1939-45). He, too, was a champion of peace, having been central in laying plans for the United Nations.

It's an interesting note, however, that when Teddy Roosevelt ran for president in 1912, he was opposed by his young Democratic cousin Franklin, then a state senator in New York, who supported Woodrow Wilson (1856-1924) in the presidential race. After Wilson was elected, he appointed Franklin Roosevelt assistant secretary of the navy—a post that delighted him for combining his vocation (politics) with his avocation (ships), and one that certainly furthered his political career. By the end of World War I (1914-18), Franklin Roosevelt was a well-known national figure.

Theodore and Franklin also shared an interest in outdoor activities. But Franklin's participation in sports was curtailed when he was stricken with polio in August 1921. The 39-year-old Roosevelt was paralyzed for a time, and though he later regained movement and was able to walk with braces, he never fully recovered. Through fierce determination he continued his life of public service, becoming president in 1933. He saw the country through two of its most trying periods: the Great Depression (1929-39) and World War II (1939-45). He died suddenly of a brain hemorrhage in April 1945.

Why was **Eleanor Roosevelt** called "the people's First Lady"?

While several First Ladies before her had also been active in the nation's life, Eleanor Roosevelt (1884-1962), wife of thirty-second president of the United States Franklin D.

Why is the Kennedy presidency called "Camelot"?

The term was actually assigned by Jacqueline Bouvier Kennedy (1929-1994). Shortly after President John F. Kennedy was assassinated (November 22, 1963), the former First Lady was talking with a journalist when she described her husband's presidency as an American Camelot, and she asked that his memory be preserved. Camelot refers, of course, to the time of King Arthur and the Knights of the Round Table, and has come to refer to a place or time of idyllic happiness. John Fitzgerald Kennedy's widow, who had with fortitude and grace guided her family and the country through the sorrow and anguish of the president's funeral, quite naturally held sway over the American public. So when she suggested that the shining moments of her husband's presidency were reminiscent of the legends of Camelot, journalists picked up on it. Despite subsequent revelations that there were difficulties in the Kennedy marriage, public opinion polls indicate that the image of Camelot—albeit somewhat tarnished—has prevailed.

Roosevelt (1882-1945), stands out as one of the country's most active first ladies and as a woman of enormous accomplishment in her own right. During her husband's administration, which began in the dark days of the Great Depression (1929-39) and continued as the world again went to war, Eleanor Roosevelt acted not only as an adviser to the president, but as the president's eyes and ears on the nation—traveling in a way that his physical condition prevented him from doing.

From the start, Eleanor Roosevelt remained in constant communication with the American people: She was known for her weekly press conferences, numbering some 350 by the end of the Roosevelt presidency, that were open only to women reporters. In 1934 she began a radio program, which became so popular that she was soon dubbed "the First Lady of Radio." Beginning in 1936 she authored a daily column called "My Day," which was syndicated to newspapers around the country. These forums gave the First Lady an unprecedented voice in American life and gave Americans a clear understanding of their First Lady and her concerns.

Concerned about the effects of the Great Depression on American children, she was instrumental in creating the National Youth Administration, which helped high school and university students complete their studies before joining the workforce. She was a champion of minority groups, declaring that the right to work "should know no color lines" and resigning from the Daughters of the American Revolution when the group refused to allow black singer Marian Anderson (1897-1993) to perform at Constitution Hall.

Eleanor Roosevelt was known for getting out among the people; she lectured frequently and made other public appearances in which she met and spoke face to face with the American people. A famous cartoon depicted a coal miner pausing in his work to exclaim, "For gosh sakes, here comes Mrs. Roosevelt." During World War II (1939-45) she made a remarkable 23,000-mile trip across the South Pacific, where she untiringly visited American GIs in field hospitals and on the lines.

Mrs. Roosevelt was an advocate for the people, and it just so happened that she lived in the White House. A beloved First Lady who actively supported liberal causes and humanitarian concerns, she has been a model to subsequent first ladies and women politicians and activists.

How many **U.S. presidents** have been **assassinated**?

Four American presidents were assassinated in office: Abraham Lincoln, James Garfield, William McKinley, and John F. Kennedy.

Abraham Lincoln (1809-1865) was shot on the evening of April 14, 1865, as he sat in the presidential box of Ford's Theatre in Washington, D.C., watching a performance of *Our American Cousin.* The man who fired the shot was actor John Wilkes Booth (1838-1865), who then jumped onto the stage, fell (breaking a leg), and limped away, calling out, "*Sic semper tyrannis*" (a Latin phrase meaning "Thus always to tyrants"). The president lived through the night, attended by family. He died just after 7:00 A.M. on April 15. He was succeeded in office by Vice President Andrew Johnson (1808-1875). On April 26 a search party found Booth in a Virginia barn, where he was fatally shot.

James Garfield (1831-1881) was en route to a class reunion at Williams College (Williamstown, Massachusetts), on July 2, 1881, when his assailant fired two shots at him in a Washington, D.C., train station. The shooter was Charles J. Guiteau (1841-1882), who held a grudge against the president. One of Guiteau's bullets had only grazed the president; the other was fixed in his back, and doctors were unable to locate it. Today the president's life might well have been spared, but the medical treatment of the late 1800s, which lacked both the X-ray machine and antiseptics, could not save him. He lived 80 days more, dying at a cottage on the New Jersey shore on September 19. He was succeeded in office by Vice President Chester Arthur (1830-1886). Guiteau's trial lawyer would later claim that Garfield's assassin was insane, but it was an unsuccessful plea for his life: In 1882 he was convicted and hung.

On September 6, 1901, President William McKinley (1843-1901) was attending a reception in Buffalo, New York, where the previous day he had delivered a speech. As he approached a man to shake his hand, the fellow fired two shots at McKinley. One bullet delivered only a minor flesh wound, but the other lodged in his stomach. Surgeons operated, but gangrene and infection set in, claiming the president's life the morning of September 14. He was succeeded in office by Vice President Theodore Roosevelt (1858-1919). The shooter was identified as avowed anarchist Leon F. Czolgosz (1873-1901); he was tried, convicted, and put to death in 1901.

On September 6, 1901, anarchist Leon Czolgosz shot President William McKinley with a concealed revolver; McKinley died eight days later. (Original drawing by T. Dart Walker.)

President John F. Kennedy (1917-1963), accompanied by his wife, Jacqueline Bouvier Kennedy (1929-1994), traveled in a motorcade through the streets of Dallas, Texas, on November 22, 1963. They were en route to the Dallas Trade Mart, where the president was scheduled to make a lunchtime speech. At 12:30 P.M., shots rang out; the president, who was riding in the back seat of a convertible, was hit in the neck and head. He was rushed to a nearby hospital, where he died at 1:00 P.M. The nation's loss was immediately felt, as television and radio stations broadcast the message live that Kennedy had been shot and killed. He was succeeded by Vice President Lyndon Baines Johnson (1908-1973), who took the oath of office aboard an airplane just after 2:30 P.M.

Additionally there were assassination attempts on the lives of Presidents Andrew Jackson (April 14, 1835), Theodore Roosevelt (October 14, 1912), Franklin D. Roosevelt (February 15, 1933), Harry S. Truman (November 1, 1950), Gerald R. Ford (two attempts, both in September 1975), and Ronald Reagan (March 30, 1981). Theodore Roosevelt and Ronald Reagan recovered from their injuries; the others were not injured in the attempts.

What happened at **Watergate**?

Watergate is a complex of upscale apartment and office buildings in Washington, D.C. In July 1972 five men were caught breaking into the Democratic Party's national headquarters there. Among these men was James McCord Jr. (1924-), the security coordinator of the Committee for the Re-election of the President (CRP). McCord was among those working to get President Richard Nixon (1913-1994), a Republican, elected to a second term in office.

All five men who were caught in the break-in were indicted on charges of burglary and wiretapping, as were CRP aide G. Gordon Liddy (1930-) and White House consultant E. Howard Hunt (1918-). Five of the men pleaded guilty to the charges. McCord and Liddy were tried and found guilty.

In February 1972—five months before the break-in at Watergate—President Nixon had traveled to China, becoming the first U.S. president to visit that country. In May he traveled to Moscow, where he signed the Strategic Arms Limitation Treaty (SALT-1 treaty), the first such treaty between the United States and the U.S.S.R. When the election was held in November, Nixon won in a landslide victory over the Democratic candidate George McGovern (1922-1998).

But early in Nixon's second term, which began in 1973, the Watergate affair became a full-blown political scandal when convicted burglar James McCord wrote a letter to District Court judge John Sirica (1904-1992), charging a massive cover-up in the Watergate break-in. A special Senate committee began televised investigations into the affair. Before it was all over, about 40 people, including high-level government officials, had been charged with crimes including burglary, wiretapping of citizens, violating campaign finance laws by accepting contributions in exchange for political favors, the use of government agencies to harm political opponents, and sabotage.

Among those prosecuted were John Dean (1938-), former White House counsel, and Attorney General John Mitchell (1913-1988). It was revealed that members of the Nixon administration had known about the Watergate burglary. It was also discovered that the president had taped conversations in the Oval Office. When Dean and Mitchell were convicted, public confidence in President Nixon plummeted. In July 1974 the Judiciary Committee of the House of Representatives was preparing articles of impeachment (including one that charged the president with obstruction of justice) against the president. The impeachment proceedings would not make it as far as the Senate: Nixon chose to resign on August 9, 1974. He was the first and so far only U.S. president to resign from office.

Shortly after taking office, Nixon's successor, Gerald R. Ford (1913-), pardoned Nixon. But Watergate remains a dark chapter in the nation's history.

What was the **Iran-Contra** affair?

It was a series of actions on the part of U.S. federal government officials, which came to light in November 1986. The discoveries had the immediate effect of hurting President Ronald Reagan (1911-2004), whose policy of antiterrorism had been undermined

Former White House aide John Dean is sworn in by Senate Watergate Committee chairman Sam Ervin, June 25, 1973.

by activities initiated from his own executive office. Following in-depth hearings and investigations into "who knew what, when," special prosecutor Lawrence Walsh (1912-) submitted his report on January 18, 1994, stating that the dealings with Iran and with the contra rebels in Nicaragua had "violated United States policy and law."

The tangled string of events involved Reagan's national security advisers Robert McFarlane (1937-) and Admiral John Poindexter (1936-), Lieutenant Colonel Oliver North (1943-), Poindexter's military aide, the Iranian government, and Nicaraguan rebels.

The U.S. officials evidently had begun their dealings with both the Iranian government and the Nicaraguan rebels with the goal of freeing seven Americans who were held hostage by Iranian-backed rebels in Lebanon. President Reagan had met with the families of the captives and was naturally concerned about the hostage situation. Under pressure to work to free the hostages, McFarlane, Poindexter, and North arranged to sell an estimated $30 million in spare parts and antiaircraft missiles to Iran (then at war with neighboring Iraq). In return, the Iranian government would put pressure on the terrorist groups to release the Americans.

Profits from the arms sale to Iran were then diverted by Lieutenant North to the contras in Central America who were fighting the dictatorial Nicaraguan government.

Congress had already passed laws that prohibited U.S. government aid to the Nicaraguan rebels; the diversion of funds certainly appeared to violate those laws.

The Iran-Contra affair led to North's dismissal and to Poindexter's resignation. Both men were prosecuted. Though the hostages were freed, Reagan's public image was seriously damaged by how the release had been achieved.

During the Iran-Contra hearings in 1987, National Security Commission officials revealed that they had been willing to take the risk of providing arms to Iran in exchange for the safe release of the hostages because they all remembered the U.S. government's failed attempt in 1980 to rescue hostages held at the American Embassy in Tehran, Iran.

Nevertheless, the deal with Iran had supplied a hostile country with American arms that could then be used against the United States. In 1987 Iran did launch an offensive when it attacked Kuwaiti oil-tankers that were registered as American and laid mines in the Persian Gulf. The United States responded by sending in the navy, which attacked Iranian patrol boats. During this military initiative, the U.S. Navy accidentally shot down a civilian passenger jet, killing everyone on board.

Why was **President Clinton** impeached?

Some believe the proceedings were nothing more than a "vast right-wing conspiracy," a term coined by First Lady Hillary Rodham Clinton (1947-) early in 1998. Still, others—including enough members of the U.S. House of Representatives to bring 11 counts of impeachment against President Clinton in December 1998—felt the nation's chief had perjured himself and obstructed justice. Many also believed he had jeopardized the authority of the U.S. presidency. Accused of having an affair with White House intern Monica Lewinsky, President Clinton vehemently denied it. Upon continued investigation, conducted by Special Prosecutor Kenneth Starr's office, the allegations proved to be true. Since the president had been so adamant in his statements to the contrary, evidence began to accumulate that he had lied about his relationship with the young woman and that he had tried to cover up the matter.

On July 31, 1998, President Bill Clinton gestures to reporters that he will take no questions about the Monica Lewinsky investigation.

Many believed the charges against Clinton did not constitute the high crimes and misdemeanors called for by the U.S. Constitution to remove a president from office. Nevertheless, in January 1999 the U.S. Senate organized itself to hear the charges against the president. When the trial concluded in February, Clinton was acquitted of both perjury and obstruction of justice. He served out his second term and left office with high approval ratings, despite being the subject of the longest criminal investigation of a president in history.

The Clinton impeachment was the first time the federal legislature had convened itself as a court in more than 130 years—since the impeachment hearings of President Andrew Johnson (1808-1875) in 1868.

Are the **Bushes** the **first father-son presidents**?

No, the nation's 41st (George H. W. Bush) and 43rd (George W. Bush) presidents were preceded as father-son presidents by John Adams (1735-1826), the 2nd president of the United States, and John Quincy Adams (1767-1848), the 6th.

There have been other presidents whose relatives held the office before them: Benjamin Harrison, the 23rd president, was the grandson of the nation's 9th, William Henry Harrison. Zachary Taylor, the 12th president, and James Madison, the 4th, were second cousins. Franklin Delano Roosevelt was preceded in the office by his distant cousin, Teddy Roosevelt. Genealogists determined that FDR had ties to 10 other presidents as well, four of them were blood relatives and six were relatives by marriage: John Adams, John Quincy Adams, Ulysses S. Grant, William Henry Harrison, Benjamin Harrison, James Madison, William Howard Taft, Zachary Taylor, Martin Van Buren, and George Washington.

ABSOLUTISM

Was the **holocaust** directed by the German government?

Yes. When fervent nationalist Adolf Hitler (1889-1945) rose to power in Germany in 1933 he quickly established a reign of terror based on his philosophy that the German (Aryan) race is superior to all others. He established a violent policy against Jews: Those who did not flee the country were rounded up and sent to concentration camps, where they were kept without cause. This was before Hitler's acts of military aggression in Europe. But after German troops invaded Poland and World War II began, the führer's anti-Semitic campaign was accelerated. Jews in Germany and in Nazi-occupied countries of Europe were severely persecuted. Those who were put into concentration camps—including Auschwitz, Treblinka, Buchenwald, and Dachau—were exterminated, many of them in gas chambers. By the end of the war, in 1945, Hitler's "final solution to the Jewish question" had been under way for some 12 years, and 6 million Jews had been systematically murdered by the Nazis during the Holocaust, or Shoah (Hebrew). As his defeat was imminent, the despotic ruler took his own life in 1945. By then he had destroyed Europe's Jewish community. Many of Hitler's leaders were later tried by an international court at Nuremberg.

Why do historians draw comparisons among **Stalin, Hitler, Napoleon, and Alexander the Great?**

All four men were fiercely powerful—and seemingly indomitable—leaders. And their early lives and careers shared some interesting characteristics as well.

First, none of them were native sons of the countries they ended up ruling (and some would say, defining). Soviet leader Joseph Stalin (1879-1953) was born in Georgia, German chancellor and führer Adolf Hitler (1889-1945) in Austria, French emperor Napoleon Bonaparte (1769-1821) in Corsica (which, though technically a new possession of France, was decidedly more Italian in nature), and king of the Macedonians Alexander the Great (356-323 B.C.) was from the fringe city-state of Macedonia. Yet it was, respectively, Russian, German, French, and Greek culture that each leader spread. All four men rose to power through the military, or, in Alexander's case (who succeeded his father), after having carried out military strategy. Once installed as rulers, all led fantastic military campaigns to expand their spheres of influence. The wars brought on by their nationalism left millions dead. Finally, all four men inspired, and some would say continue to inspire, terror in the human soul.

Still, history has been more forgiving of both Alexander and Napoleon, who today seem to be portrayed as often as heroes as they are as megalomaniacs. With Hitler's and Stalin's horrible legacies a more recent memory, the view of these men is decidedly and far more consistently dark and loathsome.

What were the **gulags?**

Gulags were prisons for political dissidents in the Soviet Union; the prisons existed from 1919 into the 1950s. Gulag is an abbreviation of the Russian name of the system, *Glavnoye Upravleniye Ispravitelno-trudovykh Lagerey,* which translates to Chief Administration of Corrective Labor Camps. The camps were first used during the collectivization of agriculture in the late 1920s and early 1930s. Under Soviet leader Joseph Stalin's (1879-1953) purges of the 1930s, anyone who posed, or seemed to pose, a threat to his hard-line Communist regime was rounded up and sent to a gulag. During World War II (1939-45), prisoners of war were held in the gulags. And after the war, Stalin continued to use the camps to punish those who opposed him. Though exact figures are unknown, it is believed that as many as 30 million people were imprisoned in gulags, where they faced forced labor, grueling conditions, and mal-

Inmates of the Nazi government's Buchenwald concentration camp, April 1945. By the end of World War II, about 6 million Jews had died in the holocaust.

treatment including starvation. (Official Soviet figures place the number around 10 million.) Millions are believed to have died in the gulags. After Stalin died in 1953, the system was dismantled, with some of the prisoners receiving amnesty.

What was the **Long March**?

The Long March began in October 1934 when Mao Tse-tung (1893-1976) led Chinese Communist forces (the Red Army of China), numbering 100,000 men and women, on an epic walk across China. With the nationalist army in pursuit, the Communist marchers crossed 18 mountain chains and 24 rivers to cover 6,000 miles. Almost all women and children died along the way. In 1935, 20,000 to 30,000 people finally reached Shaanxi (Shensi) Province in the north, where the Red Army established a stronghold. It was there that Mao, one of the earliest members of the Chinese Communist Party, formulated his own philosophy that came to be known as Maoism. He had adapted Marxism to the Chinese conditions—replacing German politician and socialist Karl Marx's (1818-1883) urban working class with the peasant farmers as the force behind revolution. The Red Army went on to defeat the nationalists in 1949; Mao was named chairman of the People's Republic of China, a Communist state, that same year.

THE POSTWAR ERA

How was the **United Nations** formed?

Officially, the United Nations (UN) was not formed until October 1945. However, events during World War II (1939-45) had paved the way for the founding of the international peacekeeping organization that today is so familiar to people around the globe.

Fervent German nationalist Adolf Hitler (1889-1945) and his troops invaded Poland in 1939, and soon Nazi Germany had conquered much of Europe. Leaders of nine nations—Belgium, Czechoslovakia, France, Greece, Luxembourg, the Netherlands, Norway, Poland, and Yugoslavia—met with Britain and its Commonwealth states in London. There, on June 12, 1941, the countries signed the Inter-Allied Declaration, vowing to work together for a free world. Two months later, on August 14, U.S. president Franklin Delano Roosevelt (1882-1945) and British prime minister Winston Churchill (1874-1965) signed the Atlantic Charter. In it the two leaders outlined their aims for peace.

On January 1, 1942, the "declaration by the United Nations" was signed by 26 countries who pledged to work together to fight the Axis powers (Germany, Italy, and Japan), and they agreed not to make peace separately. The term *United Nations,* otherwise known as the UN, is believed to have originated with Roosevelt.

In late November and early December 1943, the Big Three—Roosevelt, Churchill, and Soviet premier Joseph Stalin (1879-1953)—met in Tehran, Iran, for the first time during the war. There these Allied nations leaders cited the responsibility of a United Nations organization in keeping the peace once the war was over. Though ending the war was first and foremost in the minds of these leaders, all had seen two world wars fought in close succession and were determined that the nations of the world could work together to prevent such an event from happening again. In August 1944, at the Dumbarton Oaks Conference in Washington, D.C., representatives of Britain, the United States, the Soviet Union, and China met to make plans for the peacekeeping organization that had been envisioned. The outcome of that meeting, which lasted into October, was the basic concept for the UN Security Council as we know it—with the world's (five) major powers having permanent seats on the council and a limited and rotating membership beyond that.

When the Big Three met again at the Yalta Conference (in the Soviet Union) in February 1945, they discussed matters that were central to ending the fighting with Germany and with Japan. But Roosevelt, Churchill, and Stalin also announced that a conference of the United Nations would open in San Francisco on April 25 of that year.

Having directed the United States' massive war effort, Roosevelt did not live to see the end of World War II or the creation of the international peacekeeping body. Roosevelt died suddenly on April 12, 1945. The war in Europe ended May 7. And during the closing days of World War II, the UN was chartered—the representatives of the

Joseph Stalin, Franklin D. Roosevelt, and Winston Churchill during the Tehran Peace Conference, 1943.

Allied nations met as promised in San Francisco. On June 26, 1945, the governing treaty was signed by the delegates. On October 24, 1945, shortly after the war ended with Japan, the United Nations officially came into existence when the required number of nations approved the charter. Fifty nations were members of the UN at the outset; today the membership numbers 191.

What does the **UN** do?

Representatives of member countries work to keep peace and ensure security for people around the globe. Over the decades, the UN has expanded its role as a provider of humanitarian aid and stepped up its efforts in the area of human rights. When disputes arise, the UN works toward diplomatic resolution. Though not always successful in its role as peacekeeper or peace negotiator, the organization has provided a forum for debate, which has prevented some disputes from developing into major wars. And through its various agencies, the UN provides assistance to developing nations, promotes humanitarian causes, and sends relief to war-torn areas.

However, critics have charged the international organization with arbitrarily defining borders between countries, saying that these drawn boundaries divide ethnic groups and result in conflicts (such as in the Middle East and Africa).

What are the **bodies and agencies of the United Nations**?

The UN's charter establishes six main bodies and explains their duties and operating methods. The General Assembly is the major forum: all member nations are represented there, and the assembly can discuss any issue that is deemed relevant and important to the UN; the Security Council has the major responsibility for preserving peace; the Economic and Social Council investigates economic questions and works to improve living standards; the Secretariat is the UN's administrative body, helping all organs do their work; the Trusteeship Council assists non-self-governing territories; and the International Court of Justice hears disputes between member nations. Except for the last one, all bodies convene in the UN headquarters in New York City. The International Court of Justice meets in The Hague.

Since the charter was written in 1945, the United Nations has established numerous agencies, committees, and commissions to help carry out its work around the world. Among those that are most well known to the public are the United Nations Educational, Scientific, and Cultural Organization (UNESCO), which encourages the exchange of ideas among nations; the United Nations International Children's Emergency Fund (UNICEF), which assists children and adolescents worldwide, particularly those in devastated areas or developing countries; the World Health Organization (WHO), which promotes high health standards around the globe; the International Labor Organization (ILO), which works to improve labor conditions and protect workers; and the International Monetary Fund (IMF), which addresses currency and trade issues.

Who are the **members of the United Nations Security Council**?

According to the UN charter, the Security Council has 15 members: 5 permanent and 10 that are elected by the General Assembly for two-year terms. The permanent members are China, France, the Russian Federation, the United Kingdom, and the United States. The 10 temporary slots are elected annually, 5 nations at a time, so that on January 1, 2004, the following nations began two-year memberships: Algeria, Benin, Brazil, the Philippines, and Romania. On January 1, 2005, Argentina, Denmark, Greece, Japan, and the United Republic of Tanzania began two-year memberships. In 2005 Japan, Germany, India, and Brazil made bids for permanent seats on the council.

What does the **Security Council** do?

According to the UN charter, the functions and powers of the Security Council are:

> to maintain international peace and security in accordance with the principles and purposes of the United Nations; to investigate any dispute or situation which might lead to international friction; to recommend methods of adjusting such disputes or the terms of settlement; to formulate plans for the

establishment of a system to regulate armaments; to determine the existence of a threat to the peace or act of aggression and to recommend what action should be taken; to call on Members to apply economic sanctions and other measures not involving the use of force to prevent or stop aggression; to take military action against an aggressor; to recommend the admission of new Members; to exercise the trusteeship functions of the United Nations in 'strategic areas'; and to recommend to the General Assembly the appointment of the Secretary-General and, together with the Assembly, to elect the Judges of the International Court of Justice.

What is the **G-8**?

It is the Group of Eight, an annual meeting of the world's leading industrial democracies: Canada, France, Germany, Italy, Japan, Russia, the United Kingdom, and the United States. It began as the Group of Six, with a 1975 conference in France, where representatives of six nations (France, Germany, Italy, Japan, the United Kingdom, and the United States) met to discuss international economic and political issues. The goal of the meeting was to shore up cooperation on matters of concern to the member nations. Canada joined the group in 1976 and Russia in 1994 (though the nation did not participate fully in the sessions until 1998). Hosting responsibilities rotate among the eight member countries. In 2004 the United States hosted the 30th meeting, on an island off the coast of Georgia. Among the agenda items were the training of international peacekeepers, setting up a global initiative to develop a human immunodeficiency virus (HIV) vaccine, and developing a plan to end famine in the Horn of Africa (easternmost Africa, including Somalia, Ethiopia, and Djibouti) by 2009. The leaders and representatives of non-G-8 countries were invited to participate in discussions relevant to them.

Why was **Mohandas Gandhi** called "Mahatma"?

Mohandas Gandhi was called "Mahatma" (meaning "great-souled") by the common people, who viewed him as India's national and spiritual leader. He is considered the father of his country. He was born in India on October 2, 1869. As a young man, Gandhi studied law in Britain. Practicing briefly in India, he then traveled to British-controlled South Africa on business. Observing oppressive treatment of Indian immigrants there, he held his first campaign of passive resistance. Gandhi would later become very well known for this method of protest, called *satyagraha* (meaning "firmness in truth").

Back in India as of 1915, Gandhi organized a movement of the people against the British government there: Britain had taken control of India during the 1700s and remained in power. After World War I (1914-18), Indian nationalists fought what would be a long and sometimes bitter struggle for political independence. While Gandhi's protests took the form of nonviolent campaigns of civil disobedience, such as boycotts and fasts (hunger strikes), he was more than once arrested by the authorities for causing disorder, as his actions inspired more extreme measures on the part of his followers, whose protests took the form of rioting.

As a member and, later, the president of India's chief political party, the Indian National Congress, Gandhi led a fight to rid the country of its rigid caste system, which organizes Indian society into distinct classes and groups. In Gandhi's time, not only were there four *varna,* or social classes, but there was a fifth group of "untouchables" who ranked even below the lowest class of peasants and laborers. Improving the lot of the untouchables was of tantamount importance to the leader, who by this time had abandoned Western ways in favor of a life of simplicity.

Beginning in 1937 Gandhi became less active in government, giving up his official roles, but he continued to be regarded as a leader of the independence movement. During World War II (1939-45), he was arrested for demanding British withdrawal from the conflict. Released from prison in 1944, Gandhi was central to the postwar negotiations that in 1947 resulted in an independent India. A believer in the unity of humankind under one God, he remained tolerant to Christian and Muslim beliefs. Amidst an outbreak of violence between Hindus and Muslims, Gandhi was on a prayer vigil in New Delhi when a Hindu fanatic fatally shot him in 1948.

Was **Indira Gandhi** related to Mohandas Gandhi?

No, the two were not related, except by events. After India achieved independence in 1947, the country's first prime minister was Jawaharlal Nehru (1889-1964), who had been a follower of Mohandas Gandhi (1869-1948), the great leader of India's long struggle for autonomy from Great Britain. During his entire tenure (1947-64) as leader of India, Nehru was assisted by his only child, Indira (1917-1984), who in 1942 married a man named Feroze Gandhi—of no relation to Mohandas Gandhi. Indira Gandhi took an active role in India's national affairs. After her father died, she went on to become prime minister in 1966. However, hers was a troubled tenure. Found guilty of employing illegal election practices, Indira Gandhi was ousted by her political opponents in 1977. Determined to return to power, she was re-elected to parliament in 1980 and again served as prime minister until her death in 1984. She was assassinated by two of her own secu-

Mohandas Gandhi (pictured c. 1945) was called "Mahatma," meaning "great-souled," by the common people, who viewed him as India's national and spiritual leader.

rity guards, Sikhs who were motivated by religious reasons. Her son and successor, Rajiv Gandhi (1944-1991), was also assassinated, in 1991.

When was **modern Israel** established?

As a modern state, Israel was formed by decree in 1948. In the wake of World War II (1939-45), the United Nations (UN) formed a special committee to address the British control of Palestine, the region in the Middle East (southwest Asia) that borders the Mediterranean Sea to the west, Lebanon to the north, Syria and Jordan to the east, and Egypt (the Sinai Peninsula) to the southwest; the narrow piece of land comes to a point in the south, where it fronts the Gulf of Aqaba. In November 1947 the United Nations (UN) carved Israel out of the Palestine region; areas of Palestine that were not designated as Israel were divided between neighboring Arab countries.

Modern Israel's first leader, David Ben-Gurion (1886-1973), proclaimed an independent Israel on May 14, 1948. Born in Poland, Ben-Gurion had arrived in Palestine as a young man of about 20 and became extremely active in efforts to assert Jewish autonomy in the region. He served as prime minister from 1949 to 1953 and again between 1955 and 1963. But Israel's history goes back much farther than these twentieth-century events. And, having such a long history, it is also a complicated one.

Israel was an ancient kingdom in Palestine, formed under King Saul in 1020 B.C. Israel included the lands in Canaan, the Promised Land of the Hebrew tribes who descended from the people that Moses (fourteenth-thirteenth century B.C.) led out of Egypt. But the kingdom was subsequently divided and by the eighth century B.C. it had ceased to exist. Nevertheless, the area remained home—and holy land—to the Hebrews (Israelites) who had settled there.

The entire region of Palestine, including the kingdom of Israel, subsequently came under the control of various empires. Palestine saw the rule of the Assyrians, the Chaldeans, the Persians, the Macedonians under Macedonian king Alexander the Great (356-323 B.C.), and the Romans (the area was the Roman province of Syria in the time of Jesus). After Roman rule, Palestine was, with only one exception, ruled by various Muslim (Islamic) dynasties, including the Ottoman Empire (1516-1917). It was in 1917 that Palestine came under control of the British, who proclaimed in the Declaration of Balfour to support the establishment of a national home for the Jews living there. However, Britain reversed this policy in 1939 at the same time the area was seeing an influx of Jewish people who were escaping persecution in Europe. Jews in Palestine opposed British control, and at the same time fighting intensified between Jews and Arabs.

The 1947 decision by the UN to establish a Jewish homeland resulted in nearly two years of fighting between Israelis and Arabs in the region. And though boundaries among the various states were determined anew in 1949, fighting in the region continued with the Arab-Israeli wars of 1956, 1967, 1973-74, and 1982. Unrest prevailed throughout the 1980s and into the 1990s, when the two sides began discussions to resolve the long conflict.

What is the **Palestine Liberation Organization**?

It is a group formed in 1964 by Arabs in Palestine, a region coextensive with the nation of Israel. Known as the PLO, the organization seeks to establish an area of self-rule for Muslims. Dominated by then guerrilla leader Yasser Arafat (1929-2004), the PLO regarded Israel as an illegitimate state and became determined to establish a Palestinian state in the region. In 1974 the PLO was recognized by the United Nations and by Arab countries as the governing body of the Palestinian people; however, the Palestinians remained without a homeland and continued to fight for one, often resorting to terrorist tactics.

In 1993 Israel and the PLO, still under Arafat's leadership, officially recognized each other: In an internationally brokered agreement, Israel agreed that by early 1996 it would withdraw its troops from the Gaza Strip, a tiny ribbon of land along the Mediterranean and bordering Egypt, and most cities and towns of the West Bank, a larger region lying west of the Jordan River and Dead Sea. (The city of Jerusalem, recognized by both Israelis and Palestinians as their capitals, straddles the western border of the West Bank and is divided into an Arab East Jerusalem and a Jewish-Israeli West Jerusalem.) The 1993 Arab-Israeli agreement, called the Oslo Accords, effectively carved out an autonomous Palestinian homeland, or at least an autonomous region. To govern this region, the Palestinian Authority (PA) was set up.

In 1994 Arafat and Israeli leaders Yitzhak Rabin (1922-1995) and Shimon Peres (1923-) were awarded the Nobel peace prize for their efforts. In January 1996 Palestinians in the Gaza Strip and the Palestinian-controlled parts of the West Bank elected a legislature and a president (Arafat) to govern these areas.

But the accords foundered: both sides contributed to an escalation of violence in the long-troubled region. In 2003 the Roadmap for Peace, developed by the United States, in cooperation with Russia, the European Union, and the United Nations, was presented to Israel and the Palestinian Authority (PA). The plan outlined clear goals and timelines for their achievement for both sides. Still the violence continued, with both sides failing to take the reciprocal steps necessary to peaceably coexist in the region. Cautious hopes for peace were again raised in February 2005 when Palestinian leader Mahmoud Abbas (who in January succeeded Arafat) and Israeli Prime Minister Ariel Sharon met at an Egyptian resort for summit talks. The two announced a verbal cease-fire pledge: Sharon promised that the Israeli military would end assaults on Palestinians, and Abbas vowed to bring an end to militant attacks on Israelis. But there were obstacles to the agreement: Israeli settlements in the Gaza Strip and West Bank needed to be dismantled; the Palestinians needed to gain control of the militant group Hamas, responsible for hundreds of acts of terrorism against Israelis; and the

Israeli military needed to step down its responses. The Palestinian government remained tied to the PLO.

Who coined the term **"iron curtain"**?

It was former British prime minister Winston Churchill (1874-1965). In a March 1946 speech in Fulton, Missouri, he remarked that "an iron curtain has descended across the Continent." The statesman, who had been instrumental in coordinating the Allied victory in World War II (1939-45), was commenting on Soviet leader Joseph Stalin's (1879- 1953) tactics in Eastern Europe, which indicated the Soviets were putting up barriers against the West—and building up Soviet domination behind those barriers.

Just as he had issued warnings of the threat posed by Nazi Germany prior to World War II, Churchill astutely observed the rapidly emerging situation in Eastern Europe: In 1946 the Soviets installed Communist governments in neighboring Romania and in nearby Bulgaria; in 1947 Hungary and Poland came under Communist control as well; and the following year, Communists took control of Czechoslovakia. These countries, along with Albania, Yugoslavia, and East Germany, soon formed a coalition of Communist allies—and the Eastern bloc was formed. The United States and its democratic allies formed the Western bloc. The stage was set for the Cold War (1947-89).

How was the **Soviet Union formed**?

The Soviet Union was officially created in 1922 when Russia joined with Ukraine, Belorussia, and the Transcaucasian Federation (Armenia, Azerbaijan, and Georgia) to form the Union of Soviet Socialist Republics (U.S.S.R.). These republics were later joined by nine others, and territories were redrawn so that by 1940 the union consisted of 15 Soviet Socialist republics: Armenia, Azerbaijan, Belorussia (now Belarus), Estonia, Georgia, Kazakhstan, Kirghiz (now Kyrgyzstan), Latvia, Lithuania, Moldavia (now Moldova), Russia, Tadzhikistan (also spelled Tajikistan), Turkmenistan, Ukraine, and Uzbekistan.

How many **leaders** did the **Soviet Union** have?

From its formation in 1922 (just five years after tsarist Russia had fallen in the revolution of 1917), the Union of Soviet Socialist Republics (U.S.S.R.) had only 10 leaders. But just five of these had meaningful tenure, either due to length of time served or true authority: Lenin, Stalin, Khrushchev, Brezhnev, and Gorbachev.

After tsarist Russia ended with the revolution of 1917, Bolshevik leader Vladimir Lenin (1870-1924) became head of the Soviet Russian government as chairman of the Council of People's Commissars (the Communists), dissolving the elected assembly and establishing a dictatorship. This lasted six years: When Lenin died of a stroke in

Vladimir Lenin and Josef Stalin in 1922. When Lenin died of a stroke in 1924, his associate Stalin established himself as a virtual dictator of the Soviet Union.

1924, Joseph Stalin (1879-1953)—who had been an associate of Lenin—promptly eliminated his opposition and in 1929 established himself as a virtual dictator. Stalin ruled the U.S.S.R. during World War II (1939-45), and though he was aligned with the United States, Britain, and the other Allied nations during that conflict, soon after the war, he began a buildup of power in Eastern Europe, leading to the Cold War (1947- 89). Even though Stalin's domestic policies were extremely repressive and he ruled largely by terror, he remained in power until his death in 1953.

After Stalin died, the Soviet Union entered a brief period of struggle among its top leaders: Deputy Premier Georgy Malenkov (1902-1988), a longtime Stalin aide, came to power. In 1955 Malenkov was forced to resign, and he was succeeded by his (and Stalin's) former defense secretary, Nikolai Bulganin (1895-1975). However, Bulganin was a premier in name only; the true power rested with Communist Party secretary Nikita Khrushchev (1894-1971), who expelled Bulganin and officially took power as premier in 1958.

Khrushchev denounced the oppression of the long Stalin years, which had ended only five years earlier, and worked to improve living standards. On the international front, he pursued a policy of "peaceful coexistence" with the West and even toured the United States in 1959, meeting with President Dwight D. Eisenhower (1890-1969). In 1960 a U.S. reconnaissance plane was shot down over the U.S.S.R., raising doubts among the Soviets about Khrushchev's policy toward the West. Further troubles at home resulted from widespread hunger due to crop failures. Meantime, Khrushchev advanced the cause of Soviet space exploration, beginning the so-called space race with the United States. Eventually, his stance on international issues, which included a rift with Communist China, led to his downfall. He was removed from power in October 1964.

Khrushchev's ouster (which was a forced retirement) had been engineered by his former ally and political adviser Leonid Brezhnev (1906-1982). With Khrushchev out of the way, technically Brezhnev was to lead the country along with premier Alexei Kosygin (1904-1981). But as head of the Communist Party, it was Brezhnev who truly held the power. By the early 1970s, Brezhnev emerged as the Soviet chief—even though Kosygin remained in office until 1980. During his administration, Brezhnev kept tight control over the Eastern bloc (Communist countries), built up the Soviet Union's mili-

What was the détente?

A détente is a relaxation of strained relations, particularly between nations. The détente of the Cold War era began after Premier Nikita Khrushchev (1894-1971) rose to power in the Soviet Union in 1958 and initiated a plan of peaceful coexistence with the West. During the 1960s the United States and the Union of Soviet Socialist Republics (U.S.S.R.) entered a phase of improved relations, which saw the signing of the Nuclear Nonproliferation Treaty (1968), the Strategic Arms Limitation Treaty (known as the SALT-1 treaty; 1972), and the Helsinki Accords (1975)—which pledged increased cooperation between the nations of Eastern and Western Europe.

Some historians refer to the détente as the end of the Cold War, while others view it as an intermission: When the Soviet Union under Premier Leonid Brezhnev (1906-1982) invaded neighboring Afghanistan in 1979 to put down an anti-Communist movement there, tensions between the two superpowers (the U.S. and the U.S.S.R.) heightened dramatically. Further, Brezhnev had been steadily building up Soviet arms during his tenure. These events brought an end to the détente.

tary (in what became an arms race with the United States), and did nothing to try to reverse the downward trend of the Soviet Union's economy.

When Brezhnev died in 1982, he was succeeded by Yuri Andropov (1914-1984). However, Andropov died two years later and Konstantin Chernenko (1911-1985) replaced him as premier. When Chernenko, too, died an untimely death in March 1985, Mikhail S. Gorbachev (1931-) became head of the Communist Party and leader of the Soviet Union. With Gorbachev, the reign of the old guard of Stalin-trained leaders had come to an end. Gorbachev's policies of openness to the West and economic development led to the disintegration of the Soviet Union, with Communist rule ending in 1991 and each Soviet republic setting up its own government.

What were the **five-year plans**?

These were the plans initiated by premier Joseph Stalin (1879-1953) of the Soviet Union to speed industrialization of the U.S.S.R. and organize agriculture under the collective control of the Communist government. The first five-year plan began in 1928, and subsequent plans were carried out until 1958, at which time the new Soviet leadership developed a seven-year plan (1959-65) aimed at matching—and surpassing—American industry. Under Premier Leonid Brezhnev (1906-1982), the five-year plans were reinstated in 1966 and continued until the dissolution of the Soviet Union during 1990 and 1991. Other Communist countries also instituted five-year plans, all with the goal of bringing industry, agriculture, and the distribution of goods and services under government control.

THE POST–9/11 ERA IN THE UNITED STATES

When was the **Office of Homeland Security** formed?

The Office of Homeland Security was organized in the days following the September 11, 2001, terrorist attacks. President George W. Bush (1946-) chose Pennsylvania governor Tom Ridge (1945-) as the first Office of Homeland Security advisor. Ridge was sworn in on October 8, 2001. The office was elevated to the department level on November 25, 2002, when President Bush signed into law the Homeland Security Act, creating the Department of Homeland Security (DHS) and making Ridge a cabinet-level administrator.

The DHS consolidated several existing agencies and pledged to carry out new initiatives to, the extent possible, protect the nation from further attacks. Agencies and sub-departments within the DHS's purview eventually included the Transportation Security Administration, Customs and Border Protection, Immigration and Customs Enforcement, the Federal Emergency Management Agency (FEMA), Information Analysis and Infrastructure Protection offices, U.S. Citizenship and Information Services (formerly the Immigration and Naturalization Service, or INS), an office for Civil Rights and Civil Liberties, the U.S. Coast Guard, and the U.S. Secret Service.

On February 15, 2005, Ridge was succeeded by Michael Chertoff (1953-), a former U.S. Circuit Court judge. Chertoff had also worked as an assistant attorney general; in that position, he helped trace the 9/11 terrorist attacks to the al Qaeda network and worked to increase information sharing within the Federal Bureau of Investigation (FBI) and with state and local officials.

What is the **Patriot Act**?

The Patriot Act is a controversial law passed by a wide majority of Congress and signed by President George W. Bush (1946-) in October 2001; it was designed to strengthen national security following the 9/11 terrorist attacks. The legislation relaxes federal surveillance laws, granting authorities broad leeway to gather information on U.S. citizens and resident foreigners. It also expands the government's prosecutorial powers against suspected terrorists and their associates. The complex act, which contains 168 sections, allows the nation's intelligence and law enforcement agencies to, among other things, monitor email and financial transactions without securing a subpoena, use wiretapping without a court order, and require Internet service providers (ISPs) to hand over usage data on customers.

One of the most controversial sections of the Patriot Act is the so-called "library provision," which allows government officials to secretly subpoena books, records, papers, documents, and other items from businesses, hospitals, and other organizations. Critics feared that the government could use the provision to snoop into the reading habits of innocent Americans. The reaction to the provision was so strong that, according to the American Civil Liberties Union (ACLU), 5 states and 375 communities in 43 states had passed anti-Patriot Act resolutions by spring 2005. Another contentious section of the Patriot Act allows the delayed notification of search warrants; this is called the "sneak and peek" provision because it lets federal officials search a suspect's home without telling the individual until later.

While many legislators and security experts hailed the Patriot Act provisions as necessary in combating terrorism and securing the homeland, others immediately saw the legislation as a serious infringement of civil rights. Supporters pointed to the hundreds of charges brought against suspected terrorists, as well as hundreds of convictions, as a result of the Patriot Act. But critics, including legislators, the ACLU, conservative groups, and many citizens, called the act unconstitutional—and unpatriotic. A top ACLU representative said, "Cooler heads can now see that the Patriot Act went too far, too fast and that it must be brought back in line with the Constitution." The fallout included charges of abuses by law enforcement, the introduction of alternate legislation in Congress to revise or repeal sections of the act, as well as challenges in court (in 2004 at least two sections were found to be unconstitutional in district court).

As the debate continued over the constitutionality of the Patriot Act, some provisions were set to expire the end of 2005. In April two of the Bush administration's top law enforcement officials urged Congress to renew every provision of the antiterror act: Attorney General Alberto Gonzales (1955-) said that some of the most controversial provisions of the Patriot Act had proven invaluable in fighting terrorism; FBI director Robert Mueller (1944-) said sections of the law that allow intelligence and law enforcement agencies to share information were especially important.

What was the controversy about the **Guantanamo detainees**?

After the 9/11 attacks, the U.S. military began holding terror suspects at a detention center at the naval base at Guantanamo Bay, Cuba. (The U.S. Navy has occupied Guantanamo since the Spanish-American War, in 1898, paying an annual lease to Cuba.) The White House labeled the detainees "enemy combatants"; the controversy came when they were not charged with any crimes, yet they continued to be held.

The first detainees were transported to Guantanamo, or "Camp Gitmo," in January 2002, after being captured in Afghanistan. But no charges were made against any

Taliban and al Qaeda detainees kneel under the watchful eyes of U.S. military police at the naval base at Guantanamo Bay, Cuba, January 2002.

detainees until more than two years later, in February 2004. American lawyers challenged the Bush administration policy at Guantanamo, saying that it was a violation of the due process clause of the U.S. Constitution. In January 2005 one district court judge agreed with the prosecution, saying that the Constitution applied to the prisoners: they could not be deprived of their liberty without due process of the law. The Bush administration immediately moved to appeal the ruling. Some in the international community also strongly criticized the U.S. government for holding the suspects. One of Britain's most senior judges called the policy a "monstrous failure of justice."

In response to the widespread criticism, the U.S. Defense Department considered making major changes to the tribunals set up to prosecute terror suspects at Guantanamo. The changes were to bring the tribunals in line with the judicial standards of U.S. court-martials.

But questions also arose about the treatment of the detainees and the methods used in interrogating them. Human rights groups made charges of abuses. In spring 2005 United Nations officials working in the area of war crimes were awaiting a visit to Guantanamo; the hold up was that they requested full access to the facilities and the prison population, conditions Washington was reluctant to allow. According to a February 2005 American Forces Information Service report, there were about 545 people from some 40 countries being held at the Guantanamo detention center at that time. The government also held terror suspects, some of them senior members of the terrorist network al Qaeda, in navy brigs in South Carolina, Iraq, and Afghanistan, and on navy vessels at sea.

WAR AND CONFLICT

THE CLASSICAL AGE

What was the **Trojan War**?

According to Greek legend, the Trojan War was a 10-year siege, c. 1200 B.C., on the ancient city of Troy (also called Ilium). The Greek poet Homer (c. 850-? B.C.) chronicled the Trojan War in his epic the *Iliad.* According to Homer, the (Greek) Mycenaeans, under their great king Agamemnon, set out to conquer the city of Troy, situated on the Turkish coast at the southwestern part of the Hellespont. The Hellespont, now called the Dardanelles, and the Bosporus are narrow straits that connect the Aegean Sea with the Black Sea. As such, they are the gateway between Europe and Asia, and in Mycenaean times they held the key to control of the profitable Black Sea trade. In hopes of taking over that trade, Agamemnon's army attacked the powerful city of Troy, launching the decade-long campaign. The mythological war likely reflected a real war that was fought over the Dardanelles about 1200 B.C.

What was the **Peloponnesian War**?

It was the war fought between the Greek city-states of Athens and Sparta between 431 and 404 B.C.; it left Athens ruined. The beginning of the war signaled the end of the golden age of Greece.

As the city-states (which were self-ruling regions made up of a city and the surrounding territory) developed, an intense rivalry grew between Athens and Sparta. The Spartans recruited allies into the Peloponnesian League (the Peloponnese Peninsula forms the southern part of mainland Greece), and together they attacked the Athenian Empire, which had been gaining in power.

The war consisted of three stages: The first was the Archidamian War (431-421 B.C.), named for Archidamus, the Spartan king who led the unsuccessful attacks on fortified Athens. In 421 the so-called Peace of Nicias (421 to 413 B.C.) began, which was negotiated by Athenian politician Nicias. But this truce was broken when an Athenian commander promoted counterattacks on Athens's aggressors in 418 and 415 B.C. The attacks on the Peloponnesian League were unsuccessful, and so the Ionian War broke out (413-404 B.C.). After years of fighting, the Ionian War finally ended in victory for Sparta, after the Peloponnesian League had not only gained the support of Persia to defeat Athens but had successfully encouraged Athens's own subjects to revolt. Athens surrendered to Sparta, ending the Peloponnesian War.

Why was Macedonian king **Alexander** known as "the Great"?

The Macedonian king Alexander the Great (356-323 B.C.) has passed through history as a legendary figure, a reputation attributable to the fact that he conquered virtually all of the known world in his day. In effect, he was king of the world, though his tenure in that role was relatively brief.

Born in the Greek city-state of Macedonia, Alexander was the son of King Philip II (382-336 B.C.), who had risen to power three years earlier. He had an upbringing and education befitting a young Greek prince: Alexander was tutored by Greek philosopher Aristotle (384-322 B.C.) and was trained in athletics and war. His studies of Greek literature and art would later combine with his skill as a warrior to produce a formidable conqueror: Inspired by Greek culture, he also possessed the military prowess and cunning necessary to spread Hellenism (Greek culture) throughout the known world.

At the age of 16, Alexander began running the government of Macedonia while his father, King Philip, waged military campaigns to protect and expand his kingdom. At the age of 17, Alexander joined his father on the battlefield, where he commanded a section of the army to defeat Thebes. When Philip was assassinated in 336 B.C., Alexander acted quickly to assert his claim to the throne. Having done so by 335 B.C., he continued to carry out his father's campaigns, securing Greece and the Balkan Peninsula by the fall of that year. He followed this with an all-out offensive on the Persian Empire, long the enemy of Greece. Supremely courageous and confident in his own abilities as well as in his troops (which numbered in the tens of thousands), by the fall of 331 B.C. Alexander had defeated the Persian army and along the way claimed Egypt. The centuries-old Persian Empire crumbled, and the young Macedonian king proclaimed himself "Lord of Asia." Still, he pressed on, claiming Afghanistan (where he solidified his claim by marrying a young princess) and then India. He was poised to take the Arabian peninsula in 324 B.C. when he died of fever. He was 33. His vast kingdom, which he had ruled leniently but nevertheless authoritatively, was divided among his former generals.

Alexander the Great in battle. The Macedonian king conquered virtually all of the known world in his day.

How was **Rome** able to conquer Greece?

After Alexander the Great died in 323 B.C., his generals divided his empire into successor states, but Greece remained under Macedonian control. Though the Greeks would fight the armies of the Macedonian kings into the 200s B.C., they would not achieve independence, and instead associations of Greek city-states again fought each other.

Meantime, just to the west, Rome had been conquering lands to become a formidable power in the Mediterranean and soon began to look eastward to expand its authority. When Rome conquered Macedonia in 197 B.C., Greece was liberated. Fifty years later, in 146 B.C., Greece was conquered by Rome and was divided into provinces. While the city-states had no military or political power, they nevertheless flourished under Roman rule. And the Romans, who had first started borrowing from Greek thought and culture around 300 B.C., were soon spreading Greek ideas, art, and religion throughout their empire, giving rise to the Greco-Roman culture inherited by modern western civilization.

What were the **Punic Wars**?

The Punic Wars were three major campaigns that Rome waged to expand its empire. Messina (a present-day province of Sicily, Italy) was the site of the First Punic War, which began in 264 B.C. when warring factions in the trade and transportation center called for assistance from both Carthage and Rome. The Carthaginians arrived first and secured the city. But the Romans, who had girded their navy for the battle, arrived and drove the Carthaginians out (241 B.C.), conquering Sicily. Messina became a free city but was allied with Rome.

The rivalry between Rome and Carthage did not end there: The Second Punic War (218-201 B.C.) was largely fought over control of Spain. When the great Carthaginian general Hannibal (247-183 B.C.) captured the Roman-allied city of Sagunto, Spain, in 218, he then crossed the Alps and invaded Italy, where he was met by and defeated the Roman armies. The deciding battle in the Second Punic War was fought in the North African town of Zama (southwest of Carthage) in 202 B.C. It was there that the Romans under general Scipio Africanus (236-183 B.C.) crushed the Carthaginians under Hannibal. Rome exacted payments from Carthage, and Carthage was also forced to surrender its claims in Spain. In 201 B.C. the two powers signed a peace treaty, which held for five decades.

The Third Punic War erupted in 149 B.C. when the Carthaginians rebelled against Roman rule. By 146 B.C. Carthage, which had been richer and more powerful than Rome when the Punic Wars began, was completely destroyed in this third and final conflict with the Roman army.

Why did the **Roman Empire fall**?

One could argue that the Roman Empire collapsed under its own weight: It had become too vast to be effectively controlled by any one ruler.

By the close of the Punic Wars in 146 B.C., Greece, Macedonia, and the Mediterranean coasts of Spain and Africa had been brought under Roman control. Within a century, Rome again began to expand overseas. Under the Roman general Pompey (106-48 B.C.), eastern Asia Minor, Syria, and Judea (Palestine) were conquered. Next, Gaul was conquered by Pompey's rival, Julius Caesar (100-44 B.C.), adding the territory west of Europe's Rhine River to the Roman world. In 31 B.C., in the Battle of Actium, Octavian (63 B.C.-A.D.14; Julius Caesar's adopted son and heir) defeated the forces of Marc Antony (c. 83-30 B.C.) and Cleopatra (69-30 B.C.), queen of Egypt, and in 30 B.C. Egypt became a Roman province.

In 27 B.C. Octavian became the first Roman emperor and was known as Augustus, meaning "exalted." Though Octavian's rule marked the beginning of the long period of stability called the Pax Romana, the Roman Empire had become so large—stretching across Europe and parts of Africa and the Middle East—that only a strong, central authority could govern it. During the 200 years of the Pax Romana, Rome's emperors gradually grew more powerful, to the point that after death an emperor was worshiped by the people.

But soon there were threats to this central control, not the least of which was the spread of Christianity, as well as invasions from the Germanic Goths and the Persians. Theodosius I (379-395) was the last emperor to rule the entire Roman Empire. When he died in A.D. 395, the empire was split into the West Roman Empire and the East Roman Empire, setting the stage for the decline of the Romans.

The West Roman Empire came under a series of attacks by various Germanic tribes including the Vandals and the Visigoths (the western division of the Goths), who invaded Spain, Gaul (in western Europe), and northern Africa. These assaults eventually led to the disintegration of the West Roman Empire by 476.

The East Roman Empire remained more or less intact, but it became known as the Byzantine Empire and was predominately a Greek-oriented culture from 476 until 1453, when it fell to the Turks.

Was **Attila the Hun** really a savage?

While Attila (c. 406-453) may have possessed some of the worthwhile qualities of a military leader, the king of the Huns was no doubt a ruthless and fierce figure. He is believed to have ascended through the ranks of the Hun army, coming to power as the leader of the nomadic group in 434. By this time, the Huns (who originated in central Asia) had occupied the Volga River valley in the area of present-day western Russia.

At first, like his predecessors, he was wholly occupied with fighting other barbarian tribes for control of lands. But under Attila's leadership, the Huns began to extend their power into central Europe. He waged battles with the eastern Roman armies, and, after murdering his older brother and co-ruler Bleda in 445, went on to trample the countries of the Balkan Peninsula and northern Greece—causing terrible destruction along the way. As Attila continued westward with his bloody campaigns, which each Hun fought using his own weapons and his own savage technique, he nearly destroyed the foundations of Christianity.

But the combined armies of the Romans and the Visigoths defeated Attila and the Huns at Châlons (in northeastern France) in June 451, which is known as one of the most decisive battles of all time. From there, Attila and his men moved into Italy, devastating the countryside before Pope Leo I (c. 400-461) succeeded in persuading the brutal leader to spare Rome. (For this and other reasons, Leo was later canonized, becoming St. Leo.) Attila died suddenly—and of natural causes—in 453, just as he was again preparing to cross the Alps and invade Italy anew.

THE MIDDLE AGES

What was the **Norman Conquest**?

The Norman Conquest is the brief but critical period in British history that began when the French duke William of Normandy (c. 1028-1087) sailed across the English

Channel in 1066 and invaded England. This was upon the death of what would turn out to be England's last Anglo-Saxon king, Edward the Confessor (c. 1003-1066). While William became known as William the Conqueror (and he did conduct a brutal conquest of Anglo-Saxon England), he might have had reason to believe he could claim the English throne upon King Edward's death: The named successor, Harold (c. 1022-1066), of the powerful Wessex family, had two years earlier become shipwrecked off the coast of France, where he reportedly took an oath that he would, upon King Edward's death, support William of Normandy (who was King Edward's distant cousin) as heir.

Hearing of Edward's death, William and his army set sail for England, where Harold had already assumed the throne as King Harold II. But Harold had previously quarreled with his brother Tostig, and the noble Wessex family was divided and engaged in a power struggle. Tostig was joined in his fight by the Norwegians who, at the same time that William was landing on England's southern coast, invaded from the north. Thus, William and his troops entered England without opposition (since Harold was focusing his efforts elsewhere). Though the king defeated the Norwegians and Tostig (who was slain in battle), he would not emerge the victor in his subsequent battle with William: On October 14 the two met in battle at Hastings, near the entrance to the Strait of Dover. Though he fought valiantly, Harold was killed.

William was crowned at Westminster Abbey on Christmas Day 1066. Within a few years, by 1070, he had killed many Anglo-Saxon nobles and the rest he deprived of their land. In the 21 years of his reign, William imposed Norman aristocracy on England, required that French be spoken at court, and drew England closer to Europe. He ruled until his death in 1087, after which the Norman nobility mixed with what was left of the Anglo-Saxons. It is this intermingling that produced the English language—from the German tongue of the Anglo-Saxons combined with the Norman French. William's descendants (albeit distantly so) have ruled England ever since his takeover in 1066.

Who was **Genghis Khan**?

He was a Mongol conqueror who rose to power in the early thirteenth century to rule over one of the greatest continental empires the world has seen. Born Temüjin (c. 1167-1227), he was named Genghis Khan, meaning "universal ruler," in 1206. He was a fearless military leader, a brilliant strategist, and a ruthless subjugator, known for his brutal methods.

Temuüjin was the first-born son of the leader of a small nomadic clan. When he was a young boy, his father was killed by a neighboring tribe (Tatars) and thus he rose to the status of chief. But instead of allowing a boy to lead them, clan members abandoned Temüjin and his family. He survived the hard-scrabbled youth of a destitute nomad. But by all accounts, he seemed destined to become a great leader.

By the time he was 20 years old, Temüjin had managed to forge alliances with various tribal leaders and claimed the leadership of a small clan. By 1189 he united two Mongol tribes, which he organized to conquer the rival Tatars by the year 1202. At a conference of Mongol leaders in 1206, Temüjin was pronounced the Great Ruler, or Genghis Khan, of the Unified Mongolian State. He began a transformation of the Mongol tribes, dividing them into military units, each one supported by a number of households. He imposed law and order, promoted education, and stimulated economic prosperity. Within five years, Mongol society was changed from a nomadic-tribal to a military-feudal system. Thus organized, Genghis Khan prepared his troops to expand the Mongolian empire.

Genghis Khan's armies embarked on a series of military campaigns, claiming land and subjugating peoples—sometimes using barbaric methods. By 1213 he controlled northern China to the Great Wall. By 1219 he controlled most of China and began campaigns into the Muslim world. When he died in the field in 1227, Genghis Khan commanded the vast territory from China to the Caspian Sea. He was succeeded by his sons, who continued to expand the Mongol holdings. His grandson was Kublai Khan (1215-1294), under whose leadership the Mongolian empire reached its pinnacle.

Who was **Tamerlane**?

Tamerlane (1336-1405) was a central Asian conqueror who gained power in the late 1300s. His Islamic name was Timur; Tamerlane is the English version. He was a barbaric warrior and a brilliant military leader whose fearsome tactics earned him the name Tamerlane the Terrible. By 1370 he was a powerful warlord whose government was centered in the province of Samarkand, in present-day Uzbekistan. In 1383 he launched a series of conquests that lasted more than 20 years and gained him control of a vast region including Iraq, Armenia, Mesopotamia, Georgia, Russia, and parts of India. He died in 1405, on an expedition to conquer China. His body was entombed in an elaborate mausoleum, which is considered a treasure of Islamic art. After his death, his sons and grandsons fought for control of his dynasty, which remained intact for another hundred years. Tamerlane and his heirs built Samarkand into a great city; in its day it was a center for culture and scholarship in central Asia.

Who was **Eleanor of Aquitaine**?

Eleanor of Aquitaine (c. 1122-1204) was among the most powerful figures of the Middle Ages (500-1350). Her father was William X (1099-1137), the duke of Aquitaine—one of the largest and wealthiest regions that became modern France (it extended from the Loire River to the Pyrenees Mountains). Eleanor inherited her father's vast holdings when he died in 1137; she was a teenager at the time. The same year, she married Louis VII (c. 1120-1180), who, within a month, succeeded his father as the king of France. As queen, Eleanor took an active role in her husband's business, even accompanying him on the Second Crusade (1147-49), purportedly so that she and her numerous female attendants could care for the wounded. The expedition ended in failure, largely because of a disagreement between the king and queen about the objective. Thereafter women were prohibited from joining the crusades. Though Eleanor and Louis had two children, both daughters, they were granted an annulment of their unhappy marriage in 1152 on the grounds that they were distantly related. According to feudal law, Eleanor regained Aquitaine. Within a year she married again, to Henry Plantagenet (1133-1189) of England, who was some ten years her junior. In 1154 he became King Henry II, and Eleanor was again queen, this time of England.

Though the couple had eight children (five sons and three daughters), their marriage was stormy. Henry had liaisons with other women, the result of which was an illegitimate line of heirs to the throne. Eleanor also resented him for his attempts to control Aquitaine, which she felt was rightly hers. In 1173, when Henry and Eleanor's three surviving sons attempted to depose their father, Eleanor threw her support behind her sons. The rebellion failed, and Eleanor fled for France. In 1174 she was captured and returned to England, where she was put in semi-confinement by her husband, the king, until his death in 1189. (Henry died while attempting to put down another rebellion by his sons, Richard the Lionhearted [1157-1199] and John Lackland [1167-1216]).

After King Henry's death, Eleanor again became a powerful force in European politics. Her son, Richard "the Lionhearted," inherited the English throne, and she took an active role in his administration. She even stepped in for him when he left England to fight in the crusades. When Richard died in 1199, his brother John ascended the throne. Eleanor, then in her late seventies, continued to wield power and influence. In an effort to ensure the future of the Plantagenets and to reconcile the English and French aristocracies, she arranged for one of her granddaughters to marry the son of the French king. She also managed to secure the family's land holdings in France for King John. She retired from her active political life in 1202 and died two years later.

What was the **Hundred Years' War**?

The term refers to a succession of wars between England and France. The fighting began in 1337 and did not end until 1453. However, the period was not one of constant warfare: truces and treaties brought about breaks in the military action between the countries. The reasons for the conflicts were many: England was trying to hang onto its provinces on the European continent; the French threw their support behind the Scots, who had their own battles with the English; the French wished to control the commercial center of Flanders (present-day Belgium), where the English had set up a profitable wool trade; and finally, the two countries disagreed about who should control the English Channel, the body of water that lies between them.

To further complicate matters, marriages between the English and French aristocracy meant that heirs to either throne could find themselves with a foreign relative, allowing them to lay claim to authority over the other country as well. When the first war broke out in 1337, King Edward III (1312-1377) of England claimed the French throne on the basis of the fact that his mother, Isabella, was the daughter of France's King Philip IV (called Philip the Fair; 1268-1314) and the sister of three French kings. Over the course of the next century, even though England won most of the battles and for a brief time controlled France (1420-22), it was the French who ultimately won the war in 1453. England lost all its territory on the continent, except Calais, which was also later taken by the French (in 1558).

Joan of Arc is surrounded by a crowd after leading the French into victory over the English in the Battle for Orleans in 1429. (Original painting by J.J. Scherrer.)

How did **Joan of Arc** become a warrior?

Joan of Arc (called the Maid of Orleans; c. 1412-1431) gained fame for leading the French into victory over the English in the Battle for Orleans in 1429. A year before the battle, the English forces had invaded northern France and took possession of an area that included the city of Reims, where all of France's kings were crowned in the cathedral. Thus, Charles VII (1403-1461), whom France recognized as their king, had never had a proper coronation. It is said that Joan, an extraordinarily devoted Catholic who was then just a teen, appealed to Charles to allow her to go into battle against the English who were besieging Orleans. Though he was skeptical of her at first (she claimed to have heard the voices of saints), he eventually conceded. In the battlefield, Joan also overcame the doubts of the French troops and their leaders, who were understandably hesitant to follow the young girl's lead. She proved to them that she was not only capable but also successful. In

April 1429, in just 10 days' time, Joan led the French to victory over the English, who fled Orleans.

Still determined to see Charles properly crowned, Joan proceeded to lead a military escort for the king into Reims, where he was at last coronated on July 17, 1429—with Joan of Arc standing beside him. Next she determined that Charles should authorize her to try to free Paris from English control. Again the king acquiesced, but this time with dire results: She was captured by the French Burgundians (English sympathizers and loyalists), who turned her over to the English. Believing she was a heretic (by all reports Joan of Arc was clairvoyant), the English burned her at the stake in Rouen, France, on May 30, 1431. She is still considered a national hero of France. Recognizing Joan of Arc for her unswerving faith and for having valiantly pursued what she believed her mission to be, the Catholic Church canonized Joan of Arc in 1920. The feast day of St. Joan of Arc is celebrated on May 30.

What were the **Hussite Wars**?

The Hussite Wars were fought in the former kingdom of Bohemia (part of present-day Czech Republic) between 1420 and 1433. The country was plunged into the 13-year war by festering hostilities between papal forces and Bohemian peasants (the Hussites, named such since they were followers of religious reformer Jan Huss, c. 1373-1415). In the Four Articles of Prague (1420), the Hussites called for freedom of preaching, limits to church property holding, and civil punishment of mortal sin. The fighting ended in 1433 with the compromise of the Counsel of Basel and three years later was officially ended by the Compact of Iglau (1436), in which a faction of the Hussites agreed to accept the Holy Roman Emperor as king. The peasants had succeeded nevertheless in asserting Bohemian nationalism and had severed the country's ties to Germany.

RENAISSANCE AND THE ENLIGHTENMENT

What was the **Gunpowder Plot**?

In 1605 a group of 12 men, who believed the English government to be hostile to Roman Catholics, laid plans to blow up the Houses of Parliament—with King James I (1566-1625) and government officials in it. Their scheme was discovered, however, and all of the conspirators were put to death. The event is remembered today in two ways: On the night of November 4, which was when the plot was supposed to be carried out, the English hold a festival in which Guy Fawkes (1570-1606), the conspirator who originated the Gunpowder Plot, is burned in effigy. Further, the vaults beneath the Houses of Parliament are searched before each new session.

What was the **Thirty Years' War**?

The Thirty Years' War (1618-48), like the Hundred Years' War, was actually a series of related conflicts, rather than one long campaign. The conflict in Europe began as a religious one, with hostility between Roman Catholics and Protestants; but it eventually turned political before it was ended with the Peace of Westphalia. The war had four periods: the Bohemian (1618-24), the Danish (1625-29), the Swedish (1630-34), and the Swedish-French (1635-48).

In Bohemia (part of present-day Czech Republic) the trouble began in the capital of Prague when the archbishop authorized the destruction of a Protestant church. The act angered Bohemian Protestants and those elsewhere in Europe, who believed it was their right—granted by the Peace of Augsburg (1555)—to worship as Lutherans. When Holy Roman Emperor Matthias (1557-1619) failed to intervene on behalf of the Protestants, Prague became the scene of mayhem in May 1618. Disorder continued in Bohemia even as a new emperor ascended to the throne of the Holy Roman Empire. King Ferdinand II (1578-1637), a Habsburg, wielded an enormous amount of power, and in 1620 he squelched the Bohemian rebellion, which cost the Bohemians their independence. Further, Catholicism was reinstated as the state religion. These events caused other Protestant lands within the Holy Roman Empire to take notice. Soon the kings of Denmark, Sweden, and France entered into their own campaigns fighting King Ferdinand II for control of German lands. But the conflicts weren't strictly about religious freedom: Reducing the authority of the powerful Habsburg family became a primary objective as well.

What was the **Peace of Westphalia**?

In 1644, with Europe torn by the Thirty Years' War (1618-48), a peace conference was convened in Westphalia, Germany. But the negotiations were four long years in the making: the fighting continued until 1648, when the Peace of Westphalia was finally signed. Under this treaty, France and Sweden received some German lands. The agreement also made important allowances for Europe's religions: Not only was Lutheranism given the same due as Catholicism, but Calvinism, the religious movement begun by Frenchman John Calvin (1509-1564), was also was given the official nod. In short, the treaty not only ended the religious warfare in Europe, but it provided for some measure of religious tolerance.

Since the pact recognized the sovereignty of all the states of the Holy Roman Empire, it effectively dissolved the empire. Therefore, historians view the Peace of Westphalia as the beginning of Europe's modern state system.

What was the **Seven Years' War**?

It was a worldwide conflict that began in 1756 between Prussia and Austria, who fought over control of Germany—and over who would be the supreme power in Europe. Great Britain threw its support behind King Frederick II (the Great; 1712-1786) of Prussia. But by the following year Austria was supported not only by France, but also by Sweden, most of the German states, and, very importantly, Russia. (Spain joined the fighting on the side of Austria also, but it was not until late in the game—after 1762.) With such alliances forged among the European states, the conflict soon spilled over, manifesting itself in the colonies of North America and India, where the French and British fought each other for control.

In order to assert his authority in Europe, Prussia's King Frederick had launched many military initiatives and was in a weakened state by the time his army faced the Austrians in 1756. He was spared certain defeat only by an event in Russia in 1762: Upon the death of Czarina Elizabeth Petrovna (1709-1762), who had feared King Frederick, Peter III (1728-1762) ascended the Russian throne. Peter, unlike his predecessor, held Frederick in high esteem, and he proceeded to withdraw Russia's support from Austria and reach a peace agreement with Austria's enemy, Prussia. He died that same year.

The Seven Years' War ended the next year, on February 15, 1763, with the signing of a peace agreement in Saxony, Germany. The area that Austria had fought to control remained, for the most part, under Prussian rule, positioning Prussia as a leading European power. There were no other territorial changes in Europe as a result of the war. In North America and India, Britain emerged from the conflicts as the victor—and as *the* colonial power.

REVOLUTION AND THE MODERN ERA

What was the **French and Indian War**?

The French and Indian War (1754-63) was the last major conflict in North America before the Revolutionary War (1775-83). During colonial times, both Britain and France had steadily expanded their territories into the Ohio River valley. Since the fur trade prospered in this region, both countries wished to control it. But as the French encroached on their territory, the British colonists sent an ultimatum to them. This message was delivered by none other than George Washington (1732-1799), who had been sent by the British governor. But the French made it clear that they did not intend to back down. So in 1754 Washington (now a lieutenant colonel) and 150 troops established a British outpost at present-day Pittsburgh, not far from where the French had installed themselves at Fort Duquesne. That spring and summer fighting broke out.

Washington met the French, and though he and his troops mustered a strong resistance, there were early losses for the British. But a reinvigorated British force, under the leadership of Britain's secretary of state William Pitt (1759-1806), took French forts along the Allegheny River in western Pennsylvania and met French troops in battle at Quebec. In 1755 Washington was made colonel and led the Virginia troops in defending the frontier from French and Indian attacks. Though the British finally succeeded in occupying Fort Duquesne in 1758 (at which time Washington temporarily retired to his farm in Virginia), fighting continued until 1763 when the Treaty of Paris ended the war.

The British won the spoils, gaining control of all French lands in Canada as well as French territories east of the Mississippi River, with the exception of New Orleans. (The city was ceded to Spain, along with its holdings west of the Mississippi; Spain had become an ally to France late in the war, in 1762.) In exchange for Havana, Cuba, Spain turned over Florida to the British. France, which had once controlled a vast region of America, retained only two small islands off the coast of Newfoundland, Canada, and the two Caribbean islands of Martinique and Guadeloupe.

Why is **Paul Revere's ride** so well known?

The April 18, 1775, event was famous in its own right but was memorialized by American writer Henry Wadsworth Longfellow (1807-1882) in his poem, "Paul Revere's Ride." The verse contains an error (or perhaps Longfellow simply took literary license) about the night that the American Revolution (1775-83) began: The light signal that was to be flashed from Boston's Old North Church (one light if the British were approaching the patriots by land and two if the approach was by sea) was sent not to Revere; it was received by Revere's compatriots in Charlestown (now part of Boston proper). However, Revere did ride that night—on a borrowed horse. He left Boston at about 10:00 P.M. and arrived in Lexington at midnight to warn Samuel Adams and John Hancock, who were wanted for treason, that the British were coming. The next day, April 19, the battles of Lexington and Concord were fought, starting the Revolutionary War in America.

Paul Revere's 1775 ride to Lexington to warn that the British were coming.

As an American patriot, Revere (1735-1818) was known for his service as a special messenger, so much so that by 1773

Who were the minutemen?

They were volunteer soldiers, ready to take up arms at a minute's notice, who fought for the American colonies against the British during the Revolutionary War. The minutemen, who were trained and organized into the militia, are most well known for the battles at Lexington and Concord, on April 19, 1775, which marked the beginning of the war. They had been alerted to the approach of the British troops, or "redcoats," by the patriot Paul Revere (1735-1818). After the fighting at Lexington and Concord, which left 250 British killed or wounded and about 90 Americans dead, word spread quickly of the fighting, and the Revolutionary War had begun.

he had already been mentioned in London newspapers. Revere also participated in the Boston Tea Party in 1773.

Why was **Bunker Hill** important in the American Revolution?

The June 1775 battle on the hills outside Boston proved to be the bloodiest battle of the war. After the fighting in April at Lexington and Concord, more British troops arrived in Boston in late May. The Americans fortified Breed's Hill, near Bunker Hill, and on June 17, the British were ordered to attack the Americans there. The patriots, who needed to conserve ammunition, were given the famous direction not to fire until they saw the whites of their enemies' eyes. The patriots succeeded in driving the British back on their first two charges. But on the third charge, the patriots fled. The Battle of Bunker Hill resulted in more than 1,000 injured or dead British soldiers and 400 American soldiers killed or wounded.

What was the **Reign of Terror**?

It refers to the short but bloody period in French history that began in 1793 and ended July 1794. During this time revolutionary leader Maximilien Robespierre (1758-1794) led a tribunal that arrested, tried, and put to death more than 17,000 people—most of them by guillotine.

In the reforms that followed the 1789 Oath of the Tennis Court and the capture of the Bastille, France was transformed into a constitutional state, and French subjects became French citizens. An elected legislature (the Constituent Assembly) was given control of the government. Robespierre was elected first deputy from Paris and was the leader of the radical popular party. In this new era, those who had been associated with the old regime or those who opposed the French Revolution became the subjects of

Scene of rioting during the French Revolution, a tumultuous decade that ended when General Napoleon Bonaparte seized control of the government.

persecution. In January 1793 King Louis XVI (1754-1793) and his wife, Marie Antoinette (1755-1793), were executed, beginning the Reign of Terror that saw thousands more (mostly those who had made up the powerful first and second estates) suffer a similar fate at the hands of the revolutionaries. To escape certain death, many fled the country; this included top-ranking military officials, which made room for the rapid advancement of young military officers such as Napoleon Bonaparte (1769-1821).

The Reign of Terror ended on July 28, 1794, when Robespierre himself was put to death. As he gained power and influence, the revolutionary leader also had become increasingly paranoid, even putting two of his friends to death in 1794. He was overthrown on July 27 by the Revolution of 9th Thermidor and the next day died by guillotine.

When did the **Napoleonic Wars** begin and end?

The Napoleonic Wars began shortly after Napoleon Bonaparte (1769-1821) took power and lasted until 1815, when he was finally defeated at the Battle of Waterloo. Ever the general, Napoleon used his power to keep France at war throughout his reign.

After the Coup d'État of 18th Brumaire (November 1799), which had put Napoleon in power, at first he effected peace: In May 1800 he marched across the Alps to defeat the Austrians, ending the war with them that had begun eight years earlier. Britain, fearing a growing European power on the continent, had declared war on France in 1793; by 1802, having grown tired of battle, the country agreed to peace with Napoleon in the Treaty of Amiens. But the calm in Europe was not to last. By 1803 the diminutive but power-hungry Napoleon (nicknamed the Little Corporal) had begun to plot an invasion of Britain. Declaring himself emperor in 1804, he initiated a series of campaigns across Europe, and by 1806 most of the continent was under his control. He remained, of course, unable to beat the British, whose superior navy gave them supremacy at sea.

But the various alliances (called coalitions) formed by European countries against Napoleon eventually broke him. After he had been defeated in Russia in 1812, the European powers that had long been held in submission by Napoleon formed a sixth and final coalition against him: Great Britain, Russia, Sweden, Prussia, and Austria met Napoleon's army at the momentous Battle of the Nations at Leipzig, Poland, from October 16 to 19, 1813. Napoleon was defeated there in what is sometimes called the War of Liberation, and he retreated to France. The following March, the allies making up the Sixth Coalition took Paris; Napoleon's generals were defeated. He abdicated the throne on April 6. However, that was not the end of the Napoleonic era: Exiled to the Mediterranean island of Elba, Napoleon returned to Paris on March 20, 1815, believing he could recover power in the unstable atmosphere that followed his abdication. Three months later he was defeated at the Battle of Waterloo, on June 18. It was the last battle of the Napoleonic Wars. He was exiled to St. Helena island, where he died in 1821.

What caused the **War of 1812**?

The war between the young United States and powerful Great Britain largely came about because of France. After the French navy was crushed by the British under Admiral Nelson (1758-1805) at the Battle of Trafalgar, Napoleon turned to economic warfare in his long struggle with the British: He directed all countries under French control not to trade with Great Britain. Its economy dependent on trade, Britain struck back by imposing a naval blockade on France, which soon interfered with U.S. shipping. Ever since the struggle between the two European powers began in 1793, the United States tried to remain neutral. But the interruption of shipping to and from the continent and the search and seizure of ships posed significant problems to the American export business: In 1807 Great Britain had issued an Order in Council that required even neutral vessels destined for a continental port to stop first in England; Napoleon countered with the Milan Decree, which stated that any neutral vessel that had submitted to British search be seized.

Back in America, the people of New England, the region most dependent on shipping, nevertheless vehemently opposed entering into war with the British. But the country's economy was depressed as a result of the interruption of exports, and the U.S. Congress declared war on June 18, 1812. In these days before telegraph and radio, the United States did not know that two days before, on June 16, Britain had withdrawn its Orders in Council, lifting its policy of shipping interference, which had been the chief reason for the war declaration. Thus the two countries engaged in fighting for the next two and a half years. On December 24, 1814, the Treaty of Ghent officially ended the war. But once again, poor communication led to fighting: Two weeks after the treaty was signed, troops in New Orleans, unaware of this event, fought for control over the Mississippi River in the worst battle of the entire conflict. Though both the United States and Great Britain claimed victory in the War of 1812, neither side had gained anything.

What does **"Remember the Alamo"** mean?

The saying was a rallying cry for Texans in their war for independence from Mexico. The movement for independence had begun in the winter of 1835-36 when the people of Texas decided to cut off relations with Mexico, and soon turned into a war when the Mexican government sent a force of some 4,000 troops, under the command of General Antonio Lopez de Santa Anna (1794-1876), to squelch the rebellion. As the Mexican army approached, the force of about 150 men who were determined to defend the city of San Antonio retreated to the Alamo, a Spanish mission built in the previous century. There they were joined by another 50 men but were still no match for the Mexicans, who kept the Alamo under siege for 13 days—from February 23 to March 6, 1836. The Texans, low on ammunition, ceased to return fire. On the morning of March 6, Santa Anna's troops seized the Alamo. The fierce frontiersmen, Davy Crockett (1786-1836) among them, are believed to have fought using the butts of their rifles. All the Texans who fought that day at the Alamo died.

Meantime, General Sam Houston (1793-1863) had assembled his forces, and with the rallying cry "remember the Alamo" (and their fellow Texans who had bravely fought and died there), he set out to face the Mexican army and secure independence. This he did, at San Jacinto, Texas, on April 21, 1836, in a quick and decisive battle that had caught Santa Anna's troops by surprise. The following day the Mexican general was captured and made to sign a treaty giving Texas independence.

What caused the **Mexican War**?

The two-year war (1846-48) was fought over the United States' annexation of Texas. The events that led up to the conflict began in 1837 when President Andrew Jackson (1767-1845) recognized Texas as independent (this was just after Texas had won its war with Mexico). Republic of Texas president Sam Houston (1793-1863) felt that protection against a Mexican invasion may be necessary, so he eyed annexation to the United States. In the meantime, Mexican president Antonio Lopez de Santa Anna (1794-1876) warned that such an action on the part of the United States would be "equivalent to a declaration of war against the Mexican Republic." In June 1844 the U.S. Senate rejected a proposed annexation treaty. But later that year Democratic

Party nominee James K. Polk (1795-1849), an ardent expansionist, was elected president. Because the annexation of Texas had figured prominently in his campaign platform, outgoing President John Tyler (1790-1862) viewed Polk's victory as a public mandate for annexation, and he recommended that Congress pass a joint resolution to invite Texas into the union. Congress did so in February, and President Tyler signed the resolution on March 1, 1845, three days before leaving office.

Mexico responded by breaking off diplomatic relations with the United States. A border dispute made the situation increasingly tenuous: Texas claimed that its southern border was the Rio Grande River, while Mexico insisted it was the Nueces River, situated farther north. In June President Polk ordered Brigadier General Zachary Taylor (1784-1850) to move his forces into the disputed area. In November the U.S. government received word that Mexico was prepared to talk. Polk dispatched Congressman John Slidell (1793-1871) to Mexico to discuss three other outstanding issues: the purchase of California (for $25 million), the purchase of New Mexico (for $5 million), and the payment of damages to American nationals for losses incurred in Mexican revolutions. This last point was critical to the negotiations, as Polk was prepared to have the United States assume payment of damages to its own citizens in exchange for Mexico's recognition of the Rio Grande as the southern border of Texas.

But upon arrival in Mexico City, Slidell was refused the meeting—President José Joaquín Herrera (1792-1854) had bowed to pressure, opposing discussions with the United States. When Polk received news of the scuttled talks, he authorized General Taylor to advance through the disputed territory to the Rio Grande. Meanwhile, Mexico overthrew President Herrera, putting into office the fervent nationalist General Mariano Paredes y Arrillaga (1797-1849), who reaffirmed Mexico's claim to Texas and pledged to defend Mexican territory.

While Polk worked through Slidell to get an audience with the Mexican government, the attempts failed, and on May 9 the Cabinet met and approved the president's recommendation to ask Congress to declare war. The next day news arrived in Washington that on April 25 a sizeable Mexican force had crossed the Rio Grande and surrounded a smaller American reconnaissance party. Eleven Americans were killed and the rest were wounded or captured. On May 11 Polk delivered a message to Congress, concluding, "Mexico has...shed American blood upon the American soil....War exists...by the act of Mexico herself." By the time the war was officially declared on May 13, just more than one year after Polk had been sworn into office, General Taylor had already fought and won key battles against the Mexicans and had occupied the northern Mexico city of Matamoros.

What was the **Crimean War**?

The Crimean War was fought from 1853 to 1856 between Russian forces and the allied armies of Britain, France, the Ottoman Empire (present-day Turkey), and Sardinia (part of present-day Italy). The Crimean Peninsula, which juts out into the Black Sea and is today part of Ukraine, was the setting for many of the battles. The source of the conflict was Russia's continued expansion into the Black Sea region—which, if left unchecked, would have resulted in strategic and commercial advantages for Russia. But Russia was unable to muster the strength it needed to combat the powerful alliance formed by the European countries and the Ottoman Empire. The war was ended with the signing of the Treaty of Paris (1856), which required Russia to surrender lands it had taken from the Ottoman Empire and abolished Russian navy and military presence in the Black Sea region. It was the first conflict that was covered by newspaper reporters at the front.

Was the Civil War fought because of **slavery**?

For years, American schoolchildren learned that the question of slavery was the only cause of the Civil War (1861-65): With 19 free states and 15 slave states making up the Union, Abraham Lincoln (1809-1865) had called the country "a house divided" even before he became president. While slavery was central to the conflict, many believe the bloody four-year war had other causes as well.

By the mid-1800s important differences had developed between the South and the North—and many maintain these differences, or vestiges of them, are still with the country today. The economy in the South was based on agriculture while the North was industrialized; the ideals and lifestyles of each region reflected these economic realities. Southerners believed their agrarian lifestyle was dependent on the labor of slaves. For a long time, slavery was viewed by some as a necessary evil. But by the early 1800s the view that slavery is morally wrong was beginning to take hold. Northern abolitionists had begun a movement to end slavery in the states. But, except for a small antislavery faction, these views were not shared in the South.

There were other factors that contributed to the declaration of secession and the formation of the Confederacy, although some still argue these factors were merely smoke screens for the defense of slavery. Disputes between the federal government and the states had limited the power of the states, and this policy was called into question by Southerners. Further, the political party system was in disarray in mid-1850s America. The disorder prompted feelings of distrust for the elected politicians who set national policy. Before the 1860 presidential election, Southern leaders urged that the South secede from the Union if Lincoln, who had publicly taken a stand against slavery, won.

How did the **Civil War begin and end**?

Unhappy with the outcome of the 1860 presidential election, in which Abraham Lincoln (1809-1865) was elected, and fearing a loss of their agrarian way of life, the Southern states began to make good on their promise to secede if Lincoln won the presidency: South Car-

The 1863 Battle of Gettysburg is considered the turning point in the American Civil War.

olina was the first (in December of that year). In January 1861 five more states followed: Mississippi, Florida, Alabama, Georgia, and Louisiana. When representatives from the six states met the next month in Montgomery, Alabama, they established the Confederate States of America and elected Jefferson Davis (1808-1889) president. Two days before Lincoln's inauguration, Texas joined the Confederacy. (Virginia, Arkansas, North Carolina, and Tennessee joined in April, shortly after the Civil War had already begun.)

The Civil War, also called the War of Secession and the War between the States, began on April 12, 1861, when Southern troops fired on Fort Sumter, a U.S. military post in Charleston, South Carolina. Brutal fighting continued for four years. On April 9, 1865, General Robert E. Lee (1807-1870) surrendered his ragged Confederate troops to General Ulysses S. Grant (1822-1885) of the Union at old Appomattox Court House, Virginia. The war had not only been between the states, it had also been between brothers: the conflict divided the nation. The Civil War took more American lives than any other war in history.

Why was the **battle at Gettysburg** important?

The 1863 battle, fought when the two sides met accidentally in the southern Pennsylvania town, was a turning point in the Civil War. From July 1 to 3 General George

Meade (1815-1872) led his troops (about 90,000 strong) to defeat the advancing Confederate troops (numbering some 75,000) under General Robert E. Lee (1807-1870). The Union win effectively stopped Lee's invasion of the North.

The following November 19 President Abraham Lincoln (1809-1865) made the historical address at Gettysburg, as he dedicated part of the battlefield as a national cemetery. Beginning with the now-famous words "Four score and seven years ago our fathers brought forth upon this continent a new nation, conceived in Liberty, and dedicated to the proposition that all men are created equal," the short speech (which Lincoln rewrote many times) closed by issuing a rallying cry for the nation as a whole, saying, "we here highly resolve that the dead shall not have died in vain—that the nation shall, under God, have a new birth of freedom—and that governments of the people, by the people, and for the people, shall not perish from the earth."

What was the Battle of **Tippecanoe**?

The battle near present-day Lafayette, Indiana, took place on November 7, 1811, when U.S. troops under the command of General William Henry Harrison (1773-1841) defeated the Shawnee Indians while their leader, Tecumseh (1768-1813), was away.

Before the November battle, the Shawnee Indians had been steadily pushed back from their ancestral lands along the Cumberland River in Kentucky. Once they settled in the Ohio River valley, they formed a wall of resistance to further pressure. Resistance fighting began in 1763 and did not end until 30 years later (1793) when the American forces of General Anthony Wayne (1745-1796) defeated the Shawnee at Fallen Timbers in northwest Ohio. Tecumseh was 25 years old at the time of this critical defeat of his people. He became determined, despite the counsel of the tribe elders, to halt the westward movement of the Shawnee. Tecumseh and his brother, Tenskwatawa (c. 1768-1834), built a settlement on Tippecanoe Creek near the Wabash River, Indiana. Called Prophet's Town, it became a rallying point for those Indians who resisted displacement by colonists. Soon the Shawnee who had settled at Prophet's Town were joined by bands of Wyandot, Potawatomi, Miami, and Delaware Indians. The British became aware of Tecumseh's defiance and soon supplied Prophet's Town Indians with arms to use against the Americans.

In 1810 the governor of the Indiana Territory, William Henry Harrison (1773-1841), requested a meeting with Tecumseh. But both were suspicious of each other and could reach no agreement for peace. Settlers who were aware of Tecumseh's armed resistance movement pressured President James Madison (1751-1836) to take action, which he did: Under orders from the president, Harrison set out in the fall of 1811 with a force of 1,000 men. Arriving at Tippecanoe on November 6, he met with the Indians under a flag of truce and then made camp about a mile away from Prophet's Town. Tecumseh was visiting the Creek Indians in Alabama at the time, trying to rally their support in the white resistance movement. But his brother, Tenskwatawa, rallied the men at Prophet's Town, and at the break of day, they attacked Harrison's camp. Hand-

U.S. General William Henry Harrison leads his troops against the Shawnee Indians at the Battle of Tippecanoe, 1811.

to-hand fighting ensued in an icy drizzle. The Indian alliance retreated and though Harrison took heavy losses, he had managed to destroy Prophet's Town.

The battle undermined Tecumseh's initiative and launched the career of Harrison. In 1840, after successful military duty and service in the U.S. Congress, Harrison rode a wave of public support all the way to the White House to become the ninth president. His campaign slogan was "Tippecanoe and Tyler, too" (John Tyler was his running mate). Eventually the Shawnee were pushed into Kansas. Tecumseh became an ally of the British in the War of 1812 (1812-14) and was killed in the fighting.

What was **"Custer's Last Stand"**?

The term refers to the defeat of General George A. Custer (1839-1876) at the Battle of Little Bighorn on June 25, 1876. Custer had a national reputation as a Civil War general and Indian fighter in the west, and when he and his troops were outnumbered and badly beaten by the Sioux led by Sitting Bull (c. 1831-1890)—just as the country was about to celebrate the hundredth anniversary of the Declaration of Independence—the result was a stunning reversal in the national mood.

Little Bighorn was part of a series of campaigns known collectively as the Sioux War. Several events led to the conflict that became Custer's Last Stand. The Sioux were nontreaty Indians, which means they had refused to accept the white-dictated limits on their territory. They were outraged at the repeated violation of their lands by the onrush of miners to new gold strikes in the Black Hills of South Dakota. Further, there had been eight attacks by the Sioux on the Crow who were living on reservation land. Finally, Sitting Bull, the chief of the Hunkpapa band of Sioux, refused government demands that he and his people return to reservation lands. Meanwhile, unbeknownst to the government's military strategists, by spring 1876 Sitting Bull had been joined in his cause by other groups of northern Plains tribes, including the Cheyenne led by Crazy Horse (c. 1842-1877). With the government ready to use force to return Sitting Bull and his band of Sioux to reservations, the stage was set for a conflict—bigger than any Washington official had imagined.

On June 25 Custer rode into Montana territory with his Seventh Cavalry to meet the Sioux. Despite orders to simply contain the Indians and prevent their escape, he attacked. While historians remain divided on how Custer could have been defeated on that fateful June day, one thing remains certain: Custer and his men were badly outnumbered. Having divided his regiment into three parts, Custer rode with about 225 men against a force of at least 2,000—the largest gathering of Indian warriors in Western history. Custer and his soldiers all died. The fighting continued into the next day, with those Indians that remained finally disbanding and returning to their designated territory. Meantime, Sitting Bull and his band retreated into Canada. Returning to the United States five years later, in 1890, Sitting Bull was killed by authorities.

The battle became the subject of countless movies, books, and songs. It's remembered by some Native Americans as a galvanizing force—proof that brave men who fight for what they believe in can win.

What caused the **Spanish-American War**?

The 1898 war, which lasted only a matter of months (late April to mid-August), was fought over the liberation of Cuba. During the 1870s the Cuban people rebelled against Spanish rule. But once that long rebellion had been put down, peace on the Caribbean island did not hold: worsening economic conditions prompted revolution in 1895. American leaders, the bloody American Civil War (1861-65) still in their memories, feared that while the Cuban rebels could not win their battle against the Spanish, neither were the Spanish strong enough to fully put down the insurrection. Meanwhile, the American public, fed by a steady stream of newspaper accounts reporting oppressive conditions on the island, increasingly supported U.S. intervention in the Cuban conflict.

In November 1897 President William McKinley (1843-1901) did intervene, but it was through political, rather than military, pressure. As a result, Spain granted Cuba limited self-government within the Spanish empire. However, the move did not satisfy the Cuban rebels, who were determined to achieve independence from Spain; the fighting continued. Rioting broke out in Havana, and in order to protect Americans living there, the United States sent the battleship *Maine* to the port on January 25, 1898. On February 15, an explosion blew up the *Maine,* killing more than 200 people. Blame for the blast was promptly—and history would later conclude wrongly—assigned to Spain. While President McKinley again made several attempts to pressure Spain into granting Cuba full independence, it was to no avail. Nevertheless, on April 19, the U.S. Congress passed a joint resolution recognizing an independent Cuba, disclaiming American intention to acquire the island, and authorizing the use of the American army and navy to force Spanish withdrawal. On April 25, the United States formally declared that the country was at war with Spain.

In the months that followed, American forces battled the Spanish and Spanish loyalists in Cuba and the Spanish-controlled Philippines. There was also military activity on Puerto Rico, however, the American forces there met little resistance. Once Santiago, Cuba, was surrendered by the Spanish after the battle at San Juan Hill in July 1898, it would only be a matter of weeks before a cease-fire was called and an armistice was signed (on August 12), ending the brief war.

What does "**¡Viva Zapata!**" mean?

It was the cry that went up in support of the rebel general Emiliano Zapata (1879-1919), whose chief concern during the Mexican Revolution (1910-20) was the distribution of land to the people.

An advocate of Mexico's lower classes, Zapata began revolutionary activities against the government of Porfirio Díaz (1830-1915) as early as 1897. Zapata rose to prominence in helping the liberal and idealistic Francisco Madero (1873-1913) overthrow Díaz in 1911. With Madero placed in power, Zapata promptly began pressing his co-conspirator for a program to distribute the hacienda (large estate) lands to the peasants. Rebuffed by Madero that same year, Zapata drafted the agrarian Plan of Ayala and renewed the revolution. Madero's government never achieved stability and proved to be ineffective, prompting a second overthrow in 1913: Victoriano Huerta (1854-1916) seized power from Madero, whom he had helped put into office, and in the chaos surrounding the coup, Madero was shot and killed.

But Zapata refused to support Huerta and remained a leader of the revolution, continuing his crusade for the people—who supported him with cheers of "¡Viva Zapata!," meaning "long live Zapata!" The bitter fighting of the revolution continued and soon those who had supported the slain Madero—including Zapata and Pancho Villa (1878-1923)—threw their backing behind another revolutionary, Venustiano Carranza (1859-1920). In 1914 Carranza's forces occupied Mexico City and forced Huerta to leave the country. No sooner had Carranza taken office than the revolutionaries began fighting among themselves. Zapata and Pancho Villa demanded dramatic reforms and together they attacked Mexico City in 1914. Five years later, and one year before the end of the revolution, Carranza's army ambushed and assassinated Zapata in his home state of Morelos.

What was the **Chinese-Japanese War**?

It was a war fought in 1894 to 1895 over control of Korea, which was a vassal state of China. When an uprising broke out in Korea in 1894, China sent troops in to suppress it. Korea's ports had been open to Japan since 1876 and in order to protect its interests there, Japan, too, sent troops to the island nation when trouble broke out. But once the rebellion had been put down, the Japanese troops refused to withdraw. In July 1894 fighting broke out between Japan and China, with Japan emerging as the victor, having crushed China's navy. A peace treaty signed on April 17, 1895, provided for an independent Korea (which only lasted until 1910, when Japan took possession) and for China to turn over to Japan the island of Taiwan and the Liaodong Peninsula (the peninsula was later returned to China for a fee after Russia, Germany, and France forced Japan to do so). The war, though relatively brief, seriously weakened China, and in the imperialist years that followed, the European powers scrambled for land concessions there.

What caused the **Russo-Japanese War**?

From 1904 to 1905 the war was fought by Russia and Japan over their interests in China (particularly Manchuria) and Korea—areas of strategic importance to each country. Before fighting broke out Japan moved to settle the conflict, but the overture was rejected by Tsar Nicholas II (1868-1918), and Japan soon severed all diplomatic relations (on February 6, 1904) with Russia. Two days later the Japanese issued a surprise attack on Russian ships at Lushun (Port Arthur), Manchuria. On February 10 Japan officially declared itself at war with Russia. The battles—both on land and at sea—went badly for the Russian forces, which could not be adequately reinforced or supplied to meet the powerful and disciplined Japanese. Early in 1905, the war effort already unpopular back home, revolution broke out in Russia, further weakening the country's resolve.

After an eight-month siege at Lushun, it became clear that Russia could no longer muster a fight. Further, the war was expensive for Japan, which sought the intervention of the United States in settling the conflict. President Theodore Roosevelt (1858-1919) became involved in mediating the dispute; a peace treaty was signed September 5, 1905, at a shipyard in Portsmouth, New Hampshire, following one month of deliberations. The terms of the treaty were these: both nations agreed to evacuate Manchuria; Russia ceded to Japan the southern half of Sakhalin Island, which lies between the two countries (the island was ceded back to Russia after World War II); Korea became a Japanese protectorate; and Russia transferred to Japan the lease of China's Liaodong Peninsula. And so Japan emerged as a power onto the world scene.

What was the **Bolshevik Revolution**?

It was the November 1917 revolution in which the Bolsheviks, an extremist faction within the Russian Social Democratic Labor Party (later renamed the Russian Com-

What was the Boxer Rebellion?

It was a Chinese uprising in 1900, which was put down through the combined forces of eight foreign countries including Germany, Italy, Japan, Russia, and the United States. The Chinese-Japanese War (1894-95) had seriously weakened China, and in 1898 the country agreed to lease its Kiaochow region to Germany. Soon other European countries followed suit and before long Western influence was being felt in China. This angered many Chinese, including members of a secret society that opposed the Manchu government for having allowed the foreign incursions. This secret society was made up of athletic young men, and so they were called Boxers by China's Westerners.

Between June 21 and August 14, 1900, Boxers rebelled against anything foreign and began a raid of the country that was intended to drive out all foreign influence. The uprising was aimed at not only Westerners and foreign diplomats, but missionaries, Chinese Christians, and any Chinese who were thought to support Western ideas. Houses, schools, and churches were burned. Much of the destruction took place in Beijing, and when foreign diplomats there called for help, it arrived from eight countries. The Manchu government did not welcome this interference in its affairs and promptly declared war on the eight nations.

On September 7, 1901, the Manchu government signed a peace settlement with the foreign countries. The Boxer Protocol called for China to punish officials who had been involved in the rebellion and pay damages in the hundreds of millions of dollars. The United States, Britain, and Japan later returned part of the money to China, specifying that it be used for educational purposes.

munist Party), seized control of the government, ushering in the Soviet age. The event is also known as the October Revolution since by the old Russian calendar (in use until 1918), the government takeover happened on October 25.

The Bolshevik Revolution was the culmination of a series of events in 1917. In March, with Russia still in the midst of World War I (1914-18), the country faced hardship. Shortages of food and fuel made conditions miserable. The people had lost faith in the war effort and were loathe to support it by sending any more young men into battle. In the Russian capital of Petrograd (which had been known as St. Petersburg until 1914), workers went on strike and rioting broke out. In the chaos (called the March Revolution), Tsar Nicholas II (1868-1918) ordered the legislative body, the Duma, to disband; instead, the representatives set up a provisional government. Having lost all political influence, Nicholas abdicated the throne on March 15. He and his family were imprisoned and are believed to have been killed in July of the following year.

The Bolsheviks lead workers and disgruntled soldiers in a takeover of Petrograd's Winter Palace, Russia, 1917.

Hearing of Nicholas's abdication, longtime political exile Vladimir Lenin (1870-1924) returned from Europe to Petrograd, where he led the Bolsheviks in rallying the Russian people with calls for peace, land reform, and worker empowerment; their slogan was "Land, Peace, and Bread." The Bolsheviks grew in numbers and became increasingly radical, in spite of efforts by the provisional government headed by revolutionary Alexander Kerensky (1881-1970) to curb the Bolsheviks' influence. The only socialist member of the first provisional government, Kerensky's government proved ineffective and failed to meet the demands of the people. He also failed to end the country's involvement in World War I, which the Bolsheviks viewed as an imperialistic war.

On November 7 the Bolsheviks led workers and disgruntled soldiers and sailors in a takeover of Petrograd's Winter Palace, the scene of Bloody Sunday in 1905, and which had become the headquarters of Kerensky's provisional government. By November 8 the provisional government had fallen.

WORLD WAR I

How did **World War I begin**?

Though the Great War, as it was called until World War II (1939-45), was sparked by the June 28, 1914, assassination of Archduke Francis Ferdinand of Austria-Hungary (1863-1914), the war in Europe had been precipitated by several developments. National pride had been growing among Europeans; nations increased their armed forces through drafts; and colonialism continued to be a focus of the European powers, as they competed with each other for control of lands in far-off places. Meantime, weapons and other implements of war had been improved by industry, making them deadlier than ever. So on that June day in the city of Sarajevo (then the capital of Austria-Hungary's province of Bosnia and Herzegovina), when a gunman named Gavrilo Princip (1894-1918) shot down Archduke Ferdinand, it is not surprising that Austria-Hungary responded with force. Since Princip was known to have ties to a Serbian terrorist organization, Austria-Hungary declared war on Serbia. Both sides, however, believed that the battle would be decided quickly. But instead fighting would spread, involving more countries. Four years of fighting—aided by the airplane, the submarine, tanks, and machine guns—would cause greater destruction than any other war to that date.

Why did the **United States** get involved **in World War I**?

When war broke out in Europe in August 1914, Americans opposed the involvement of U.S. troops, and President Woodrow Wilson (1856-1924) declared the country's neutrality. But as the fighting continued and the German tactics threatened civilian lives, Americans began siding with the Allies.

After the sinking of the passenger liner SS *Lusitania,* Germany adopted restricted submarine warfare. But early in 1917 Germany again began attacking unarmed ships, this time American cargo boats, goading the United States into the war. Meantime, German U-boats were positioning to cut off shipping to and from Britain, in an effort to force the power to surrender. Tensions between the United States and Germany peaked when the British intercepted, decoded, and turned over to President Wilson a telegram Germany had sent to its ambassador in Mexico. The so-called "Zimmermann note," which originated in the office of German foreign minister Arthur Zimmermann (1864-1940), urged the German officials in Mexico to persuade the Mexican government into war with the United States—in order to reconquer lost territory in Texas, New Mexico, and Arizona. The message was published in the United States in early March. One month later, on April 6, 1917, the U.S. Congress declared war on Germany after President Wilson had asserted that "the world must be made safe for democracy."

The SS *Lusitania* was torpedoed by a German U-boat in May 1915; the event forced U.S. involvement in World War I.

How did **World War I end**?

Though the United States had been little prepared to enter the war, the American government mobilized quickly to rally the troops—and the citizens—behind the war effort: In April 1917 the U.S. Regular Army was comprised of just more than 100,000 men; by the end of the war, the American armed forces stood some 5 million strong. It was the arrival of the U.S. troops that gave the Allies the manpower they needed to win the war. After continued fighting in the trenches of Europe, which had left almost 10 million dead, in November 1918, Germany agreed to an armistice and the Central Powers finally surrendered. In January 1919 Allied representatives gathered in Paris to draw up the peace settlement.

How did the **Treaty of Versailles** pave the way for World War II?

In the aftermath of World War I (1914-18), Germany was severely punished: One clause in the Treaty of Versailles even stipulated that Germany take responsibility for causing the war. In addition to its territorial losses, Germany was also made to pay for an Allied military force that would occupy the west bank of the Rhine River, intended to keep Germany in check for the next 15 years. The treaty also limited the

German soldiers ready a machine gun as they watch enemy positions during World War I.

size of Germany's military. In 1921 Germany received a bill for reparations: It owed the Allies $33 million.

While the postwar German government had been made to sign the Treaty of Versailles under the threat of more fighting from the Allies, the German people nevertheless faulted their leaders for accepting such strident terms. Not only was the German government weakened, but public resentment over the Treaty of Versailles soon developed into a strong nationalist movement—led by German chancellor and führer Adolf Hitler (1889-1945).

What was the **League of Nations**?

The League of Nations was the forerunner to the United Nations. It was an international organization established by the Treaty of Versailles at the end of World War I (1914-18). Since the United States never ratified that treaty, it was not a member.

The league was set up to handle disputes among countries and to avoid another major conflict such as the Great War (which is how World War I was referred to until the outbreak of World War II). But the organization proved to be ineffective; it was unable to intervene in such acts of aggression as Japan's invasion of Manchuria in

1931, Italy's conquest of Ethiopia during 1935 to 1936 and occupation of Albania in 1939, and Germany's takeover of Austria in 1938.

The League of Nations dissolved itself during World War II (1939-45). Though unsuccessful, the organization did establish a basic model for a permanent international organization.

THE ERA BETWEEN THE WORLD WARS

What was **Nazism**?

Short for national socialism, "Nazi" was a derisive abbreviation that held. The Nazi doctrine rests on three philosophies: extreme nationalism, anti-Semitism, and anti-communism. As one of the Central Powers, Germany's defeat in World War I (1914-18) resulted in severe punishment of that country and its seriously diminished role in Europe. The doctrines of Nazism took hold there, appealing to the masses with promises of a rebuilt Germany.

The "bible" of Nazism was Adolf Hitler's *Mein Kampf* (*My Struggle;* 1923), which asserted the superiority of a pure Aryan race (Aryans are non-Jewish Caucasians, particularly those of northern European descent), led by an infallible ruler (called "the führer"); the reestablishment of a German empire (the Third Reich); and the systematic annihilation of people who Nazis perceived to be Germany's worst enemies: Jews and Communists. Nazis ruled Germany from 1933, when Hitler rose to power as head of the National Socialist German Workers' Party. In their own country, they enforced their policies through a secret police (the Gestapo), storm troops (called the SS), and Hitler's bodyguard (called the SA). Elsewhere in Europe, the Nazis used sheer force in imposing their system. Their aggression and ruthlessness resulted in World War II (1939-45). During the Holocaust (1933-45), Nazi soldiers, led by "Hitler's henchmen," persecuted and exterminated upwards of 12 million people, at least half of whom were European Jews. Nazism ended in 1945, when Hitler killed himself and Germany lost the war. The doctrine, which demonstrated how detrimentally powerful a theory can be, was outlawed thereafter. Sadly, the late twentieth century saw a resurgence of "neo-Nazism" among extremists in Germany and the United States.

What caused the **Spanish Civil War**?

From 1936 to 1939, two sides fought for control of Spain: the nationalists and the loyalists. The insurgent nationalists were aristocrats, military leaders, Roman Catholic clergy, and members of a political group called the Falange Party; they were supported

Adolf Hitler salutes his troops in Warsaw on October 5, 1939, after Germany's invasion of Poland.

by Nazi Germany (under Adolf Hitler [1889-1945]) and fascist Italy (under Benito Mussolini [1883-1945]) in their effort to wrest control. The loyalists were liberals, socialists, and communists; they were supported by the Soviet Union (under Joseph Stalin [1879-1953]). A number of non-Spanish idealists, who believed saving the republic from the fascist rebels was worth dying for, joined the ranks of the loyalists to form the International Brigade. (In his novel *For Whom the Bell Tolls,* Ernest Hemingway [1899-1961], who had covered the war as a correspondent, wrote about one young American man who took up arms in behalf of the loyalist effort.) The nationalists, under Generalissimo Francisco Franco (1892-1975), won the war when they captured Madrid in March 1939, beginning an era of harsh right-wing rule. And, as with any war, the fascist victory had come at a dear price: hundreds of thousands dead and massive destruction throughout the country.

Who was **Generalissimo Franco**?

Generalissimo Francisco Franco (1892-1975) was the fascist leader of Spain from 1939 until 1973. He rose to power in the Spanish Civil War (1936-39) as he led a rebel nationalist army against the loyalist forces. Capturing Madrid in 1939, Franco assumed the role of head of government. Though he and the nationalists had received considerable help from Nazi Germany and fascist Italy to win the civil war, when fighting broke out in World War II (1939-45), Spain stayed neutral (at least nominally so). In 1947, with the fighting in Europe over, Franco declared himself monarch of Spain and ruled as an authoritative dictator. Two years before he died, he stepped down as head of state, though he retained the title generalissimo, meaning "commander in chief." Franco named as his successor Prince Juan Carlos (1938-). When Franco died in 1975, Juan Carlos I became the first Spanish monarch to control Spain since his grandfather, King Alfonso XIII (1886-1941), was deposed in 1931 to make way for the brief republic (which was later overthrown by Franco and the nationalists). King Juan Carlos played an important role in transforming Spain into a modern democracy.

WORLD WAR II

How did **World War II begin**?

The war began on September 1, 1939, when Germany invaded Poland, which was soon crushed by German chancellor and führer Adolf Hitler's (1889-1945) war machine. But while the Nazis moved in from the west, Poland was under attack by the Soviets from the north and east. The events in the Eastern European country had set the stage for a major conflict.

After Poland, the Germans moved into Denmark, Luxembourg, the Netherlands, Belgium, Norway, and France, taking control as they went. By June 1940 only Great Britain stood against Hitler, who was joined by Axis power Italy. Before long, fighting had spread into Greece and northern Africa.

In June 1941 Germany invaded the Soviet Union, enlarging the scope of the conflict again. With the world's focus on war-torn Europe, Japan executed a surprise attack on the U.S. naval base at Pearl Harbor, Hawaii, in December 1941, which drew Americans into the war. The war would not end until 1945.

How many countries were part of the **Axis powers**?

The Axis, which was forged in 1936, included an alliance of three nations: Germany, Italy, and Japan. These major powers were joined by six smaller countries, the Axis satellites: Albania, Bulgaria, Finland, Hungary, Romania, and Thailand. But together these countries never comprised the unified front and strength that the Allied powers did.

Germany started the war on September 1, 1939, and was joined in June 1940 by Italy and Albania. In the middle of 1941 Bulgaria, Hungary, Romania, and Finland joined the Axis effort. Japan, which was already fighting with China (in the Sino-Japanese War),

More than 2,300 people were killed in the 1941 bombing of Pearl Harbor; the attack drew the United States into World War II.

entered the fray on December 7, 1941, with its attack on the U.S. naval base at Pearl Harbor, Hawaii. Thailand was the last Axis country to enter the war, on January 25, 1942.

Which countries comprised **the Allies in World War II**?

The three major Allied powers were Great Britain, the United States, and Soviet Union. Their leaders, Winston Churchill (1874-1965), Franklin Roosevelt (1882-1945), and Joseph Stalin (1879-1953), were referred to as the Big Three. They and their military advisors developed the strategy to defeat the Axis countries—though Stalin, for the most part, acted alone on the Soviet front. China, which had been at war with Asian rival Japan since 1937, also joined the Allies. Forty-six other countries became part of the Allied front before the war was over.

Germany invaded Poland on September 1, 1939, and within days Great Britain entered into fighting against Germany. Australia, New Zealand, India, France, South Africa, and Canada also allied with Great Britain, as did Norway, Denmark, Belgium, the Netherlands, and Luxembourg in 1940—all of them under siege by Nazi Germany. Greece entered the war later that year, as did Yugoslavia in the spring of 1941. On June 22, 1941, the Soviet Union entered the war. And in the days after the Japanese bombing of the U.S. naval base at Pearl Harbor, Hawaii, on December 7, 1941, 12 more Allied countries became involved in the war, chief among them, the United States and China. (The others, with the exception of Czechoslovakia, were all Caribbean and Latin American countries: Panama, Costa Rica, the Dominican Republic, Haiti, Nicaragua, El Salvador, Honduras, Cuba, and Guatemala.) The year 1942 saw three more countries join the Allies—Mexico in May, Brazil in August, and Ethiopia in December. In 1943 and 1944—in what were perhaps the darkest days of the war—Iraq, Bolivia, Iran, and Columbia signed on as Allied nations, followed by the tiny country of San Marino (significant since it is situated wholly within the boundaries of Axis power Italy), Colombia, and Liberia. February and March of 1945 saw another wave of nations siding with the Allies: the South American countries of Ecuador, Paraguay, Peru, Chile, Venezuela, Uruguay, and Argentina; along with the Middle Eastern countries of Egypt, Syria, Lebanon, and Saudi Arabia. Mongolia (the Mongolian People's Republic), in Central Asia, was the last to join the Allies, on August 9, 1945. Of course, the level of support each Allied nation lent to the war effort varied. But it was significant that the list of Allied nations grew longer with each year that the war was fought.

Why did the **Japanese attack Pearl Harbor**?

There is still disagreement among historians, military scholars, and investigators about why the island nation of Japan issued this surprise attack on the U.S. military installation at Pearl Harbor, Hawaii. Some believe that Japan had been baited into making the attack in order to marshal public opinion behind U.S. entry into World War II (1939-45); others maintain that the United States was unprepared for such an assault, or at least, the Japanese believed Americans to be in a state of unreadiness; and still others theorize that Pearl Harbor was an all-or-nothing gamble on the part of Japan to knock America's navy out of the war before it had even entered into the fray.

These are the facts: In 1941 Japanese troops had moved into the southern part of Indochina, prompting the United States to cut off its exports to Japan. In fall of that year, as General Hideki Tojo (1884-1948) became prime minister of Japan, the country's military leaders were laying plans to wage war on the United States. On December 7 Pearl Harbor, the hub of U.S. naval power in the Pacific, became the target of Japanese attacks, as did the American military bases at Guam, Wake Island, and the Philippines. But it was the bombing of Pearl Harbor that became the rallying cry for Americans during the long days of World War II—since it was at this strategic naval station, which had been occupied under treaty by the U.S. military since 1908, that Americans had felt the impact of the conflict.

When did the **first U.S. troops** begin fighting in World War II?

Late in 1942 the United States sent its first troops across the Atlantic, making amphibious landings in North Africa, followed by Sicily and the Italian peninsula. The

Long lines of American soldiers move into Normandy, France, as part of the D-Day assault of June 6, 1944.

first allied landings were in Morocco (Casablanca) and Algeria (Oran and Algiers) on November 8 of that year. (Algiers became the Allied headquarters in North Africa for the duration of the war.) The combined forces of the initial landing included more than 100,000 troops, launching the American military effort in the Atlantic theater of conflict. One American newspaper headline announced: "Yanks Invade Africa."

What is **D-Day**?

The military uses the term *D-Day* to designate when an initiative is set to begin, counting all events out from that date for planning. For example, "D-Day minus two" would be a plan for what needs to happen two days before the beginning of the military operation. While the military planned and executed many D-Days during World War II (1939-45), most of them landings on enemy-held coasts, it was the June 6, 1944, invasion of Normandy that went down in history as *the* D-Day.

What happened at **Normandy**?

Normandy, a region in northwestern France that lies along the English Channel, is known for the June 6, 1944, arrival of Allied troops, which proved to be a turning point in World War II (1939-45). Officially called Operation Overlord (but known historically as D-Day) and headed by General Dwight D. Eisenhower (1890-1969) of the United States, the initiative had been in the planning since 1943 and it constituted the largest seaborne invasion in history. After several delays due to poor weather, the Allied troops crossed the English Channel and arrived on the beaches of Normandy on the morning of June 6. Brutal fighting ensued that day, with heavy losses on both sides. At the end of the day, the Allied troops had taken hold of the beaches—a firm foothold that would allow them to march inland against the Nazis, eventually pushing them back to Germany. While it was a critical Allied victory (which history has treated as the beginning of the end for German chancellor and führer Adolf Hitler), the invasion at Normandy was still to be followed by 11 more months of bloody conflict; Germany would not surrender until May 7 of the following year.

What was the **Battle of the Bulge**?

The term refers to the December 16, 1944, German confrontation with the American forces in the Ardennes Mountains, a forested plateau range that extends from northern France into Belgium and Luxembourg. Even though Germany appeared to be beaten at this late point in the war, Hitler rallied his remaining forces and launched a surprise assault on the American soldiers in Belgium and Luxembourg. But Germany could not sustain the front, and within two weeks the Americans had halted the German advance near Belgium's Meuse River (south of Brussels). The offensive became known as the Battle of the Bulge because of the protruding shape of the battleground on a map.

The Ardennes were also the site of conflict earlier in World War II, in 1940, as well as in World War I, in 1914 and 1918.

Why did **General MacArthur** vow to return?

Two weeks after the Japanese bombing of the U.S. military bases at Pearl Harbor and the Philippines, Japan invaded the Philippine Islands. General Douglas MacArthur (1880-1964), the commander of the U.S. Army forces in the Far East, led the defense of the archipelago. He had begun to organize his troops around Manila Bay when, in March 1942, he received orders from the president to leave the islands. When he reached Australia, MacArthur said, "I shall return," in reference to the Philippines. Under new commands, MacArthur directed the Allied forces' offensive against Japan throughout the Southwest Pacific Islands. After a string of successes, on October 20, 1944, MacArthur made good on his promise, landing on the Philippine island of Leyte, accompanied by a great invasion force. By July of the following year, the general had established practical control of the Philippines. When Japan surrendered in August, MacArthur was made the supreme commander of the Allies, and as such, he presided over the Japanese surrender aboard the USS *Missouri* on September 2. He received the Medal of Honor for his defense of the

U.S. Army troops make their way across the coral reef in the South Pacific Mariana Islands in July 1944.

Philippines, but he wasn't the only hero in the MacArthur family: His father, Arthur MacArthur (1845-1912), had received the nation's highest military award during the Civil War (1861-65).

What was the **Bataan Death March**?

It was one of the most brutal chapters of World War II (1939-45). On April 9, 1942, American forces on the Bataan Peninsula, Philippines, surrendered to the Japanese. More than 75,000 American and Filipino troops became prisoners of war (POWs). On April 10, they were forced to begin a 65-mile march to a POW camp. Conditions were torturous—high temperatures, meager provisions, and gross maltreatment. The troops were denied food and water for days at a time; they were not allowed to rest in the shade; they were indiscriminately beaten; and those who fell behind were killed. On stretches where some troops were transported by train, the boxcars were packed so tightly that many POWs died of suffocation. The forced march lasted more than a week. Twenty thousand men died along the way.

But the end of the march was not the end of the horrors for the surviving POWs. About 56,000 men were held until the end of the war. They endured starvation, torture, and horrific cruelties; some were forced to work as slave laborers in Japanese industrial plants and some became subjects of medical experiments. In August 1945 their POW camp was liberated by the Allied forces, and the surviving troops were put on U.S. Navy vessels for the trip home. As part of the United States' 1951 peace treaty with Japan, surviving POWs were barred from seeking reparations from Japanese firms that had benefited from their slave labor. This injustice continued to be the subject of proposed Congressional legislation into the early 2000s, with no positive outcome for the veterans as of 2005.

Why was the **battle of Midway** important in World War II?

It was the turning point for the allied forces fighting the Japanese in the Pacific. The battle for Midway Island (actually two small islands situated about 1,300 miles west-northwest of Honolulu, Hawaii) began on June 4, 1942. The Japanese aimed to control Midway as a position from which its air force could launch further attacks on Hawaii. As the Japanese fleet approached the islands, which was home to a U.S. Navy base (established in 1941), U.S. forces attacked. Fighting continued until June 6. The Japanese were decisively defeated, losing four aircraft carriers; the United States lost one. The victory proved that Allied naval might could overcome Japan's.

What happened on **Iwo Jima**?

During the month of February 1945 Allied forces and the Japanese fought for control of Iwo Jima, a small island in the northwest Pacific Ocean, 759 miles south of Tokyo. Japan was using Iwo Jima as a base from which to launch air attacks on U.S. bombers in the Pacific. Capturing the island from the Japanese became a key objective for the United States. On February 19, 1945, the Fourth and Fifth U.S. Marine Divisions invaded the island. Fighting over the next several days claimed more than 6,000 U.S. troops. On the morning of February 23, after a rigorous climb to the top of Mount Suribachi (Iwo Jima's 550-foot inactive volcano), U.S. Marines planted an American flag. Though small, it was visible from around the island. Later that day, a larger flag was raised atop Mount Suribachi by five marines and a navy hospital corpsman. The moment was captured by American news photographer Joe Rosenthal. His famous photo became the inspiration for the U.S. Marine Corps Memorial (dedicated November 10, 1954) in Arlington, Virginia.

What was the ***Enola Gay***?

It was the American B-29 bomber that dropped the first atomic bomb ever used in warfare. On August 6, 1945, the *Enola Gay* flew over Hiroshima, Japan, to drop an A-bomb over the city. The explosion killed an estimated 80,000 people and leveled an area of about five square miles in Hiroshima, an important manufacturing and military center. Thousands more died later from radiation exposure.

New York's Times Square is packed with crowds celebrating the news of Germany's surrender in World War II, May 7, 1945.

How many were killed by the A-bomb that was dropped on **Nagasaki**?

The death toll from the explosion, on August 9, 1945, was about 40,000. But, as in Hiroshima, thousands more died later due to radiation exposure from the atomic bomb. American military strategists believed that the first A-bomb, on Hiroshima, would force Japan's leaders to surrender. But when they did not, the second bomb was dropped on Nagasaki, an important seaport and commercial city. That catastrophic attack on Japan brought an end to the war, on August 14. Japan signed the surrender agreement on September 2 aboard the U.S. battleship *Missouri,* in Tokyo Bay.

What are **V-E Day and V-J Day**?

V-E Day stands for Victory in Europe Day, and V-J Day stands for Victory over Japan Day. After the German surrender was signed in Reims, France (the headquarters of General Dwight D. Eisenhower [1890-1969]), in the wee hours of May 7, 1945, U.S. president Harry S. Truman (1884-1972) declared May 8 V-E Day—the end of the World War II fighting in Europe.

But it was not until the Japanese agreed to surrender on August 14, 1945, that World War II ended. September 2, 1945, was declared the official V-J Day since it was then that Japan signed the terms of surrender on the USS *Missouri* anchored in Tokyo Bay.

A group of blockaded Berliners watch a U.S. Air Force plane in 1948. For eleven months, West Berlin was supplied with food and fuel entirely by airplanes.

What was the **Berlin airlift**?

It was the response during 1948 and 1949 to the Soviet blockade of West Berlin. After World War II (1939-45), the German city had been divided into four occupation zones: American, British, French, and Soviet. But following the conclusion of the war, it did not take long for the Cold War (1947-89) between the Western powers and the Soviet Union to heat up. When the Americans, British, and French agreed to combine their three areas of Berlin into one economic entity, the Soviets responded by cutting the area off from all supply routes. In June 1948 all arteries—road, rail, and water—into West Berlin were blocked by Soviet troops. Since Berlin was completely surrounded by the Soviet occupation zone, the Soviets clearly believed the blockade would be an effective move that would prompt the Western countries to pull out. But the move failed: the Americans, British, and French set up a massive airlift. For the next eleven months, West Berlin was supplied with food and fuel entirely by airplanes. The Soviets lifted the blockade in May 1949, and the airlift ended by September.

COLD WAR

What is **NATO**?

NATO stands for the North Atlantic Treaty Organization, a military alliance formed on April 4, 1949, when 12 countries signed the North Atlantic Treaty in Washington, D.C. The original 12 NATO countries were Belgium, Canada, Denmark, France, Iceland, Italy, Luxembourg, the Netherlands, Norway, Portugal, the United Kingdom, and the United States. Each member nation agreed to treat attacks on any other member nation as if it were an attack on itself. In other words, any aggressor would have to face the entire alliance. This was NATO's policy of deterrence, a way of discouraging any attacks by the Soviet Union or other Eastern bloc countries. The organization had the further benefit of discouraging fighting among the member countries.

Three years after it was formed, the alliance was joined by Greece and Turkey (in 1952). West Germany followed three years after that, in 1955, and Spain joined in 1982. After the fall of communism and the reunification of East and West Germany (c. 1990), all of Germany joined the alliance. At this point, with the Cold War (1947-89) over, many wondered what purpose the organization could serve. After all, the Soviet threat was no longer existent. However, other conflicts loomed on the horizon, including those in Bosnia and Herzegovina and in the Albanian republic of Kosovo. Fearing the civil war in the former Yugoslav republic would spread, NATO sent in troops on the side of the Bosnian government. NATO also formed the Partnership for Peace in 1994: This program was joined by more than 20 countries, including former Eastern bloc nations, including Russia. Though these nations are not full members in the NATO alliance, the Partnership for Peace provides for joint military planning among signing nations. On March 12, 1999, three former Eastern bloc nations were given full membership in NATO: Poland, Czechoslovakia, and Hungary. Observers hailed the additions as evidence that Europe is becoming more unified. On April 23, 1999, the 50th anniversary of the alliance's founding, the 19 NATO member nations gathered in Washington, D.C., to commemorate the event, just after NATO had begun air-bombing Yugoslavia to pressure the government there to accept international terms aimed at bringing peace to the nation's Kosovo province, where ethnic conflicts between Serbs and Albanians had turned deadly.

NATO is governed by the North Atlantic Council, which is made up of the heads of government of member nations or their representatives. It was headquartered in Paris until 1967, at which time the offices were moved to Brussels, Belgium.

What was the **Warsaw Pact**?

The Warsaw Pact was the Eastern bloc countries' answer to the North Atlantic Treaty Organization (NATO). Seeing the Western nations form a strong alliance, in May

1955 the Soviet Union and its allies met in Warsaw, Poland, where they signed a treaty agreeing that they, too, would mutually defend one another. The eight member nations were Albania (which withdrew in 1968), Bulgaria, Czechoslovakia, East Germany, Hungary, Poland, Romania, and the Soviet Union. The Warsaw Pact was headquartered in Moscow and, in addition to discouraging attacks from Western bloc/NATO countries, the organization also sought to quell any democratic uprisings in Warsaw Pact nations.

But in 1990 the pact and the Soviet Union's control of it weakened as democracy movements in member nations could not be put down. As the former Eastern bloc countries underwent relatively peaceful revolutions, Warsaw Pact members began announcing their intentions to withdraw from the organization. East Germany withdrew when it was reunified with West Germany, and the restored Germany joined NATO (in 1990). The Warsaw Pact was dissolved by the remaining member nations in 1991.

What was the **Bay of Pigs**?

Bay of Pigs is the name of an unsuccessful 1961 invasion of Cuba, which was backed by the U.S. government. About 1,500 Cuban expatriates living in the United States had been supplied with arms and trained by the U.S. Central Intelligence Agency (CIA). On April 17, 1961, the group of men who opposed the regime of Cuba's Fidel Castro (1926-) landed at the Bahia de Cochinos (Bay of Pigs) in west-central Cuba. Most of the rebels were captured by the Cuban forces; others were killed. In order to secure the release of the more than 1,100 men who had been captured during the invasion, private donors in the United States accumulated $53 million in food and medicine, which was given to Castro's government in exchange for the rebels' release. The failed invasion came as a terrible embarrassment to the Kennedy administration, and many believe the Bay of Pigs incident directly led to the Cuban Missile Crisis.

What was the **Cuban Missile Crisis**?

The 1962 events, which happened very quickly, nevertheless constituted a major confrontation of the Cold War (1947-89). After the disastrous Bay of Pigs invasion, when the United States backed Cuban expatriates in an attempt to oust Fidel Castro (1926-), the Soviet Union quietly began building missile sites in Cuba. Since the island nation is situated just south of Florida, when U.S. reconnaissance flights detected the Soviet military construction projects there, it was an alarming discovery. On October 22, 1962, President John F. Kennedy (1917-1963) demanded that the Soviet Union withdraw its missiles from Cuba. Kennedy also ordered a naval blockade of the island. Six days later, the Soviets agreed to dismantle the sites, ending the crisis.

KOREA AND VIETNAM

Why did the United States get involved in the **Korean War**?

Americans became involved in the Korean conflict when the United Nations (UN), only five years old, called upon member countries to give military support to South Korea, which had been invaded by troops from Communist-ruled North Korea on June 25, 1950. The United Nations considered the invasion to be a violation of international peace and called on the Communists to withdraw. When they did not, 16 countries sent troops and some 40 countries sent supplies and military equipment to the aid of the South Korean armies. About 90 percent of the UN aid came from the United States. But North Korea received aid too—the Chinese sent troops and the Soviet Union provided equipment for them to sustain the war, which lasted until July 27, 1953. After three years of fighting, an armistice was called, but a formal peace treaty was never drawn up between the neighboring countries, prompting the United States to maintain military forces in South Korea in an effort to discourage any further acts of aggression from the north.

What caused the **Vietnam War**?

In the simplest terms, the long conflict in Southeast Asia was fought over the unification of Communist North Vietnam and non-Communist South Vietnam. The two countries had been set up in 1954. Prior to that, all of Vietnam was part of the French colony of Indochina. But in 1946, the Vietnamese fought the French for control of their own country. The United States provided financial support to France, but the French were ultimately defeated in 1954. Once France had withdrawn its troops, an international conference was convened in Geneva to decide what should be done with Vietnam. The country was divided into two partitions, along the 17th parallel. This division of land was not intended to be permanent, but the elections that were supposed to reunite the partitions were never held. Vietnamese president Ho Chi Minh (1892-1969) took power in the north while Emperor Bao Dai (1913-1997), for a while, ruled the south.

But the Communist government in the north opposed the non-Communist government of South Vietnam and believed the country should still be united. The North Vietnamese supported antigovernment groups in the south and over time, stepped up aid to those groups. These Communist-trained South Vietnamese were known as the Viet Cong. Between 1957 and 1965, the Viet Cong struggled against the South Vietnamese government. But in the mid-1960s, North Vietnam initiated a large-scale troop infiltration into South Vietnam, and the fighting became a full-fledged war.

China and the Soviet Union provided the North Vietnamese with military equipment, but not manpower. The United States provided both equipment and troops to

U.S. military helicopters sweep in to rescue injured soldiers during the Vietnam War (c. late 1960s).

non-Communist South Vietnam in its struggle against the Viet Cong and North Vietnam. By 1969 there were more than half a million American troops in South Vietnam. This policy was controversial back in America, where protests to involvement in the Vietnam War continued until the last U.S. troops were brought home in 1973. In January of that year, the two sides had agreed to a cease-fire, but the fighting broke out again after the American ground troops left. On April 30, 1975, South Vietnam surrendered to North Vietnam and the war, which had lasted nearly two decades, ended. North Vietnam unified the countries as the Socialist Republic of Vietnam.

For its part, the North Vietnamese called the conflict a "war of national liberation": They viewed the long struggle as an extension of the earlier struggle with France. They also perceived the war to be another attempt by a foreign power (this time the United States) to rule Vietnam.

Why did the **United States** get involved **in Vietnam**?

The policy of involvement in the Vietnam conflict began in the mid-1950s when President Harry S. Truman (1884-1972) provided U.S. support to the French in their struggle to retain control of Vietnam, which was then part of French Indochina. In the Cold War era (1947-89), government leaders believed that the United States must come to the assistance of any country threatened by communism. Truman's successors in the White House, Presidents Dwight D. Eisenhower (1890-1969), John F. Kennedy (1917-1963), and Lyndon B. Johnson (1908-1973), also followed this school of thought, fearing a "domino effect" among neighboring nations—if one fell, they'd all fall.

What was the **Tet Offensive**?

The Tet Offensive was a turning point in the Vietnam War (1954-75). The assault began during Tet, a festival of the lunar new year, on January 30, 1968. Though a truce had been called for the holiday, North Vietnam and the Viet Cong issued a series of attacks on dozens of South Vietnamese cities, including the capital of Saigon, as well as military and air installations. American troops and the South Vietnamese struggled to regain control of the cities, in one case destroying a village (Ben Tre) in order to "save it" from the enemy. Fighting continued into February. Though the Communist North ultimately failed in its objective to hold any of the cities, the offensive was critical in the outcome of the war: As images of the fighting and destruction filled print and television media, Americans saw that the war was far from over, despite pre-Tet reports of progress in Vietnam. The Tet Offensive strengthened the public opinion that the war could not be won. It altered the course of the American war effort, with President Lyndon Johnson (1908-1973) scaling back U.S. commitment to defend South Vietnam.

THE MIDDLE EAST AND AFRICA

What is the basis of the conflict over the **Gaza Strip and the West Bank**?

The conflict is rooted in Jewish and Arab claims to the same lands in the Palestine region, which was under British control between 1917 and 1947. The Gaza Strip is a tiny piece of territory along the eastern Mediterranean Sea and adjacent to Egypt. After the nation of Israel was established and boundaries were determined by the United Nations (UN) in 1947, the Gaza Strip—bounded on two sides by the new Israel—came under Egyptian control. The Arab-Israeli war of 1967 resulted in Israeli takeover and occupation of Gaza. But unrest continued, and in 1987 and 1988 the region was the site of Arab uprisings known as the Intifada. A historic accord between the Palestine Liberation Organization (PLO) and Israel, signed in May 1994, provided for Palestinian self-rule in the Gaza Strip. This has been in effect since—though peace in the region remains elusive, as extremists on both sides of the conflict stage sporadic acts of violence.

The West Bank, which does *not* neighbor the Gaza Strip, is an area on the east of Israel, along the Jordan River and Dead Sea. The West Bank includes the towns of Jericho, Bethlehem, and Hebron. The holy city of Jerusalem is situated on the shared border between Israel and the West Bank. By the UN mandate that established the independent Jewish state of Israel in 1948, the West Bank area was supposed to become Palestinian. But Arabs who were unhappy with the UN agreement in the first place attacked Israel, and Israel responded by occupying the West Bank. A 1950 truce brought the West Bank under the control of neighboring Jordan; this situation lasted until 1967, when Israeli forces again occupied the region. Israelis soon began establishing settlements there, which provoked the resentment of Arabs. The Intifada uprisings that began in the Gaza Strip in 1987 soon spread to the West Bank. In 1988 Jordan relinquished its claim to the area, but fighting between the PLO and Israeli troops continued. Peace talks began in 1991, and the agreements that provided for Palestinian self-rule in the Gaza Strip also provided for the gradual return of West Bank lands to Palestinians. The city of Jericho was the first of these lands.

In August 2005 Israel began pulling out of the Gaza Strip after 38 years of occupation. Some Israeli settlers resisted Prime Minister Ariel Sharon's call for withdrawal; but Sharon insisted the move was a critical step toward peace and securing Israel's future.

What were the **Camp David Accords**?

Camp David Accords is the popular name for a 1979 peace treaty between Israel and Egypt. The name stuck since President Jimmy Carter (1924-) met with Israel's Menachem Begin (1913-1992) and Egypt's Anwar Sadat (1918-1981) at the presidential retreat at Camp David, Maryland. The treaty was actually signed on March 26, 1979, in Washington, D.C., with Carter as a witness to the agreement between the warring Middle Eastern nations.

The pact, which was denounced by Arab countries, provided for the return of the Sinai Peninsula to Egypt. The mountainous area, adjacent to Israel and at the north end of the Red Sea, had been the site of a major campaign during the Arab-Israeli War of 1967 and had been occupied by Israel since. The transfer of the peninsula back to Egypt was completed in 1982. The Camp David Accords had also outlined that the two sides would negotiate Palestinian autonomy in the occupied West Bank and Gaza Strip. However, Sadat was assassinated in 1981, and this initiative saw no progress as a result of the Camp David Accords.

What was **Camp David II**?

In July 2000 President Bill Clinton (1946-) invited Israeli and Palestinian Authority leaders to the presidential retreat at Camp David, Maryland, to hammer out a final peace agreement in the Middle East. In what could have been the major breakthrough in the conflict, Israeli prime minister Ehud Barak (1942-) agreed to a Palestinian state, including the West Bank and East Jerusalem, and the administration of all Jerusalem holy sites by a third party (i.e. neither Israel nor Palestine). In exchange,

Palestinian leader Yasser Arafat (1929-2004) was asked to sign an "end of conflict" addendum to the final agreement, which would have required him to bring the militant Arab group Hamas under control and end all Palestinian attacks on Israelis. But Arafat refused the deal. The July 11-25 meeting ended without an agreement. Violence erupted again in Israel, beginning the Second Intifada.

What is the **Roadmap for Peace**?

It is a plan for lasting peace in the Palestinian-Israeli conflict. The roadmap was announced by the Bush administration on March 14, 2003, after several months of working with Russian, European Union, and United Nations (UN) officials to develop the plan, which calls for a permanent two-state solution. The roadmap outlines specific, actionable steps to be taken by each side in the conflict. The U.S. State Department described it as a "performance-based and goal-driven roadmap, with clear phases, timelines, target dates, and benchmarks aiming at progress through reciprocal steps by the two parties in the political, security, economic, humanitarian, and institution-building fields." In announcing the roadmap, President George W. Bush (1946-) called for an end to the recent wave of violence (intifada) in the Middle East, for authoritative Palestinian leadership, and for Israeli readiness to comply. He asked for Israeli and Palestinian leaders to contribute to and discuss the roadmap, and he repeated his call for "all parties in the Middle East to abandon old hatreds and to meet their responsibilities for peace." The plan, the last phase of which was to have been completed in 2004-05, foundered amid the daily violence of the Second Intifada, but was given new promise in May 2005 when Palestinian and Israeli leaders met in Egypt to discuss peace.

What did **President George H.W. Bush** mean when he said the U.S. had to "draw a line in the sand"?

President George H.W. Bush (1924-) was reacting to Iraqi leader Saddam Hussein's (1937-) act of aggression when on August 2, 1990, his troops invaded neighboring Kuwait. The United Nations (UN) gave Iraq until January 15, 1991, to withdraw from Kuwait. Iraq failed to comply. The "line in the sand" that Hussein crossed was soon defended: On January 16, 1991, Operation Desert Storm was launched to liberate the Arab nation of Kuwait from Iraq, whose military dictator had not only invaded Kuwait but proclaimed it a new Iraqi province. Bush averred, "This will not stand," and in order to protect U.S. oil supplies in the country, the president mobilized U.S. forces, which were joined by a coalition of 39 nations, to soundly and quickly defeat Iraq.

Why was the **Persian Gulf War** important?

The six-week war, telecast around the world from start to finish (February-April 1991), was significant because it was the first major international crisis to take place in the post-Cold War era. The United Nations proved to be effective in organizing the coalition against aggressor Iraq. Leading members of the coalition included Egypt, France, Great Britain, Saudi Arabia, Syria, and the United States. The conflict also tested the ability of the United States and the Soviet Union (then still in existence as such) to cooperate in world affairs.

What happened in the **Rwandan genocide**?

On April 6, 1994, the airplane carrying Rwandan president Juvenal Habyarimana (1937-1994), of Rwanda's majority Hutu ethnic group, was shot down by unknown attackers. The event touched off, or was used as an excuse for, what one journalist described as a "premeditated orgy of killing" in which ethnic Hutu extremists carried out a campaign of mass murder against minority Tutsis. Ten years after the horrific events, the *Chicago Tribune*'s Africa correspondent recounted how Rwanda's "Hutu majority, equipped with machetes and called to action by government radio announcements, slaughtered neighbors, friends, co-workers. Priests killed parishioners who sought refuge in churches. Teachers murdered pupils. Hundreds of thousands of women were raped, children burned or drowned, bodies pushed into mass graves." The massacre continued for three months, ending only when Tutsi fighters managed to seize the capital at Kigali and take power.

In 2004 the Rwandan government released its official estimate of the death toll: 937,000 people were murdered, making it the worst ethnic cleansing the world has seen since the Holocaust during World War II (1939-45). But, unlike the Holocaust, which was carried out by a dictatorial military machine, the Rwandan genocide was carried out by the masses. In the aftermath, more than 150,000 people were accused of participating in the massive violence, though the Rwandan courts had only tried a small fraction of those—no more than 10 percent in 10 years. An estimated 2 million Hutus, many who probably feared retribution, had fled to neighboring countries after the Tutsis gained power. The genocide had happened at the hands of many.

In the decade since the Rwandan genocide, Rwandans, and the world, have grappled with difficult and perhaps unanswerable questions. How could so many people (Hutus) have participated in the mass cleansing? Experts point to Rwanda's deeply divided history; the rivalry between Hutus and Tutsis dates back hundreds of years—since the Tutsis first arrived in the central African region in the fourteenth century. How could the world body have "allowed" such an event to happen, particularly with the Nazi Holocaust a not-too-distant memory? Again, there is no easy answer. The United Nations withdrew its people when the violence began in April 1994, but some UN officials estimated later that perhaps as few as 5,000 troops might have been able to prevent the annihilation. The United States did not intervene in the Rwandan genocide; the recent images of dead American soldiers being dragged through the streets of Mogadishu, Somalia (in October 1993), had left the country reticent to involve itself in the world's hotspots. But, even with the lesson of Rwanda, experts wondered how the

A worker arranges human bones and skulls in Kigali, Rwanda, in 2000, as part of a nationwide effort to retrieve corpses and arrange dignified reburials of the nearly one million victims of the 1994 genocide.

international response might differ today. Finally, how can Rwanda rebuild? The governing Tutsis have been able to enforce a calm on the tiny landlocked nation. But some believe it is an uneasy calm and wonder how long minority Tutsis can retain control over a country that is 85 percent Hutu. In Rwanda's efforts to serve justice, its jails and courts remained jammed 10 years after the genocide. And since so many had fled the country and others escaped prosecution, justice could not be served fully. Some legal experts thought that a general amnesty, issued by the Rwandan government, would help put the nation's problems behind them.

What was the crisis in **Darfur, Sudan**?

The brutal violence, really a genocide, in Darfur began in February 2003 and was still ongoing two years later as United Nations (UN) negotiators tried to broker a peace agreement. Sudanese government troops and government-backed Arab militia, called the janjaweed, were engaged in a violent campaign that targeted black African civilians from the Fur, Massalit, and Zaghawa ethnic groups in the western Sudanese state of Darfur (which is about the size of Texas). Reports from the Human Rights Watch and UN agencies working in Sudan indicated that large-scale bombing and burning campaigns had destroyed entire villages, tens of thousands of Darfurians had been raped and killed, and as many as 2 million had been displaced by early 2005. International relief efforts were hampered by ongoing violence, putting millions of women and children at risk of starvation and disease. Observers called for an international response to the crisis to avert "another Rwanda." In April 2005 the UN Security Council referred the Darfur situation to the International Criminal Court. But to date, no one had been able to stop the campaign of ethnic cleansing.

The Darfur crisis was part of a greater and older conflict in Sudan. The east African nation, whose neighbors include Egypt to the north and Ethiopia to the east, was in 2005 the scene of Africa's oldest civil war. The conflict had pit the Arab (Muslim) north against the Christian and animist south since 1984. But diplomatic efforts to resolve that decades-old conflict had so far failed in 2005: The Muslim regime based in the national capital of Khartoum was unwilling to share power and wealth. Thus, when Khartoum was hit with a rebellion in 2003, it retaliated by inciting the brutality in Darfur. Diplomats worked to resolve the north-south civil conflict, offering Sudan a package of debt relief and development aid that could reach $100 million. Critics of that plan said that incentives were not enough, and that sanctions should be levied against the nation to pressure the government to move toward ceasefire.

TERRORISM

What happened after the **1993 World Trade Center bombing**?

During the Federal Bureau of Investigation (FBI) investigation that followed the February 26, 1993, tragedy, it was learned that the World Trade Center was one of several intended targets of an Islamic extremist group. The bomb explosion in lower Manhattan killed six people and started a fire that sent black smoke through the 110-story twin towers, injuring hundreds and forcing 100,000 people to evacuate the premises.

Days later, on March 4, 25-year-old Mohammed A. Salameh, an illegal Jordanian immigrant, was arrested in Jersey City, New Jersey. Salameh was later found to be a follower of self-exiled Islamic fundamentalist leader Sheik Omar Abdel Rahman (1933-), who was wanted by Egypt for having incited antigovernment riots in 1989. In June investigators seized Arab terrorists they accused of plotting to blow up several New York City sites, including the United Nations headquarters and the Holland and Lincoln tunnels. U.S. authorities then arrested Rahman and imprisoned him on suspicion of complicity in the World Trade Center bombing. On October 1, 1995, a federal jury found Rahman and nine other militant Muslims guilty of conspiring to carry out a campaign of terrorist bombings and assassinations aimed at forcing Washington to abandon its support of Israel and Egypt.

The 1993 bombing foreshadowed the terrorist strikes of September 11, 2001, which destroyed the landmark twin towers of the World Trade Center in lower Manhattan and launched what came to be called a global war on terrorism.

What happened in the **Oklahoma City bombing**?

The attack took place at 9:02 A.M. on April 19, 1995, when a truck bomb exploded outside the Alfred P. Murrah Federal Building in Oklahoma City, Oklahoma. Of the 168 people who were killed, 19 were children. Another 500 people were injured. The blast, which investigators later learned had been caused by a bomb made of more than two tons of ammonium nitrate and fuel oil, sheered off the front half of the nine-story building and left a crater 8 feet deep and 30 feet wide. Nearby buildings were damaged or destroyed, including a YMCA day care center where many children were seriously injured. The force of the explosion shattered windows blocks away. Survivors of the blast and others in the vicinity began rescue efforts right away. Eventually more than 3,600 people from around the country participated in rescue operations, including police, firefighters, and members of the Federal Emergency Management Agency (FEMA).

Police and Federal Bureau of Investigation (FBI) agents arrested members of an American right-wing militant group who were suspected of wanting to avenge the April 19, 1993, FBI/ATF raid on the Branch Davidian religious compound in Waco, Texas. Former army buddies Timothy J. McVeigh, then 27, and Terry L. Nichols, then 40, were indicted on August 10, 1995, on 11 charges each. The two were tried separately and convicted in federal court. McVeigh was found guilty of murder and conspiracy in June 1997, and a federal jury sentenced him to death. Nichols was later found guilty of conspiracy and involuntary manslaughter, but in January 1998 the jury deadlocked on the sentence, which was then to be decided by the judge. In early June it was decided that Nichols would serve life in prison.

Officials believe the Murrah Federal Building was targeted in the antigovernment attack because it housed 15 federal agencies, including offices of the Social Security Administration (SSA), Housing and Urban Development (HUD), the Drug Enforcement Administration (DEA), and the Bureau of Alcohol, Tobacco, and Firearms (ATF), as well as several defense department offices and a government-run day care center.

What was the chronology of events on **September 11, 2001**?

The sequence of events related to the terrorist attacks on 9/11 were as follows (all times are eastern daylight time):

> 8:46 A.M.: A passenger plane crashes into the north tower of New York City's World Trade Center. At first it is assumed to be an accident. But within hours, it is learned that the plane was American Airlines Flight 11, and comman-

deered by hijackers shortly after takeoff from Boston headed to Los Angeles; it carried 81 passengers (including 5 hijackers) and 11 crewmembers.

9:03 A.M.: A second passenger plane slams into the south tower of the World Trade Center and explodes. United Airlines later announces that this was Flight 175, another Boston-Los Angeles plane; it carried 56 passengers (including 5 hijackers) and 9 crewmembers. Both towers of the World Trade Center are in flames.

9:21 A.M.: Bridges and tunnels leading into New York City are closed. Within the hour, Mayor Rudolph Giuliani (1944-) orders an evacuation of Manhattan south of Canal Street.

9:25 A.M.: All flights in the United States are grounded. It is the first time in history that the Federal Airlines Administration (FAA) halts all flights.

9:30 A.M.: President George W. Bush (1946-), scheduled to speak at a grade school in Sarasota, Florida, remarks that the nation has been the target of an "apparent terrorist attack."

9:45 A.M.: A third passenger plane crashes into the east wall of the Pentagon in Arlington, Virginia. The plane was American Airlines Flight 77, carrying 58 passengers (including 5 hijackers) and 6 crewmembers. It originated at Washington, D.C.'s Dulles International Airport and was headed to Los Angeles. After being hijacked, the plane made a u-turn over the Ohio-Kentucky border to return to the Washington, D.C.-area, where it hit its intended target.

9:45 A.M.: The White House is evacuated.

10:05 A.M.: The south tower of the World Trade Center collapses.

10:10 A.M.: A large section of the Pentagon collapses.

10:10 A.M.: A fourth passenger plane crashes in a field in Somerset County, in southwestern Pennsylvania (outside of Pittsburgh). It was United Airlines Flight 93, originating in Newark, New Jersey, and bound for San Francisco. After being hijacked, the plane made a u-turn over Ohio and was headed for a target in Washington, D.C. (later thought to be Camp David, the White House, or the U.S. Capitol building). After learning via cell phones of the other hijackings, a group of passengers stormed the cockpit in an effort to take the plane, which crashed in the countryside. The plane carried 37 passengers (including 4 hijackers) and a crew of 7. There were no survivors.

10:24 A.M.: The FAA reports that it has diverted all incoming transatlantic flights to Canada.

10:28 A.M.: The north tower of the World Trade Center falls. The collapse of each tower blankets lower Manhattan in smoke and ash, turning the brilliantly sunny day to darkness.

10:45 A.M.: All federal office buildings in the nation's capital are evacuated.

2:00 P.M.: Senior FBI sources reveal to the media that they are working under the assumption that the four airplanes that crashed were part of a terrorist attack. The FBI later learns the identities of all 19 hijackers (there were 5 on board each plane, except Flight 93, which had 4).

4:00 P.M.: Media reports indicate that U.S. officials have credible evidence tying the morning's attacks to Saudi militant Osama bin Laden (1957-).

5:20 P.M.: Building 7 (a 47-story structure) of the World Trade Center complex collapses. Nearby buildings are in flames.

How many died in the September 11 attacks?

About 3,000 people died that day as a result of the terrorist attacks on the United States. The strikes on New York's World Trade Center claimed 2,602 lives, and another 125 died at the Pentagon, outside Washington, D.C. (The numbers include firefighters and police officers who died as part of the rescue effort.) The victims on board the hijacked flights, which were used as terrorist weapons, numbered an additional 87 on American Airlines Flight 11, which crashed into the North Tower of the World Trade Center; 60 on United Airlines Flight 175, which crashed into the South Tower of the World Trade Center; 59 on American Airlines Flight 77, which slammed into the Pentagon; and 40 on United Airlines Flight 93, which crashed in rural Shanksville, Pennsylvania.

In February 2005 officials announced that they had exhausted all possible methods of identifying the human remains recovered at Ground Zero. Of the 2,749 people reported missing at the World Trade Center, positive identification had been made on 1,161 people. The rest were presumed dead; 2,749 death certificates were issued related to the World Trade Center attack.

What was the **9/11 Commission**?

It was the 10-member group created by a congressional act signed by the president on November 27, 2002. The bipartisan commission, consisting of five Republicans and five Democrats, was chosen by Congress to look into how the attacks of September 11, 2001, could have happened and how such a tragedy could be avoided in the future. During its investigation, the commissioners and their staff reviewed more than 2.5 million pages of documents, interviewed more than 1,200 people in 10 countries, held 19 days of hearings, and took public testimony from 160 witnesses. The commission wrapped up its work in all due speed, publishing a full report less than two years after it received its mandate. The 567-page report chronicles the events of 9/11, looks at the roots and growth of the "new terrorism," reviews the U.S. response to the attacks and to previous assaults (including the August 1998 U.S. embassy bombings in Kenya and Tanzania), and recommends changes to prevent further terrorist strikes. The report

A fireball erupts from the north tower of the World Trade Center after it was struck by the second of two hijacked airplanes on the morning of September 11, 2001.

was made available as a book and an online document, presented "to the American people for their consideration."

Among the key disclosures in the report were that the commission found "no credible evidence that Iraq and al Qaeda cooperated on the attacks against the United States." That finding was immediately dismissed by the White House in June 2004. The commission also reported that the original plan for the al Qaeda attacks on the U.S. homeland included a total of 10 hijacked airplanes, striking targets on the East and West coasts; the plan was dismissed by al Qaeda leader Osama bin Laden as too complex. In the aftermath of the 9/11 attacks and the U.S.-led retaliatory strikes on Afghanistan, the commission believed that al Qaeda had become more decentralized, with cell leaders assuming greater authority for decision-making.

What is the **War on Terror**?

In his remarks the evening of September 11, 2001, President George W. Bush (1946-) vowed that "America and our friends and allies join with all those who want peace and security in the world, and we stand together to win the war against terrorism." TV newscasts were soon emblazoned with the message, "America's War on Terror," or simply, "The War on Terror." The events of 9/11 catapulted the free world into a new era, in which conflicts no longer were limited to wars between nations. There was a new enemy, which knew no national boundaries, whose "army" was covert, and which mercilessly targeted civilians.

Acknowledging that the new threat could not be met by the United States alone, the Bush administration began forging an alliance of nations that together would use diplomacy, take military action, and coordinate intelligence and law enforcement efforts to combat terrorists around the globe. On September 12, 2001, Secretary of State Colin Powell (1937-) called for a "global coalition against terrorism." Eventually the Bush administration put together an alliance of 84 countries, called the Global Coalition Against Terrorism, "united against a common danger, and joined in a common purpose."

The strike on Afghanistan, called Operation Enduring Freedom, was the first military strategy in the new war. The next major initiative was the war in Iraq. While those operations were underway, terrorist strikes continued around the globe. In March 2004, following the commuter train blasts in Spain, President Bush remarked that "the murders in Madrid are a reminder that the civilized world is at war. And in this new kind of war, civilians find themselves suddenly on the front lines. In recent years, terrorists have struck from Spain, to Russia, to Israel, to East Africa, to Morocco, to the Philippines, and to the United States. They've targeted Arab states such as Saudi Arabia, Jordan, and Yemen. They've attacked Muslims in Indonesia, Turkey, Pakistan, Iraq, and Afghanistan. No nation or region is exempt from the terrorists' campaign of violence."

What is **al Qaeda**?

During a 1999 anti-American rally in Pakistan, a protester holds a poster of al Qaeda leader Osama bin Laden.

Al Qaeda (Arabic, meaning "the base") is a global network of terrorists who banded together during the 1990s and proclaimed to be carrying out a holy war on non-Islamic nations. The group knows no national boundaries, though certain nations, including Afghanistan, were known to be al Qaeda strongholds. Led by the elusive Osama bin Laden (1957-), a wealthy exiled Saudi, the group conducted terrorist training programs in several Muslim (mostly Middle Eastern) countries and was funded by loyalists around the world. One of the United States' first actions following the September 11, 2001, terrorist attacks on the World Trade Center and Pentagon (which were later confirmed to have been carried out by al Qaeda operatives) was to freeze bank accounts of persons and organizations with suspected ties to the terrorist group.

The roots of al Qaeda can be traced to the Soviet invasion of Afghanistan in 1979, when thousands of Muslims, including bin Laden, joined the Afghan resistance. The 10-year conflict was a rallying point for Islamic extremists. Bin Laden returned home to Saudi Arabia in 1989, determined to perpetuate a holy war (*jihad*) by maintaining the funding, organization, and training that had made the Afghan resistance victorious against the Soviets. By the early 1990s he emerged as a leader in the Muslim world, proclaiming his goal to reinstate the Caliphate, a unified Muslim state. He also proclaimed the United States to be an enemy to Islam; he considered the nation responsible for all conflicts involving Muslims. The Saudi government rescinded his passport in 1994, and bin Laden fled his homeland. He eventually found safe harbor in Taliban-ruled Afghanistan. According to the report issued by the 9/11 Commission, bin Laden's declaration of war came in February 1998, when he and fugitive Egyptian physician Ayman al Zawahiri "arranged from their Afghanistan headquarters for an Arabic newspaper in London to publish what they termed a *fatwa* issued in the name of a 'World Islamic Front.'" The statement claimed that America had declared war against God and his messenger, and they called for retaliation.

Under bin Laden's direction, al Qaeda carried out several attacks on American targets, including the August 7, 1998, bombings of U.S. embassies in Kenya and Tanzania, which killed 258 and injured 5,000, and the September 11, 2001, attacks on the

World Trade Center and Pentagon, which killed nearly 3,000 people. After the Global Coalition Against Terrorism, led by U.S. forces, launched its attack on Afghanistan in October 2001, bin Laden was believed to have fled for Pakistan. Capturing him and other al Qaeda leaders and operatives was the key objective of the United States in its efforts to dismantle the terrorist network.

What was the **Taliban**?

It was the ultraconservative faction that ruled Afghanistan from late 1996 until December 2001, when its government crumbled following a U.S.-led military campaign. The Persian word *taleban* means "students"; the group was made up of Afghan refugees who, during the Soviet invasion (1979-89), had fled their country for Pakistan, where they attended conservative Islamic religious schools. After the Soviet withdrawal from Afghanistan and amidst the unrest that ensued, the Taliban rose to prominence. They gained control of the nation region by region, eventually taking the capital of Kabul in 1996.

While in power, the group put into force strict laws based on a fundamental interpretation of Islam. The Taliban excluded women from Afghan society, and it allowed the nation to become a training ground for Islamic terror groups such as al Qaeda. Very few nations of the world recognized the Taliban government. Its human rights abuses, principally the complete disenfranchisement of women and girls, were decried by the international community. But the breaking point came after the September 11, 2001, terrorist attacks on the U.S. homeland: When the American government requested that the suspected mastermind of those attacks be extradited from Afghanistan to the United States, the Taliban refused. The group was forcibly ousted in the brief military campaign that followed. In December 2001 the United Nations (UN) convened a conference in Bonn, Germany, where leaders of anti-Taliban ethnic factions decided on a post-Taliban transitional government, led by Pashtun leader Hamid Karzai. (The Pashtuns are the dominant group in Afghanistan, representing about 42 percent of the population. The next largest group is the Tajik, which represents about 27 percent of the population in the highly fragmented nation of 28.5 million people.) Attendees also agreed to a UN-led peacekeeping operation. Though ethnic rivalries and sporadic conflicts continued under the transitional government, Afghanistan made strides in building a stable, democratic government. One encouraging sign of reform came in March 2005, with the appointment of Habiba Sarobi, the first woman to become a provincial governor in Afghanistan history. Sarobi was chosen by the president for her post, which she assumed in late March.

When did the **U.S.-led operation in Afghanistan** begin?

Joined principally by the United Kingdom, the U.S.-led military strikes on Afghanistan began on October 7, 2001—26 days after the terrorist attacks on the U.S. homeland.

The goals were to weaken the Taliban government and root out terrorist cells in the Mideast nation. Al Qaeda leader Osama bin Laden (1957-), the suspected 9/11 mastermind, was also a target. The strikes on Afghanistan, which the United States called Operation Enduring Freedom (OEF), were the first in the new war on terror.

OEF's primary goal—ousting the ruling Taliban government—was achieved relatively quickly. By mid-November, the combined efforts of the U.S. military, British, and Afghanistan's Northern Alliance, managed to take control of major cities, including the capital of Kabul. In late December an interim government was established at a UN-convened conference in Bonn, Germany. In June 2002 Hamid Karzai (1957-) was overwhelmingly elected as transitional president by the *loya jirga,* the traditional Afghan assembly of ethnic leaders; the transitional government was to run Afghanistan until national elections could be held in 2004. Despite strides in establishing the new government, fighting continued in the rugged mountainous terrain of eastern Afghanistan; Operation Anaconda was the name given to the U.S. military's effort to combat Taliban pockets of resistance, root out terrorist cells, and capture key al Qaeda leaders, including Osama bin Laden (though he had reportedly fled to neighboring Pakistan). Violence also preceded the October 2004 election.

When did **The War in Iraq begin**?

The U.S.-led multinational military campaign in Iraq began on March 19, 2003, with air strikes on the capital of Baghdad; ground forces moved into southern Iraq from neighboring Kuwait. After taking the southern city of Basra, U.S. marines and army infantry moved northward, toward the capital. U.S. troops took control of Baghdad on April 9, after which images of gleeful Iraqis dismantling statues and other symbols of Saddam Hussein's despotic rule flooded the American media. Coalition forces, American troops, and U.S.-backed Kurdish fighters then pressed into northern Iraq, including Tikrit, Saddam's hometown and a loyalist stronghold. On April 14 Tikrit fell. The war seemed to be near conclusion, but the hard combat had only begun—and continued for years, even after the end of major combat was declared.

When did the major combat phase of **Operation Iraqi Freedom end**?

President George W. Bush (1946-) declared an end to major combat on May 1, 2003. But the stabilization of Iraq was far from over; the fighting continued more than two years later, the result of an increasingly violent Iraqi insurgency. Faced with the ongoing resistance, in December 2004 the number of U.S. troops in the war-torn nation was increased from 130,000 to 150,000.

Most of the casualties occurred after the declared end of major combat: On April 8, 2005, the Pentagon reported that there had been 1,543 American fatalities in the war to date—1,174 in hostile actions and 369 in nonhostile actions, including accidents during routine maneuvers. Of the 1,543 U.S. military deaths, 1,404 died after the declared end of major combat, 1,065 of them from hostile action. More than 7,000 had been injured to date.

A 30-foot statue of former Iraqi leader Saddam Hussein is toppled by plastic explosives in Tikrit, Iraq, 2003.

In addition to the American fatalities, the British military had reported 86 deaths as of early April 2005; Italy, 21; Ukraine, 18; Poland, 17; Spain, 11; Bulgaria, 8; Slovakia, 3; Estonia, Thailand, and the Netherlands, 2 each; and Denmark, El Salvador, Hungary, Kazakhstan, and Latvia, 1 each.

The figures fueled criticism for the lingering war, with some observers wondering if stabilization was possible in the fractious nation. There were several factors contributing to the growing lists of casualties and injuries: coalition forces were frequently ambushed in attacks from resistance fighters and suicide bombers; U.S. troops faced continued combat in parts of Baghdad and its outskirts; the southern towns of Najaf and Kufa were holdouts of resistance; and there was intense fighting in the Sunni cities of Fallujah, Ramadi, and Samarra, which remained under insurgent control even after the transfer of political authority from the United States to the interim Iraqi authority on June 28, 2004.

What was the **Abu Ghraib** prison scandal?

News of the atrocities of Abu Ghraib, where Iraqi prisoners were being held by members of the U.S. military during Operation Iraqi Freedom, first surfaced in April 2004 when shocking photographs began appearing in the American media. The photos depicted an array of hideous abuses, all of them in violation of the Geneva Conventions for the treatment of prisoners of war.

The deep troubles first surfaced in spring 2003 when International Red Cross and human rights groups complained that American troops had been mistreating Iraqi prisoners. The U.S. Army launched an investigation into its prison system; a fact-finding mission was eventually led by Major-General Antonio Taguba, who completed his report in February 2004. It stated that one police company at Abu Ghraib had committed "sadistic, blatant, and wanton criminal abuses." The Taguba report also found that "supervisory omission was rampant" at the prison. More investigations and reports followed, taking into account other prisons under Central Command. Some of the reports tied prisoner deaths to the abuses.

The scandal sent shockwaves around the world and sparked an intense debate about how such abuses could have happened. The tortures were labeled by some as "unauthorized actions taken by a few individuals." But others believed they were a manifestation of policy that had gone wrong. The scandal soon widened: By May 2004 British newspapers began reporting abuses by British troops. While Prime Minister Tony Blair (1953-) apologized for any mistreatment Iraqi prisoners may have suffered at the hands of British troops, President Bush went on Arabic television to denounce the abuses as "abhorrent"; he stopped short of an apology, saying that the mistreatment "does not represent the America that I know." Both nations moved quickly to bring charges against several soldiers shown in the pictures. The guilty verdicts, and subsequent sentences, began being handed down in May 2004.

The prison scandals fueled criticism of the controversial war in Iraq. They also prompted a deadly backlash from the Arab world: Insurgents in Iraq began a series of kidnappings of Americans and British citizens working in Iraq, most of them ending in ghastly and widely publicized killings. Between spring 2004 and spring 2005 more than 200 foreigners were taken captive in Iraq; more than 30 of them were killed by their kidnappers.

POLITICAL AND SOCIAL MOVEMENTS

How old is **nationalism**?

Nationalism, a people's sense that they belong together as a nation because of a shared history and culture, and often because of a common language and/or religion, emerged at the close of the Middle Ages (500-1350). By the 1700s several countries, notably England, France, and Spain, had developed as "nation-states," groups of people with a shared background who occupy a land that is governed independently. As political and economic entities, the nation-states were preceded by fiefs, tribes, city-states, and empires, which overlapped each other as organizing units, dividing peoples' loyalties.

By the 1800s nationalism had become a powerful force, and the view took hold that any national group has the right to form its own state. Because of this belief, called national self-determination, some nations achieved independence (including Greece, which gained freedom from Turkey in 1829, and Belgium, which won self-rule from the Netherlands in 1830); others formed new, larger countries (both Italy and Germany were created by the unification of numerous smaller states, Italy in 1870 and Germany one year later); and still others carved smaller states out of great empires (for example, the breakup of the Austro-Hungarian Empire following World War I [1914-18] resulted in the formation of the independent countries of Austria, Hungary, Czechoslovakia, Poland, and, later, Yugoslavia).

In the United States, nationalism in the 1800s took the form of Manifest Destiny, the mission to expand the country's boundaries to include as much of North America as possible. By the end of the century the United States had claimed all of its present-day territory.

While nationalism is a source of pride and patriotism and has had many positive results, some leaders (notably German dictator Adolf Hitler [1889-1945]) have carried it to extremes, initiating large-scale movements that resulted in the persecution of other peoples and in the hideous practice of ethnic cleansing.

The boundary lines that were drawn on the world map at the end of the twentieth century were largely the result of nationalistic movements, some of which had resulted in conflicts—and some of which remained unresolved.

What is **Zionism**?

Zionism was founded as the nationalist movement to establish an independent Jewish state; it began in the 1890s, and roughly 50 years later, in 1948, the movement's activism resulted in the proclamation of the state of Israel. Since that time, Zionism has focused its efforts on building bridges between Israel and Jewish people around the world.

The roots of Zionism date to 1882, when a movement began encouraging Jewish settlement of Palestine, the region in the Middle East (in southwest Asia) that borders the Mediterranean Sea to the west, Lebanon to the north, Syria and Jordan to the east, and Egypt (the Sinai Peninsula) to the southwest. Groups advocating immigration to the Jewish homeland in Palestine called themselves Lovers of Zion (*Hoveve Zion*): Mount Zion is the site in Jerusalem where the Temple of David (king of the ancient Hebrews; d. 962 B.C.) was built, and it is therefore considered the center of Jewish spiritual life.

As a political movement, Zionism was founded in the late 1890s by Austrian journalist Theodor Herzl (1860-1904). In 1894 Herzl was among the reporters covering the trial of Alfred Dreyfus, a French army officer falsely convicted of treason. Though the artillery captain, who was Jewish, was later declared innocent (the guilty verdict rendered in his first trial was annulled), many felt the Dreyfus case had exposed a "deep vein of anti-Semitism" in Europe. Herzl's conclusion was that if anti-Semitism could take hold in France, it could prevail anywhere. Based on this belief, he began working for the reclamation of a Jewish state in the Middle East. In 1897 Herzl convened the First Zionist Congress, held in Basel, Switzerland, bringing the movement to worldwide attention. In 1917, against the backdrop of World War I (1914-18), British foreign secretary Arthur James Balfour (1848-1930) issued a declaration vowing his country's support for a national Jewish homeland in Palestine; this came after British troops liberated the Middle East from the control of the Ottoman Empire. In 1920 the Ottoman Empire dissolved as part of the conclusion of World War I and by international agreement the British were given rule over Palestine.

Numerous Jews immigrated to Palestine, where fighting broke out with Arabs who opposed Jewish resettlement. Previously boosted by British support of an independent Jewish state, Zionists received a heavy blow in 1937 when, with another conflict in Europe on the horizon, Britain reversed its policy in Palestine—in an effort to gain Arab support should fighting break out with Germany. At the end of World War II (1939-45), Britain turned over the problem in the Middle East to the newly created United Nations, which decided that out of Palestine both an independent Jewish state and a self-ruling Arab state should be formed. In 1948 the state of Israel was declared by Polish-born and Zionist moderate David Ben-Gurion (1886-1973), who became head of the nation's provisional government. The World Zionist Congress was later separated from the government. The organization has since turned its attention to immigration and cultural activities. German-born scientist Albert Einstein (1897-1955) was among Zionism's most prominent adherents.

What was the nonviolent **Indian reform movement**?

It was the movement led by Indian nationalist leader Mohandas Gandhi (1869-1948), whose methods of protest included staging boycotts, fasting, conducting prayer vigils, and visiting troubled areas in an attempt to end conflicts. Gandhi, whom the people called Mahatma (meaning "great-souled"), was determined to bring about change in India—to bring an end to British control of the country and to topple the ages-old caste system (the strict social structure) there. Gandhi believed that it took great courage to *not* engage in violence, and he began campaigns of passive resistance, which he called *satyagraha* (meaning "firmness in truth"). Gaining a wide following, Gandhi's acts of civil disobedience did bring about changes in his homeland, where he is revered as the founder of an independent India (1947). He remained faithful to his nonviolent beliefs throughout his life. He also adhered to a firm policy of religious tolerance. It was for this reason that the spiritual and nationalist leader was killed by a Hindu extremist in 1948.

What was the **May Fourth movement**?

It was a mass movement that emerged in China after May 4, 1919, when students in Beijing protested one of the outcomes of the peace conference held at Versailles earlier that year to officially settle World War I (1914-18): Japan, which had seized German territories in China during the war, was given control of the holdings. Student demonstrators criticized a weakened Chinese government for allowing the Japanese occupation. Following the death of powerful leader Yuan Shih-k'ai (1859-1916), the country's central government crumbled: In northern China local military leaders (called war lords) rose to power, continually challenging the authority of the capital at Beijing. Meanwhile, revolutionary leader Sun Yat-sen (1866-1925) had begun promoting his three great principles—nationalism, democracy, and people's livelihood—in southern China, where he gained the support of military leaders in the region. At about the same time, Chinese intellectuals had begun attacking traditional culture and society, urging government reforms and the modernization of industry. The May Fourth movement fanned the fires of revolution. The movement would have far-reaching—and unforseen—results. And some might argue that the story has not yet played out.

In 1919 Sun reorganized the Kuomintang (Nationalist) Party and began recruiting student followers. Two years later he became president of a self-proclaimed national government of the Southern Chinese Republic, establishing the capital at

Guangzhou (Canton). His sights were set on conquering northern China. Toppling the northern war lords to reunify the country, in 1924 Sun began cooperating with both the Soviets and the Communist groups that had been formed by students following the 1919 protest. Under Sun's leadership, the Nationalist Party began preparing for war. But Sun, who is regarded as the "father of modern China," would not live to see the culmination of his plans: He died of cancer in 1925. Under military leader Chiang Kai-shek (1887-1975), the Kuomintang turned on its Communist members, whose leaders fled in fear of the generalissimo. In 1928, following a two-year military campaign, Chiang led the nationalists to capture Beijing, reuniting China under one government for the first time in 12 years. His rule of China lasted until 1949, when Communists won control of the mainland and Mao Tse-tung (1893-1976) became the first chairman of the People's Republic of China. The expelled Chiang and his followers established a Chinese nationalist government on the island of Taiwan. Back on the mainland, Mao's Great Leap Forward, his massive collectivization of agriculture and industry, brought economic failure and a two-year famine to China in the late 1950s.

What is **Solidarity**?

It was a worker-led movement for political reform in Poland during the 1980s and it led to the downfall of communism. The movement was inspired by Pope John Paul II's June 1979 visit to his native Poland, where, in Warsaw, he delivered a speech to millions, calling for a free Poland and a new kind of "solidarity." (As scholar and author Timothy Garton Ash noted, "Without the Pope, no Solidarity. Without Solidarity, no Gorbachev. Without Gorbachev, no fall of Communism.")

Shipyard electrician Lech Walesa (1943-) became the leader of Solidarity, formed in 1980 when 50 labor unions banded together to protest Poland's Communist government. The unions staged strikes and demonstrations. By 1981 Solidarity had gained so many followers that it threatened Poland's government, which responded (with the support of the Soviet Union) by instituting martial law in December of that year. The military cracked down on the activities of the unions, abolishing Solidarity in 1982 and arresting its leaders, including the charismatic Walesa. But the powerful people's movement, which had also swept up farmers (who formed the Rural Solidarity), could not be suppressed. Martial law was lifted in mid-1983 but the government continued to exert control over the people's freedom. That year Walesa received the Nobel peace prize for his efforts to gain workers' rights and prevent violence. Solidarity continued its work for reform. In 1989 the collapse of communism on the horizon (people's movements in Eastern Europe had combined with Soviet leader Mikhail Gorbachev's policy of *glasnost* to herald the system's demise), the Polish government reopened negotiations with Solidarity's leadership. Free elections were held that year, with the labor party candidates gaining numerous seats in Parliament. In 1990 Walesa was elected president, at which time he resigned as chairman of Solidarity. Poland's Communist Party was dissolved that year.

Pro-Solidarity rally in Czestochowa, Poland, 1988. Solidarity was a worker-led movement for political reform in Communist Poland; by 1990 the country's Communist government was dissolved.

What was the **antiapartheid movement**?

It was an international movement to throw out the decades-old system of racial segregation in South Africa. (The word *apartheid* means "separateness" in the South African language of Afrikaans.) Under apartheid, which was formalized in 1948 by the Afrikaner Nationalist Party, minority whites were given supremacy over nonwhites. The system further separated nonwhite groups from each other so that mulattoes (those of mixed race), Asians (mostly Indians), and native Africans were segregated. The policy was so rigid that it even separated native Bantu groups from each other. Blacks were not allowed to vote, even though they were and are the majority population. Apartheid was destructive to the society as a whole and drew protest at home and abroad. But the South African government adhered to the system, claiming it was the only way to keep peace among the country's various ethnic groups. In 1961 the government even went so far as to withdraw from the British Commonwealth in a dispute over the issue.

Protesters against apartheid staged demonstrations and strikes, which sometimes became violent. South Africa grew increasingly isolated as countries opposing the system refused to trade with the apartheid government. The no-trade policy had been urged by South African civil rights leader and former Anglican bishop Desmond Tutu (1931-), who led a nonviolent campaign to end apartheid and in 1984 won the Nobel peace prize for his efforts. During the 1980s the economic boycott put pressure on the white minority South African government to repeal apartheid laws. It finally did so, and in 1991 the system of segregation was officially abolished.

White South African leader F. W. de Klerk (1936-), who was elected in 1989, had been instrumental in ending the apartheid system. In April 1994 South Africa held the first elections in which blacks were eligible to vote. Not surprisingly, black South Africans won control of Parliament, which in turn elected black leader Nelson Mandela (1918-) as president; de Klerk was retained as deputy president. The two men won the Nobel peace prize in 1993 for their efforts to end apartheid and give all of South Africa's peoples full participation in government. In 1996 the work of the Truth and Reconciliation Commission, a panel headed by Desmond Tutu and charged with investigating the political crimes committed under apartheid, began work. Its investigations continued in 1999, with many findings proving controversial.

What happened at China's **Tiananmen Square**?

In 1989 Beijing's Tiananmen Square, the largest public square in the world, became the site of a student protest and massacre. Three years before the demonstration, freedom of speech and other democratic beliefs began being espoused on university campuses. In increasing numbers China's youth were demanding political reform. They found a sympathizer in the general secretary (the highest ranking officer) of the Communist Party, Hu Yaobang (1915-1989), who, despite criticism from conservatives in government, adhered to his liberal views, particularly concerning freedom of expression. In January 1987 Hu was removed from his post; he died in April 1989, at which time students organized marches in his honor and demonstrated in favor of democratic reforms. On June 4, 1989, Chinese troops fired on the protesters in Tiananmen Square, killing more than 200 and later arresting anyone thought to be involved in China's pro-democracy movement. The actions raised fury around the world. International observers continued to monitor the tenuous situation in China, where evidence surfaced that the government was continuing its pattern of human rights violations.

THE ANTISLAVERY MOVEMENT

Which U.S. state was the first to **abolish slavery**?

Vermont was first, in 1777. On July 8 of that year Vermont adopted a state constitution that prohibited slavery. The first document in the United States to outlaw slavery, it read in part: "No male person, born in this country, or brought from over sea, ought to be holden by law, to serve any person, as a servant, slave or apprentice, after he arrives to the age of twenty-one years, nor female, in like manner, after she arrives to the age of eighteen years, unless they are bound by their own consent, after they arrive to such age, or bound by law, for the payment of debts, damages, fines, costs, or the like." Vermont's constitution also gave suffrage to all men, regardless of race. Vermonters were the first to put a black legislator in the state house: Alexander Twilight (1795-1857) was elected as a representative in 1836. Twilight also earned another first: In 1823 he graduated from Vermont's Middlebury College to become the first black person in the nation to earn a college degree.

Underground Railroad conductor Harriet Tubman (pictured in 1911) worked against slavery by helping hundreds of blacks head to freedom in northern states and Canada.

When did the **antislavery movement** begin?

In the United States, the campaign to prohibit slavery strengthened in the early 1800s. Across the Atlantic, abolitionists had successfully lobbied for the outlaw of slave trade in Great Britain by 1807. The following year, the U.S. government also

Who started the Underground Railroad?

American abolitionist, lecturer, and nurse Harriet Tubman (c. 1820-1913) set up the network to emancipate slaves. Tubman was motivated to do so after she had made her way to freedom in 1849, and then wished the same for her family: "I had crossed the line of which I had so long been dreaming. I was free; but there was no one to welcome me to the land of freedom."

For the next 10 years Tubman acted as a conductor on the Underground Railroad, making at least 15 trips into southern slave states, and guiding not only her parents and siblings, but more than 300 slaves to freedom in the North. She was called "the Moses of her people" for her emancipation efforts. The journeys to freedom were demanding and often dangerous missions. Though Tubman was small in stature, she possessed extraordinary leadership qualities. Author, clergyman, and army officer Thomas Wentworth Higginson (1823-1911) called her "the greatest heroine of the age."

outlawed the trade, but possession of slaves remained legal and profitable. In the 1830s the call to abolish slavery and emancipate slaves became an active movement in the United States, precipitated by a revival of evangelical religion in the North. Abolitionists, believing slavery is morally wrong and violates Christian beliefs, called for an end to the system, which had become critical to the agrarian economy of the southern states, where plantations produced cotton, tobacco, and other crops for domestic and international markets.

Who were the **leaders of abolition**?

Leaders of the antislavery movement included journalist William Lloyd Garrison (1805-1879), founder of the influential antislavery journal *The Liberator* and of the American Anti-Slavery Society (established 1833); brothers Arthur (1786-1865) and Lewis (1788-1873) Tappan, prominent New York merchants who were also founders of the American Anti-Slavery Society; and Theodore Dwight Weld (1803-1895), leader of student protests, organizer of the American and Foreign Anti-Slavery Society, and author of *The Bible Against Slavery* (1837) and other abolitionist works.

Underground Railroad conductor Harriet Tubman (c. 1820-1913) worked against slavery by helping to free hundreds of blacks who escaped slavery in the South, heading for northern states and Canada. Writers such as Harriet Beecher Stowe (1811-1896), author of *Uncle Tom's Cabin* (1851-52), helped strengthen the abolitionist cause and were instrumental in swaying public sentiment. In the hands of some activists, the movement became violent: In 1859 ardent abolitionist John Brown

(1800-1859) led a raid on the armory at Harpers Ferry (in present-day West Virginia), which proved a failed attempt to emancipate slaves by force.

What did the **founding of Liberia** have to do with the antislavery movement?

With the goal of transporting freed slaves back to their homeland, members of the American Colonization Society (organized 1816-17), made land purchases on the west African coast. The holdings were named *Liberia,* a Latin word meaning "freedom." The first black Americans arrived there in 1822. But the society's plan was controversial; even some abolitionists and blacks opposed it, as they believed the only answer to the question of slavery was to eradicate it from the United States and extend the full rights of citizenship to the freed slaves in their new American home. Nevertheless, by 1860 11,000 freed black slaves from the United States had been settled there; eventually a total of 15,000 made the transatlantic voyage to a secured freedom in Liberia. The country was established as an independent republic on July 26, 1847.

Why did President Lincoln issue the **Emancipation Proclamation** before the end of the Civil War?

As the war raged between the Confederacy and the Union, it looked like victory would be a long time in the making: In the summer of 1862 things seemed grim for the federal troops when they were defeated at the Second Battle of Bull Run (which took place in northeastern Virginia on August 29-30). But on September 17, with the Battle of Antietam (in Maryland), the Union finally forced the Confederates to withdraw across the Potomac into Virginia. That September day was the bloodiest of the war. President Abraham Lincoln (1809-1865) decided that this withdrawal was success enough for him to make his proclamation, and on September 22, he called a cabinet meeting. That day he presented to his advisers the Preliminary Emancipation Proclamation.

The official Emancipation Proclamation was issued later, on January 1, 1863. This final version differed from the preliminary one in that it specified emancipation was to be effected only in those states that were in rebellion (i.e. the South). This key change had been made because the president's proclamation was based on congressional acts giving him authority to confiscate rebel property and forbidding the military from returning slaves of rebels to their owners.

Abolitionists in the North criticized the president for limiting the scope of the edict to those states in rebellion, for it left open the question of how slaves and slave owners in the loyal (Northern) states should be dealt with. Nevertheless, Lincoln had made a stand, which served to change the scope of the Civil War (1861-65) to a war against slavery.

On January 31, 1865, just over two years after the Emancipation Proclamation, Congress passed the Thirteenth Amendment, banning slavery throughout the United

States. Lincoln, who had lobbied hard for this amendment, was pleased with its passage. The Confederate states did not free their 4 million slaves until after the Union was victorious (on April 9, 1865).

When was **slavery outlawed in Europe**?

The slave trade ended in Britain in 1807, when authorities agreed with the growing number of abolitionists (those who argued that slavery is immoral and violates Christian beliefs) and outlawed the trade. In 1833 slavery was abolished throughout the British colonies as the culmination of the great antislavery movement in Great Britain. In the United States, the slave trade was prohibited in 1808, but possessing slaves was still legal. Consequently, trade on the black market continued until Britain stepped up its enforcement of its antislavery law by conducting naval blockades and surprise raids off the African coast, effectively closing the trade. The slave trade as it had been known officially came to an end after 1870, when it was outlawed throughout the Americas. Throughout the world, the United Nations works to abolish slavery and other systems of forced labor.

Is there **slavery today**?

Yes, slavery continues into the twenty-first century. The United Nations Population Fund (UNFPA) has stated: "Although slavery has been formally abolished from the world, the trade in human misery continues." Today it is called "human trafficking." Estimating the size of the problem is difficult, but the UNFPA estimates that about four million people are trafficked across international borders each year. The group also reports that the problem is widespread, but the greatest volume of human trafficking exists in Asia, with Africa and Latin America following close behind. The Asia Pacific region is seen as particularly vulnerable, according to the United Nations Economic and Social Commission for Asia and the Pacific (UNESCAP), because of "its huge population pyramid, growing urbanization, and extensive poverty."

Some human rights groups estimate that the number of slaves in the world today is as high as 27 million people. And experts say that it is a growing problem, fueled by globalization. Men, women, and children, especially in developing countries, are forced into labor in sweatshops and fields, and into prostitution in brothels. In desperately poor regions of the world, families sell their children into slave labor and forced prostitution. Other victims are lured in; according to the United Nations Office on Drugs and Crime, "From Himalayan villages to Eastern European cities, people—especially women and girls—are attracted by the prospect of a well-paid job as a domestic servant, waitress, or factory worker." Traffickers recruit victims through fake advertisements, mail-order bride catalogs, and casual acquaintances. But the victims end up in situations controlled by their traffickers, and they are exploited against their wills to earn illicit revenues.

By the early 2000s, human rights groups and governments were organizing to combat the increase in human trafficking. Several agencies of the United Nations worked to address the roots of the problem and to aid victims. Nongovernment agencies were playing a role as well. One such group is Shared Hope International, founded in 1998 by U.S. Congresswoman Linda Smith (Washington) to "rescue and restore women and children in crisis by providing comprehensive services to meet their needs." Italy's government was at the forefront of the anti-trafficking movement, offering residency permits to victims and funding local shelters through legislation passed in 1999. In 2000 the U.S. Congress passed the Victims of Trafficking and Violence Protection Act (TVPA), declaring that sex trafficking is the "modern day slavery." Government figures estimated that each year 45,000 to 50,000 women and children were trafficked into the United States, where they were trapped in modern-day slavery-like situations such as forced prostitution.

But the trafficking problem in the United States, and elsewhere, is not limited to importing women and children from other countries. According to a September 2001 Justice Department report, 400,000 children are lured or forced into prostitution each year in the United States. Many of the victims are from white, working- and middle-class families, often runaways from troubled homes who end up on the streets.

In September 2004 former representative John R. Miller (Washington) was sworn into the newly created position of ambassador-at-large for the U.S. State Department's anti-trafficking office. In a speech, Miller said, "Today, the slavery is not on plantations and in homes; it is in factories and armies as well, and especially in brothels. But the slave masters use the same tools today as earlier slave masters: kidnapping, fraud, threats, and beatings, all aimed at forcing women, children, and men into labor and sex exploitation."

Experts agreed that ending human trafficking in the twenty-first century would require a coalition of government, special interest groups, human rights organizations, and other nongovernment organizations. Determining the scope of the problem and raising public awareness were important first steps.

THE CIVIL RIGHTS MOVEMENT

What was the **Niagara movement**?

It was a short-lived but important African American organization that advocated "the total integration of blacks into mainstream society, with all the rights, privileges, and benefits of other Americans." Founded in Niagara Falls, Ontario, in 1905, the Niagara movement was led by writer, scholar, and activist W. E. B. Du Bois (1868-1963), who was then a professor of economics and history at Atlanta University. Observers described the organization as the anti-Bookerite camp: Educator Booker T. Washington (1856-1915), who rose from slavery to found Alabama's Tuskegee Institute (1881), believed change for black people should be effected through education and self-improvement—not through demand. Mr. Washington opposed the social and political agitation favored by some reformers; the Niagara movement, on the other hand, placed the responsibility for the nation's racial problems squarely on the shoulders of its white population. The 30 branches of the Niagara movement challenged conservative politics of the so-called "Tuskegee Machine" led by Booker T. Washington. Though the Niagara organization dissolved in 1909, the National Association for the Advancement of Colored People (NAACP) was heir to its ideology and activism. Du Bois helped found that organization, and from 1910 to 1934 edited its official journal, *The Crisis,* in which he published his views "on nearly every important social issue that confronted the black community."

Were activists the only ones who were vocal about **opposing segregation**?

No, segregation was opposed at every level of black society, as well as by many whites. The voices of the civil rights movement included wage laborers, farmers, educators, athletes, entertainers, soldiers, religious leaders, politicians, and statesmen—all of whom had experienced the oppression of Jim Crow laws and policies in the United States.

Before W. E. B. Du Bois (1868-1963) rose to prominence as an educator and writer, he chose to leave the security of his home in Great Barrington, Massachusetts, to attend college at Nashville's Fisk University. There, in 1885, he encountered Tennessee's Jim Crow laws, which strictly divided blacks and whites. He was so intimidated by the "southern system" that he rarely left the campus, and he ultimately returned to New England to complete his studies at Harvard University. He did, however, go back to the South, becoming a professor of economics and history at Atlanta University (1897-1910, 1932-44). As one of the first exponents of full and equal racial equality, in 1909 Du Bois helped found the National Association for the Advancement of Colored People (NAACP), which provided leadership during the civil rights movement.

In 1942 a young Georgia man named John Roosevelt Robinson (1919-1972) was drafted into the military. Robinson applied for Officer's Candidate School at Fort Riley, Kansas, and although he was admitted to the program, he and the other black candidates received no training until pressure from Washington, D.C., forced the local commander to admit blacks to the base's training school. Later Robinson became a second lieutenant and continued to challenge the Jim Crow policies on military bases. When the army decided to keep him out of a game with the nearby University of Missouri because that school refused to play against a team with black members, Robinson quit the base's football team in protest; at Fort Hood, Texas, Robinson objected to segregation on an army bus. His protests led to court-martial. Acquitted, in November 1944 Robinson was honorably discharged—before the end of World War II (1939-45): The army had no desire to keep this black agitator among the ranks, and, as Robinson later put it, he was "pretty much fed up with the service." In 1947 "Jackie" Robinson became the first black baseball player in the major leagues when he joined the Brooklyn Dodgers, breaking the color barrier in the national pastime.

In the postwar years, American diplomat Ralph Bunche (1904-1971) attracted public attention when he rejected an offer from President Harry Truman (1884-1972) to become an assistant secretary of state. Bunche, a Howard University professor who had worked for the Office of Strategic Services during the war, explained that he declined the position because he did not want to subject his family to the Jim Crow laws of Washington, D.C. Bunche spoke out frequently against racism, and in 1944 he co-authored the book *An American Dilemma,* which examined the plight of American blacks.

These are just a few of the many examples of personal protest that signaled the beginning of the civil rights movement in the United States.

How did the **civil rights movement** begin?

It began on Thursday, December 1, 1955, as Rosa Parks (1913-), a seamstress who worked for a downtown department store in Montgomery, Alabama, made her way home on the Cleveland Avenue bus. Parks was seated in the first row that was designated for blacks. But the white rows in the front of the bus soon filled up. When Parks was asked to give up her seat so that a white man could sit, she refused. She was arrested and sent to jail.

Montgomery's black leaders had already been discussing staging a protest against racial segregation on the city buses. They soon organized, with Baptist minister Martin Luther King Jr. (1929-1968) as their leader. Beginning on December 5, 1955, thousands of black people refused to ride the city buses: the Montgomery Bus Boycott had begun. It lasted more than a year—382 days—and ended only when the U.S. Supreme Court ruled that segregation on the buses was unconstitutional. The protesters and civil rights activists had emerged the victors in this—their first and momentous—effort to end segregation and discrimination in the United States.

Parks, who lost her job as a result of the arrest, later explained that she had acted on her own beliefs that she was being unfairly treated. But in so doing Parks had taken a stand and had given rise to a movement.

What was the **nonviolence movement**?

The Reverend Martin Luther King Jr. (1929-1968) was committed to bringing about change by staging peaceful protests; he led a campaign of nonviolence as part of the civil rights movement. King rose to prominence as a leader during the Montgomery Bus Boycott in 1955, when he delivered a speech that embodied his Christian beliefs and set the tone for the nonviolence movement, saying, "We are not here advocating

The Reverend Martin Luther King Jr. brought change through peaceful protests. A charismatic speaker, here he addresses supporters in Selma, Alabama, in 1965.

violence.... The only weapon we have...is the weapon of protest." Throughout his life, King staunchly adhered to these beliefs—even after terrorists bombed his family's home. King's "arsenal" of democratic protest included boycotts, marches, the words of his stirring speeches (comprising an impressive body of oratory), and sit-ins. With other African American ministers King established the Southern Christian Leadership Conference (1957), which assumed a leadership role during the civil rights movement.

The nonviolent protest of black Americans proved a powerful weapon against segregation and discrimination: A massive demonstration in Birmingham, Alabama, in 1963 helped sway pubic opinion and motivate lawmakers in Washington to act when news coverage of the event showed peaceful protesters being subdued by policemen using dogs and heavy fire hoses. In response to the outcry over the event in Birmingham, President John F. Kennedy (1917-1963) proposed civil rights legislation to Congress; the bill was passed in 1964. That same year Martin Luther King Jr. received the Nobel peace prize for his nonviolent activism.

King's policy of peace was challenged two years later when the Student Nonviolent Coordinating Committee (SNCC), tired of the violent response with which peaceful protesters were often met, urged activists to adopt a more decisive and aggressive stance and began promoting the slogan "Black Power." The civil rights movement, having made critical strides, became fragmented, as leaders, including the highly influential Malcolm X (1925-1965), differed over how to effect change.

On April 4, 1968, King was in Memphis, Tennessee, to show his support for a strike of black sanitation workers when he was gunned down outside his hotel room shortly after 5:30 in the evening. As news of King's death swept over the nation, blacks in 168 American cities and towns responded with rioting, setting fire to buildings, and looting white businesses. Commenting on the terror, radical African American leader Stokely Carmichael said, "When white America killed Dr. King last night, she declared war on us." The chaos continued for a week: When the rioting ended on April 11, there were 46 dead (most of them black), 35,000 injured, and 20,000 jailed. Nevertheless, the violent crime that claimed the leader's life and the violence that erupted after news spread of his death have not, decades later, overshadowed King's legacy of peace and his message of the brotherhood of all people.

What were the **"freedom rides"**?

The "freedom rides" were a series of bus rides designed to test the U.S. Supreme Court's prohibition of segregation in interstate travel. In 1960, in the case of *Boynton* v. *Virginia,* the Supreme Court ruled in favor of a Howard University student who charged that segregation laws at the Richmond, Virginia, bus station violated federal antisegregation laws. The Congress of Racial Equality (CORE) decided to test the enforcement of the federal law by initiating the freedom rides. On May 4, 1961, 13 people, black and white, boarded a bus for the South. Meant as a nonviolent means of protest against local segregation laws, the riders were nevertheless met with violence: When the bus reached Montgomery, Alabama, on May 20, a white mob was waiting; the freedom riders were beaten. Rioting broke out in the city, and U.S. marshals were sent to restore order. The interracial campaign to desegregate transportation was ultimately successful, but government intervention was required to enforce the laws, as numerous southern whites had demonstrated that they weren't going to comply voluntarily.

When did **Martin Luther King Jr.** give his "I Have a Dream" speech?

The occasion was the March on Washington on August 28, 1963. That summer day more than a quarter million people—lobbying for congressional passage of a civil rights bill—gathered at the Lincoln Memorial to hear speakers, including the charismatic and influential King (1929-1968). His eloquent words defined the movement and still inspire those who continue to work for reforms. Among his words were these: "I have a dream that one day this nation will rise up and live out the true meaning of its creed, 'We hold these truths to be self-evident; that all men are created equal.'"

Congress did pass the Civil Rights Act, in 1964. The most comprehensive American civil rights legislation since the Reconstruction (the 12-year period that followed the Civil War), the act outlawed racial discrimination in public places, assured equal voting standards for all citizens, prohibited employer and union racial discrimination, and called for equality in education.

What does the letter *X* in **Malcolm X**'s name stand for?

The influential but controversial African American leader, who was a staunch defendant of black rights, took the surname X in 1952, upon his release from prison. He explained that the letter stood for the unknown African name of his ancestors. Malcolm X's family's name, Little, was that given to his slave ancestors by their owner. By adopting X as his surname, it was at once a bitter reminder of his family's slavery and an affirmation of his (unknown) African roots.

How were southern **blacks prevented from voting**?

Besides intimidation, there were three different methods used in southern states in the early part of the century to disenfranchise black citizens: 1) the poll tax; 2) literacy tests; and 3) grandfather clauses. The poll tax required a voter to pay a fee in order to exercise the right to vote. Literacy tests were implemented as a prerequisite for voting; this method also kept many poorly educated whites (unable to pass the exam) from casting their ballots as well. Most southern states also adopted legislation by which voting rights were extended only to those citizens who had been able to vote as of a certain date—a date when few if any black men would have been able to vote. Since these laws made provisions for said voters' descendants as well, they were dubbed "grandfather clauses." Such attempts to deny citizens the right to vote were made unlawful in 1964 (by the Twenty-fourth Amendment, which outlaws the poll tax in all federal elections and primaries), in 1965 (by the Voting Rights Act, which outlawed measures used to suppress minority votes), and in 1966 (when poll taxes at the state and local levels were also declared illegal). Literacy tests and grandfather clauses were also struck down as unconstitutional.

What is the history of the **Ku Klux Klan**?

The Ku Klux Klan (KKK) is a white supremacist group originally formed in 1865 in Pulaski, Tennessee, when Confederate Army veterans formed what they called a "social club." The first leader (called the "grand wizard") was Nathan Bedford Forrest (1821-1877), a former general in the Confederate Army, who, on April 12, 1864, in the final days of the Civil War, led a massacre of 300 black soldiers in service of the Union Army at Fort Pillow, Tennessee.

As the unofficial arm of resistance against Republican efforts to restore the nation and make full citizens of its black (formerly slave) population, the Ku Klux Klan waged a campaign of terror against blacks in the South during Reconstruction (1865-77), the 12-year period of rebuilding that followed the Civil War. Klan members, cloaked in robes and hoods to disguise their identity, threatened, beat, and killed numerous blacks. While the group deprived its victims of their rights as citizens, their intent was also to intimidate the entire black population and keep them out of politics. White people who supported the federal government's measures to extend rights to all black citizens also became the victims of the fearsome Klan. Membership in the group grew quickly, and the Ku Klux Klan soon had a presence throughout the South.

In 1871 the U.S. Congress passed the Force Bill, giving President Ulysses S. Grant (1822-1885) authority to direct federal troops against the Klan. The action was successful, causing the group to disappear—but only for a time. In 1915 the society was newly organized at Stone Mountain, Georgia, as a Protestant fraternal organization (called "The Invisible Empire, Knights of the Ku Klux Klan, Inc."), this time widening its focus of persecution to include Roman Catholics, immigrants, and Jews, as well as blacks. Members of all of these groups became the target of KKK harassment, which now included torture, whippings, and public lynchings. The group, which proclaimed its mission of "racial purity," grew in number and became national, electing its own to public office in many states, not just the South. But the society's acts of violence raised the public ire, and by the 1940s, America's attention focused on World War II (1939-45), and the Klan died out or went completely underground. The group had another resurgence during the 1950s and into the early 1970s, as the nation struggled through the era of civil rights. The Klan still exists today, fostering the extremist views of its membership and staging marches to demonstrate its presence on the American landscape. Such demonstrations are often attended by protestors.

What are **reparations**?

Reparations are payments or other compensations made to a group of people who have been wronged or injured. The issue was in the news in the 1990s and early 2000s as lawmakers, academics, and other leaders pressed for a redress for slavery, which some scholars call the American, or black, holocaust. The precedents for making reparations were several: The German government made reparations to survivors and families of victims of the Nazi holocaust. And the American government made reparations to Japanese Americans who had been interned during World War II (1939-45), as well as to Native Americans, for damages done to them.

The recent discussion of reparations began in 1989, when U.S. representative John Conyers (Michigan) introduced a bill, H.R. 40, in Congress to "establish a commission to examine the institution of slavery...and economic discrimination against African Americans" and, if so determined, "to make recommendations to the Congress on appropriate remedies." As the idea of reparations gained currency in the American public in the 1990s, supporters argued that redress for slavery would help heal the "open wound" of race relations and would compensate the descendants of slaves whose ancestors' work had helped build the national economy. They further argued that slavery resulted in long-term discrimination that beleaguered black Americans; they were the victims of a centuries-old, government-sanctioned system that established a legacy of race-based injustices. African American activist and author Randall Robinson explained it this way: "No nation can enslave a group of people for hundreds of years, set them free—bedraggled and penniless—to pit them, without assistance, in a hostile environment against privileged victimizers, and then reasonably expect the gap between the heirs of the two groups to narrow. Lines begun parallel and left alone can never touch." In bolstering support for reparations, Robinson pointed to the consequences of this "massive injustice": that blacks in the United States experience high rates of infant mortality, low incomes, high rates of unemployment, substandard education, high death rates, below-average life spans, and overrepresentation in prisons and on death row.

Critics of reparations said that compensating the descendants of slaves was unrealistic; determining who would be paid would alone constitute an expensive government program. They also questioned why descendants of slaves should be paid by the government a century and a half after the end of the brutal system. Further, they argued that other programs, born of the civil rights movement, have strived to bring equity to African Americans.

Despite criticism, Representative Conyers resolved to reintroduce his bill as often as necessary until Congress would act on it. He emphasized that his goal was to create a commission, informed by town hall meetings, to first determine if there should be reparations—and if so, who should be paid and how much. H.R. 40 had received the support of the city councils of Detroit, Cleveland, Chicago, and Atlanta.

WOMEN'S RIGHTS

When did the American **suffragist movement** begin?

In the 1840s American women began organizing and, in increasing numbers, demanding the right to vote. The movement was started by women who sought social reforms, including outlawing slavery, instituting a national policy of temperance (abstinence from alcoholic beverages), and securing better work opportunities and pay. These reformers soon realized that in order to make change they needed the power of the vote.

Among the leaders of the suffragist movement was feminist and reformer Elizabeth Cady Stanton (1815-1902). She joined with antislavery activist Lucretia Mott (1793-1880) to organize the first women's rights convention in 1848 in Seneca Falls, New York, launching the woman suffragist movement. In 1869 Stanton teamed with Susan B. Anthony (1820-1906) to organize the National Woman Suffrage Association.

New York suffragists hold a demonstration outside the White House in February 1917. Ratified in 1920, the Nineteenth Amendment gives women the right to vote in all state and federal elections.

That same year, another group was formed: the American Woman Suffrage Association, led by women's rights and antislavery activist Lucy Stone (1818-1893) and her husband Henry Brown Blackwell (1825-1909). In 1870 the common cause of the two groups was strengthened by the passage of the Fifteenth Amendment, which gave all men, regardless of race, the right to vote. When the two organizations joined forces in 1890, they formed the National American Woman Suffrage Association (NAWSA).

The founders of the American women's movement were followed by a new generation of leaders, which included Stanton's daughter, Harriot Eaton Blatch (1856-1940), as well as Alice Paul (1885-1977), who founded the organization that became the National Woman's Party, and organizer and editor Lucy Burns (1879-1966), who worked closely with Paul.

The suffragists appealed to middle-class and working-class women, as well as to students and radicals. They waged campaigns at the state level, distributed literature, organized meetings, made speeches, and marched in parades. They also lobbied federal legislators, picketed, and chained themselves to the White House fence. When jailed, many resorted to hunger strikes and were sometimes met with cruel treatment. The suffragists' fight was a fierce one; the opposition played on the widespread belief that if given the right to vote, women would neglect the traditional duties of wife and mother.

The movement gained strength during World War I (1914-18). As men went off to fight the war in Europe, the women at home demonstrated themselves to be intelligent and involved citizens in the life of the country. A wartime suffragist poster declared in one long column, "As a war measure, the country is asking of women service as...farmers, mechanics, nurses, doctors, munitions workers, mine workers, yeomen, gas makers, bell boys, messengers, conductors, motormen, army cooks, telegraphers, ambulance drivers, advisors to the council of national defense," and in another short column it stated, "As a war measure, women are asking of the country...the vote." By 1918 support for woman suffrage was broad. That year Congress proposed a constitutional amendment stating that the "right of citizens of the United States to vote shall not be denied or abridged by the United States or by any State on account of sex." It was passed, as the proposed Nineteenth Amendment, in the House in 1918 and in the Senate in 1919. The amendment was approved by the required number of state legislatures on August 18, 1920, when Tennessee ratified it.

What was the **Night of Terror**?

It is a little-known episode in the American suffragist movement that took place on November 14, 1917, at the Occoquan Workhouse in Lorton, Virginia.

After President Woodrow Wilson (1856-1924) took office in January 1917, activists began picketing daily outside the White House, demanding the right to vote for women. It was the first time in history that demonstrators had marched at the White House. The suffragists carried banners that read, "Mr. President, how long must women wait for liberty?" and, more radically, "Kaiser Wilson: 20,000,000 American women are not self-governed." Their intent was to expose the government's hypocrisy: In April the United States had entered World War I (1914-18) in an effort to guarantee democracy abroad, yet democracy did not exist at home—where the entire female population remained disenfranchised.

In June police began arresting demonstrators on minor charges, such as obstructing traffic. But the arrests did nothing to deter the suffragists. Upon their release from prison, they returned to protest at the White House gates. In all, 168 women, including Alice Paul (1885-1977) and Lucy Burns (1879-1966) of the National Woman's Party, were arrested.

On the night of November 14, 1917, guards took 33 protesters to the Occoquan Workhouse to be held. Previously, the women had been subject to forced feedings and solitary confinement at Occoquan, but this time new cruelties awaited them. They were beaten, dragged, choked, and handcuffed. Word leaked out about the atrocities committed at the workhouse. Less than two weeks later, a judge ruled that the women had been brutally treated, yet they had done nothing more than exercise their constitutional right to free speech. The women returned to their fight, now with more weight of public opinion behind them. Nevertheless, it was three long years before the Nineteenth Amendment was adopted, guaranteeing women the right to vote.

In 1982 a historical marker was placed on the prison grounds in tribute to the brave women who endured Occoquan's Night of Terror.

Who was **Alice Paul**?

Alice Paul (1885-1977) was a groundbreaking feminist before the word "feminist" came into fashion. The Mount Laurel, New Jersey, institute named in her honor describes her as "the architect of some of the most outstanding political achievements on behalf of women in the twentieth century."

Paul was born in 1885 to Quaker parents who instilled in her a belief in gender equality. After completing high school the top in her class, Paul graduated from Swarthmore College in 1905 and began work toward an advanced degree. In 1906 she traveled to England, where she continued her studies, did social work, and became actively involved in the suffrage movement. She was arrested three times for her involvement in protests.

In 1916, when the American women's suffrage movement was divided and "dead in the water," Paul founded the National Woman's Party (NWP), an organization that spearheaded the campaign for national woman's suffrage and that continued working for women's rights and equality into the twenty-first century. Paul's leadership of the suffrage movement was critical in the passage of the Nineteenth Amendment (1920), which guaranteed women the right to vote; she organized thousands of activists to put enormous pressure on the White House and Congress. Paul employed what was then considered a most unladylike strategy of "sustained, dramatic, nonviolent protest." The suffrage campaign was characterized by national speaking tours, marches, and pickets (including the first ever at the White House). When protesters were arrested, they sometimes endured brutal prison conditions and staged hunger strikes.

After passage of the Nineteenth Amendment, Paul continued her studies, adding to her master's degree in social work (1907) a doctorate in economics (1912). She earned three more advanced degrees, culminating in a doctor of law degree in 1927 from American University. Called a brilliant political strategist, the forward-thinking Paul authored the first equal rights amendment for women, which she introduced to Congress in 1923. In 1942 she became chairperson of the National Woman's Party. She later added language of gender equality to the charter for the United Nations as well as the 1964 Civil Rights Act. After a life of courageous activism on behalf of women, Paul died in 1977.

Who was **Emmeline Pankhurst**?

Pankhurst (1858-1928), a key figure in the women's suffrage movement, was a militant reformer who waged a decades-long battle to win the vote for women in Great Britain. Pankhurst's sometimes radical campaign greatly influenced her American counterparts. Though she held various municipal offices and was married to an influential barrister (Richard Marsden Pankhurst), she worked for change primarily through the organizations she founded. In 1889 she organized the Women's Franchise League, and five years later the group's work secured the right of all women (married and unmarried) to vote in local elections. She went on to found the Women's Social and Political Union in 1903. The union was known for its extreme tactics. The British suffragist movement culminated in 1928 with the passage of the Representation of the People Act, which gave all women the right to vote in elections. Pankhurst died later that year.

How old is **feminism**?

Feminists—people who believe that women should have economic, political, and social equality with men—have existed throughout history; such women are often described in literature and by history as being "women before their time." But as a movement, feminism, which is synonymous with the women's rights movement, did not get under way until the mid-1800s, when women in the United States and Great Britain began organizing and campaigning to win the vote. Early feminists (and feminists today) were likely influenced by the revolutionary work titled *A Vindication of the Rights of Woman,* published in 1792 by British author and educator Mary Wollstonecraft (1759-1797; her daughter was writer Mary Shelley of *Frankenstein* fame). Wollstonecraft attacked the convention of the day, charging that it kept middle-class and upper-class women in a state of ignorance, training them to be useless. A staunch promoter of education (she was self-educated), Wollstonecraft is credited with being the first major philosophical feminist.

What is the **ERA**?

The ERA stands for the equal rights amendment, a constitutional amendment proposed by Congress in 1972. It stated that "equality of rights under the law shall not be denied or abridged by the United States or any state on account of sex." In proposing the amendment, Congress gave the states 10 years in which to ratify it. But in 1982 only 35 of the necessary 38 states had approved the amendment, which then died. The failure to ratify the ERA was the result of disagreement over how the language would be interpreted. Supporters believed the amendment would guarantee women equal treatment under the law; opponents feared the amendment might require women to forfeit the financial support of their husbands and require them to serve in the military.

How did Betty Friedan's ***Feminine Mystique*** launch the modern women's rights movement?

American author and activist Betty Friedan's (1921-) landmark work was published in 1963. She argued that in the postwar era American society expected women only to be devoted housewives and mothers. This was the ideal, the mystique, that was both promoted and accepted. In the *Feminine Mystique* Friedan challenged this prevailing notion, causing many women to reexamine their lives. After all, during World War II (1939-45) women had ably stepped into the workplace to keep industry running as the men went to war. When the servicemen came back, women returned to the home and were not expected to seek careers. But after nearly two decades of accepting the status quo, Friedan asked the question, "If women could successfully hold jobs, why shouldn't they?" Assessing their happiness, many women opted to pursue work outside the home. The modern women's movement had begun. Soon women were organizing to promote social and political reforms to do away with discrimination in the workplace and eliminate barriers to entry in education and politics. Friedan herself helped found the National Organization for Women (NOW) in 1966; the association grew rapidly and continues to fight for women's equality in the twenty-first century.

What is **Title IX**?

Considered one of the biggest successes of the modern women's movement, Title IX is part of the Education Amendments of 1972, federal legislation that prohibits any school or college that receives federal funds from discriminating on the basis of sex. The law applies to all aspect of education, including admission, athletics, and curriculum.

POPULISM, PROGRESSIVISM, AND THE LABOR MOVEMENT

What was **populism**?

A commoners' movement, in the United States populism was formalized in 1891 with the founding of the Populist Party, which worked to improve conditions for farmers and laborers. In the presidential election of 1892, the party supported its own political candidate, the former (third-party) Greenback candidate James B. Weaver (1833-1912). Though Weaver lost, the Populists remained a strong force. In the next presidential election, of 1896, they backed Democratic Party candidate William Jennings Bryan (1860-1925), a self-proclaimed commoner who was sympathetic to the causes of the Farmers' Alliances and of the National Grange (reform-minded agricultural organizations) as well as the nation's workers. Bryan lost to William McKinley (1843-1901), and soon after the election the Populist Party began to fall apart, disappearing altogether by 1908. Nevertheless, the party's initiatives continued to figure in the nation's political life for the next two decades and many populist ideas were made into laws, including the free coinage of silver and government issue of more paper money ("greenbacks") to loosen the money supply, adoption of a graduated income tax, passage of an amendment allowing for the popular election of U.S. senators (the Constitution provided for their election by the state legislatures), passage of antitrust laws (to combat the monopolistic control of American business), and implementation of the eight-hour workday. Since the early 1900s political candidates and ideas have continued to be described as populist, meaning they favor the rights of and uphold the beliefs and values of the common people.

What was the **Progressive movement**?

It was a campaign for reform on every level—social, political, and economic—in the United States. It began during the economic depression that was brought on by the Panic of 1873 and lasted until 1917, when Americans entered World War I (1914-18).

During the first 100 years of the U.S. Constitution (1788), federal lawmakers and justices proved reluctant to get involved in or attempt to regulate private business. This policy of noninterference had allowed the gap to widen between rich and poor. The turn of the century was a time in America when early industrialists built fantastic mansions while many workers and farmers struggled to earn a living; when tenement houses sprang up in urban areas to meet (albeit horribly inadequately) the housing needs made present by a steady stream of immigrants; and when labor unions, which had only recently begun to organize, were beset by outbreaks of violence, hurting their fight for better treatment by employers. Observing these problems, progressive-minded reformers, comprised largely of middle-class Americans, women, and journalists (the so-called "muckrakers"), began reform campaigns at the local and state levels, eventually effecting changes at the federal level.

Progressives favored many of the ideas that had previously been espoused by the Populists, including antitrust legislation to bust up the monopolies and a graduated income tax to more adequately collect public funds from the nation's well-to-do businessmen. Additionally, Progressives combated corrupt local governments; dirty and dangerous working conditions in factories, mines, and fields; and inner-city blight. The minimum wage, the Pure Food and Drug Act, and Chicago's Hull House (which served as "an incubator for the American social work movement") are part of the legacy of the Progressive movement.

When did the **U.S. labor movement** begin?

It began in the early 1800s, when skilled workers, such as carpenters and blacksmiths, banded together in local organizations with the goal of securing better wages. By the time fighting broke out in the Civil War (1861-65), the first national unions had been founded—again, by skilled workers. However, many of these early labor organizations struggled to gain widespread support and soon fell apart. But by the end of the century, several national unions, including the United Mine Workers (1890) and the American Railway Union (1893), emerged. In the last two decades of the 1800s, violence accompanied labor protests and strikes while opposition to the unions mounted. Companies shared blacklists of the names of workers suspected of union activities; hired armed guards to forcibly break strikes; and retained lawyers to successfully invoke the Sherman Anti-Trust Act (of 1890) to crush strikes—lawyers argued that strikes interfered with interstate commerce, which was declared illegal by the Sherman legislation (which had not been the intent of the lawmakers).

In the early decades of the 1900s, unions made advances, but many Americans continued to view organizers and members as radicals. The climate changed for the unions during the Great Depression (1929-39). With so many Americans out of work, many blamed business leaders for the economy's failure and began to view the unions in a new light—as organizations to protect the interests of workers. In 1935 the federal government strengthened the unions' cause in passing the National Labor Relations Act (also called the Wagner Act), protecting the rights to organize and to bargain collectively (when worker representatives, usually labor union representatives, negotiate with employers). The legislation also set up the National Labor Relations Board (NLRB), which still works today to penalize companies that engage in unfair labor practices. The constitutionality of the act was challenged in court in 1937, but the Supreme Court upheld the legislation.

The unions grew increasingly powerful over the next decade: By 1945 more than one-third of all nonagricultural workers belonged to a union. Having made important gains during World War II (1939-45), including hospital insurance coverage, paid vacations and holidays, and pensions, union leaders continued to urge workers to strike to gain more ground—something leaders felt was the worker's right amidst the unprecedented prosperity of the postwar era. But strikes soon impacted the life of the average American: Consumers faulted the unions for shortages of consumer goods, suspension of services, and inflated prices. Congress responded by passing the Labor-Management Relations Act (or the Taft-Hartley Act) in 1947, which limits the impact of unions by prohibiting certain kinds of strikes, setting rules for how unions could organize workers, and establishing guidelines for how strikes that may impact the nation's health or safety are to be handled.

What was **the first big union**?

The first national union of note was the Knights of Labor, founded by garment workers in Philadelphia, Pennsylvania, in 1869. Recruiting women, blacks, immigrants, and unskilled and semiskilled workers alike, the Knights of Labor's open-membership policy provided the organization with a broad base of support, something previous labor unions, which had limited membership based on craft or skill, lacked. The organization set its objectives on instituting the eight-hour workday, prohibiting child labor (under age 14), instituting equal opportunities and wages for women laborers, and abolishing convict labor. The group became involved in numerous strikes from the late 1870s to the mid-1880s.

At the same time, a faction of moderates within the organization was growing, and in 1883 it elected American machinist Terence Powderly (1849-1924) as president.

Who were the Molly Maguires?

They were Irish-American coal miners in eastern Pennsylvania who organized a secret society in 1854. The Molly Maguires aimed to wage a campaign of violence against mine owners and operators. The name of the group came from a society in Ireland that used physical force to fight ruthless landlords. The American miners became determined to defeat their oppressors at all costs. Their numbers grew, and in the decade following the Civil War (1861-65), the Molly Maguires were active both as agitators, and it would later be revealed, as assassins. In 1875 the group incited a coal miners strike, which was broken by the detective work of Irish-American James McParlan (1844-1919), a Pinkerton guard hired by Philadelphia and Reading Coal and Iron Company to infiltrate the Molly Maguires. McParlan revealed the identities of gunmen responsible for the deaths of nine mine company foremen. Several members of the secret society were arrested, tried and convicted (in 1876), and hanged (in 1877) for the crimes. American sympathies for the plight of the miners were diminished by the headlines proclaiming the terrorist activities of the Molly Maguires. The society dissolved by 1877. Their presence, however, was long felt in the anthracite coal fields of Pennsylvania, where company police monitored activities in the mines, and effectively intimidated many miners from organizing.

Under Powderly's leadership, the Knights of Labor began to splinter. Moderates pursued a conciliatory policy in labor disputes, supporting the establishment of labor bureaus and public arbitration systems; radicals not only opposed the policy of open membership, they strongly supported strikes as a means of achieving immediate goals—including a one-day general strike to demand implementation of an eight-hour workday. In May 1886 workers demonstrating in Chicago's Haymarket Square attracted a crowd of some 1,500 people; when police arrived to disperse them, a bomb exploded and rioting ensued. Eleven people were killed and more than 1,000 were injured in the melee. For many Americans, the event linked the labor movement with anarchy. That same year several factions of the Knights of Labor seceded from the union to join the American Federation of Labor (AFL). The Knights of Labor remained intact for three more decades, before the organization officially dissolved in 1917, by which time the group had been overshadowed by the AFL and other unions.

How old is the **AFL-CIO**?

The roots of the American Federation of Labor-Congress of Industrial Organizations (AFL-CIO), today a federation of national unions, date to 1881 when the Federation of Organized Trade and Labor Unions was formed in Pittsburgh, Pennsylvania, by trade

Striking mill workers demonstrate in Gastonia, North Carolina, 1929.

union leaders representing some 50,000 members in the United States and Canada. Reorganizing in 1886, the association of unions changed its name to the American Federation of Labor (AFL) and elected Samuel Gompers (1850-1924) president.

Unlike the open-membership policy of the Knights of Labor (from whom the AFL gained numerous members in 1886), the AFL determined to organize by craft: At the outset, its member unions included a total of 140,000 skilled laborers. Gompers, who immigrated from England in 1863 and became the first registered member of the Cigar-Makers' International Union in 1864, had been active in labor for more than two decades. Once chosen as president of the AFL, Gompers remained in that office, with the exception of only one year, until his death in 1924. During the nearly 40-year period, he shaped the labor federation and helped it make strides by determining a general policy that allowed member unions autonomy. Unlike the Knights of Labor, which pursued long-term goals such as Knights leader Terence Powderly's abstract objective of making "every man his own master—every man his own employer," the AFL focused its efforts on specific, short-term goals such as higher wages, shorter hours, and the right to bargain collectively (when an employer agrees to negotiate with worker/union representatives).

In the 1890s the AFL was weakened by labor violence, which evoked public fears. A July 1892 strike at the Carnegie Steel plant in Homestead, Pennsylvania, turned into a riot between angry steelworkers and Pinkerton guards. The militia was called in to monitor the strike, which five months later ended in failure for the AFL-affiliated steelworkers. Nevertheless, under Gompers's leadership, membership of the AFL grew to more than 1 million by 1901 and to 2.5 million by 1917, when it included 111 national unions and 27,000 local unions. The federation collected dues from its members, creating a fund to aid striking workers. The organization avoided party politics, instead seeking out and supporting advocates regardless of political affiliation. The AFL worked to support the establishment of the U.S. Department of Labor (1913), which administers and enforces statutes promoting the welfare and advancement of the American workforce, and the passage of the Clayton Anti-Trust Act (1914), which strengthened the Sherman Anti-Trust Act of 1890, eventually delivering a blow to monopolies.

The CIO was founded in 1938. In the early 1930s several AFL unions banded together as the Committee for Industrial Organization and successfully conducted campaigns to sign up new members in mass-production facilities such as the automobile, steel, and rubber industries. Since these initiatives (which resulted in millions of new members) were against the AFL policy of signing up only skilled laborers by craft (the CIO had reached out to all industrial workers, regardless of skill level or craft), a schism resulted within the AFL. The unions that had participated in the CIO membership drive were expelled from the AFL; the CIO established itself as a federation in 1938, officially changing its name to the Congress of Industrial Organizations.

In 1955, amidst a climate of increasing anti-unionism, the AFL and CIO rejoined to form one strong voice. Today the organization has craft and industrial affiliates at the international, national, state, and local levels, with membership totaling in the millions.

Who was **Eugene Debs**?

Debs (1855-1926) was a radical labor leader who in 1893 founded the American Railway Union (ARU), an industrial union for all railroad workers. Debs was a charismatic speaker, but he was also a controversial figure in American life around the turn of the century. In 1894 workers at the Pullman Palace Car Company, which manufactured railcars in Pullman, Illinois (near Chicago), went on strike to protest a significant reduction in their wages. Pullman was a model "company town" where the railcar manufacturer, founded by American inventor George W. Pullman (1831-1897) in 1867, owned all the land and buildings, and ran the school, bank, and utilities. In 1893, in order to maintain profits following declining revenues, the Pullman Company cut workers wages by 25 to 40 percent, but did not adjust rent and prices in the town, forcing many employees and their families into deprivation. In May 1894 a labor committee approached Pullman Company management to resolve the situation. The company, which had always refused to negotiate with employees, responded by firing the labor committee members. The firings incited a strike of all 3,300 Pullman workers. In support of the labor effort, Eugene Debs assumed leadership of the strike (some Pullman employees had joined the ARU in

1894) and directed all ARU members not to haul any Pullman cars. A general rail strike followed, which paralyzed transportation across the country. In response to what was now being called "Deb's rebellion," a July 2, 1894, federal court order demanded all workers to return to the job, but the ARU refused to comply. U.S. president Grover Cleveland (1837-1908) ordered federal troops to break the strike, citing it interfered with mail delivery. The intervention turned violent. Despite public protest, Debs, who was tried for contempt of court and conspiracy, was imprisoned in 1895 for having violated the court order. Debs later proclaimed himself a socialist and became leader of the American Left, running unsuccessfully for president as the Socialist Party candidate five times, in 1900, 1904, 1908, 1912, and 1920. He actively supported the causes of the International Workers of the World (IWW), a radical labor organization founded in 1905.

Who was **Cesar Chavez**?

Mexican American farm worker Cesar Chavez (1927-1993) was a labor union organizer and spokesperson of the poor. Born in Arizona, his family lost their farm when he was just 10 years old; they became migrant workers in California, where farm production—particularly of grape crops—depended on the temporary laborers. Chavez knew the migrant worker's life intimately, and as a young man he began working to improve conditions for his people. In 1962 he organized California grape pickers into the National Farm Workers Association. Four years later this union merged with another to form the United Farm Workers Organizing Committee, or UFWOC (the name was changed to the United Farm Workers of America, or UFW, in 1973). An impassioned speaker known for squishing bunches of grapes in his hands as he delivered his messages, Chavez went on to lead a nationwide boycott of table grapes, since growers had refused to accept the collective bargaining of the UFWOC. By the close of the 1970s, California growers of all crops had accepted the migrant workers' union, now called the United Farm Workers. Like Martin Luther King Jr., Chavez maintained that nonviolent protest was the key to achieving change.

COUNTERCULTURE AND CONSUMERISM

What was the **beat movement**?

The post-World War II era bred unprecedented prosperity and an uneasy pace in the United States. Out of this environment rose the beat generation, alienated youths who rejected society's new materialism and threw off its "square" attitudes to reinvent

Vietnam War protesters gather on 5th Avenue in New York City in 1968.

"cool." The beat generation of the 1950s bucked convention, embraced iconoclasm, and attracted attention. Mainstream society viewed them as anarchists and degenerates. But many American youths listened to and read the ideas of its leaders, including writers Allen Ginsberg, Jack Kerouac (whose novel *On the Road,* 1957, was the bible of the Beat movement), William Burroughs, and Lawrence Ferlinghetti. The "beatniks," as they were dubbed by their critics, believed in peace, civil rights, and radical protest as a vehicle for change. They also embraced drugs, mystical (Eastern) religions, and sexual freedom—all controversial ideas during the postwar era. Beat writers and artists found their homes in communities like San Francisco's North Beach, Los Angeles's Venice Beach, and New York City's Greenwich Village. The movement merged—or some would argue, gave birth to—the counterculture movements of the 1960s, including the hippies. Beat literature is the movement's legacy.

Who were the **hippies**?

Most hippies of the 1960s and 1970s were young (15 to 25 years old), white, and from middle-class families. The counterculture (antiestablishment) movement advocated peace, love, and beauty. Having dropped out (of modern society) and tuned in (to their own feelings), these flower children were as well known for their political and social beliefs as they were for their controversial lifestyle: They opposed American involvement in the Vietnam War (1954-75) and rejected an industrialized society that seemed to care only about money; they favored personal simplicity, sometimes living in small communes where possessions and work were shared, or living an itinerant lifestyle, in which day-to-day responsibilities were few if any; they wore tattered jeans and bright clothing usually of natural fabrics, grew their hair, braided beads into their locks, walked around barefoot or in sandals, and listened to a new generation of artists including the Beatles, the Grateful Dead, Jefferson Airplane, Bob Dylan, and Joan Baez. Some hippies were also known for their drug use: Experimenting with marijuana and LSD, some hoped to gain profound insights or even achieve salvation through the drug experience—something hippie guru Timothy Leary told them was possible. New York City's East Village and San Francisco's Haight-Ashbury neighborhood became havens of the counterculture. The movement began on American soil, but was soon embraced elsewhere as well—principally Canada and Great Britain.

What happened to the hippies? The conflict in Vietnam ended, flower children grew older, drugs took their toll on some, and by 1980 there was no such thing as free love. Still, a few continued to lead an alternative lifestyle, while at the opposite end of the spectrum others bought back into the establishment. Still others adapted their flower-child beliefs to the ever-changing world around them and got on with their lives, working at jobs and raising children in the most socially and politically conscious way possible.

What are **"Nader's Raiders"**?

They were (and are) investigators working with American lawyer and consumer advocate Ralph Nader (1934-). With the help of his research team, Nader wrote the landmark work *Unsafe at Any Speed* in 1965; it charged that many automobiles weren't as safe as they should be or as consumers had the right to expect them to be. In part the book was responsible for passage in 1966 of the National Traffic and Motor Vehicle Safety Act, which set motor vehicle safety standards. Nader has continued his watchdog work, founding the Public Citizen organization, which researches consumer products, promotes consumer awareness, and works to influence legislators to improve consumer safety.

While Nader may be the most recognizable face of consumer advocacy, the movement's roots predate his activism. As the consumer age dawned at the end of the 1800s and early 1900s, when mass-production techniques came into wide use, some observers decried industry standards (or lack thereof) that put the public who used their products at risk. The muckraking journalists of the early twentieth century disclosed harmful or careless practices of early industry, raising awareness and bringing about needed reforms. Upton Sinclair (1878-1968), for example, penned the highly influential novel *The Jungle* (1906), revealing scandalous conditions of meat-packing plants. The public was outraged; upon reading Sinclair's work, President Theodore Roosevelt (1858-1919) ordered an investigation. Finding the novelist's descriptions to be true to life, government moved quickly to pass the Pure Food and Drug Act and the Meat Inspection Act that same year (1906). Industry watchdogs continued their work in the early decades of the century: In 1929 Consumers' Research Inc. was founded, and in 1936, the Consumers Union was formed; both of these independent organizations test and rate consumer products. (Consumers Union publishes its reports in the monthly magazine *Consumer Reports.*)

Such consumer advocacy has served to heighten public awareness, compelling industry to make changes and improving the safety of products in general. Abuses still occur, but at roughly 100 years into the consumer age, the work of consumer watchdogs like Nader's Raiders has made the consumer experience far less risky than it once was.

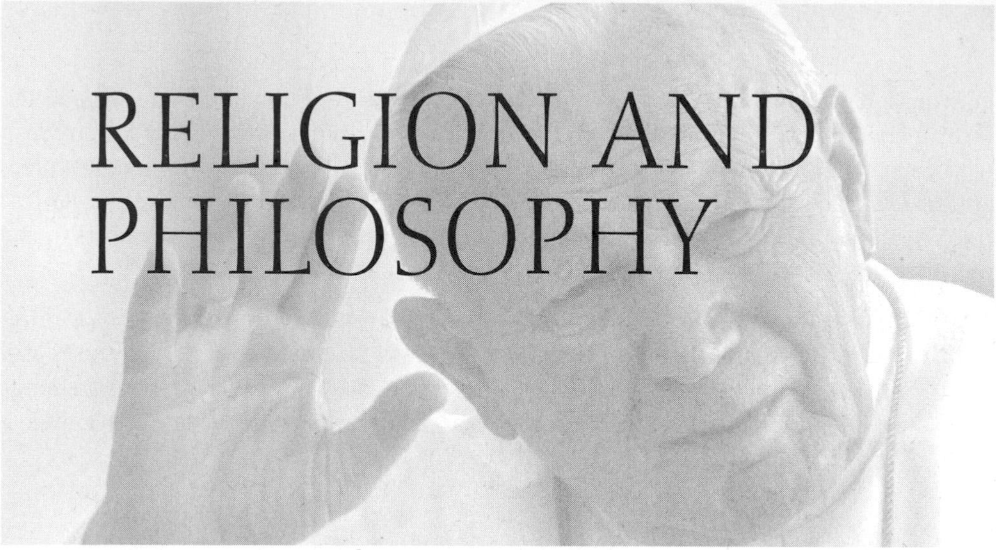

RELIGION AND PHILOSOPHY

RELIGION

How are **religions classified**?

Religion, which is a system of beliefs that usually centers on whatever is beyond the known or the natural, is commonly divided between elementary forms and higher religions.

Some elementary forms, or "traditional religions," are animism (the belief in spirits in nature or in natural objects), ancestor worship (revering the spirits of the dead), and totemism (belief in a mystical relationship between a group of people and an emblem). Animists might believe in spirits living in the sea or in the mountains. Believers in ancestor worship will both honor and fear the spirits of dead family members—for if they are neglected by the living, these spirits are believed to be able to bring harm to their descendants. Within clans, some tribal peoples adopt totems, such as a lion or a turtle. Totemists will be careful throughout their lives not to harm the animal or object that serves as their clan's emblem.

Higher religions are those that embody a concept of transcendence. Higher religions are classified as polytheistic (believing in many gods), dualistic (believing in equally powerful gods of good and evil), monotheistic (believing in one god), and pantheistic (believing in god as the forces and laws of the universe, or the worship of all gods). Religions are further classified as revealed or nonrevealed. Revealed religions are those that followers know through divine agency; both Christianity and Islam are revealed religions. Nonrevealed religions, such as Buddhism, Brahmanism, or Taoism, are known only through inquiry.

What did **ancient civilizations believe**?

In the absence of scientific knowledge, ancient civilizations—including the Greeks, the Romans, the Egyptians, the Aztecs, and the Mayas—created mythologies to explain origination (how they came into existence as a people); the existence of good and evil; the natural cycle of the seasons; weather; and the motions of the sun, the moon, and the stars. Such natural phenomena were explained by a body of stories that centered around gods, goddesses, and heroes.

For example, the Romans, who largely adapted Greek mythology, believed that gods and goddesses had power not only over agriculture, but also over all aspects of life. They worshiped Ceres as the goddess of the harvest, Vesta as the goddess of the hearth and home, and Jupiter (who later became their supreme god and protector) as the god of the weather. These gods are traced to the Greek beliefs in Demeter as the goddess of the harvest and of fertility, Hestia as the goddess of the hearth (she symbolized security and happiness), and Zeus—the supreme Greek god who was believed to rule from his court on Mount Olympus, and was a symbol for power, rule, and law. The ancient Greeks were also the source of what is perhaps one of the most well known myths of western civilization: Pandora's box. They believed that all that is bad or evil was once enclosed in a box, which was opened by Pandora (who, according to Greek mythology, was the first woman on Earth), releasing evil into the world. Greek mythology was preserved in the works of the poets Homer (c. 850-? B.C.) and Hesiod (c. 800 B.C.).

Other frequently studied mythologies include the Vedic (Indian), Egyptian, and Mesopotamian.

What are the basic **beliefs of Buddhism**?

Buddha taught the Four Noble Truths: existence is suffering; the cause of suffering is desire; through total transcendence (called nirvana) one may suspend suffering; and to end suffering one must follow a certain path—called the Eightfold Noble Path. The path prescribes moral conduct, specifically: 1) knowing the truth; 2) resolving to resist evil; 3) using speech properly—so as not to hurt others; 4) demonstrating respect for life, morality, and property through ones actions; 5) working in a job that does not harm others; 6) making an effort to free one's mind of evil; 7) mindfulness (or controlling one's thoughts and feelings); and 8) concentration. In some places, the beliefs and practices of Buddhism are combined with those of Hinduism and the Shinto religion.

Who is the **Dalai Lama**?

The Dalai Lama is the spiritual leader of Lamaism, a Buddhist sect in Tibet. The title, first bestowed on a Lamaist leader in 1578, translates as "teacher whose wisdom is great as the ocean." The title has been bestowed 13 times since: Followers believe that the Dalai Lama is continually reborn. Monks go in search of a young boy who was born at about the same time as the Dalai Lama died. They seek other signs of continuity as well before identifying the "new" Dalai Lama, who the monks educate and train to assume the leadership role.

The Dalai Lama, pictured in December 2004, was awarded the Nobel peace prize in 1989 for his nonviolent efforts to free Tibet from China.

What is **Zen**?

Also called Zen Buddhism, it is a sect of Buddhism practiced predominately in Japan and China. The religion is based on meditation rather than on the strict moral doctrine of Buddhism. It was founded in China in the fifth century A.D. by Bodhidharma, an Indian Buddhist monk and missionary. He taught that sudden enlightenment can be achieved through the practice of meditation (or "wall-gazing"). The religion defines enlightenment as the direct seeing of one's original nature.

What is **Hinduism**?

Hinduism, an ancient religion that originated about 1500 B.C. and developed over thousands of years, encompasses the beliefs and practices of the numerous religious sects of India. Each sect has its own philosophy and form of worship. It is a polytheistic religion—believing in many gods as well as in one great god, or universal spirit, called Brahman. Hindu doctrine is centered on sacred scriptures including the Veda, which includes the Upanishads (dialogues describing sacrificial rituals and religious ceremonies), the Puranas (stories about Hindu gods and goddesses), and the Mahabharata, which contains the Bhagavad Gita (or "the Song of the Lord," in which the god Krishna discusses the meaning of life with a warrior-prince on the eve of battle). Hindus worship alone at temples, which are dedicated to divinities. Followers also practice yoga, believing that it leads to knowledge and union with God.

What is **Shinto**?

Shinto is the dominant religion of Japan. Its traditions call for the reverence of ancestors, prayer, and the observance of rituals. It is polytheistic, believing in many gods (kami), who are thought to be the forces behind nature as well as behind human conditions such as sickness, healing, and creativity. Followers of the Shinto religion believe these spirits are housed in shrines. Private shrines are erected in homes while public shrines can be highly elaborate, including multiple buildings as well as gardens. The latter are the goals of many religious pilgrimages; pilgrims pray and make offerings (of money and flowers) to the spirits.

Originating in Japan in ancient times, Shinto has an interesting modern history: In 1882 religious organizations were divided into two groups—state shrines and sectarian shrines. State Shinto was controlled by the government, which went so far as to proclaim divine origins for the Japanese emperor. After World War II (1939-45), state Shinto crumbled and Emperor Hirohito (1901-1989) was compelled to renounce his divinity. Sectarian Shinto religion still thrives in Japan today, where it has more than 3 million followers.

Jews and Christians consider the Ten Commandments to be the summary of divine law, handed down by God to the prophet Moses.

What is the difference between the **Hebrew Bible** and the **Old Testament**?

The Hebrew Bible is made up of 24 books. The Old Testament used by Christians consists of the same books as those of the Hebrew Bible, but they are arranged differently and many books are divided, resulting in more books in the Old Testament than in the Hebrew Bible.

Among Christians, the Old Testament varies between Protestantism and Roman Catholicism: Protestants include 39 books in the Old Testament while Roman Catholics add seven books, called the Apocrypha, to their version, for a total of 46 books. The books of the Apocrypha resemble those of the Old Testament, but since they were written later than most of the Old Testament (probably 300 B.C.-A.D. 70), both Protestants and Jews treat them separately. The Bibles used by all three religions—Judaism, Roman Catholicism, and Protestantism—begin with the same seven books: Genesis, Exodus, Leviticus, Numbers, Deuteronomy, Joshua, and Judges. The first five of these were written by Moses.

What are the **Dead Sea Scrolls**?

The scrolls are ancient manuscripts of great historical and religious importance. They were found in dry riverbed caves on the northwestern side of the Dead Sea (a salt lake situated between Israel, the West Bank, and Jordan). More than 800 scrolls have been found, with the most famous discoveries made in 1947. The Dead Sea Scrolls were found miles apart at a number of different sites, including Khirbat Qumran in the West Bank (formerly Israel). The texts date to different centuries but include fragments of every book of the Hebrew Bible (or Old Testament) except the Book of Esther. Some texts are almost identical to Bible texts used today, showing that much of the Old Testament is the same as it was 2,000 years ago.

Why is the **Exodus from Egypt** so well known?

The Exodus of the Jews from Egypt, an event recorded in the Bible and corroborated by historical evidence, is well known to Jews and non-Jews alike, since the event, which Jews commemorate with Passover, came to symbolize departure from oppressive conditions, for the Israelites had been enslaved in Egypt.

According to the Bible (the Old Testament books of Genesis and Exodus), the ancestors of the Israelites had settled in the Nile River Delta of Egypt 430 years before the Exodus, or about the seventeenth century B.C. A change of dynasty caused the Israelites, because of their growing numbers, to be looked upon with hostility. They were put to work as state serfs in the construction of cities.

The biblical account tells about a series of confrontations between Ramses II, the pharaoh of Egypt, and the prophet Moses, who had been commissioned by God to lead his people to the Promised Land. The pharaoh refused to allow the Israelites to leave Egypt but was later convinced, through a series of divine signs including the Ten Plagues, to permit them to go. The flight from Egypt and the Promised Land have come to symbolize freedom and the realization of hopes.

What were the **Ten Plagues**?

The Ten Plagues were delivered by God to the people of Egypt as a way of convincing the pharaoh that he was to let the Israelites go—so Moses could lead them out of bondage and into the Promised Land. The plagues were, in the order described in Exodus: 1) water turned into blood, 2) frogs, 3) gnats, 4) flies, 5) pestilence, 6) boils, 7) hail, 8) locusts, 9) darkness, and 10) death of the firstborn. It was not until the Tenth Plague had been delivered that the pharaoh agreed to let the Israelites leave.

What are the **Ten Commandments**?

Also called the Decalogue, the Ten Commandments appear in the Bible in the book of Exodus (20:2-17) and in the book of Deuteronomy (5:6-21). They are considered the summary of divine law as handed down by God to Moses, who not only heard them but received them in the form of writing on two stone tablets as he stood atop Mount Sinai (what is known today as Gebel Musa, on Egypt's Sinai Peninsula), where he had been summoned by God.

According to the Bible, the commandments, which are paramount in the ethical systems of Judaism and Christianity, are these: 1) Do not have any other god besides the Lord God; 2) Do not have or worship idols (carved images); 3) Do not make wrong use of the name of the Lord your God (or, do not take the name of the Lord in vain); 4) Keep the Sabbath day holy; 5) Honor your mother and your father; 6) Do not commit murder; 7) Do not commit adultery; 8) Do not steal; 9) Do not give false evidence against your neighbor; and 10) Do not covet your neighbor's household or lust after your neighbor's spouse.

People sometimes see the Ten Commandments as divided into two groups: the first group covers the relationship between people and God and the second covers relationships among people.

What is the **Ark of the Covenant**?

According to Judeo-Christian tradition, the Ark of the Covenant is a decorative box that holds the tablets containing the Ten Commandments, also called the Law. The Ark was constructed by skilled craftsmen in Sinai; it was made exactly to God's specifications, which are first mentioned in the Bible in Exodus 25:10-22. The Israelites carried the Ark with them into the Promised Land, where King Solomon (tenth century B.C.) built a permanent temple to house it. When the Babylonians captured Jerusalem in 586 B.C., the Ark was either destroyed or taken. If it survived, its location is a mystery that has intrigued scholars and archeologists, as well as popular culture. However, some scholars believe the Ark never really existed.

Why did people first believe that **Jesus of Nazareth** was **the Messiah**?

In his lifetime, Jesus of Nazareth (c. 6 B.C.-c. A.D. 30) was believed to be the Messiah for many reasons. These reasons are explained in detail in the New Testament, particularly in the four Gospels, Matthew, Mark, Luke, and John.

First, Jesus was thought to have been miraculously conceived by Mary, a virgin. In Luke 2:8-20, an angel is described as having spoken to shepherds tending their fields, telling them that "in this night in the city of David, a Savior is born unto you...a Messiah, the Lord," and goes on to say that the sign (of the Messiah) is that they will find a baby wrapped in swaddling clothes. Also in Luke (2:36-38), a prophetess arrives and proclaims Mary's baby to be the "child to all who were looking for the liberation of the Jews."

Further, Jesus proclaimed himself to be the Son of God (as described, for example, in John 5:17-23). He demonstrated extraordinary healing powers, used parables to teach moral and spiritual ways, and carried a message of God's redeeming love. All of this was convincing enough that many—mostly the common people—became disciples, or followers, of Christ during his lifetime.

Why was Jesus feared by the authorities?

There were two reasons Jesus (c. 6 B.C.-c. A.D. 30) was feared by Palestine's leaders. First, as an advocate of the poor, he was an outspoken critic of the privileged as well as of Palestine's oppressive Roman rulers. (Palestine was part of the Roman province of Syria during the lifetime of Jesus.) Jesus openly accused the ruling class of hypocrisy and injustices. Second, some feared that if Jesus was the Messiah, he would lead a revolution. So the governors viewed him and his teachings as a threat to their authority.

Who were **the apostles**?

The apostles were 12 men chosen by Jesus Christ (c. 6 B.C.-c. A.D. 30) to be his close followers. The apostles helped spread the word that they believed Jesus to be the Son of God. Matthew 10:1 explains that Jesus gave the 12 authority to drive out unclean spirits and to cure every kind of illness.

In Matthew 10:2-4, the names of the 12 apostles are given as Simon Peter (who is later simply called Peter), Andrew, James, John, Philip, Bartholomew, Thomas, Matthew, James the son of Alphaeus, Thaddaeus, Simon the Zealot, and Judas Iscariot. But the lists of apostles found in Luke 6:13-16 and in Acts 1:13 differ from that found in Matthew. While both Luke and Acts cite (Simon) Peter, Andrew, James, John, Philip, Bartholomew, Thomas, Matthew, James the son of Alphaeus, Simon the Zealot, and Judas Iscariot, they do not name Thaddaeus, but rather Judas the son of James. In other words, the lists agree on 11 of the 12 names.

After Judas Iscariot betrayed Jesus Christ, Matthias was chosen by the apostles to take his place (this is described in Acts 1:21-26). He was considered eligible since, like the 11 remaining apostles, he accompanied Jesus from the time of Jesus's baptism until "the day he was taken up from us."

What is **Golgotha**?

Golgotha is the Hebrew name for Calvary, the site on a hillside outside ancient Jerusalem where Jesus Christ (c. 6 B.C.-c. A.D. 30) was crucified. Though the exact site is unknown, it is believed to be where the church of the Holy Sepulcher is located.

How old is **Islam**?

Islam, one of the world's largest religions, originated with the teachings of the prophet Muhammad (c. 570-632) during the early 600s. Muhammad was born in Mecca (in present-day Saudi Arabia) and was orphaned at the age of six. He was raised by relatives, who trained him as a merchant. When he was 25 years old he married a wealthy widow, Khadijah, who bore him several children. In about 610, Muhammad began having visions in which he was called upon by God (Allah). More than 600 of these visions were written down, becoming the sacred text known as the Koran (or Qur'an). By 613 Muhammad had attracted followers with his messages of one God, Allah's power, the duty of worship and generosity, and the doctrine of the last judgment. Followers of this new religion became known as Muslims, an Arabic word meaning "those who submit" (to Allah); and the religion itself became known as Islam (meaning submission).

Today, there are Muslims in every part of the world, but the largest Muslim communities are in the Middle East, North Africa, Indonesia, Bangladesh, Pakistan, India, and central Asia. Additionally, most of the people of Turkey and Albania are Muslim. It is the world's second-largest religion (after Christianity).

Who wrote the **Koran**?

The Koran (or Qur'an) contains the holy scriptures of Islam and was written by the followers of the prophet Muhammad (c. 570-632). It is not known whether these texts were written down during Muhammad's lifetime or after his death. It is known that the texts were codified (organized into a body) between 644 and 656. Muslims believe the angel Gabriel revealed the book to Muhammad, beginning in 610 and continuing until the prophet's death in 632. The Koran, meaning "recitation," consists of 114 verses (*ayas*) that are organized in chapters (*suras*).

Muslims believe the beautiful prose of the Koran to be the words of God himself, who spoke through Muhammad. Further, it is believed to be only a copy of an eternal book, which is kept by Allah. The Koran is also held up by Muslims as proof that Muhammad was indeed a prophet since no human is capable of composing such text. Among the most widely read texts today, the Koran is also taught orally so that even Muslims who are illiterate may know and be able to recite verses.

When did the **Sunni and Shiah sects of Islam** form?

It was during the 600s, not long after Muhammad's death, when Muslims split into two main divisions: Sunni and Shiah.

Sunnite Muslims, who account for most of the Islamic world today, believe that Islamic leadership passes to caliphs (temporal and spiritual leaders) who are selected from the prophet Muhammad's tribe.

The Shiites believe, however, that the true leaders of Islam descend from Ali (c. 600-661), Muhammad's cousin and the husband of Muhammad's daughter, Fatimah (called the Shining One; c. 616-633). Ali, who was the fourth caliph (656-61), is revered by Shiites as the rightful successor to the prophet Muhammad and are led by his descendants.

Shiites form the largest subgroup, but there are other sects within Islam as well: the Wahhabi Muslims are a puritanical sect; the Baha'is emerged from the Shiites; and the Ismaili Khoja Muslims have been in existence almost from the beginning of Islam. While Islamic practices may vary somewhat among the sects, all Islamic people uphold the Five Pillars of Faith.

What are Islam's **Five Pillars of Faith**?

Muslims practice adherence to the Five Pillars of Faith: 1) belief in Allah as the only God and Muhammad as his prophet; 2) prayer five times daily—at dawn, at noon, in the afternoon, in the evening, and at nightfall; 3) giving alms to the poor; 4) fasting from dawn until dusk during the holy month of Ramadan); and 5) making the pilgrimage (*hajj*) to the holy city of Mecca at least once during their lifetime.

Hajj pilgrims pray during the annual Muslim pilgrimage to the holy city of Mecca, 2002.

Why is **Mecca** a holy city for Muslims?

Mecca, in western Saudi Arabia, is the birthplace of the prophet Muhammad (c. 570) and was his home until the year 622, when those who opposed him forced him to flee to Medina (a city about 200 miles north of Mecca). Muhammad later returned to Mecca and died there in 632.

Mecca is also the site of the Great Mosque, which is situated in the heart of the city. The outside of the mosque is an arcade, made up of a series of arches enclosing a courtyard. In that courtyard is the most sacred shrine of Islam, the Kaaba (or Caaba), a small stone building that contains the Black Stone, which Muslims believe was sent from heaven by Allah (God).When Muslims pray (five times a day, according to the Five Pillars of Faith), they face the Kaaba. It is also the destination of the *hajj,* or pilgrimage.

What were **the Crusades**?

The Crusades were a series of nine Christian military expeditions that took place during the end of the eleventh century and throughout the twelfth and thirteenth centuries. The stated goal of the Crusades was to recover from the Muslims the Holy Land of Palestine, where Jesus Christ (c. 6 B.C.-A.D. 30) lived. The word crusade comes from the Latin word *crux* meaning "cross," and Crusaders were said to have "taken up the cross."

The Crusades began with an impassioned sermon given by Pope Urban II (c. 1035-1099) at Clermont, France, in November 1095. Earlier that year Byzantine emperor Alexius I Comnenus (1048-1118) had appealed to Urban for aid in fighting back the fierce Seljuk Turks. (The Seljuk Turks preceded the Ottoman Turks; the Seljuks were named for their traditional founder, Seljuq). Seeing the expansion of the Turks, who were Muslim, as a threat to Christianity, the Pope agreed to help. Not only did Urban rally support for the Byzantines in staving off the further advances of the Turks, he also advocated that the Holy Lands should be recovered from them. While the Arab Muslims who had previously controlled the Holy Land had allowed Christians to visit there, the Turks tolerated no such thing. Urban feared that if Palestine were not recovered, Christians would lose access to their holy places altogether.

But Urban also viewed the Crusades as a way of unifying western Europe: The feudal nobility there had long fought against each other. He believed a foreign war would unite them behind a common cause as Christians. Further, he hoped the Crusades would unite western with eastern (Byzantine) Europe behind one goal. If successful, the expeditions would also expand the pope's moral authority across a greater region.

En route from Clermont to Constantinople (present-day Istanbul, Turkey), where the Crusade was set to begin in August 1096, Urban continued to preach his message—at Limoges, Poitiers, Tours, Aquitaine, and Toulouse, France. The message found broad appeal, even if it appealed to something other than the people's religious sensibilities. Some of those who answered Urban's call took up arms not for the Christian cause, but for their own personal gain such as acquiring more land, expanding trade, or recovering religious relics. Many peasants "took up the cross" to escape hardships— in 1094 northern France and the Rhineland had been the site of flooding and pestilence, which was followed in 1095 by drought and famine.

The First Crusade actually turned into two. A Peasants' Crusade (which had never been Urban's intent) had gone ahead of the official expedition, and many lives were lost. It ended in failure. But the planned expedition, called the Crusade of Princes, ultimately succeeded in capturing Jerusalem in 1099. Western Christian feudal states were established at Edessa, Antioch, and Tripoli—all of which were placed under the authority of the Kingdom of Jerusalem. But Urban did not live to see the recovery of the Holy Land. And the Christian hold on Palestine was not to last, as the Muslims refused to give up the fight for control of lands they too considered to be holy. The Second (1147-49), Third (1189-92), Fourth (1202-04), Fifth (1217-21), Sixth (1228-29), Seventh (1248-54), and Eighth (1270) Crusades were prompted by a mix of religious, political, and social circumstances. The Crusades ended in 1291—almost 200 years after they had started—when the city of Acre, the last Christian stronghold in Palestine, fell to the Muslims, ending Christian rule in the East.

Yet another crusade, in 1212, was particularly tragic: Called the Children's Crusade, the expedition was led by a young visionary who had rallied French and German children to believe they could recover Jerusalem—since, as poor and faithful servants, they would have God on their side. As the children marched south across Europe, many of them died even before reaching the Mediterranean coast. Some believe that the Crusade was sabotaged, resulting in the children being sold into slavery in the East.

How many popes have there been?

The number given by the Vatican is 265, including Pope Benedict XVI, the former German cardinal who was elected on April 19, 2005, to succeed John Paul II (1920-2005). (Other lists cite 266 popes; the discrepancy arises around Stephen II, who died in 752 after he was elected but before he could be consecrated.) Except for a few brief interruptions when the papacy was vacant, the Roman Catholic Church has been led by the pope as its visible head (and Jesus Christ as its invisible head) since Jesus said to the apostle Peter: "And I say also unto thee, That thou art Peter, and upon / this rock I will build my church; and the gates of hell / shall not prevail against it" (Matthew 16:18).

The apostle Peter—who was earlier called Simon and is also called Simon Peter—became the leader of the Christian community after the crucifixion of Christ, and he made Jerusalem the headquarters of his preaching in Palestine. According to second-century sources, Peter traveled to Rome about 55 A.D. and became the city's first bishop. During the persecution of Christians under Roman emperor Nero (37-68 A.D.), Peter was crucified on Vatican Hill in the year 64. He died a martyr and was canonized. St. Peter's Church, the principal church of the Christian world, is said to have been built over Peter's burial place. These events in Rome during St. Peter's time long after gave the city special status within the church. It further established the site of the papal palace in Vatican City, which is an independent state that lies within the city of Rome. And the majority of popes (all but 18) have been Italian: When John Paul II, who was born in Poland, was elected pope in 1978, he was the first non-Italian pope since 1523.

What was the controversy with **Thomas Becket**?

Archbishop of Canterbury Thomas Becket (c. 1118-1170) was killed by knights in the service of England's King Henry II (1133-1189); he had refused to be subservient to the monarch. In the long struggle between church and state, the story of St. Thomas Becket is a dramatic chapter. Born in London in about 1118, when he was in his twenties Becket entered into service for the archbishop of Canterbury, the spiritual head of the Church of England. He subsequently held various church offices, including archdeacon. When Henry II was coronated in 1154, becoming the worldly leader of the Church of England, he found in Becket one of his most vigorous champions. In 1162 Henry made him archbishop of Canterbury. But a transformation soon occurred in

Thomas Becket, who put his spiritual duties first and began defending the church against the king's power. Henry, eager to increase royal authority, was determined to regain control over the church. A bitter struggle ensued between the two former friends. At one point, Becket fled the country because he was in fear for his life. When he returned to England six years later (in 1170), he renewed his opposition to the king, but nevertheless forced a reconciliation with him. Henry was still irked by Becket's open defiance to his authority, and he suggested to his knights that one among them might be brave enough to do away with him, ending the king's troubles. Four knights took the king at his word, and on December 29, 1170, they found Becket in Canterbury Cathedral and killed him as he made his evening prayers. Henry later did penance for the crime; Becket was canonized three years later.

What caused the **East-West schism in the Catholic Church**?

During the Middle Ages (500-1350) cultural, geographical, and even political differences caused an increasingly wide divide between East (the Catholic churches in eastern and southeastern Europe, as well as in parts of western Asia) and West (the Catholic churches of western Europe). In the 800s a series of theological disputes began between the highest authority of the Eastern (Byzantine) churches, called the patriarch of Constantinople (also called the ecumenical patriarch), and the pope—particularly about the pope's authority over Christians in the East. Finally, in 1054, Pope Leo IX (1002-1054) issued an anathema (a formal curse) against the patriarch of Constantinople, Michael Cerularius (c. 1000-1059), excommunicating him and his followers from the Roman Catholic Church. The church had officially split. Thereafter the Eastern Orthodox churches would accept the patriarch of Constantinople as the highest church authority (in other words, they did not acknowledge the primacy of the pope) and they would follow the Byzantine rite (ceremonies); in the West, Roman Catholics followed the Latin rite and continued to regard the pope as the Holy Father.

When the Ottoman Empire captured Constantinople (present-day Istanbul, Turkey) in 1453, Orthodox Christians in the East came under Muslim rule; this lasted into the 1800s. Though there are still differences between the Eastern Orthodox churches (the Greek Orthodox church, the Russian Orthodox church, etc.) and the Roman Catholic Church today, the rift between them was healed in 1964 when Pope Paul VI (1897-1978) met with Ecumenical Patriarch Athenagoras I (1886-1972) in Jerusalem. The following year, the two religious leaders lifted the mutual anathemas between their churches.

What was the **Reformation**?

It was a religious movement in Europe during the sixteenth and seventeenth centuries. It fomented inside the Catholic Church as people began questioning the church's doctrines, practices, and authority. While the movement was preceded by a swelling dissatisfaction with the church, the Reformation was officially, and some would say abruptly, begun in October 1517 when German monk and theology professor Martin Luther (1483-1546) nailed his Ninety-Five Theses to the door of the Castle Church at Wittenberg (Saxony, Germany), launching an attack on the church. The movement continued through the Thirty Years' War (1618-48). And though the resolution to that conflict brought about a measure of religious stability in Europe, the force of the Reformation did not end there. Both the freedom of dissent and the Protestantism people know today are the byproducts of the movement.

What was the importance of Martin Luther's **Ninety-Five Theses**?

The Reformation as a movement began on October 31, 1517, when the German monk and theology professor Martin Luther (1483-1546) nailed his Ninety-Five Theses to the door of the Castle Church at Wittenburg (Saxony, Germany). The theses (which are arguments or assertions) questioned the value of indulgences (the pardons that were disseminated by the church) and condemned the sale of them. Luther had already begun to preach the doctrine of salvation by faith rather than by works, and during 1518 he went on to publicly defend his beliefs, which were in direct opposition to the church. The following year he expanded his argument against the church by denying the supremacy of the pope.

In 1521 Pope Leo X (1475-1521) declared Luther a heretic and excommunicated him. Ordered to appear before the Diet of Worms in April 1521, Luther refused to retract his statements of his beliefs, saying, "Unless I am convinced by the testimony of the Scriptures or by clear reason...I am bound by the Scriptures I have quoted and my conscience is captive to the Word of God." The following month, Holy Roman Emperor Charles V (1500-1558) issued the Edict of Worms, declaring Luther to be an outlaw and authorizing his death. But the Prince of Saxony, known by history as Frederick the Wise (1463-1525), saw fit to protect Luther, whom he had appointed as a faculty member at the University of Wittenberg (founded by Frederick the Wise in 1502). There Luther translated the New Testament into German and undertook a translation of the entire Bible. Luther continued the Protestant movement until his death in 1546.

What was the **Counter Reformation**?

Also called the Catholic Reformation, it was the Roman Catholic Church's response to the Protestant Reformation of the sixteenth century. Some parishioners and members of the Roman Catholic clergy had already been calling for reforms within the church for more than two centuries when in 1517 German monk and theology professor Martin Luther (1483-1546) nailed his Ninety-Five Theses to the door of the Castle Church at Wittenberg (Saxony, Germany). His theses attacked the doctrines and authority of the church, sparking the Reformation. The movement's leaders, called Protestants because they protested against the Catholic Church, changed the religious landscape

What was the Diet of Worms?

In 1521 a diet, which is another word for an imperial council or an assembly of princes, was convened at Worms, situated on the Rhine River in Germany. This particular meeting had been called by Holy Roman Emperor Charles V (1500-1558) to consider the crisis that had been brought on by the Reformation. Since Martin Luther (1483-1546) was instrumental in both igniting the movement and furthering its causes, he was called before the diet to testify and defend himself. But the religious leader refused to yield his stance; he vowed to continue to make his argument against the church. He closed his statement with these famous words: "Here I stand. I cannot do otherwise. God help me. Amen."

The result of this was that on May 25 the Edict of Worms was issued, declaring Martin Luther an outlaw. However, Luther sought refuge in the protection of Frederick the Wise, and the edict itself served only to galvanize the cause of the reformers.

of Europe by creating new Christian churches. But a movement to make changes inside the Catholic Church also began. The turning point came in 1534 when Paul III (1468-1549) became pope. Realizing that the church must respond to what it viewed as a religious crisis, Pope Paul convened the Council of Trent (in Italy), which was charged with reviewing all aspects of religious life. The ecumenical group met from 1545 to 1547, 1551 to 1552, and 1562 to 1563, and out of those deliberations emerged the modern Catholic Church. The Counter Reformation was aided by a group of priests and brothers known as the Jesuits, members of the Society of Jesus, a religious order of the Roman Catholic Church. The Jesuits were instrumental in spreading the word of the reforms and in promoting a new spirit within the Catholic Church.

Who are the **Jesuits**?

The Jesuits are members of a Roman Catholic religious order called the Society of Jesus. The group was founded by Saint Ignatius of Loyola (1491-1556). Born into nobility as Iñigo de Oñaz y Loyola, the Spaniard became a knight in 1517. In that capacity he fought against the French in their siege 1521 of Pamplona, northeast of Madrid. But he was seriously wounded in the battle and retreated to a commune in northeast Spain from 1522 to 1523. There Ignatius heard a religious calling and subsequently undertook a pilgrimage to Jerusalem (1523 to 1524). Committed to a religious life, he embarked on a program of disciplined writing and study in Spain and in Paris, France. Even before he was ordained in 1537, Ignatius had gained followers—the Spanish missionary Francis Xavier (1506-1552) among them. With his companions Ignatius founded the Society of Jesus in 1539; the religious order was approved by Pope Paul III (1468-1549) the following year. Jesuits are known for leading structured lives and for their self-discipline, commitment to the pope, and missionary work. They have a profound belief in education, and as such have long been leaders in learning and in the sciences. The order was suppressed in 1773 but restored in 1814.

What were the **results of the Reformation**?

The emergence of the Protestants (who got their name for protesting against the Catholic Church) was officially recognized by Holy Roman Emperor Charles V (1500-1558) with the Peace of Augsburg (1555), which granted the people the right to worship as Lutherans (the church named for reformer Martin Luther [1483-1546]). But the hostility between Catholic and Protestant countries erupted in 1618 with the Thirty Years' War. That series of conflicts, which had become increasingly political as it raged, was ended with the Peace of Westphalia, which, among other things, stipulated that Lutheranism and Calvinism (or Presbyterianism, founded by Frenchman John Calvin [1509-64]) be given the same due as Catholicism.

Through acts of state, both Catholicism and Protestantism took hold in Europe, with the northern countries, including those of Scandinavia, turning toward the new churches and the southern countries remaining Catholic. For the most part, the Reformation fostered an attitude of religious tolerance among Christians. However, conflict would continue (to the present day) in the British Isles: After Queen Elizabeth I (1533-1603) adopted a moderate form of Protestantism (called Anglicanism) as the official religion of England, English Protestants colonized Ulster (Northern) Ireland and in so doing gave rise to hostilities with their Irish-Catholic countrymen to the south.

For its part, the Catholic Church, too, underwent a period of reform (called the Counter Reformation), which rid the church of many of its pre-Reformation problems to emerge as a stronger religious body.

The Reformation had without question brought about greater religious freedom than had been known before. Among the churches that emerged during the Reformation are the Lutheran, the Anabaptist (ancestors to the Amish and Mennonite churches), the Presbyterian, the Episcopal, and the Congregational and Unitarian (formerly Puritan)—all of which have strong followings today, both in Europe and in North America, where they were established by the colonists.

Who were the **Puritans**?

The Puritans were members of a religious movement that began in England in the 1500s and lasted into the first half of the 1600s, when it spread to America as well. Influenced by the teachings of religious reformers John Wycliffe (c. 1330-1384) and John Calvin (1509-1564), the Puritans were so named because they wanted to "purify" the Anglican church (also known as the Church of England). They believed too much power rested with the church hierarchy (its priests, bishops, and cardinals), that the people (called the laity or lay members) should have more involvement in church matters, and that the ceremonies ought to be simplified to stress Bible reading and individual prayer. Further, they defied the authority of the pope, believing that each church congregation should have control of its own affairs, which should be guided by a church council (called a presbytery) made up of lay members.

These ideas are familiar to Americans today since they provided the basis not only for many Protestant churches but also influenced the formulation of U.S. government. When the Puritans faced persecution at home, they became religious pilgrims, traveling to the New World, where they established both their religious and social belief system.

What was the **Great Awakening**?

The Great Awakening was an American religious movement that began in New England in the mid-1730s. At its center were the fire-and-brimstone sermons delivered by charismatic preachers such as Congregational minister Jonathan Edwards (1703-1758) and Anglican missionary George Whitefield (1714-1770). Revivals were another cornerstone of the movement: These were evangelistic meetings that moved around the countryside, from Maine to Georgia, converting (or awakening) people to Christianity—not through the doctrines of the church, but rather through the individual's own experience. The theology of the Great Awakening was Calvinist, stressing the depravity of man and the sovereignty of God and promoting the belief that faith, and not conduct, is the road to salvation. In its emphasis on the individual and its espousal that the individual is the final arbiter of truth, the movement had a profound effect on the spiritual and political character of what would soon become the United States. Since many vehemently opposed the movement, it also served to divide churches between the revivalists and the traditionalists. Thus, it diversified American religious life and promoted religious tolerance.

How is **someone sainted**?

Criteria for sainthood (also called canonization) are leading a holy life, conducting miracles, and suffering or even dying because of one's faith (martyrdom). The Catholic Church keeps a list of saints, from which certain names were dropped in 1969 since their inclusion could not be justified by history.

PHILOSOPHY

What is **philosophy**?

From the Greek *philo,* meaning "love of," and *sophia,* meaning "wisdom," philosophy is literally a love of wisdom. In practice, it is the pursuit of understanding the human

Confucius was a highly revered Chinese philosopher who believed that the family is the model for all human relationships.

condition—how, why, and what it means to exist or *to be.* Philosophers use methods such as observation and questioning to discern the truth. Philosophy is traditionally divided between Eastern thought and Western thought. Further, Western thought consists of five branches: metaphysics (concerned with the nature of the universe or of reality); logic (the laws of reasoning); epistemology (the nature of knowledge and the process by which knowledge is gained); ethics (the moral values or rules that influence human conduct); and aesthetics (the nature of beauty or the criteria for art).

How old is **Taoism**?

It dates back to the sixth century B.C. when it was founded by Chinese philosopher Lao-tzu (c. 550 B.C.-?). Master Lao, as he was known, believed in inaction and simplicity, which he combined with religious practices to form the mystical philosophy of the Tao (Dao), the path of virtuous conduct. Lao-tzu reasoned that since humans face a "cloud of unknowability," they ought not to react to things at all: He viewed the world as a pendulum, with the Tao as its hinge. Anyone who struggles against the current of life is like an insect caught at the end of a pendulum—swinging back and forth, and suffering with each movement. But by crawling along the hinge (Tao) to reach the top, a place of complete stillness is found. Lao-tzu advised that people do away with their desires, avoiding that which is extreme, extravagant, or excessive, and steer clear of any competition. Many of these ideas are embodied in a work usually ascribed to him, *Tao-te Ching* (Classic of the Way of Power). However, modern scholars now believe that tome to be the work of his followers.

Taoism is still relevant to many today. When it was developed some 26 centuries ago, the philosophy filled a spiritual void that was not addressed by the practical doctrines of traditional Confucianism. One legend has it that Lao-tzu rebuked a young Confucius (551-479 B.C.) for his pride. The Tao also contributed greatly to Buddhism, especially in its emphasis on meditation and sudden enlightenment.

One of the great thinkers of the Chinese Taoist school was teacher and philosopher Chuang-tzu (fourth century B.C.), who constructed an nonpolitical, transcendental philosophy that promoted an individual's spiritual freedom. His self-titled work (*Chuang-tzu*) is another classic of Taosim.

Who was Confucius and who do people still quote him?

Confucius (551-479 B.C.) was a Chinese philosopher whose real name was K'ung Ch'iu; Confucius is the Latinized version. Born into a class of lesser nobility in the province of Lu, his father died before Confucius had turned three and he was raised in humble circumstances by his mother. He lived in the middle of China's feudal period, when there were enormous problems, including famine and poverty, which had been brought on by weak emperors and, consequently, chronic warfare among rival feudal states. Because of his upbringing, Confucius possessed a profound sympathy for the common people. In his view, the feudal princes, only interested in their own personal gain, were responsible for the suffering of the people. Confucius set out on a reform mission: Believing that good government can only be achieved by ethical leaders, Confucius endeavored to train a new generation of them. He taught literature and music (important in building character), conduct, and, most importantly, ethics, to anyone who wanted to learn. He is regarded as the first Chinese teacher to offer education freely, that is to say, to all comers, rather than just the privileged. The great philosopher is revered for his belief that the family is the model for all human relations. Confucianism regards the chief relations in life to be those between ruler and subject, father and son, elder and younger brother, husband and wife, and friends. Most importantly, he taught students that rulers are responsible for the happiness of their subjects. He believed that government leaders need not be expert administrators. Instead, they must be humane, honest, and above corruption and personal gain. Some of his students went on to hold positions of power in city governments.

Over the centuries, he became the most venerated person in Chinese history, but his teachings transcend cultural lines, which is why Confucian wisdom, including the principle "What you do not want done to yourself, do not do to others," is often quoted. The philosophy's maxims are set forth in the work *Lun-Yü* (Analects), recorded by his followers.

Why was **Socrates** condemned to death?

Socrates (c. 470-399 B.C.), the Greek philosopher who is credited, along with philosophers Plato (c. 428-347 B.C.) and Aristotle (384-322 B.C.), for laying the foundations of Western thought, had many followers in his own time. However, his ideas and methods were controversial, too, which led him to be tried before judges and sentenced to death, which he carried out by drinking hemlock (poison). He had been charged for not worshiping the Athenian gods and for corrupting the young.

Except for his time spent in military service, Socrates lived his entire life in Athens, where he was as well known for his disheveled appearance as for his moral integrity, self-control, and quest for wisdom. He lived during a time when attention was turning away from the physical world (of the heavens) and toward the human world (of the self, the community, and the law). He participated in this turning point by walking the streets of Athens, engaging people—including rulers who were supposed to be wiser than he—in conversation. In these conversations, he employed what came to be known as the "Socratic method" or dialectic, a series of seemingly simple questions designed to elicit a rational response. Through the line of questioning, which usually centered around a moral concept such as courage, the person being questioned was intended to realize that he did not truly know that which he thought he knew. Socrates's theory was that once the person being questioned realized his weak understanding, he could divest himself of false notions, and was then free to participate in the quest for knowledge. These philosophical "disputes," however, gained Socrates many enemies.

Though he left no writings, Socrates's student, Plato, documented his recollections of dialogues with his teacher. A staunch believer in self-examination and self-knowledge, Socrates is credited with saying that "the unexamined life is not worth living" (some ascribe the quote to Plato). Socrates also believed that the psyche (or "inner self") is what should give direction to one's life—not appetite or passions. A seminal figure in Greek (and Western) thought, philosophy that predates him is termed "pre-Socratic."

What was **Plato**'s relationship to Socrates and Aristotle?

The Athens-born Plato (originally, Aristocles) was Socrates's disciple and Aristotle's teacher. The philosophies of these three men combined to lay the foundations of Western thought.

With the death sentence of his spiritual guide, Socrates, in 399 B.C., Plato's (c. 428-347 B.C.) dissatisfaction with the Athenian government reached its peak. Traveling throughout the Mediterranean after the death of Socrates, Plato returned to Athens in 387 B.C., and one mile outside of the city he established the Academy, a school of philosophy supported entirely by philanthropists; students paid no fees. One of the pupils there was young Aristotle (384-322 B.C.), who remained at the Academy for 20 years before venturing out on his own.

Plato wrote a series of dialogues in which Socrates figures prominently. The most highly regarded of these is the *Republic,* in which Plato discusses justice and the ideal state. It was his belief that people would not be able to eliminate injustice from society until rulers became philosophers: "Until all philosophers are kings, or the kings and princes of this world have the spirit and power of philosophy, and political greatness and wisdom meet in one, and those commoner natures who pursue either to the exclusion of the other are compelled to stand aside, cities will never have rest from their evils—no, nor the human race." Also on the subject of the ideal state, Plato wrote but did not finish *Laws.* His other works include *Symposium,* which considers ideal love; *Phaedrus,* which attacks the prevailing notions about rhetoric; *Apology,* which is a rendering of the speech Socrates delivered at his own trial in 399 B.C.; and *Phaedo,* which discusses the immortality of the soul and which is supposed to be a record of Socrates's last conversation before he drank hemlock and died.

What is Plato's **theory of forms**?

The theory, or doctrine, of forms (also called the theory of ideas) is Greek philosopher Plato's (c. 428-347 B.C.) expression of his belief that there are forms that exist outside the material realm, and therefore are unchanging—they do not come into existence, change, or pass out of existence. It is these ideas that, according to Plato, are the objects or essence of knowledge. Further, he posited that the body, the seat of appetite and passion, which communes with the physical world (rather than the world of ideas or forms), is inferior to the intellect. He believed the physical aspect of human beings to be irrational while the intellect, or reason, was deemed to be rational.

The origins of Plato's theory can be traced to Socrates (c. 470-399 B.C.), who believed that the psyche (inner spirit) has intuitive access to divinely known principles or truths, which he attempted to formulate through his conversations with others. Indeed, the Socratic dialogues, written by Plato, reveal that Socrates was striving to define the exact nature of the traditional Greek moral virtues of piety, temperance, and courage.

Did **Aristotle develop his own philosophy**?

A student of Plato's for 20 years, Aristotle's ideas were unquestionably influenced by his teacher. However, Aristotle developed his own doctrine, which he applied to many subjects.

Aristotle rejected Plato's theory of forms (or theory of ideas). While Aristotle, too, believed in material (the physical being) and forms (the unchanging truths), unlike his teacher, he believed that it is the concrete (material) that has substantial being. Aristotle viewed the basic task of philosophy as explaining why and how things are, or how they become what they are. It is for this reason that Aristotle had not only a profound and lasting influence on philosophy but on scientific spirit.

What does **"epicurean"** mean?

While "epicurean" has come to refer to anything relating to the pleasure of eating and drinking, it is an oversimplification of the beliefs of the Greek philosopher Epicurus (341-270 B.C.), from whose name the word was derived. While Epicurus did believe that pleasure is the only good, and that it alone should be humankind's pursuit, later scholars misinterpreted the philosophy as a license for sensory excess. In actuality, Epicurus defined pleasure not as unbridled sensuality but as freedom from pain and as peace of mind, which can only be obtained through simple living.

In about 306 B.C., Epicurus established a school in Athens, which came to be known as the Garden School because residents provided for their own food by gardening. There he and his students strived to lead lives of simplicity, prudence, justice, and honor. In this way, they achieved tranquility—the ultimate goal in life, according to the philosophy of Epicureanism. He further believed that intellectual pleasures are superior to sensual pleasures, which are fleeting. In fact he held that one of the greatest and most enduring pleasures is friendship. These ideas were put forth by the Greek philosopher and writer Lucretius (c. 99-c. 55 B.C.) in his poem *On the Nature of Things.*

While the Epicurean school endured for several centuries, ultimately Christian leaders deemed the philosophy a pagan creed. However, some critics have posited that the writer of Ecclesiastes in the Old Testament of the Bible was likely a member of the Garden School and that the Epistles of Saint Paul in the New Testament were strongly influenced by Epicurean thought. In more recent times, Thomas Jefferson (1743-1826), author and signatory of the Declaration of Independence and third president of the United States, was a self-proclaimed Epicurean.

Who were the great **Islamic philosophers of the Middle Ages**?

Three thinkers of the Islamic world stand out as important interpreters of Greek thought, and therefore, as a bridge between ancient philosophy and the Scholasticism of the Middle Ages: their Latin names are Avennasar, Averroës, and Avicenna.

Avennasar (c. 878-950), who studied with Christian Aristotelians in Baghdad (Iraq), proved so adept at applying the teachings of Aristotle (384-322 B.C.) to Muslim thought that he became known as "the second Aristotle" or the "second teacher." He posited that philosophy and religion are not in conflict with each other; rather, they parallel one another. Also known for his work in interpreting the great Aristotle for the Muslim world, Avicenna (980-1037) is sometimes referred to as the "third teacher." He was also the first to expand the distinction between essence and existence. Averroës (1126-1198) also was no stranger to Aristotle, writing commentaries on him as well as Plato (specifically, the *Republic*); he also wrote on religious law and philosophy as well as religion and logic.

Who were the great thinkers of **Scholasticism**?

Just as Islamic philosophers reinterpreted faith by applying reason, subordinating revelation to reason, Western philosophers endeavored to incorporate the doctrines of Greek philosophy into the theology of the Christian church. Leaders in this movement included St. Augustine (Augustine of Hippo), St. Anselm, and St. Thomas Aquinas.

Augustine of Hippo (354-430) lived during a time when the last vestiges of the pagan world of the Romans was giving way to Christianity. His theological works, including sermons, books, and pastoral letters, reveal a Platonic influence, foreshadowing the movement of Scholasticism that emerged more than six centuries later (during the eleventh century). Augustine believed that understanding can lead one to faith and that faith can lead a person to understanding. He also argued that Christians can understand the nature of the Trinity by examining their own nature (through introspection).

One of Scholasticism's founders, Anselm (c. 1033-1109) was a Benedictine monk who in 1093 became archbishop of Canterbury. He became famous for writing about the attributes of God (in his work *Monologion*) and for trying to prove the existence of God (in *Proslogion*) by rational means alone, arguing that God is that of which nothing greater can be thought; that of which nothing greater can be thought must include existence (if it did not, then something greater could be thought); and therefore God necessarily exists.

But the greatest figure of Scholasticism was St. Thomas Aquinas (1225-1274), who is also one of the principal saints of the Roman Catholic Church. In 1879 his philosophical works were declared the official Catholic doctrine by Pope Leo XIII (1810-1903). While he was teaching at universities in Cologne (Germany) and Paris between 1248 and 1272, Thomas Aquinas penned his major works, *Summa contra gentiles* (1259-64) and *Summa theologica* (1266-73). He discarded the Platonic leanings of St. Augustine (to whom truth was a matter of faith), interpreting Aristotle's naturalistic philosophy: Similar to the Islamic philosopher Avennasar (c. 878-950), who argued that religion and philosophy are not in conflict with each other, Thomas Aquinas believed faith and reason are in harmony with each other. His work is considered the greatest achievement of medieval philosophy, making the thirteenth century Scholasticism's golden age. Thomas Aquinas was canonized in 1323 and was proclaimed a doctor of the Catholic Church in 1567.

What were **Sir Francis Bacon**'s beliefs?

The English philosopher, author, and statesman was one of the great minds of the Scientific Revolution of the 1500s and 1600s, during which the way that Europeans viewed themselves and the universe underwent a dramatic change. Bacon (1561-1626) believed that humankind's accepted notions about nature should be aggressively challenged. As a young man studying at Trinity College, he concluded that the Aristotelian system (or deductive logic) was without merit; Bacon favored observation (or inductive logic) as a system for interpreting and understanding nature. He argued that the understanding of nature was being held back by the blind acceptance of the beliefs of ancient philosophers such as Aristotle (384-322 B.C.) and Plato (c. 428-347 B.C.). A religious person, Bacon maintained that theology should *not* be questioned: He believed that rational inquiry can unlock the secrets of nature—but not of the human soul. Bacon therefore insisted on the separation of philosophy and

English philosopher Sir Francis Bacon believed that nature was best understood by direct observation. (Original engraving by S. Freeman.)

theology, an idea that ran counter to the academic traditions of the time. Consequently he was a staunch proponent of educational and scientific reform.

Trained in law, Bacon served as a royal diplomat in France, was admitted to the bar, elected to Parliament, and served in public office (including the jobs of solicitor general and attorney general). He penned several seminal works, including *Essayes* (1597), which consists of practical wisdom and observations; *Advancement of Learning* (1605), a survey of the state of knowledge (Bacon was attempting to enlist the support of the king in the total reform of education and science in England); and *Novum Organum* (1620), in which he put forth his method for understanding nature by an inductive system, based on direct observation (versus Aristotle's deductive method, which was based on circumstantial evidence and prior conclusions).

Why is **Descartes** considered the **"father of modern philosophy"**?

French mathematician and philosopher René Descartes (1596-1650) was living in Holland in 1637 when he published his first major work, *Discourse on Method.* In this treatise, he extends mathematical methods to science and philosophy, asserting that all knowledge is the product of clear reasoning based on self-evident premises. This idea, that there are certitudes, provided the foundation for modern philosophy, which dates from the 1600s to the present.

Descartes may be best known for the familiar phrase "I think, therefore I am" (*Cogito ergo sum,* in Latin). This assertion is based on his theory that only one thing cannot be doubted, and that is doubt itself. The next logical conclusion is that the doubter (thinker) must, therefore, exist. The correlation to the dictum (I think, therefore I am) is dualism, the doctrine that reality consists of mind and matter: Since the thinker thinks and is, he or she is both mind (idealism) and body (matter, or material). Descartes concluded that mind and body are independent of each other, and he formulated theories about how they work together. Modern philosophers have often concerned themselves with the question of dualism.

Descartes's other major works include *Meditations on First Philosophy* (1641), which is his most famous, and *Principles of Philosophy* (1644). His philosophy became known as Cartesianism (from *Cartesius,* the Latin form of his name).

What is **empiricism**?

Empiricism is the philosophical concept that experience, which is based on observation and experimentation, is the source of knowledge. According to empiricism, the information that a person gathers with his or her senses is the information that should be used to make decisions, without regard to reason or to either religious or political authority. The philosophy gained credibility with the rise of experimental science in the eighteenth and nineteenth centuries, and it continues to be the outlook of many scientists today. Empiricists have included English philosopher John Locke (1632-1704), who asserted that there is no such thing as innate ideas—that the mind is born blank and all knowledge is derived from human experience; Irish clergyman George Berkeley (1685-1753), who believed that nothing exists except through the perception of the individual, and that it is the mind of God that makes possible the apparent existence of material objects; and Scottish philosopher David Hume (1711-1776), who evolved the doctrine of empiricism to the extreme of skepticism—that human knowledge is restricted to the experience of ideas and impressions, and therefore cannot be verified as true.

Why are **Kant's philosophies** still relevant?

Immanuel Kant (1724-1804) remains one of the great modern thinkers because he developed a whole new philosophy, one that completely reinterpreted human knowledge. A professor at Germany's Königsberg University beginning in 1755, Kant lectured widely and was a prolific writer. His most important work came somewhat late in life—after 1775. It was in that year that he undertook "a project of critical philosophy," in which he aimed to answer the three questions that, in his opinion, have occupied every philosopher in Western history: What can I know? What ought I do? For what may I hope?

Kant's answer to the first question (What can I know?) was based on one important conclusion: What a person can know or make claims about is only his or her experience of things, *not* the things in themselves. The philosopher arrived at this conclusion by observing the certainty of math and science: He determined that the fundamental nature of human reality (metaphysics) does not rely on or yield the genuine knowledge of science and math. For example, Newton's law of inertia—a body at rest tends to remain at rest, and a body in motion tends to remain in motion—does not change based on human experience. The law of inertia is universally recognized as correct and as such, is a "pure" truth, which can be relied on. But human reality, argued Kant, does not rest on any such certainties. That which a person has not experienced with their senses cannot be known absolutely. Kant therefore reasoned that free will cannot be proved or disproved—nor can the existence of God.

Even though what humans can know is extremely limited, Kant did not become skeptical. On the contrary, he asserted that "unknowable things" require a leap of faith. He further concluded that since no one can disprove the existence of God, objections to religion carry no weight. In this way, Kant answered the third question posed by philosophers: For what may I hope?

After arriving at the conclusion that each person experiences the world according to his or her own internal laws, Kant began writing on the problem of ethics, answering the second question (What ought I do?). In 1788 he published the *Critique of Practical Reason,* asserting that there is a moral law, which he called the "categorical imperative." Kant argued that a person could test the morality of his or her actions by asking if the motivation should become a universal law—applicable to all people: "Act as if the maxim from which you act were to become through your will a universal law." Kant concluded that when a person's actions conformed with this "categorical imperative," then he or she was doing his or her duty, which would result in goodwill.

Kant's theories have remained relevant to philosophy for more than two centuries: modern thinkers have either furthered the school of thought that Kant initiated or they have rejected it. Either way, the philosopher's influence is still felt. It's interesting to note that among his writings is an essay on political theory (*Perpetual Peace*), which first appeared in 1795: In it, Kant described a federation that would work to prevent international conflict; the League of Nations and the United Nations, created more than a century after Kant, are the embodiments of this idea.

What is the **Hegelian dialectic**?

It is the system of reasoning put forth by German philosopher Georg Hegel (1770-1831), who theorized that at the center of the universe there is an absolute spirit that guides all reality. According to Hegel, all historical developments follow three basic laws: Each event follows a necessary course (in other words, it could not have happened in any other way); each historical event represents not only change but progress; and one historical event, or phase, tends to be replaced by its opposite, which is later replaced by a resolution of the two extremes. This third law of Hegel's dialectic is the "pendulum theory" discussed by scholars and students of history: that events swing from one extreme to the other before the pendulum comes to rest at middle. The extreme phases are called the thesis and the antithesis; the resolution is called the synthesis. Based on this system, Hegel

German philosopher Georg Hegel (in an 1884 portrait) theorized that at the center of the universe there is an absolute spirit that guides all reality. (Original painting by Ernst Hader.)

asserted that human beings can comprehend the unfolding of history. In this way, he viewed the human experience as absolute and knowable.

What is **existentialism**?

Existentialism is not a single school of thought but rather a label applied to several systems that are influenced by the theories of Danish philosopher Soren Kierkegaard (1813-1855). Existentialist thinkers consider one problem: human existence in an unfathomable universe. However, in considering this "plight," philosophers have arrived at different conclusions.

The founder of existentialism, Kierkegaard rejected the principles put forth by traditional philosophers such as Georg Hegel (1770-1831), who had considered philosophy as a science, asserting that it is both objective and certain. Kierkegaard overturned this assertion, citing that truth is not objective but rather subjective; that there is no such thing as universal truths; and that human existence is not understandable in scientific terms. He maintained that human beings must make their own choices, based on their own knowledge. When he wrote on the subject, Kierkegaard frequently used pseudonyms, a practice he defended by intimating that he was putting the onus on his readers to determine what is true—that they shouldn't rely on the "authority" of his philosophies.

In the twentieth century, heirs to Kierkegaard's school of thought included German philosopher Martin Heidegger (1889-1976), who rejected the label "existentialist," and the French writer Jean-Paul Sartre (1905-1980), the only self-proclaimed existentialist. They grappled with the dilemma that human beings must use their free will to make decisions—and assume responsibility for those decisions—without knowing conclusively what is true or false, right or wrong, good or bad. In other words, there is no way of knowing absolutely what the correct choices are, and yet individuals must make choices all the time, and be held accountable for them. Sartre described this as a "terrifying freedom." However, theologians such as American Paul Tillich (1886-1965) reconsidered the human condition in light of Christianity, arriving at far less pessimistic conclusions than did Sartre. For example, Tillich asserted that "divine answers" exist. Similarly, Jewish philosopher Martin Buber (1878-1965), who was also influenced by Kierkegaard, proposed that a personal and direct dialogue between the individual and God yields truths.

What was **Nietzsche's philosophy** about the "will to power"?

The German philosopher Friedrich Nietzsche (1844-1900) developed many theories of human behavior, and the will to power was one of these. While other philosophers (including the ancient Greek Epicurus) argued that humans are motivated by a desire to experience pleasure, Nietzsche asserted that it was neither pleasure nor the avoidance of pain that inspires humankind, but rather the desire for strength and power. He argued that in order to gain power, humans would even be willing to embrace pain. However, it's critical to note that he did not view this will to power strictly as a will to dominate others: Nietzsche glorified a superman or "overman" (*ubermensch*), an individual who could assert power over himself (or herself). He viewed artists as one example of an overman—since that person successfully harnesses his or her instincts through creativity and in so doing has actually achieved a higher form of power than would the person who only wishes to dominate others. A notable exception to Nietzsche's esteem for artists was the composer Richard Wagner (1813-1883), whom the philosopher opposed. Since Wagner led an immoral lifestyle, unlike the ubermensch, Nietzsche maintained that the composer had not gained power over his own instincts.

Nietzsche was a professor of classics at the University of Basel in Switzerland from 1868 to 1878. Retiring due to poor health, he turned to his writing, which included poetry. In 1889 he suffered a mental breakdown and died the next year. After his death, his sister, Elisabeth Förster-Nietzsche (1846-1935), altered her brother's works in editing, changing their meaning. In 1895 she married an anti-Semitic agitator, Bernhard Förster (1843-1889), who, with his wife, attempted to establish a pure Aryan (a non-Jewish Caucasian) colony in Paraguay. The effort failed, and Förster took his own life. These events and, more importantly, the changes to the philosopher's own words resulted in the popular misconception that Nietzsche's philosophies had given rise to Nazism.

What is **natural law**?

Natural law is the theory that some laws are fundamental to human nature, and as such they can only be known through human reason—without reference to manmade law. Roman orator and philosopher Cicero (106-43 B.C.) insisted that natural law is universal, meaning it is binding to governments and people everywhere.

Why are **Thomas Paine**'s philosophies important to democratic thought?

English political philosopher and author Thomas Paine (1737-1809) believed that a democracy is the only form of government that can guarantee natural rights. Paine arrived in the American colonies in 1774. Two years later he wrote *Common Sense,* a pamphlet that galvanized public support for the American Revolution (1775-83), which was already underway. During the struggle for independence, Paine wrote and distributed a series of 16 papers, called *Crisis,* upholding the rebels' cause in their fight. Paine penned his words in the language of common speech, which helped his message reach a mass audience in America and elsewhere. He soon became known as an advocate of individual freedom. The fight for freedom was one that he waged in letters: In 1791 and 1792 Paine, now back in England, released *The Rights of Man* (in two parts), a work in which he defended the cause of the French Revolution (1789-99) and appealed to the British people to overthrow their monarchy. For this he was tried and convicted of treason in his homeland. Escaping to Paris, the philosopher became a member of the revolutionary National Convention. But during the Reign of Terror (1793-94) of revolutionary leader Maximilien Robespierre (1758-1794), Paine was imprisoned for being English. An American minister interceded on Paine's behalf, insisting that Paine was actually an American. Paine was released on this technicality. He remained in Paris until 1802, and then returned to the United States. Though he played an important role in the American Revolution by boosting the morale of the colonists, he nevertheless lived his final years as an outcast and in poverty.

Political philosopher and author Thomas Paine believed that a democracy is the only form of government that can guarantee natural rights. (Original painting by George Romney.)

What is **Marxism**?

Marxism is an economic and political theory named for its originator, Karl Marx (1818-1883). Marx was a German social philosopher and revolutionary who in 1844 in Paris met another German philosopher, Friedrich Engels (1820- 1895), beginning a long collaboration. Four years later they wrote the *Communist Manifesto,* laying the foundation for socialism and communism. The cornerstone of Marxism, to which Engels greatly contributed, is the belief that history is determined by economics. Based on this premise, Marx asserted that economic crises will result in increased poverty, which in turn, will inspire the working class (proletariat) to revolt, ousting the capitalists (bourgeoisie). According to Marx, once the working class has seized control, it will institute a system of economic cooperation and a classless society. In his most influential work, *Das Kapital* (The Capital), an exhaustive analysis of capitalism published in three volumes (1867, 1885, and 1894), Marx predicted the failure of the capitalist system, based on his belief that the history of society is "the history of class struggle." He and Engels viewed an international revolution as inevitable.

While Marxism still has followers in the late twentieth century, most scholars have discredited Marx's predictions, citing improved conditions for workers in industrialized nations, which has been brought about by the evolution of capitalism.

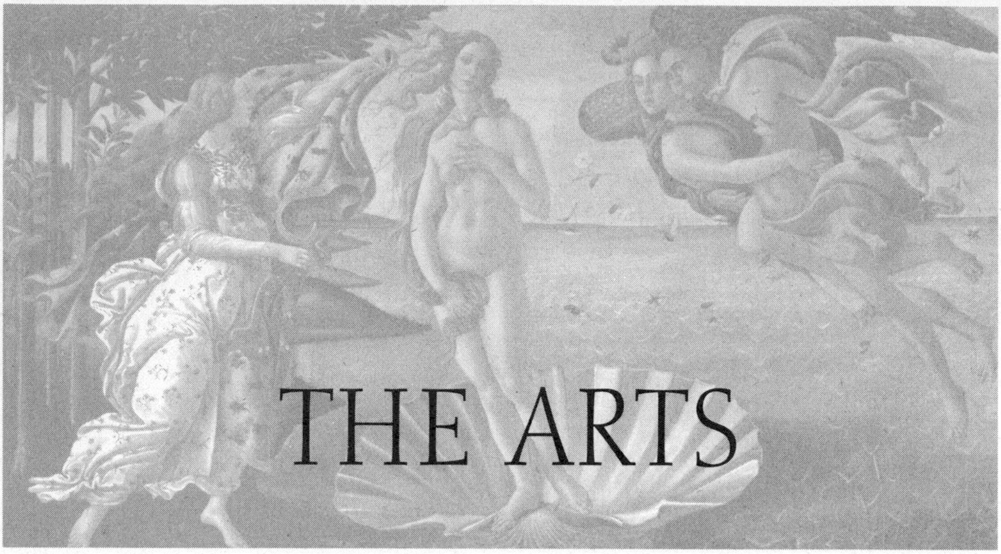

THE ARTS

How long have humans been producing **art**?

The first true art was originated by *Homo sapiens sapiens* (called "man the double wise") in Europe about 35,000 years ago (during the Stone Age). Man the double wise painted his own hand prints, warrior images, and animals (including bison, horses, and reindeer) on the walls and ceilings of uninhabited caves in France and Spain between 35,000 B.C. and 8000 B.C. He used red, black, and yellow paints, which were made by mixing powdered earth and rock pigments with water. Among the most famous paintings are those in the caves at Lascaux (in Dordogne, France), Niaux (Ariège, France), Pech-Merle (Lot, France), Gasulla (Castellón, Spain), and Altamira (Cantabria, Spain).

These early modern humans—who, if dressed in contemporary clothing, would be nearly indistinguishable from anyone on a modern city street—also decorated tools and created lifelike sculptures of animals and women. European man of this period, who had a fully developed human brain, is also referred to as Cro-Magnon man for a shallow rock shelter near Les Eyzies in the Dordogne region of southwestern France, where, in 1868, skeletal remains of the tall, erect-walking species were found.

WRITING AND LITERATURE

When did **people begin to write**?

If writing is viewed as a means of communicating between humans, using conventional, visible marks, then writing spans the entire history of visual communication—from early pictographic (picture writing) beginnings to alphabetical writing. The oldest picture writing identified thus far was found in Mesopotamia (present-day Iraq), the valley between the lower Tigris and Euphrates rivers. This writing, called cuneiform, dates back to the last centuries of the fourth millennium B.C. (c. 3700 B.C.). The finding consisted of about a dozen pictures inscribed on both sides of a limestone tablet. The characters are made up of wedge-shaped strokes; the system was probably created by the Sumerians, a non-Semitic people whose origins are unknown; they probably immigrated to southwest Asia (Mesopotamia) from the East. Cuneiform pictographs closely resemble Egyptian hieroglyphics, picture script developed by ancient Egyptian priests and perfected by the first Egyptian dynasty (3110 to 2884 B.C.). Egyptian hieroglyphics consisted of some 600 symbols (phonograms). Cuneiform and hieroglyphic systems were the predecessors to the alphabet.

When was the **first alphabet** created?

The earliest form of an alphabet (a set of letters with which one or more languages are written) was developed between 1800 and 1000 B.C. by a Semitic people of unknown identity. In 1928 in the northern Syrian city of Ras Shamra, clay tablets were discovered with a cuneiform (wedge-shaped) alphabet of characters. According to most scholars, these early Semitic inventors got the idea of developing an alphabet because of their contact with Egyptian hieroglyphics. Although some of the Semitic symbols were Egyptian, the system of writing was distinctly their own, consisting of 22 characters representing only consonants. (There were no written directions for vowels; the reader had to supply the vowels from his or her knowledge of the language.)

The characters were developed this way: Important Semitic words were selected so that each would begin with a different consonant. Then, stylized pictures portraying the words (mostly nouns) were assigned the phonetic value of the initial sound of each word. For example, the first character in the Semitic (Hebrew) alphabet, *aleph,* originally meant and was the symbol for an oxhead. The second, *beth,* which came to represent the sound "b," meant "house" and renderings of the symbol reveal a shelter with a roof. The Phoenician alphabet (developed c. 1000 B.C.) is believed to have been derived from this early Semitic alphabet; in turn, the Greeks (in about 500 B.C.) adapted the Phoenician alphabet for their own use.

How was **paper invented**?

The oldest writing surfaces in existence include Babylonian clay tablets and Indian palm leaves. Around 3000 B.C. the Egyptians developed a writing material using papyrus, the plant for which paper is named. Early in the Holy Roman Empire, the long manuscript scrolls that were made of fragile papyrus and used by Egyptians, Greeks, and Romans were replaced by the codex, separate pages bound together at one side and having a cover (like the modern book). Eventually, papyrus was replaced by vellum (made of a fine-grain lambskin, kidskin, or calfskin) and parchment (made of sheepskin or goatskin), both of which provided superior surfaces for painting.

The wood-derived paper we know today was developed in A.D. 105 by the Chinese, who devised a way to make tree bark, hemp, rags, and fishnets into paper. The process used then contained the basic elements that are still found in paper mills today. The Moors introduced papermaking to Europe (Spain) in about 1150; by the 1400s paper was being made throughout Europe. But it was not until the late 1700s that paper was produced in continuous rolls. In 1798 a French paper mill clerk invented a machine that could produce a continuous sheet of paper in any desired size from wood pulp. The machine was improved and patented by English papermakers Henry (1766-1854) and Sealy Fourdrinier (d. 1847) in 1807. The invention spurred the development of newspapers.

What was the **first book**?

It was *The Diamond Sutra,* published in the year A.D. 868. Archaeologists discovered it in the Caves of the Thousand Buddhas, at Kansu (Ganzu), China.

Who developed **printing**?

If printing is defined as the process of transferring repeatable designs onto a surface, then the first known printing was done by the Mesopotamians, who as early as 3000 B.C. used stamps to impress designs onto wet clay.

Printing on paper developed much later; Chinese inventor Ts'ai Lun (A.D. c. 50-c. 118) is credited with producing the first paper in A.D. 105. During the T'ang dynasty (618-906) Chinese books were printed with inked wood blocks, and it was the Chinese—not German printer Johannes Gutenberg (c. 1390-1468), as is widely believed—who developed movable type, allowing printers to compose a master page from permanent, raised characters. However, movable-type printing did not catch on in medieval China because the Chinese language has some 80,000 characters; printers found it more convenient to use carved blocks.

How old is the oldest **illuminated manuscript**?

The oldest painted manuscript known is the *Vatican Vergil,* which dates to the early fifth century A.D. The content is pagan, representing a scene from Roman poet Virgil's (70-19 B.C.) *Georgica,* his verses idealizing country life and nature. But illuminated manuscripts were typically renderings of sacred texts. When the fathers of the Eastern Church advised that pictures could be used in books and art to teach people, the decorations and pictures (called illuminations since they were meant to illuminate, or make clear, the text) took on great importance. Since the beauty of the manuscript was meant to represent the spiritual beauty of the text (usually gospels, psalms, prayers, or meditations), sacred books became increasingly ornamental. Some "books of hours," devotional books developed during the 1300s, are considered masterpieces of illumination. The works (c. 1409-16) of Belgian illuminators Pol, Hermann, and Jehanequin Limburg represent the height of painted religious manuscripts.

Why is **Gutenberg** considered the pioneer of **modern printing**?

Johannes Gutenberg (c. 1390-1468), a German who built his first printing press around 1440 to 1450, is considered the inventor of a lasting system of movable-type printing. Printing technology had only a brief existence in Europe before Gutenberg, whose process, culminating in the publication of the Gutenberg Bible (1452-1456), made printed material available to everyone, not just the clergy or the privileged class. Gutenberg is credited with helping spread the ideals of the Renaissance (1350-1600) throughout Europe.

How old are **Aesop's *Fables***?

They date back to the sixth century B.C. However, it was not until the late 1600s that English-language versions appeared: In 1692 a complete translation of the stories, which are believed to have been written by a Greek slave, were published in London by Sir Roger L'Estrange (1616-1704). The short, moralistic tales, which were handed down through the oral tradition, include the well-known story of the tortoise and the hare (which teaches the lesson slow and steady wins the race) and the one about a wolf in sheep's clothing (people are not always what they seem). Since some of the timeless fables have been traced to earlier literature, many believe it is almost certain that Aesop is a legendary figure.

Who were the **Brothers Grimm**?

The German brothers Jacob (1785-1863) and Wilhelm (1786-1859), best known for their fairytales, were actually librarians and professors who studied law, together wrote a dictionary of the German language, and lectured at universities.

In 1805 Jacob traveled to Paris to conduct research on Roman law, and in a library there he found medieval German manuscripts of old stories that were slowly disintegrating; he decided the tales were too valuable to lose, and he vowed to collect them. The brothers' interest in fairytales also led them to search for old traditions, legends, and tales, especially those meant for children. They traveled the German countryside, interviewing villagers in an effort to gather stories—most of which were from the oral tradition and had never been written down. The brothers were diligent in their efforts, recording everything faithfully so that nothing was added and nothing was left out. When the first volume of *Kinderund Hausmärchen* (literally, the Children's Household Tales, but known better as *Grimm's Fairy Tales*) was published in 1812, children loved it. Subsequent volumes were published in German through 1815. The fairytales collected in the multivolume work included such classics as "The History of Tom Thumb," "Little Red Riding-Hood," "Bluebeard," "Puss in Boots," "Snow White and the Seven Dwarfs," "Goldilocks and the Three Bears," "The Princess and the Pea," "The Sleeping Beauty in the Wood," and "Cinderella."

What is **"the Homeric question"**?

During the eighteenth and nineteenth centuries, scholars became involved in a debate, referred to as "the Homeric question," about whether the *Iliad* and the *Odyssey* were written by the same author, or even if any one author can be credited with the entire composition of either poem, and what kind of an author Homer was. The dispute continues today. Scholars believe the *Iliad* was probably written much earlier than the *Odyssey,* though there is not enough evidence to prove that the Greek poet Homer (c. 850-? B.C.) did not write both epics. Further, it was suggested that Homer was a bard (oral poet) who was unable to read or write and who sang the great stories of the *Iliad* and *Odyssey* to the accompaniment of a lyre. According to this theory, the tales would have been dictated by Homer to a scribe late in the poet's life. However, some have left open the possibility that the human histories told in the *Iliad* and the *Odyssey* were in fact the composite result of the storytelling of numerous bards.

Several other poems, including the *Margites* and the *Batrachomyomachia,* have also been attributed to Homer, but they were most likely written by his successors.

What is known about **Homer**?

It is most likely that Homer was an oral poet and performer. Though little is known about Homer, it's believed that he was an Ionian Greek who lived circa the eighth or ninth century B.C. In the 1920s scholar Milman Parry proved that Homer's poems were "formulaic in nature, relying on generic epithets (such as 'wine-dark sea' and 'rosy-fingered dawn'), repetition of stock lines, and descriptions and themes typical of oral folk poetry." All of this suggested that Homer was most likely a bard or rhapsode—an itinerant professional reciter—who improvised pieces to be sung at Greek festivals.

Why is the ***Iliad*** studied today?

Greek poet Homer's (c. 850-? B.C.) *Iliad* and *Odyssey* (both works credited to him) are considered to be among the greatest works of literature and have had a profound influence on western poetry, serving as the primary models for subsequent works, including the *Aeneid* (Virgil) and the *Divine Comedy* (Dante).

The *Iliad* in particular can be seen as both the beginning of western literature as we know it and the culmination of a long tradition of oral epic poetry that may date as far back as the thirteenth century B.C. The *Iliad* has been a part of western education for nearly 3,000 years. The epic poem, telling the story of a 10-year Trojan War, reveals the author's keen understanding of human nature.

Is Virgil's ***Aeneid*** an unfinished work?

Yes, the *Aeneid* was technically unfinished by its author, Virgil (70-19 B.C.), who is considered the greatest Roman poet. Virgil spent the last ten years of his life working on the *Aeneid,* and he planned to devote three more years making revisions to this epic when, during his travels to gather new material for the poem, he became ill with fever and died. On his deathbed, Virgil requested that his companions burn the *Aeneid.* However, Augustus (63 B.C.-A.D. 14), the emperor of Rome, countermanded the request, asking Virgil's friends to edit the manuscript. Augustus did specify that the writers not add, delete, or alter the text significantly. The *Aeneid,* Virgil's great epic about the role of Rome in world history, was first published in 17 B.C. The work consists of 12 books, each between 700 and 1,000 lines long.

What **innovations** are credited to **Virgil**?

Scholars acclaim Virgil (70-19 B.C.) for transforming the Greek literary traditions, which had long provided Roman writers with material, themes, and styles. Virgil populated his pastoral settings (always idealized by other writers) with contemporary figures; he combined observation with inquiry; employed a more complex syntax than had been in use previously; and developed realistic characters. These technical innovations informed all subsequent literature.

However, writing was not supposed to have been Virgil's occupation: In his youth, he studied rhetoric and philosophy, and he planned to practice law, but proved too shy for public speaking. So he returned to the small family farm his mother and father operated, where he studied and wrote poetry.

In addition to the *Aeneid,* Virgil wrote *Eclogues* (or *Bucolica*), a set of 10 pastoral poems written (from 42-37 B.C.) as a response to the confiscation of his family's lands; and *Georgics,* a four-volume work (written from 36-29 B.C.) glorifying the Italian countryside. Within 50 years of his death in 19 B.C.,Virgil's poems became part of the standard curriculum in Roman schools, ensuring the production of numerous copies. Virgil's works have remained accessible to scholars and students ever since.

Why is ***Beowulf*** considered an important work?

Beowulf, the earliest manuscript of which dates to about A.D. 1000, is the oldest surviving epic poem in English or any other European vernacular. It was written in Old English (the language of the Anglo-Saxons in England; used c. A.D. 500-1100); its author is unknown. Categorized as a folk-epic, *Beowulf* tells the story of a Scandinavian warrior hero who, on behalf of the Danish king, fights and kills the fearsome monster Grendel, then slays the monster's mother, and finally engages a fire-breathing dragon in mortal combat. Because of its combination of Christian and pagan themes, scholars believe the epic may have been written as early as 700 or 750.

Why is *The Divine Comedy* widely studied?

Simply put, *The Divine Comedy,* which consists of 100 cantos arranged in three books (*Inferno, Purgatorio,* and *Paradiso*), is studied not only for the beauty of its verse, but for its timeless message.

In a letter to his benefactor, Dante Alighieri (1265-1321) explained that by writing *The Divine Comedy* (*Divina Commedia,* begun c. 1308) he would attempt "to remove those living in this life from the state of misery and lead them to the state of felicity." While the subject of the poem, according to Dante, is "the state of souls after death," allegorically, the poem is about humankind, who can exercise free will to bring "rewarding or punishing justice" upon themselves.

Dante's masterpiece is considered the seminal work of Italian literature: At the time that he wrote *The Divine Comedy,* Latin was the undisputed language of science and literature. Italian, on the other hand, was considered vulgar. By skillfully writing this poem in the vernacular (Tuscan Italian) rather than Latin, Dante parted from tradition, marking a critical development for vernacular writing. In its translations *The Divine Comedy* has become a point of reference for writers in any language. Scholars and students agree that Dante expresses universal truths in this work, which is also a finely crafted piece of literature.

Why is **Chaucer's *Canterbury Tales*** important to literature?

The unfinished work, which was begun about 1486 and written during the last 14 years of its author's life, is considered a masterpiece of Middle English, the language spoken by Anglo-Saxons in England from c. 1200 into the late 1400s. In the *Canterbury Tales,* Geoffrey Chaucer (1340-1400), who was the son of a wealthy wine merchant, weaves together stories told by 28 pilgrims whom the storyteller (the poet himself) met at an inn. The pilgrims, along with the innkeeper who joins them and the poet, represent all facets of English social life—aristocracy, clergy, commoners, and even a middle class, which was not officially recognized by the social structure of the day, but which, in fact, existed.

To connect the tales, Chaucer uses the framing device of a journey to the shrine of Thomas Becket (c.1118-1170), the archbishop of Canterbury who in 1170 was killed by overzealous knights in the service of England's King Henry II. In his prologue, Chaucer indicates that each traveler was to tell two tales out and two tales back from Canterbury Cathedral, for a total of 120 stories, which were intended to entertain the pilgrims during their trip. But Chaucer wrote only 24 tales, two of which are incomplete. The tales include bawdy humor, fables, and lessons. While the pilgrims reach the shrine, they do not return—a device some scholars have interpreted as deliberate on the author's part, as it suggests the human journey from earth to heaven. Whatever the intention, *The Canterbury Tales* reveal the author's ability as a storyteller, as the editors of the *Norton Anthology of English Literature* assert, rivaling Shakespeare "in the art of providing entertainment on the most primitive level, and at the same time, of significantly increasing the reader's ability to comprehend reality."

The tales were extremely popular in late medieval England, printed and reprinted numerous times, particularly during the 1400s. Chaucer's rendering of details reveal both story and storyteller (pilgrim) at once, giving the reader a remarkable insight into the characters and revealing basic human paradoxes—which transcend time.

It is thought that William Shakespeare is widely studied because his words express universal and unchanging human concerns.

Why is **Shakespeare widely studied**?

English dramatist Ben Jonson (1572-1637) said it best when he proclaimed that Shakespeare "was not of an age, but for all time." Most teachers and students, not to mention critics and theatergoers down through the ages, likely agree with Jonson's remark: Shakespeare's canon (consisting of 37 plays, divided into comedies, tragedies, or histories, plus poems and sonnets) expresses universal and unchanging human concerns as no other works have. Shakespeare's words are familiar even to those who have not studied them, not simply because of the many contemporary adaptations of his works, but because Shakespearean phrases and variations thereof have, through the years, fallen into common usage. Consider these few examples from *Hamlet* alone: "Neither a borrower nor a lender be"; "To thine own self be true"; and "The play's the thing." No other writer's plays have been produced so often or read so widely in so many countries.

What is a **poet laureate**?

A poet laureate is someone who is recognized by his or her country or state as its most eminent and representative poet. Officially, a poet laureate is appointed or named by the government. England's first, if unofficially titled, poet laureate was Ben Jonson (1572-1637), a contemporary of Shakespeare. (Shakespeare acted a leading role in the first of Jonson's great plays, *Every Man in His Humour,* 1598.) In 1605 Jonson began writing a series of masques (short, allegorical dramas that were performed by actors wearing masks) for the court. Years later, in 1616, he was appointed poet laureate and in that capacity received a "substantial pension." Among Jonson's works are *Volpone* (1605), *Works* (a collection of poetry published in 1616, and which includes the oft-quoted line, "Drink to me only with thine eyes"), and *Pleasure Reconciled to Virtue* (1618).

Some sources trace the first British poet laureate back to Edmund Spenser (1552 or 1553-1599), who is called the "Poet's Poet." However, the title of poet laureate was not officially conferred on an English writer until 1638, when poet and dramatist William Davenant (1606-1668), who was reputed to be the godson or even the illegitimate son of Shakespeare, was given the honor. Other poet laureates of England include John Dryden (1631-1700), William Wordsworth (1770-1850), and Lord Alfred Tennyson (1809-1892).

How did the word **"Machiavellian"** get its meaning?

Machiavellian is defined as "characterized by cunning, duplicity, or bad faith." It's based on the theory of Italian diplomat Niccolò Machiavelli (1469-1527), who developed a code of political conduct that operates independent of ethics, thus disregarding moral authorities such as classical philosophy and Christian theology.

In 1513, after having been exiled from Florence, Italy, by the powerful Medici family, Machiavelli abruptly turned his attention to writing *The Prince,* which puts forth a calm and uncompromising analysis of techniques and methods that the successful ruler must use in order to gain—and keep—power. Written in the form of advice to the ruler, Machiavelli advises the Prince that only one consideration should govern his decisions: the effectiveness of a particular course of action, regardless of its ethical character. The book had little immediate impact in Italy, although it soon became legendary throughout Europe, and its major ideas—the power of politics—are familiar today even to people who have never read the book.

Why is **Milton** important to **English literature**?

Except for Shakespeare, the works of John Milton (1608-1674) have been the subject of more commentary than those of any other English writer. Milton is considered one of only a few writers to take their place in "the small circle of great epic writers." According to *Norton Anthology of English Literature,* in Milton's writings "two tremendous intellectual and social movements come to a head." The movements referred to are the Renaissance and the Reformation. Scholars point to Milton's use of classical references and the rich tapestry of his works as being Renaissance in nature, while his "earnest and individually minded Christianity" are resonant of the Reformation. For example, in his masterpiece *Paradise Lost* (1667), Milton, like poets Homer and Virgil before him, takes on humankind's entire experience: war, love, religion, hell, heaven, and the cosmos. But rather than having Adam triumph over evil through an act of heroism, he "accepts the burden of worldly existence, and triumphs over his guilt by admitting it and repenting it."

In addition to his famous epics, Milton wrote sonnets and other short poems, including "On Shakespeare," "L'Allegro," "Il Penseroso," and "Lycidas." His writings also include political discourse, chief of which is the essay *Areopagitica* (1644). Among the ideas that Milton championed were the limitation of the monarchy, dethroning of bishops, freedom of speech, and the institution of divorce. One commentator mused that "the guarantees of freedom in the United States Constitution owe more to Milton's *Areopagitica* than to John Locke."

What were **Voltaire's beliefs**?

The prolific French writer's corpus of 52 works were produced as part of his lifelong effort to expose injustices. Voltaire's famous words, *"Ecrasez l'infame"* (squash that which is evil), encapsulate his tenets: He believed in God, but abhorred priestly (high church) traditions; he spread the doctrines of rational skepticism to the world; he strongly advocated religious and political tolerance; and he held great faith in humankind's ability to strive for perfection. To the European literary world, he embodied the highest ideal of the Age of Reason (also called the Enlightenment). But victims of his wit feared and denigrated him. Celebrated by some during his lifetime, he has certainly been celebrated since. His masterpiece, *Candide* (1759), a satirical tale exploring the nature of good and evil, has been translated into more than 100 languages.

What was **Goethe's** contribution to world literature?

Johann Wolfgang Goethe (1749-1832) is considered Germany's greatest writer. He also was a scientist, artist, musician, and philosopher. As a writer, Goethe experimented with many genres and literary styles, and his works became a shaping force of the major German literary movements of the late eighteenth and early nineteenth centuries. His masterwork, the poetic drama *Faust* (1808; rewritten 1832), embodies the author's humanistic ideal of a world literature—one that transcends the boundaries of nations and historical periods. Indeed, the story of Faust, a German astrologer, magician, and soothsayer (c. 1480-1540), remains one of universal interest, and has been treated often in both literature and music: the legendary figure was believed to have sold his soul to the devil in exchange for the opportunity to experience all of life's pleasures.

Who was Alexis **de Tocqueville**?

Aristocrat Alexis de Tocqueville (1805-1859) was only 26 years old when he traveled to New York with his colleague and friend, Gustave de Beaumont (1802-1866), to study and observe American democracy.

Though Tocqueville set out with the pretext of studying the American penal system on behalf of the French government (both he and Beaumont were magistrates at the time), he had the deliberate and personal goal of conducting an onsite investigation of the world's first and then only completely democratic society: the United States. Tocqueville and Beaumont traveled for nine months through New England, eastern Canada, and numerous American cities, including New York; Philadelphia, Pennsylvania; Baltimore, Maryland; Washington, D.C.; Cincinnati, Ohio; and New Orleans, Louisiana.

The pair returned to France in 1832 and the following year published their study, *On the Penitentiary System in the United States and Its Application in France.* Once this official obligation was behind him, Tocqueville left his post as magistrate and moved into a modest Paris apartment. There he devoted two years to writing *Democracy in America* (1835, 1840). The work was soon proclaimed the classic treatment of its subject throughout the Western world and secured Tocqueville's fame as political observer, philosopher, and, later, sociologist.

Tocqueville proclaimed that during his travels, "Nothing struck me more forcibly than the general equality of conditions.... All classes meet continually and no haughtiness at all results from the differences in social position. Everyone shakes hands...." But he also foresaw the possibility that the principles of economic equality could be undermined by the American passion for equality, which not only "tends to elevate the humble to the rank of the great," but also "impels the weak to attempt to lower the powerful to their own level." While he warned against the possible "tyranny of the majority" as a hazard of democracy, he also added that law, religion, and the press provide safeguards against democratic despotism.

Who was the first to write a **modern novel**?

While there are differing opinions on the answer to this question, it is generally accepted that the credit for the novel as we know it belongs to Spanish writer Miguel de Cervantes (1547-1616). Cervantes wrote *Don Quixote* (in two parts, 1605 and 1615): It was the first extended prose narrative in European literature in which characters and events are depicted in what came to be called the modern realistic tradition. Considered an epic masterpiece, *Don Quixote* had an undeniable influence on early novelists, including English novelist and playwright Henry Fielding (who wrote the realistic novel *Tom Jones,* 1749). *Don Quixote* is also said to have anticipated later fictional masterpieces, including French novelist Gustave Flaubert's *Madame Bovary* (1857), Russian novelist Fyodor Dostoevsky's *The Idiot* (1868-69), and American writer Mark Twain's *The Adventures of Tom Sawyer* (1876) and *The Adventures of Huckleberry Finn* (1884).

Why is **Jane Austen widely read** today?

Austen is considered one of the greatest novelists in English. She wrote just six books during her lifetime, including her best-known works *Sense and Sensibility* (published 1811), *Pride and Prejudice* (1813), and *Emma* (1816), but in so doing she created the novel of manners, which continues to delight readers today. The daughter of a clergyman, Jane Austen (1775-1817) rejected the literary movement of the day, romanticism, opting instead to portray life as she knew it. As such, she was the first realist in the English novel. Austen's works are ripe with shrewd observation, wit, and an appreciation for the charms of everyday life, making her an engaging storyteller for all time.

Why is ***Moby Dick*** considered the greatest American novel?

The 1851 novel by Herman Melville (1819-1891), which opens with the familiar line "Call me Ishmael," has been acclaimed as one of the greatest novels of all time; many regard it as the best American novel. Of course, determining the best is a purely subjective matter, and Melville's work has many worthy rivals for the distinction, but *Moby Dick* remains a compelling and finely wrought work—in spite of the fact that it was not appreciated in its day. The story of a whaling captain's obsessive search for the whale that ripped off his leg, *Moby Dick* is both an exciting tale of the high seas and an interesting allegory, interpreted as the human quest to understand the ultimately unknowable ways of God. The work first received notoriety some 30 years after Melville's death.

Why was James Joyce's ***Ulysses*** **banned** in the United States?

Irish writer James Joyce's (1882-1941) masterpiece was originally published in 1922 (it had been serialized prior to then) by the Paris bookstore Shakespeare and Company. By 1928 it was officially listed as obscene by the U.S. Customs Court. The reason was twofold: the use of four-letter words and the stream-of-consciousness narrative of one of the characters, revealing her innermost thoughts. When the official stance on the book was challenged in U.S. court in 1933, the judge (John Woolsey) called it a "sincere and honest book," and after long reflection he ruled that it be openly admitted into the United States. Random House, the American publisher who had advocated the obscenity charge be challenged in court, promptly began typesetting the work in order to release a U.S. edition. But the court decision had important and lasting legal impact as well: it was a turning point in reducing government censorship. Prior to the case, laws that prohibited obscenity were not seen to be in conflict with the First Amendment of the U.S. Constitution (which is most often interpreted as a guarantee of freedom of speech), and the U.S. Post Office and the Customs Service alike both had the power to determine obscenity. The government appealed the decision to the U.S. Circuit Court of Appeals, but Judge Woolsey's decision held.

What is **Proust**'s claim to literary fame?

Marcel Proust (1871-1922) is generally considered the greatest French novelist of the twentieth century and is credited with introducing to fiction the elements of psychological analysis, innovative treatment of time, and multiple themes. Proust is primarily known for his multivolume work *A la recherche du temps perdu* (1954), which was published in English as *Remembrance of Things Past.* Proust was an creative stylist as well as shrewd social observer.

In the mid-1890s Proust joined other prominent artists, including the great French novelist of the nineteenth century, Emile Zola (1840-1902), to form the protest group known as the Revisionists or Dreyfusards. The artists were staunch supporters of Alfred Dreyfus (1859-1935), and therefore vocal critics of the French military, who they accused of anti-Semitism for keeping the French army officer, wrongly accused of treason, imprisoned on Devil's Island.

When did **American poetry** begin?

As the self-described poet of democracy, Walt Whitman (1819-1892) was the first to compose a truly American verse—one that showed no references to European antecedents (throwing off both the narrative and ode forms of verse) and that clearly articulated the American experience.

His first published poetry was the self-published collection *Leaves of Grass* (1855). In an effort to gain recognition, Whitman promptly sent a copy to the preeminent man of American letters, Ralph Waldo Emerson (1803-82), who could count as his acquaintances and friends the great British poets William Wordsworth (1770-1850) and Samuel Taylor Coleridge (1772-1834), the renowned Scottish essayist Thomas Carlyle (1795-1881), and prominent American writers Henry David Thoreau (1817-1862) and Nathaniel Hawthorne (1804-1864). It was a bold move on Whitman's part, but it paid off: While *Leaves of Grass* had been unfavorably received by reviewers, Emerson composed a five-page tribute, expressing his enthusiasm for the poetry and remarking that Whitman was "at the beginning of a great career." Thoreau, too, praised the work. More than a century later, biographer Justin Kaplan acclaimed that in its time *Leaves of Grass* was "the most brilliant and original poetry yet written in the New World, at once the fulfillment of American literary romanticism and the beginnings of American literary modernism." Whitman's well-known and frequently studied poems include "Song of Myself," "O Captain! My Captain!," "Song of the Open Road," and "I Sing the Body Electric."

While she was virtually unknown for her poetry during her lifetime, Emily Dickinson (1830-1886) was writing at about the same time as Whitman (the 1850s), publishing only a handful of poems before her death. Collections of Dickinson's works were published posthumously, and today she, too, is regarded as one of the great early poets of the United States. Had more of her work been brought out in print, perhaps she would have been recognized as the first truly American poet.

What were the lasting effects of the **Harlem Renaissance**?

The Harlem Renaissance (1925-35) marked the first time that white Americans (principally intellects and artists) gave serious attention to the culture of African Americans. The movement, which had by some accounts begun as early as 1917, was noted in a 1925 *New York Herald Tribune* article that announced, "We are on the edge, if not in the midst, of what might not improperly be called a Negro Renaissance." The first African American Rhodes scholar, Alain Locke (1886-1954), who was a professor of philosophy at Howard University, led and shaped the movement during which Upper Manhattan became a hotbed of creativity in the post-World War I (1914-18) era.

Not only was there a flurry activity, but there was a heightened sense of pride as well. The movement left the country with a legacy of literary works including those by Jean Toomer (his 1923 work *Cane* is generally considered the first work of the Harlem Renaissance), Langston Hughes ("The Negro Speaks of Rivers," 1921; *The Weary Blues,* 1926), Countee Cullen (*Color,* 1925; *Copper Sun,* 1927), Jessie R. Fauset (novelist and editor of *The Crisis,* the journal of the National Association for the Advancement of Colored People, or NAACP), Claude McKay (whose 1928 novel *Home to Harlem* evoked strong criticism from W. E. B. Du Bois and Alain Locke for its portrayal of black life), and Zora Neale Hurston (the author of the highly acclaimed 1937 novel *Their Eyes Were Watching God,* who was the first black woman to be honored for her creative writing with a prestigious Guggenheim Fellowship).

Zora Neale Hurston (pictured c. 1940) was the first black woman to be honored for creative writing with a prestigious Guggenheim Fellowship; she was one of the key figures of the Harlem Renaissance.

The Harlem Renaissance was not only about literature: jazz and blues music also flourished during the prosperous times of the postwar era. During the 1920s and 1930s Louis Armstrong, "Jelly Roll" Morton, Duke Ellington, Bessie Smith, and Josephine Baker rose to prominence. Their contributions to music performance are still felt by artists and audiences, regardless of color, today.

FINE ART

What are the characteristics of **Botticelli's paintings**?

The works of Sandro Botticelli (1445-1510), one of the early painters of the Italian Renaissance, are known for their serene compositions, refined elegance, and spirituality. A student of Florentine painter Fra Filippo Lippi (1406-1469), Botticelli refined Lippi's method of drawing such that he is considered one of the great "masters of the line."

Botticelli's work was soon eclipsed by that of Leonardo da Vinci (1452-1519), who was just a few years younger than he, but whose range of talents made Botticelli's work seem dated. Nevertheless, late in the nineteenth century, Botticelli began to be revered again by artists and critics alike, who hailed his works for their simplicity and

Botticelli's well-known painting *Birth of Venus* was commissioned by Florence's powerful Medici family.

sincerity. English art critic John Ruskin (1819-1900) held Botticelli up as an example of an artist who presented nature as an expression of a divinely created world.

Why is Botticelli's *The Birth of Venus* famous?

This immediately recognizable painting (c. 1482) is most likely known for its elegant figures, use of pictorial space, and decorative detail, which give the painting a tapestry effect. At the time it was painted, the presentation of a nude Venus was an innovation since the use of unclothed figures in art had been prohibited during the Middle Ages (500-1350). Botticelli, however, felt free to render Venus in this way since the work was commissioned by Florence's powerful Medici family, who were his patrons. Under their protection, Botticelli could pursue the world of his imagination without fearing charges of paganism and infidelity.

Though *The Birth of Venus* is extremely well known, *The Magnificat* (1483), Botticelli's round picture of the Madonna with singing angels, is his most copied work.

Why was the **Medici family** important to **Renaissance art**?

The Medici family was powerful in Florence, Italy, between the fourteenth and sixteenth centuries. The founder of the family was Giovanni di Bicci de Medici (1360-

Why is da Vinci called the "universal man"?

Leonardo da Vinci (1452-1519) possessed an intensely curious mind and an inventive imagination. He is known by students both for his famous works of art including *The Last Supper* (1495-98) and *Mona Lisa* (1503-05), as well as for his scientific notes and drawings dealing with matters of botany, anatomy, zoology, hydraulics, and physiology. By his own claim, he pursued scientific investigations only to make himself a better painter. Nevertheless, he clearly endeavored to understand the laws of nature. Consequently, he made a study of man, contributing to the understanding of physiology and psychology.

Leonardo da Vinci's body of work provided the foundation of High Renaissance sculpture, painting, drawing, and architecture. As an artist-genius, da Vinci earned the epithet "universal man," and has become a wonder of the modern world, for, as *Gardner's Art through the Ages* put it, having stood at the beginning of "a new epoch like a prophet and a sage."

1429), who amassed a large fortune through his skill in trade and who virtually ruled Florence between 1421 and 1429.

Later, Lorenzo de Medici (1449-1492) ruled Florence between 1478 and 1492. Though he was tyrannical, he was a great patron of the arts and letters. Lorenzo (also called "the Magnificent") maintained Fiesole, a villa outside Florence, where he surrounded himself with the great talents and thinkers of Florence, including a young artist named Sandro Botticelli (1445-1510). Lorenzo was also a patron of Michelangelo.

Did **Michelangelo** study anatomy?

Yes: In 1492 Michelangelo Buonarroti (1475-1564), a master sculptor of the human form, undertook the study of anatomy based on the dissection of corpses from the Hospital of Santo Spirito.

Perhaps most well known for his sculptures of *David* (1501-04) and *Moses* (1515-15), as well as his frescoes on the ceiling and walls of the Sistine Chapel, Michelangelo was also an architect who believed that buildings should follow the form of the human body "to the extent of disposing units symmetrically around a central and unique axis, in a relationship like that of the arms to the body." He also wrote poetry; he was a true Renaissance man.

Michelangelo was totally absorbed in his work and was known to be impatient with himself and with others. He has been likened to German composer Ludwig van Beethoven (1770-1827) since the personal letters of both men reveal a "deep sympathy and concern for those close to them, and profound understanding of humanity informs their works" (*Gardner's Art through the Ages*).

Michelangelo's statue of *David* is housed at the dome of Florence's Accademia Gallery, Italy.

Of the great trio of **High Renaissance artists**—Leonardo, Michelangelo, and Raphael—who is considered *the* master?

Most historians and critics agree that it was Raphael Sanzio (1483-1520) who most clearly stated the ideals of the High Renaissance. Though arch rivals Leonardo da Vinci (1452-1519) and Michelangelo Buonarroti (1475-1564) influenced the younger Raphael, he developed his own style. A prolific painter, he was also a great technician whose work is characterized by a seemingly effortless grace. His most well-known work is *The School of Athens* (1509-11), which has been called "a complete statement of the High Renaissance in its artistic form and spiritual meaning." The painting, which projects a stagelike space onto a two-dimensional surface, reconvenes the great minds of the ancient world—Plato, Aristotle, Pythagoras, Herakleitos, Diogenes, Euclid —for an exchange of ideas. Raphael even included himself in this gathering of greatness. But it seems only appropriate for the master to be in such company: In this work, Raphael has achieved the art of perspective, bringing the discipline of mathematics to pictorial space where human figures appear to move naturally.

Why is **Titian** thought of as the "father of modern painting"?

During Titian's time (1488 or 1490-1576), artists began painting on canvas rather than on wood panels. A master of color, the Venetian painter was both popular and prolific. His work was so sought after that even with the help of numerous assistants, he could not keep up with demand.

His body of works established oil color on canvas as the typical medium of western pictorial tradition. Among his most well-known paintings are *Sacred and Profane Love* (c. 1515) and *Venus of Urbino* (1538).

Why is **Rembrandt** considered the archetype of the modern artist?

To understand the similarities between Rembrandt van Rijn (1606-1669) and the modern artist, it's important to note that this master portrait-painter, who broke ground in his use of light and shadow, was in his own time criticized for his work: Some thought it too personal or too eccentric. An Italian biographer asserted that Rembrandt's works were concerned with the ugly, and he described the artist as a tasteless painter. Rembrandt's subjects included lower-class people, the events of everyday life and everyday business, as well as the humanity and humility of Christ (rather than the choirs, trumpets, and celestial triumph that were the subjects of other religious paintings at the time). His portraits reveal his interest in the effects of time on human features—including his own. In summary, the Dutch artist approached his work with "psychological insight and...profound sympathy for the human affliction." He was also known to use the butt end of his brush to apply paint. Thus, he strayed outside the accepted limits of great art at the time.

Art critics today recognize Rembrandt as not only one of the great portrait painters, but a master of realism. The Dutch painter, who also etched, drew, and made prints, is regarded as an example for the working artist; he showed that the subject is less important than what the artist does with his materials.

Among his most acclaimed works are *The Syndics of the Cloth Guild* (1662) and *The Return of the Prodigal Son* (c. 1665). The first painting shows a board of directors going over the books, and Rembrandt astutely captures the moment when the six businessmen are interrupted, thus showing a remarkably real everyday scene. *The Return of the Prodigal Son* is one of the most moving religious paintings of all time. Here Rembrandt has with great compassion rendered the reunion of father and son, capturing that moment of mercy when the contrite son kneels before his forgiving father. Through his series of self-portraits, Rembrandt documented his own history—from the confidence and optimism of his youth to the "worn resignation of his declining years."

What exactly is **impressionism**?

The term "impressionism" was derived by a rather mean-spirited art critic from the title of one of Claude Monet's (1840-1926) early paintings, *Impression, Fog* (*La Havre,* 1872). The French impressionist painters were interested in the experience of the natural world and in rendering it exactly as it is seen—not fixed and frozen with an absolute perspective, but rather as constantly changing and as it is glimpsed by a moving eye.

Georges Seurat (1859-1891) and Paul Signac (1863-1935) are also typically thought of as impressionists; however, they are more appropriately dubbed neoimpressionists since they, along with Camille Pisarro (1830-1903), advanced the work of the original group through more scientific theories of light and color, introducing deliberate optical effects to their works. Seurat and Signac are commonly referred to as pointillists for the technique, pioneered by Seurat, of using small brush strokes to create an intricate mosaic effect. The postimpressionists, artists representing a range of explorations but all having come out of the impressionist movement, included both Seurat and Signac, as well as Henri de Toulouse-Lautrec (1864-1901), Paul Gaugin (1848-1903), Vincent van Gogh (1853-1890), and Paul Cézanne (1839-1906, who was also associated with the original impressionists).

Together the impressionists paved the way for the art of the twentieth century, since as a group they "asserted the identity of a painting as a thing, a created object in its own right, with its own structure and its own laws beyond and different from...the world of man and nature" (*History of Modern Art*).

Was **Monet** the "father of French impressionism"?

Though the movement was named for one of Claude Monet's (1840-1926) paintings and his *Water Lilies* (1905) are arguably the most well-known and highly acclaimed impressionist works, impressionism is actually rooted in the works of the group's spiritual leader, Édouard Manet (1832-1883), who first began experimenting with color and light to bring a more naturalistic quality to painting.

In 1863 Manet exhibited two highly controversial and groundbreaking works: *Déjeuner sur l'herbe* and *Olympia.* Both paintings were based on classic subjects, but Manet rendered these pastoral scenes according to his own experience, giving them a decidedly more earthy and blatantly erotic quality than the Parisian critics and academicians of the day could accept. He was roundly criticized for his scandalous exhibition. Nevertheless, Manet persevered, and in 1868, with his portrait of the French writer Emile Zola, he again challenged the art world and its values. A critic for *Le National* denounced the portrait and cited among his complaints that Zola's trousers were not made of cloth. This, the artists observed, was both truth and revelation: the pants were made of paint. A few years later, in 1870, Manet began experimenting with painting outside, in the brilliance of natural sunlight. Manet pioneered many of the ideas and techniques taken up by the impressionists.

How did American **Mary Cassatt** join the Paris art world of the impressionists?

Mary Cassatt (1844-1926), the daughter of a wealthy investment banker from Pittsburgh, Pennsylvania, traveled to Paris in 1866 in the company of her mother and some women friends; the young Cassatt was determined to join the city's community of artists. Since women were not allowed to enroll in classes at Paris's Institute of Beaux Arts (the policy was changed in 1897), Cassatt privately studied painting and traveled in Europe, pursuing her artistic interests. Returning to Paris in 1874, she became acquainted with Edgar Degas (1834-1917), who remarked that the American artist possessed an "infinite talent" and that she was "a person who feels as I do." He made these observations after viewing one of her paintings at the Salon d'Automne in Paris. Cassatt went on to exhibit with the impressionists in 1879, 1880, 1881, and 1886, gaining her first solo exhibit in 1891.

Judith Barter, curator of American arts at the Art Institute of Chicago and organizer of the traveling exhibit "Mary Cassatt: Modern Woman," describes Cassatt as "a very good businesswoman...who knew how to market her career." During three and a half years of research, which she conducted to launch the exhibit, Barter explored the prevailing social climate of the day: The late nineteenth century was a time when feminists, who organized to campaign for political and social reforms (eventually winning women the vote in 1920), focused on maternity, encouraging women to be involved in caring for their children. To Cassatt, observed Barter, maternity was "the highest expression of womanhood." Women and children were the subjects of Cassatt's body of works, which includes oil paintings, pastels, prints, and etchings.

Cassatt's place among the impressionists has often been overshadowed by her male colleagues, and her contributions to the art world are mentioned only in passing in many art books, but her talent, insights, and sheer determination combined to create an impressive legacy. As Gaugin quipped, "Mary Cassatt has charm but she also has force."

Why were **Matisse's** paintings considered so **shocking** when they were debuted?

Even if they seem commonplace to art today, the color and style of the paintings of French expressionist Henri Matisse (1869-1954) were revolutionary in their day.

In 1905 Matisse, along with several other artists, exhibited works at Paris's Salon d'Automne. The wildly colorful paintings on display there are said to have prompted an art critic to exclaim that they were *fauves,* or "wild beasts." The name stuck: Matisse and his contemporaries who were using brilliant colors in an arbitrary fashion became known as the fauves. His famous work *Madame Matisse,* or *Green Stripe* (1905), showed his wife with blue hair and a green stripe running down the middle of her face, which was colored pink on one side of her nose and yellow on the other. Matisse was at the forefront of a movement that was building new artistic values. The fauves were not using color in a scientific manner (as Georges Seurat had done), nor were they using it in the nondescriptive manner of Paul Gaugin (1848-1903) and Vincent Van Gogh (1853-1890). The fauves were developing the concept of abstraction.

Throughout his career, Matisse continued to experiment with various art forms—painting, paper cutouts, and sculptures. All of his works indicate a progressive elimination of detail and simplification of line and color. So influential was his style on modern art that some 70 years later one art critic commented that it was as if Matisse belonged to a later generation—and a different world.

Many of Picasso's works fall into the category of cubism, exemplified by this 1948 painting, *Woman in an Armchair.*

How is **Picasso's** work characterized?

It's impossible to characterize or classify the work of Spaniard Pablo Picasso (1881- 1973) since his career as an artist spanned his entire life and he experimented with many disciplines. Picasso often claimed that he could draw before he could speak, and by all accounts he spent much of his childhood engaged in drawing. He was only 15 years old when he submitted his first works for exhibition. And by the turn of the century, when he was still a young man, he began exploring the blossoming modern art movement. The rest of his career breaks into several periods. His Blue period (1901-04) was named for the monochromatic use of the color for its subjects, and was likely the result of a despair brought on by the suicide of a friend. Next came his Rose period (beginning 1905), when images of harlequins and jesters appear in his works—all to a somewhat melancholic effect. He soon began to incorporate aspects of primitive art, and later experimented with geometric line and form in his works, which were constructions—or deconstructions—sometimes only identifiable by their title.

In the spring of 1912 cubism exploded, and Picasso was on its forefront. In 1923 he broke new ground with surrealism. The key masterpiece in his body of works came in 1937 when he painted *Guernica,* his rendering of the horror of the German attack (supported by Spanish fascists) on the small Basque town (of Guernica) in Spain. His career reached its height during the 1940s, during which he lived in Nazi-occupied Paris.

Biographer Pierre Cabbane summed up the last period (1944-73) of Picasso's work: "He invented a second classicism: autobiographical classicism.... His final 30 years were to be a dizzying, breakneck race toward creation." During this time, Picasso did not chart any new artistic territory, but simply created art at an amazing rate. After his death in 1973, his estate yielded an inventory of 35,000 remaining works—paintings, drawings, sculptures, ceramics, prints, and woodcuts.

He left an enormous—even mind-boggling—legacy to the art world. In a 1991 article in *Vanity Fair,* Picasso's friend and biographer John Richardson observed, "Almost every artist of any interest who's worked in the last 50 years is indebted to Picasso...whether he's reacting against him knowingly or is unwittingly influenced by him. Picasso sowed the seeds whose fruits we are continuing to reap."

PHOTOGRAPHY

When was **photography** invented?

The concept of still photography dates back to the tenth century when Islamic scientists developed the camera obscura (Latin for "dark chamber"), a darkened enclosure with a small aperture (opening) to admit light. The light rays would cast an inverted image of external objects onto a flat surface opposite the aperture. This image could be studied and traced by someone working inside the camera obscura, or the image could be viewed from the outside of the camera, through a peephole.

In the sixteenth century, the Italian scientist Giambattista della Porta (c. 1535-1615) published his studies on fitting the aperture of the camera obscura with a lens to strengthen or enlarge the image projected. Made increasingly versatile through additional improvements, the camera obscura become popular among seventeenth- and eighteenth-century European artists.

But the camera obscura could only project (rather than reproduce) images onto a screen or a piece of paper. During the 1800s scientists experimented with ways of making the images permanent. Among those who made advances in the photographic process were French physicist Joseph-Nicéphore Niepce (1765-1833), who produced the first negative image in 1826; French painter Louis-Jacques Daguerre (1759-1851), who in 1839 succeeded in making a direct positive image on a silver plate, known as the daguerreotype; English scientist William Henry Fox Talbot (1800-1877), who developed a paper negative (c. 1841) that could be used to print any number of paper positives; and English astronomer Sir John Herschel (1792-1891), who was the first to produce a practical photographic fixing agent and the first to apply the terms "positive" and "negative" to photographic images. All of these milestones made photography a practical way of permanently recording real-life images.

The breakthrough in still photography was the Kodak, introduced in 1888 by American inventor George Eastman (1854-1932). The Kodak camera used film that was wound on rollers, eliminating the glass photographic plates that had been in use. The box-shaped camera made photography accessible to everyone—including amateurs. By

Thomas Edison and George Eastman stand with a motion picture camera, c. 1925. Both inventors contributed to the innovation of movies.

the early 1900s the Eastman Kodak Company had become the largest photographic film and camera producer in the world. George Eastman has been credited with mass-producing the moment: Before the Kodak (a word he made up because he was fond of the letter *k*), photography had largely been the domain of professionals who were commissioned to take portraits of the well-to-do prominent members of society. Once the Kodak became widely available, photographs preserved the faces of ordinary people and the events of everyday life.

When was **photography** established as an **art form**?

In the early 1900s. Alfred Stieglitz (1864-1946) is the acknowledged "father of modern photography." His interest in the medium began when he was just a toddler: at the age of two, he became obsessed with a photo of his cousin, carrying it with him at all times. When he was nine years old, he took exception to a professional photographer's practice of using pigment to color a black-and-white photo, complaining that this spoiled the quality of the print.

Between 1887 and 1911 Stieglitz worked to establish photography as a valid form of artistic expression, a pursuit for which he was sometimes publicly derided. He believed that photography should be separate from painting, but on an equal footing as an art form. He also strove to differentiate photography by instilling it with an American essence; the streets of New York City became his subject. By the time Stieglitz founded the Photo-Secession Group in 1902, he had developed a uniquely American art form. Stieglitz also published and edited photography magazines, most notably *Camera Work* (1903-17). After an unhappy first marriage, in 1924, Stieglitz married American artist Georgia O'Keeffe (1887-1986), who became the subject of one of his best-known series of works.

ARCHITECTURE

How old is the **Great Wall of China**?

The immense structure, built as a barricade of protection against invasion, was begun during the third century B.C. by Emperor Shih Huang Ti (Cheng; c. 259-210 B.C.) of

The Great Wall of China, originally built as a barricade against invasion, stretches 1,500 miles and is visible from space.

the Ch'in dynasty, and was expanded over the course of succeeding centuries. The wall stretches 1,500 miles, ranges in height between 20 to 50 feet, and is between 15 and 25 feet thick. In the thirteenth century, the wall was penetrated when Mongols conquered China, expanding their empire across all of Asia.

How old is the **Parthenon**?

The ancient temple, originally built on the Acropolis, a hill overlooking the city of Athens, was constructed between 447 and 432 B.C. by Greeks. The white marble edifice, considered a prime example of Greek architecture, has an interesting history: About A.D. 500, it became a Christian church; in the mid-1400s, when the region was captured by Turkish Muslims, it was turned into a mosque; and in 1687, when Venetians tried to take the city, the Parthenon was severely damaged; only ruins remain today.

How was the **Colosseum** ruined?

The Roman structure, begun during the reign of Vespasian (ruled A.D. 69-79), was disassembled during the Middle Ages (500-1350) when its stones and brocks were removed and used to construct other buildings. The Colosseum, situated in the center of the city of Rome, was a giant, outdoor theater. Between 80 and 404, it was an entertainment center where battles were staged, gladiators competed, and men fought wild animals. It could seat 50,000 spectators who were separated from the arena by a 15-foot wall.

When was London's **Westminster Abbey** built?

The famed national church of England was begun between 1042 and 1065 when Edward the Confessor (c. 1003-1066) built a church on the site of the Abbey. King Henry III (1207-1272) began work on the main part of Westminster in 1245. Since the time of William the Conqueror (1066), all of England's rulers, except Edward V and Edward VIII, have been crowned at the church. The Abbey is also a burial place of great English statesmen and literary giants (the latter are buried in the Poet's Corner).

Why does the **Leaning Tower of Pisa** lean?

The famous bell tower in Pisa (in northwestern Italy) leans because of the unstable soil on which it was built. Construction began in 1173 on the approximately 180-foot campanile; it began to lean as soon as the first three floors were completed. Nevertheless, building continued, and the seven-story structure was finished between 1360 and 1370. Leaning a bit more each year, by the time it was closed for repairs in 1990, the tower tilted 14.5 feet out of line when measured from the top story. Engineers on the project worked to stabilize the foundation and straighten it slightly (to prevent damage). The tower, which was built alongside a church and a baptistery, would probably not be remarkable if it were not for its slant. But with its characteristic angle, it continues to attract tourists to the small town on the Arno River.

Why is the **Cathedral of Notre-Dame** famous?

The Paris cathedral was built using the first true flying buttresses (masonry bridges that transmit the thrust of a vault or a roof to an outer support). The device allowed the structure to achieve a great height—one of the first Gothic churches to do so. Gothic was a medieval architectural style that predominated in northern Europe from the early twelfth century until the sixteenth century; it was epitomized in elaborate churches with stained-glass windows—ornamentation meant to instill the building itself with transcendental qualities. One of the leading examples of Gothic architecture is the Amiens Cathedral (in Amiens, northern France), which was begun in 1220. Its soaring nave (the central area of a church) epitomizes the era's drive for height. The Amiens cathedral is France's largest.

Why is Spain's **Alhambra** historically important?

The elaborate palace, built east of the city of Granada, in southern Spain, was built by Moors, Muslim North Africans who occupied the Iberian Peninsula (Spain and Portu-

Upon completion in 1883 the Brooklyn Bridge was considered a feat of modern engineering. (Photo, c. 1900.)

gal) for hundreds of years during the Middle Ages (500-1350). The fortified structure, built between 1238 and 1354, is a monument of Islamic architecture in the Western world. Its name is derived from an Arabic word meaning "red"; the highly ornamental palace, with its decorative columns, walls, and ceilings, was constructed of red brick. Perched on a hilltop, the Alhambra was the last stronghold of the Moors in Spain. In 1492 the palace was captured by forces of Spain's King Ferdinand (1452-1516) and Queen Isabella (1451-1504).

When was the **Brooklyn Bridge** completed?

The bridge, which spans New York's East River to connect Manhattan and Brooklyn, was completed in 1883. Upon opening, it was celebrated as a feat of modern engineering and, with its twin gothic towers, as an architectural landmark of considerable grace and beauty. It is a high statement of the era—an expression of the optimism of the Industrial Revolution. It was designed by German American engineer John Augustus Roebling (1806-1869), who, upon his death, was succeeded on the project by his son Washington Augustus Roebling (1837-1926). When the Brooklyn Bridge was finished, it was the longest suspension bridge in the world: it measures 1,595 feet. The bridge hangs from steel cables that are almost 16 inches thick. The cables are suspended from stone and masonry towers that are 275 feet tall. Specially designed watertight chambers allowed for the construction of the two towers—whose bases are built on the floor of the East River. The project proved to be an enormous and dangerous undertaking. Underwater workers suffered from the bends, a serious and potentially fatal blood condition caused by the decrease in pressure that results from rising from the water's depth too quickly. But man prevailed against the elements and, following 14 laborious years, on May 24, 1883, the Brooklyn Bridge was inaugurated. Five years later, Brooklyn became a borough of New York City, and in 1964 the bridge was designated a national historic landmark.

When did **modern architecture** begin?

The term "modern architecture" is used to refer to the architecture that turned away from past historical designs in favor of designs that are expressive of their own time. As such, it had its beginnings in the late nineteenth century when architects began reacting to the eclecticism that was prevalent at the time. Two "schools" emerged: art nouveau and the Chicago school.

Art nouveau, which had begun about 1890, held sway in Europe for some 20 years and was evident not only in architecture and interiors, but in furniture, jewelry, typography, sculpture, painting, and other fine and applied arts. Its proponents included Belgian architects Victor Horta (1861-1947) and Henry Van de Velde (1863-1957), and Spaniard Antonio Gaudi (1852-1926).

But it was the Chicago school that, in the rebuilding days after the Great Chicago Fire (1871), created an entirely new form. American engineer and architect William Le Baron Jenney (1832-1907) led the way. Four of the five younger architects who followed him had at one time worked in Jenney's office: Louis Henry Sullivan (1856-1924), Martin Roche (1855-1927), William Holabird (1854-1923), and Daniel Hudson Burnham (1846-1912). Burnham was joined by another architect, John Wellborn Root (1850-1891). Together these men established solid principles for the design of modern buildings and skyscrapers where "form followed function." Ornament was used sparingly, and the architects fully utilized iron, steel, and glass.

By the 1920s modern architecture had taken firm hold, and in the mid-twentieth century it was furthered by the works of Walter Adolf Gropius (1883-1969), Le Corbusier (Charles-Édouard Jeanneret; 1887-1965), Ludwig Mies van der Rohe (1886-1969), and Frank Lloyd Wright (1867-1959). For practical purposes, modern architecture ended in the 1960s with the deaths of the aforementioned masters.

Examples of modern architecture include Chicago's Monadnock Building (1891), Reliance Building (1895), Carson Pirie Scott store (1904), and Robie House (1909); New York City's Rockefeller Center (1940), Lever House (1952), and Seagram Building (1958); as well as Taliesin West (1938-59) in Arizona, Johnson Wax Company's Research Tower (1949) in Wisconsin, and the Lovell House (1929) in Los Angeles.

Who invented the **skyscraper**?

The credit is usually given to American architect William Jenney (1832-1907), who designed the 10-story Home Insurance Building, erected on the corner of LaSalle and Monroe Streets in Chicago in 1885. The building was the first in which the entire structure was of skeleton construction—of cast iron, wrought iron, and Bessemer steel. However, some experts believe the first skyscraper to have been designed was one by the American firm Holabird and Roche, also in Chicago. The firm, founded by two former students of Jenney, designed the skeleton-framed Tacoma Building, which was actually not completed until 1889. Both the Home Insurance Building and the Tacoma Building were demolished in 1931 and 1929, respectively.

It was the use of steel, the innovation of a safe elevator, and the use of central heating that combined to make possible the construction of tall buildings toward the end of the nineteenth century. Once the trend had started, it quickly took off: Another Chicago firm, Burnham and Root (Burnham, too, had been a student of Jenney), completed the 14-story Reliance Building in 1895; it had a steel skeleton frame. The further development of the skyscraper is visible in the Gage Buildings in Chicago—two of which were designed by Holabird and Roche, and one by Louis Henry Sullivan (1856-1924), the Chicago architect often credited for mastering the skyscraper. Other Chicago skyscrapers built by Holabird and Roche during the early days of modern architecture include the Marquette Building (1894) and the Tribune Building (1901).

What is the **tallest man-made structure** in the world?

The Burj Dubai skyscraper is currently the tallest structure. When completed, it will reach a height of over 2,064 feet (629 meters). It has surpassed the CN Tower in Toronto, Canada, which since 1976 was the world's tallest building at 1,815 feet (553.3 meters).

THEATER

How old is the **dramatic** form of **tragedy**?

Tragedy, a form of drama central to western literature, dates to ancient times—the fifth century B.C., when Greeks held a religious festival to honor the god Dionysus (god of fertility, wine, and, later, drama). Famous ancient tragedies include *Oresteia* by Aeschylus (who is credited with inventing tragedy), *Oedipus Rex* by Sophocles, and *Medea* and *Trojan Women* by Euripides. The philosopher Aristotle observed that tragedy's function is a cathartic one—by participating in the drama, the spectators are purged of their emotions of pity and fear. The well-known Renaissance tragedies of

William Shakespeare (1564-1616) harken back to the works of Roman statesman and playwright Seneca (c. 4 B.C.-A.D. 65), who wrote during the first century. He is credited with creating dramatic conventions including unity of time and place, violence, bombastic language, revenge, and ghostly appearances.

How old is **comedy**?

Like tragedy, comedy as a form of drama dates back to ancient Greece. While tragedy was meant to engage human emotions, thereby cleansing spectators of their fears (according to Aristotle), comedy's intent was simply to entertain and amuse audiences. Athenian poet Aristophanes (who flourished circa the fifth century B.C.) is considered the greatest ancient writer of comedy. His plays, written for the festival of Dionysus (the god of fertility, wine, and, later, drama), were a mix of social, political, and literary satire. Performance vehicles included farce, parody, and fantasy. During the fourth century B.C., this old comedy evolved into a new comedy, which was less biting and more romantic and realistic in nature. New comedy, which was marked by strong character development and often subtle humor, includes the works of Greek playwright Menander (flourished during the fourth century B.C.) and those of Roman comic writers Plautus (flourished third century B.C.) and Terence (flourished second century B.C.), all of whom were influences on Ben Jonson, William Shakespeare, Jean Molière, and other writers of the sixteenth and seventeenth centuries.

What is ***No*** drama?

It is the oldest form of traditional Japanese drama, dating to A.D. 1383. It is rooted in the principles of Zen Buddhism, a religion emphasizing meditation, discipline, and the transition of truth from master to disciple. History and legend are the subjects of *No* plays, which are traditionally performed on a bare, wooden stage by masked male actors who performed the story using highly controlled movements. The drama is accompanied by a chorus, which chants lines from the play. The art form was pioneered by actor-dramatist Motokiyo Zeami (1363-1443) when he was 20 years old. Zeami had begun acting at age seven and went on to write more than half of the roughly 250 *No* dramas that are still performed today.

What are the elements of **Japanese kabuki**?

The most popular traditional form of Japanese drama, kabuki features dance, song, mime, colorful costumes, heavy makeup, and lively, exaggerated movements to tell stories about historical events. The drama had its beginnings in 1575 when Okuni, a woman, founded a kabuki company. In 1603 at Kyoto women danced at the Kitani shrine, playing men's roles as well as women's. In October 1629 kabuki became an all-male affair by order of the shogun Iemitsu, who decided that it was immoral for women to dance in public. Just as in Elizabethan England, women's roles were then performed by men. The performing art became increasingly popular during the 1600s, eclipsing *bunraku* (puppet theater), in which a narrator recites a story, which is acted by large, lifelike puppets. Today kabuki remains a viable art form, borrowing from other forms of drama to adapt to changing times.

Japanese kabuki tells stories through dance, song, mime, colorful costumes, heavy makeup, and lively, exaggerated movements.

What is a **passion play**?

A passion play is a dramatization of the scenes connected with the passion and crucifixion of Jesus Christ. The roots of the passion play can be traced to ancient times: early Egyptians performed plays dedicated to the god Osiris (god of the underworld and judge of the dead), and the Greeks also acted out plays to honor their god Dionysus (the god of fertility, wine, and, later, drama). During the Middle Ages (500-1350) liturgical (religious ceremonial) dramas were performed. Toward the end of the tenth century, the Western church began to dramatize parts of the Latin mass, especially for holidays such as Easter. These plays were performed in Latin by the clergy, inside the church building. Eventually the performances became more secular, with laymen acting out the parts on the steps of the church or even in marketplaces.

The liturgical dramas developed into so-called miracle plays or mystery plays. As a symbol of gratitude or as a request for a favor, villagers would stage the life story of the Virgin Mary or of a patron saint. When the plague (also called the Black Death) ravaged Europe, the villagers at Oberammergau, Germany, in the Bavarian Alps, vowed to enact a passion play at regular intervals in the hope that by so doing they would be spared the Black Death. They first performed this folk drama in 1634 and have continued to stage it every 10 years, attracting numerous tourists to the small town in southern Germany.

Why is the **Globe Theatre** famous?

The Globe is known because of William Shakespeare's (1564-1616) involvement in it. In the 1590s an outbreak of the plague prompted authorities to close London theaters. At the time Shakespeare was a member of the Lord Chamberlain's Men, an acting company. With other members of the troupe, he helped finance the building of the Globe (on the banks of the Thames River), which opened in 1599 as a summer playhouse. Plays at the Globe, then outside of London proper, drew good crowds, and the Lord Chamberlain's Men also gave numerous command performances at court for King James. By the turn of the century, Shakespeare was considered London's most popular playwright, and by 1603 the acting group, whose summer home was the Globe Theatre, was known as the King's Men.

What was **vaudeville**?

Light, comical theatrical entertainment, vaudeville flourished at the end of the nineteenth century and beginning of the twentieth century. Programs combined a variety of music, theater, and comedy to appeal to a wide audience. Script writers attracted immigrant audiences by using ethnic humor, exaggerating dialects, and joking about the difficulties of daily immigrant life in America. (The word *vaudeville* is derived from an old French term for a satirical song, *vaudevire,* which is a reference to the Vire valley of France, where the songs originated.)

Vaudeville made its way to the American stage by the 1870s, when acts performed in theaters in New York, Chicago, and other cities. Troupes traveled a circuit of nearly 1,000 theaters around the country. As many as 2 million Americans a day flocked to the shows to see headliners such as comedians Eddie Cantor (1892-1964) and W. C. Fields (1880-1946), singer Eva Tanguay (1878-1947), and French actress Sarah Bernhardt (1844-1923).

During the first two decades of the twentieth century, vaudeville was the most popular form of entertainment in the country. In the 1930s, just as New York opened the doors of its famous Radio City Music Hall, which was intended to be a theater for vaudeville, the entertainment form began a quick decline. Motion pictures, radio, and, later, television took its place, with numerous vaudeville performers parlaying their success into these new media. Among those entertainers who had their origins in vaudeville acts were actors Rudolph Valentino, Cary Grant, Mae West, Jack Benny, George Burns, Gracie Allen, Ginger Rogers, Fred Astaire, Will Rogers, and Al Jolson.

MUSIC

When was our system for **notating music** developed?

The innovation came in the early eleventh century, when Guido of Arezzo (c. 991-1050), an Italian monk, devised a precise system for defining pitch. Guido was a leading music teacher and theorist in his day. As such, he was invited in about 1028 to Rome, where he presented a collection of religious anthems to Pope John XIX. Guido used a system of four horizontal lines (a staff) on which to chart pitch, and he used the syllables *ut* (later replaced with *do*), *re, mi, fa, sol,* and *la* to name the first six tones of the major scale. Before Guido developed his precise method for teaching music, singers had to learn melodies by memorizing them, a process that took many years. Using his notating system, singers were able to sight-read melodies. Guido's famous treatise, *Micrologus,* was one of the most widely used instruction books of the Middle Ages (500-1350).

How many **musical Bachs** were there?

Johann Sebastian Bach (1685-1750) was only one of a long and extended line of competent musicians—some 14 of them. The Bach family was a musical dynasty. J. S.'s father, Ambrosius Bach (1645-1695), was a court musician for the Duke of Eisenach, and several of J. S. Bach's close relatives were organists in churches. His eldest brother, Johann Christoph Bach (1671-1721), was apprenticed to the famous German composer Johann Pachelbel (1653-1706).

J. S. Bach left a musical legacy even beyond the vast body of church, vocal, and instrumental music that he composed: Four of his sons and one grandson were also accomplished musicians. "The English Bach" refers to J. S.'s son Johann Christian Bach (1735-1782), who composed operas, oratorios, arias, cantatas, symphonies, concertos, and chamber music. A proponent of Rococo style music, J. C. Bach influenced Wolfgang Amadeus Mozart (1756-1791).

Why do music historians talk about **"before Bach"** and **"after Bach"**?

Some scholars use these terms to classify music history since the life work of Johann Sebastian Bach (1685-1750) was so substantial, consisting of some 1,100 works, and has had lasting and profound influence on music composition. While he was not famous during his lifetime and had disagreements with employers throughout his career, J. S. Bach's works and innovations in many ways defined music as people now know it. The tempered scale is among his inventions, and he initiated a keyboard technique that is considered standard today. Chronologically, J. S. Bach marks the end of the "prolific and variegated" baroque era, which began about 1600 and ended the year of his death, 1750.

A devout Christian, J. S. Bach believed that all music was to "the glory of God and the re-creation of the human spirit." As a spiritual person and true believer in eternal life, he left behind an impressive body of church music, including 300 cantatas (or musical sermons) as well as passions and oratorios. As a devoted family man who believed all his children were born musicians (and therefore, the Bachs could stage drawing-room music at any time), J. S. Bach also wrote chamber music, including instrumental concertos, suites, and overtures. Among his most well-known and beloved works are *The Saint Matthew Passion; Jesu, Joy of Man's Desiring; Sheep May Safely Graze;* and his *Christmas Oratorio.*

How old was **Mozart** when he composed his first work?

A child prodigy, Wolfgang Amadeus Mozart (1756-1791) was composing at the age of five. He had been playing the harpsichord since the age of three. His father, Leopold (1719-1787), was a composer and violinist who recognized his son's unusual music ability and encouraged and taught young Mozart. In 1762 Leopold took his son and daughter, Maria Anna (nicknamed "Nannerl"; 1751-1829), on tour to Paris. While there, young Wolfgang Mozart composed his first published violin sonatas and improvisations.

However, the image of the effortless and "artless child of nature" is not altogether true. Contrary to the reports that the gifted composer never revised first-and-only drafts, he did work at his craft. In a letter to his father, he wrote, "It is a mistake to think that the practice of my art has become easy to me—no one has given so much care to the study of composition as I have. There is scarcely a famous master in music whose works I have not frequently and diligently studied." The fact is that he did make revisions to his works, though it is also true that he composed at a rapid pace. The result is an impressive body of works, unequaled in beauty and diversity. The complete output—some 600 works in every form (symphonies, sonatas, operas, operettas, cantatas, arias, duets, and others)—would be enough to fill almost 200 CDs. Among his most cherished works are *The Marriage of Figaro* (1786), *Don Giovanni* (1787), *Così fan tutte* (1790), and *The Magic Flute* (1791).

Was **Beethoven** really deaf for much of his life?

Yes, Ludwig van Beethoven (1770-1827) suffered a gradual hearing loss during his twenties, and eventually lost his hearing altogether (in his early thirties). The loss was devastating to the German composer. In a letter to his brother he wrote, "But how humbled I feel when someone near me hears the distant sound of a flute, and I hear nothing; when someone hears a shepherd singing, and I hear nothing!" At one point he even contemplated suicide but instead continued his work.

He had studied briefly with Mozart (in 1787) and Joseph Haydn (in 1792), and appeared for the first time in his own concert in 1800. While the loss of his hearing later prevented him from playing the piano properly, it did nothing to hold back his creativity. Between 1800 and 1824, Beethoven wrote nine symphonies, and many believe that he developed the form to perfection. His other works include five piano concertos and 32 piano sonatas, as well as string quartets, sonatas for piano and violin, opera, and vocal music, including oratorios. It was about the time that he completed his work on his third symphony, the *Eroica* (1804), that he went completely deaf. Though he was himself a classicist, music critics often refer to a turning point marked by the *Eroica,* which shows the complexity of the romantic age of music.

Ludwig van Beethoven, considered a genius of musical composition, was deaf for much of his life.

A true genius, Beethoven's innovations include expanding the length of both the symphony and the piano concerto, increasing the number of movements in the string quartet (from four to seven), and adding instruments—including the trombone, contrabassoon, and the piccolo—to the orchestra, giving it a broader range. Through his adventurous piano compositions, Beethoven also heightened the status of the instrument, which was a relatively new invention (1710). Among his most well-known and most-often-performed works are his third (*Eroica*), fifth, sixth (*Pastoral*), and ninth (*Choral*) symphonies, as well as the fourth and fifth piano concertos.

It is remarkable—even unfathomable—that these works, so familiar to so many, were never heard by their composer. A poignant anecdote tells of Beethoven sitting on stage to give tempo cues to the conductor during the first public performance of his ninth symphony. When the performance had ended, Beethoven—his back to the audience—was unaware of the standing ovation his work had received until a member of the choir turned Beethoven's chair around so he could see the tremendous response.

Why is **Brahms's** first symphony sometimes called **"Beethoven's tenth"**?

In many ways, Johannes Brahms (1833-1897) was the inheritor of Beethoven's genius, prompting some music historians to refer to Brahms's first symphony as "Beethoven's tenth." This is not to diminish the work of the great nineteenth-century composer, who left an enduring corpus of works. Brahms demonstrated that classicism continued to have artistic validity—and was not incompatible with—the romanticism of the late nineteenth century.

What does **Wagnerian** mean?

It is a reference to anything that is in the style of German composer Richard Wagner (1813-1883). Wagner was an enormously creative composer, conductor, and artistic manager who is credited with no less than originating the music drama. His interest in theater began in his boyhood, and by his teens he was writing plays. So that he could put music to these works, he sought out composition teachers. It is no surprise then that Wagner later conceived of the idea of the "total work of art," where music, poetry, and the visual arts are brought together in one stunning performance piece.

As an adult, Wagner led a scandalous life—even today challenging the music-listening public to separate his life from his art. He was someone modern audiences would recognize as a truly gifted and charismatic—if amoral—artist, working on a grand scale. Were he alive now, Wagner might well be creating blockbusters. In fact his musical compositions are heard in movies (including Francis Ford Coppola's *Apocalypse Now*) and are familiar to even the youngest audience today—or at least those who watch Bugs Bunny cartoons.

But this is not to take away from Wagner's serious accomplishments: His most widely recognized operatic works include *Lohengrin* (1848), the *Ring* cycle (1848-74), and *Tristan und Isolde* (1859). In the decades after his death, Wagner's reputation grew to the point that through the end of the nineteenth century his influence was felt by most every composer, who often referred to Wagner's works in measuring the value of their own.

Why did **Schoenberg** face sharp criticism in his day?

The Vienna-born American composer Arnold Schoenberg (1874-1951), now considered one of the great masters of the twentieth century, was derided for having thrown out the rules of composition—for working outside the confines of traditional harmony.

In his youth, he was a fan of Wagner's compositions, seeing each of his major operas repeatedly. A series of Schoenberg's early works reflect the Wagnerian influence. But just after the turn of the century, Schoenberg set out on his own path. The result was the 1909 composition *Three Pieces* for piano, which some music historians argue is the single most important composition of the twentieth century. The work is atonal, which is to say it is organized without reference to key. Schoenberg abandoned the techniques of musical expression as they had been understood for hundreds of years. This was no small moment for the music world, and many reacted with vocal and vehement criticism. (Of the outcry Schoenberg remarked in 1947 that it was as if "I had fallen into an ocean of boiling water.")

But he had his followers, too, among them his students. Though he was essentially self-taught as a composer, he became one of the most influential teachers of his time. It's interesting to note, however, that his teaching approach was grounded in the traditional practices of tonal harmony. He later brought order to the chaos of atonalism by developing a 12-tone serialism, showing how entire compositions could be organized around an ordained sequence of 12 notes. However, he never taught the method and rarely lectured or wrote about it.

Why does the music of **Bartók** figure prominently in concert programs today?

Béla Bartók (1881-1945) is revered today not only for his ability as a pianist (his teacher compared him to Franz Liszt [1811-1886], who was perhaps the greatest pianist of the nineteenth century), but for his compositions, which are steeped in the tradition of Hungarian folk music. Bartók studied and analyzed Hungarian, Romanian, and Arabian folk tunes, publishing thousands of collections of them in his lifetime. While ethnic music had influenced the works of other composers, Bartók was the first to make it an integral part of art music composition. His works were unique in that the folk music provided the sheer essence and substance of the music, lending the compositions a primitive quality. Among his masterpieces are his three stage works: the ballets *The Wooden Prince* and *The Miraculous Mandarin,* and the one-act opera *Duke Bluebeard's Castle.*

The introduction of folk music as the core of a musical composition has had far-reaching influence, which must have been felt by American composer Aaron Copland (1900-1990), whose *Appalachian Spring* (1944) features a simple Shaker tune, front and center.

Is **Stravinsky** the twentieth century's foremost composer?

The Russian-born American composer Igor Stravinsky (1882-1971) is certainly one of the greatest composers of the twentieth century. Stravinsky wrote concerts, chamber music, piano pieces, and operas, as well as ballets, for which he may be most well known.

Between 1903 and 1906 Stravinsky studied under the great Russian composer Nikolay Rimsky-Korsakov (1844-1908). In 1908 Stravinsky wrote his first work of note, the orchestral fantasy *Fireworks,* which was in honor of the marriage of Rimsky-Korsakov's daughter. The piece caught the attention of Sergey Diaghilev (1872-1929) of the Ballets Russes, who invited the young composer to participate in the ballet company's 1910 season (Ballets Russes had dazzled audiences the year before, bringing new energy to the art form). In collaboration with Diaghilev, Stravinsky went on to create masterpieces—*The Firebird* (1910), *Petrushka* (1911), and *Rite of Spring* (1913) among them. The partnership served to elevate the role of the ballet composer in the art world.

Rite of Spring is either Stravinsky's most famous or most infamous work. It was first performed by the Ballets Russes in the third week of its 1913 season. The choreography was arranged by the famous dancer Vaslav Nijinsky (1890-1950). But the per-

Jazz greats Duke Ellington (piano) and Louis Armstrong (trumpet) rehearse in New York City in January 1946.

formance stunned both the music and dance worlds. So extreme was the audience's reaction to this premier work that a riot nearly broke out inside the theater. Stravinsky had composed his music not to express spring's idyllic qualities but rather its turmoil and dissonance—similar to childbirth. Nijinsky paired Stravinsky's composition with complicated and visually frenzied dance movements, later characterized by the composer as a jumping competition. Though many thought it a disastrous performance, when the Ballets Russes continued to London, *Rite of Spring* was more widely accepted there—largely because the audience had been duly prepared for it.

The following year, *Rite of Spring* was performed in concert in Russia, but the reaction was mixed. The young composer Sergei Prokofiev (1891-1953) was in the audience and later wrote that he had been so moved by the work that he could not recover from the effects. Listeners today are still moved by the elevated rhythm of *Rite of Spring,* which makes an entire orchestra into a kind of sustained percussion instrument. Ultimately, most musicians and critics came to regard the watershed work as one of the finest compositions of the twentieth century.

Who invented **jazz**?

Ferdinand "Jelly Roll" Morton (1885-1941), a New Orleans pianist, claimed credit for having invented jazz. And to some degree, it was fair of him to think so—after all, his recordings with the group the Red Hot Peppers (1926-30) are among the earliest examples of disciplined jazz ensemble work. But in truth, the evolution of jazz from ragtime and blues was something that many musicians, in several cities, took part in. Most regard Morton as *one* of the founders of jazz, the other founders include Bennie Moten (1894-1935), Eubie Blake (1883-1983), Duke Ellington (1899-1974), and Thomas "Fats" Waller (1904-1943).

Some would go back even farther to trace the roots of jazz: From 1899 to 1914 Scott Joplin (1868-1917) popularized ragtime, which was based on African folk music. Even astute music critics may not be able to draw a clear-cut distinction between ragtime and early jazz. Both musical forms rely on syncopation (the stressing of the weak beats), and either style can be applied to an existing melody and transform it. The definitions and boundaries of the two terms have always been subject to debate, which is further complicated by the fact that some musicians of the time considered ragtime to be more or less a synonym for early jazz.

But there are important, albeit not strict, differences between the two genres as well: Rags were composed and written down in the European style of notation, while early jazz was learned by ear (players would simply show one another how a song went by playing it); jazz encourages and expects improvisation, whereas ragtime, for the most part, did not; and the basic rhythms are also markedly different, with jazz having a swing or "hot" rhythm that ragtime does not.

Whatever its origins, jazz became part of the musical mainstream by the 1930s and influenced other musical genres as well—including classical. American composer George Gershwin (1898- 1937) was both a songwriter and composer of rags as well as a composer of symphonic works. Many of his works, including *Rhapsody in Blue* (1924) and his piano preludes, contain ragtime and jazz elements.

Perhaps more than any other composer and musician, Miles Davis (1926-1991) expanded the genre: Through decades of prolific work, Davis constantly pushed the boundaries of what defines jazz and in so doing set standards for other musicians.

Is **blues music** older than jazz?

Only slightly (and only if your definition of jazz doesn't include ragtime). Really, the two musical traditions developed side by side, with blues emerging about the first decade of the 1900s and hitting the height of its early popularity in 1920s Harlem, where the songs were seen as an expression of African American life. Great blues singers like Ma Rainey (1886-1939) and Bessie Smith (1894 or 1898-1937) sang of the black reality—determined but weary. During the Harlem Renaissance the music was a symbol for African American people who were struggling to be accepted for who they were. Poet Langston Hughes (1902-1967) saw the blues as a distinctly black musical genre, and as helping to free blacks from American standardization.

As the first person to codify and publish blues songs, American musician and composer W. C. Handy (1873-1958) is considered the "father of the blues." The Florence, Alabama, native produced a number of well-known works, including "Memphis Blues," "St. Louis Blues" (which is one of the most frequently recorded songs in popular music), "Beale Street Blues," and "Careless Love."

When did the **Big Band** era begin?

On December 1, 1934, Benny Goodman's *Let's Dance* was broadcast on network radio, which effectively launched the swing era, in which Big Band music achieved huge popularity. Goodman (1909-1986) was a virtuoso clarinetist and bandleader. His jazz-influenced dance band took the lead in making swing the most popular style of the time.

How old is **country music**?

Old-time music or "hillbilly music," both early names for country music, emerged in the early decades of the 1900s. By 1920 the first country music radio stations had opened, and healthy record sales in rural areas caused music industry executives to take notice. But it was an event in 1925, in the middle of the American Jazz Age, that put country music on the map: On November 28, WSM Radio broadcast *The WSM Barn Dance,* which soon became known as *The Grand Ole Opry* when the master of ceremonies, George D. Hay, took to introducing the program that way—since it was aired immediately after an opera program. The show's first performer was Uncle Jimmy Thompson (1848-1931). Early favorites included Uncle Dave Macon (1870-1952), who played the banjo and sang, and Roy Acuff (1903-1992), who was the Opry's first singing star. Millions tuned in and soon the Nashville-based show had turned Tennessee's capital city into Music City U.S.A. In the 1960s and again in the late 1980s and 1990s, country music reached the height of popularity, while holding on to its small-town, rural-based audience who were the show's first fans.

Is **bluegrass** music a distinctly American genre?

Yes, the style of music developed out of country music during the late 1930s and throughout the 1940s. Bill Monroe (1911-1996), a country and bluegrass singer-songwriter, altered the tempo, key, pitch, and instrumentation of traditional country music to create a new style—named for the band that originated it, Bill Monroe and the Blue Grass Boys (Monroe's home state was Kentucky). Bluegrass was first heard by a wide audience when in October 1939, Monroe and his band appeared on the popular country music radio program *The Grand Ole Opry.*

Although bluegrass evolved through several stages and involved a host of contributors, through it all Bill Monroe remained the guiding and inspirational force, and therefore merits the distinction of being the "father of bluegrass."

Who was more important to **rock and roll**—Elvis Presley or the Beatles?

While music historians—and fans of either or both—may be willing to offer an opinion, the question cannot be definitively answered. The fact is that popular music today would not be what it is had it not been for both Elvis Presley and the Beatles. And the influences of both are still felt.

Elvis Presley (1935-1977) brought to music an exciting and fresh combination of country, gospel, blues, and rhythm and blues music, and topped it all off with a style and sense of showmanship that dazzled young audiences. His first commercial recording was "That's All Right, Mama" in 1954, which was followed in 1956 by the success of "Heartbreak Hotel." Between 1956 and 1969 he had 17 number-one records. Presley defined a new musical style—and an era.

Among those the American Presley had influenced were four English musicians who called themselves the Beatles. Originally founded as the Quarrymen by John Lennon (1940-1980) in 1956, the group became the most popular rock-and-roll band of the 1960s. Their first single was "Love Me Do," released on October 5, 1962, and producer George Martin was encouraged that the Beatles could produce a number-one record. In 1963 they did: "Please Please Me" was released in Britain on January 12 and was an immediate hit. Other hits off their first album included "She Loves You" and "I Want to Hold Your Hand." The follow-up album, *With the Beatles,* was released in 1964 and established them as Britain's favorite group.

Elvis Presley (shown in 1956) brought to music an exciting and fresh combination of country, gospel, blues, and rhythm and blues.

Already popular in their homeland, "Beatlemania" began in the United States on February 7, 1964, when the mop-topped "Fab Four" (Lennon along with Paul McCartney, b. 1942, George Harrison, 1943-2001, and Ringo Starr, b. 1940) arrived at New York's Kennedy International Airport and were met by a mob of more than 10,000 screaming fans and 110 police officers. Two days later, on February 9, the Beatles made their legendary appearance on *The Ed Sullivan Show.* By April the group held onto the top five positions on the U.S. singles charts. The British Invasion had begun.

In their early years, the Beatles brought a new energy to rock and roll and picked up where Presley, Buddy Holly, and Little Richard had left off. The instrumentation and orchestration of Beatles songs (for which their producer George Martin deserves at least some of the credit) were innovative at the time, and are common for rock music today. Their rock movies, *A Hard Day's Night* (1964) and *Help!* (1965), were a precursor to the music videos of today. When the band decided to break up, the April 10, 1970, announcement proved to be the end of an era.

DANCE

Why is the **Ballets Russes** famous?

The notoriety of the Ballets Russes began on a May night in 1909. It was then that the company, created by Russian impresario Sergey Diaghilev (1872-1929), performed innovative ballet choreographed by Michel Fokine (1880-1942). The Parisian audience, made up of the city's elite, was wowed by the choreography, set design, and musical scores, as well as the performances of the lead dancers—the athletic vigor of Vaslav Nijinsky, the delicate beauty of Tamara Karsavina, the expressiveness of Anna Pavlova, and the exotic quality of Ida Rubinstein. Ballet had been freed of the constraints and conventions that had held it captive. The art form was reawakened.

The reforms were on every level: choreography, performance, costuming, and design. The company's chief set designer was Léon Bakst (1866-1924), whose sense of color had influenced not only stage designs but even women's fashions. Soon Diaghilev and the Ballets Russes were at the center of the art world: Major twentieth-century painters, including Robert Edmond Jones, Pablo Picasso, Andre Derain, Henri Matisse, and Joan Miró, created set and costume designs for the dance company. And Diaghilev commissioned music that could match the spectacular dancing, choreography, and decor of his ballets. History's most celebrated composers, including Maurice Ravel, Claude Debussy, Richard Strauss, Sergei Prokofiev, and Igor Stravinsky, provided the scores for the dances performed by Ballets Russes. The company, under Diaghilev's direction, had created a completely different kind of dance drama, bringing ballet out of the shadows of opera and asserting it as an art form unto itself.

The ballet companies of today are the lasting legacy of the Ballets Russes. Diaghilev illustrated that through a collaborative process, excellent art could be created outside the traditional academy. The Ballets Russes provided twentieth-century dance with the model of the touring ballet company and seasonal repertory.

Who was **Balanchine**?

The name of the Russian-born choreographer is synonymous with modern American ballet: George Balanchine (1904-1983) was one of the most influential choreographers of the twentieth century, creating more than 200 ballets in his lifetime and choreographing 19 Broadway musicals as well as four Hollywood films. He co-founded three of the country's foremost dance institutions: the School of American Ballet (in 1934); the American Ballet Company (1935); and the New York City Ballet (1948), the first American ballet company to become a public institution.

His entrance into the world of dance was entirely accidental: In August 1914 Balanchine accompanied his sister to an audition at the Imperial School of Ballet and was invited to audition as well. Though his sister failed, he passed and, against his own wishes, was promptly enrolled. However, Balanchine remained uninterested in the art form, even running away from school shortly after starting. The turning point for the young dancer came with a performance of Tchaikovsky's ballet *The Sleeping*

Beauty (1890). He was dazzled by the experience and chose to stay with the school's rigorous training program.

Serenade (1935; music by Tchaikovsky) is considered by many to be Balanchine's signature work. His other well-known works include *Apollo* (1928), *The Prodigal Son* (1929), *The Nutcracker* (1954), and *Don Quixote* (1965), as well as *Jewels,* the first full-length ballet without a plot.

Remembering the opportunity he had been given as a child, Balanchine was known for choreographing children's roles into many of his ballets. His outreach did not end there: He organized lecture-demonstration tours for schools, gave free ballet performances for underprivileged children, conducted free annual seminars for dance teachers, and gave free advice and use of his ballets to other ballet companies. Balanchine's unparalleled body of work was instrumental in establishing the vibrant style and content of contemporary ballet in America, where he brought ballet to the forefront of the performing arts.

Who was **Dame Margot Fonteyn**?

Fonteyn (1919-1991) has been called an "international ambassador of dance." The British-trained ballerina achieved worldwide fame and recognition during more than 34 years with the Royal Ballet, expanding the company's female repertoire and becoming the model for the modern ballerina. In 1962, at the age of 43, Fonteyn formed a dance partnership with Soviet defector Rudolf Nureyev (1938-1993), challenging traditional assumptions about the ability of mature dancers to continue vigorous performance careers. In her later years, she continued to be active in the world of dance, helping set up dance scholarships, fostering international artistic relations, and encouraging the growth of dance institutions around the world.

How did **modern dance** begin?

American dancer and choreographer Martha Graham (1894-1991) is the acknowledged creator of modern dance. She was 35 years old when the Martha Graham Dance Group made its debut on April 14, 1929, ushering in a new era in dance performance. The new form of dance dissolved the separation between mind and body and relied on technique that was built from within.

Graham's interest in dance had begun in her youth, and as an astute observer and manipulator of light and space, she came to be regarded later in life as one of the masters of the modernist movement—on a par with artist Pablo Picasso (1881-1973). She is credited with revolutionizing dance as an art form; in her hands it had become nonlinear and nonrepresentational theater. Choreographing some 180 works in her lifetime, she also taught many students who rose to prominence as accomplished and masterful dancers, including Merce Cunningham and Paul Taylor.

Who founded the **Dance Theater of Harlem**?

The Dance Theater of Harlem, the first world-renowned African American ballet company, was founded by Arthur Mitchell (1934-), a principal dancer with the New York City Ballet, along with Karel Shook (1920-1985), a dance teacher and former director of the Netherlands Ballet. The impetus for the creation of the company came on April 4, 1968, while Mitchell was waiting to board a plane from New York City to Brazil (where he was establishing that country's first national ballet company) and he heard that Martin Luther King Jr. (1929-1968) had been assassinated. Mitchell later said that as he sat thinking about the tragic news, he wondered to himself, "Here I am running around the world doing all these things, why not do them at home?" Mitchell had spent his youth in Harlem, and he felt he should return there to establish a school to pass on his knowledge to others and to give black dancers the opportunity to perform. The primary purpose of the school was "to promote interest in and teach young black people the art of classical ballet, modern and ethnic dance, thereby creating a much-needed self-awareness and better self-image of the students themselves."

The idea was a success: During the 1970s and 1980s the company toured nationally and internationally, often performing to sell-out crowds and participating in prestigious events including international art festivals, a state dinner at the White House, and the closing ceremonies of the 1984 Olympic Games.

Today, the Dance Theater of Harlem is acknowledged as one of the world's finest ballet companies. Not only did Mitchell succeed in giving black dancers the opportunity to learn and to perform, he effectively erased color barriers in the world of dance, testimony to the universality of classical ballet.

How long has the **waltz** been danced?

Considered the quintessential ballroom dance, the waltz first became popular in Europe in 1813. But it dates as far back as the mid-1700s (the first written occurrence of the word *waltz* was in 1781). In the 1850s the dance captivated Vienna, and the prolific Johann Strauss (1825-1899), also known as the "Waltz King," produced scores of new waltzes to meet the increasing demand. Many of the compositions were named for professional associations and societies.

One of the most well-known waltzes is "The Blue Danube," first performed by Strauss on February 15, 1867, in Vienna. The lyrics, from a poem by Karl Beck, were sung by the Viennese Male Singing Society. The new waltz created an immediate sensation. It is an Austrian tradition whenever "The Blue Danube" is played that the opening strain is played first, followed by a pause before the work is played by the full orchestra. The pause is so that the audience may applause.

MOVIES

When was the **first movie** shown?

On March 22, 1895, the first in-theater showing of a motion picture took place in Paris, when the members of the Société d'Encouragement à l'Industrie Nationale (National Society for the Promotion of Industry) gathered to see a film of workers leaving the Lumière factory at Lyons for their dinner hour. The cinematography of inventors Louis (1864-1948) and Auguste (1862-1954) Lumière, ages 31 and 33 respectively, was a vast improvement over the kinetoscope, introduced in 1894 by Thomas Edison, whose film could only be viewed by one person at a time. The 16-frame-per-second mechanism developed by the Lumière brothers became the standard for films for decades. The following year, on April 20, 1896, the first motion picture showing in the United States took place in New York; the film was shown using Thomas Edison's vitascope, which was an improvement on his kinetoscope, and a projector made by Thomas Armat.

What are *the* **milestones in the motion picture industry**?

Motion pictures continue to develop as new, sophisticated technologies are introduced to improve the moviegoing experience for audiences. In the decades following their rudimentary beginnings, there were many early milestones, including not only advancements in technology but improvements in conditions for those working in the then-fledgling industry:

1903: Edwin S. Porter's *The Great Train Robbery* was the first motion picture to tell a complete story. Produced by Edison Studios, the 12-minute epic established a pattern of suspense drama that was followed by subsequent movie makers.

1907: Bell & Howell Co. was founded by Chicago movie projectionist Donald H. Bell and camera repairman Albert S. Howell with $5,000 in capital. The firm went on to improve motion picture photography and projection equipment.

1910: *Brooklyn Eagle* newspaper cartoonist John Randolph Bray pioneered animated motion picture cartoons, using a "cel" system he invented and which was subsequently used by all animators.

1912: *Queen Elizabeth,* starring Sarah Bernhardt, was shown July 12 at New York's Lyceum Theater and was the first feature-length motion picture seen in America.

1915: D. W. Griffith's *The Birth of a Nation* provided the blueprint for narrative films.

1925: The new editing technique used in *Potemkin* revolutionized the making of motion pictures around the world. Soviet film director Sergei Eisenstein created his masterpiece by splicing film shot at many locations, an approach subsequently adopted by most film directors.

1926: The first motion picture with sound ("talkie") was demonstrated.

1927: The Academy of Motion Picture Arts and Sciences was founded by Louis B. Mayer of MGM Studios. The first president of the academy was Douglas Fairbanks.

1927: The first full-length talking picture, *The Jazz Singer,* starring vaudevillian Al Jolson, was released. By 1932 all movies talked.

1929: The first Academy Awards (for 1928 films) were held: Winners were William Wellman for *Wings,* Emil Jannings for best actor (in *Last Command*), and Janet Gaynor for best actress (in *Sunrise*). Movie columnist Sidney Skolsky dubbed the awards "the Oscars."

1928: Hollywood's major film studios signed an agreement with the American Telephone & Telegraph Corporation (AT&T) to use their technology to produce films with sound, leading to an explosion in the popularity of motion pictures.

1929: Eastman Kodak introduced 16-millimeter film for motion picture cameras.

1933: The Screen Actors Guild (SAG) was formed when six actors met in Hollywood to establish a self-governing organization of actors. The first organizing meeting yielded 18 founding members.

1935: The first full-length Technicolor movie was released, *Becky Sharpe.* The technology, however, was still in development, and the colors appeared garish.

1939: *Gone with the Wind* was released in Technicolor, which had come along way since its 1935 debut.

What was the **Hollywood blacklist**?

In 1947 studio executives assembled at the Waldorf-Astoria Hotel in New York put together a list of alleged Communist sympathizers, naming some 300 writers, directors, actors, and others known or suspected to have Communist Party affiliations or of having invoked the Fifth Amendment against self-incrimination when questioned by the House Committee to Investigate Un-American Activities. The "Hollywood Ten" who refused to tell the committee whether or not they had been Communists were Alvah Bessie, Herbert Biberman, Lester Cole, Edward Dmytryk, Ring Lardner Jr., John Howard Lawson, Albert Maltz, Samuel Ornitz, Adrian Scott, and Dalton Trumbo. The film industry blacklisted the Hollywood Ten on November 25, and all of them drew short prison sentences for refusing to testify.

When was Hollywood's golden age?

Hollywood had its heyday in the 1930s: In the same decade that the Great Depression crippled the world economy, the American film industry enjoyed its golden age. The era was marked by technical innovations: "talking movies" had made their debut in 1927 with the first full-length film with sound, *The Jazz Singer,* and by 1932 all films were "talkies"; the first Technicolor film, *Becky Sharpe,* debuted in 1935, and by 1939 was perfected when *Gone with the Wind* was released; and special effects were brought to the screen in 1933 with *King Kong,* which was the result of painstaking stop-motion and rear-projection photography.

In the meantime, movie stars such as Clark Gable, Claudette Colbert, Greta Garbo, and the Marx Brothers achieved public followings that were "the envy of political and business leaders." The MGM, Warner Bros., and RKO studios led Hollywood production, but other studios, including Fox, Paramount, Universal, Columbia, and United Artists, also fared well during these difficult times. In 1939 Hollywood had what has often been called its greatest year: Among the top releases that year were the classics *Gone with the Wind, The Wizard of Oz, Stagecoach, Ninotchka, Mr. Smith Goes to Washington,* and *Gunga Din.* By the end of the decade Hollywood had become a "major contributor to popular culture, an occasional contributor to high culture, and a dynamic, if unsteady, force in the nation's economy."

What were **newsreels**?

Newsreels got their start in 1910 when the pioneer film newsreel *Pathé Gazette* was shown in Britain and the United States. French cinematographer Charles Pathé (1863-1957) and his brother Emil (1860-1937) were Paris agents for the Edison phonograph. They visited London to acquire filmmaking equipment and secured financial support in order to set up production units in Britain, the United States, Italy, Germany, Russia, and Japan. These short movies, covering current events, were predominately used during wartime and were shown in theaters before motion pictures were shown. Superseded by television newscasts, the last newsreels were screened in 1967.

ECONOMICS AND BUSINESS

What is **capitalism**?

The cornerstones of capitalism are private ownership of property (capital goods); property and capital create income for those who own the property or capital; individuals and firms openly compete with one another, with each seeking its own economic gain (so that competition determines prices, production, and distribution of goods); and participants in the system are profit-driven (in other words, earning a profit is the main goal). Capitalism is the antithesis of socialism, a theory by which government owns most, if not all, of a nation's capital. There is no pure capitalist system; national governments become involved in the regulation of business to some degree. But the economy of the United States is highly capitalistic in nature, as are the economies of many other industrialized nations, including Great Britain.

What does **laissez-faire** mean?

From the French, *laissez-faire* literally means "to let (people) do (as they choose)." As an economic doctrine, laissez-faire opposes government interference in economic and business matters, or at least desires to keep government's role to an absolute minimum. Laissez-faire favors a free market (a market characterized by open competition). The theory was popularized during the late eighteenth century as a reaction to mercantilism. Noted Scottish economist Adam Smith (1723-1790) was among the advocates of a laissez-faire market.

What is **mercantilism**?

An economic system that developed as feudalism was dissolving (at the end of the Middle Ages [500-1350]), mercantilism advocates strict government control of the national economy. Its adherents believe a healthy economy can only be achieved through state regulation. The goals were to accumulate bullion (gold or silver bars), establish a favorable balance of trade with other countries, develop the nation's agricultural concerns as well as its manufacturing concerns, and establish foreign trading policies.

Who was **Adam Smith**?

Scottish economist Adam Smith (1723-1790) is popular with conservative economists today because of his work titled *The Wealth of Nations* (written in 1776), which proposes a system of natural liberty in trade and commerce; in other words, a free-market economy. Smith, who was teaching at the University of Glasgow at the time, wrote, "Consumption is the sole end and purpose of all production, and the interest of the producer ought to be attended to, only so far as it may be necessary for promoting that of the consumer."

The Wealth of Nations established the classical school of political economy but has been faulted for showing no awareness of the developing Industrial Revolution. While Smith advocated both free-market competition and limited government intervention, he also viewed unemployment as a necessary evil to keep costs—and therefore prices—in check.

What is **Keynesian economics**?

Keynesian economics are the collected theories of British economist and monetary expert John Maynard Keynes (1883-1946), who in 1935 published his landmark work, *The General Theory of Employment, Interest and Money.* A macroeconomist (he studied a nation's economy as a whole), Keynes departed from many of the concepts of a free-market economy. In order to ensure growth and stability, he argued that government needs to be involved in certain aspects of the nation's economic life. He believed in state intervention in fiscal policies, and during recessionary times he favored deficit spending, the loosening of monetary policies, and government public works programs (such as those of President Franklin D. Roosevelt's New Deal) to promote employment. Keynes's theories are considered the most influential economic formulation of the twentieth century.

Having played a central role in British war financing during World War II (1939-45), Keynes participated in the Bretton Woods Conference of 1944, where he helped win support for the creation of the World Bank, which was established in 1945 as a specialized agency of the United Nations. The body aims to further economic development by guaranteeing loans to nations, extending easy credit terms to developing nations, and providing risk capital to promote private enterprise in less-developed nations. It's interesting to note that Keynes was a key representative at the Paris Peace Conference of 1919, where the Treaty of Versailles was drawn up, officially ending

World War I (1914-18). He quit the proceedings in Paris, returned to private life in London, and in 1919 published *The Economic Consequences of Peace,* in which he argued against the excessive war reparations that the treaty required of Germany. Keynes foresaw that the extreme punishment of Germany at the end of World War I would pave the way for future conflict in Europe.

MONEY

When was **money introduced**?

The use of money dates back some 4,000 years, when people began using something of recognized value, such as precious metals including gold and silver, to purchase goods and services. In the absence of money, all transactions were made on the barter system, which is an exchange of goods and services negotiated by the parties involved. The introduction of money simplified the acquisition of products and services. The ancient country of Lydia, in the western part of Asia Minor (modern-day Turkey), is credited with the first use of standardized coins, made of gold and silver, in the seventh century B.C.

When was **paper money** first used?

Paper money first appeared in China during the Middle Ages (500-1350). In the ninth century A.D., paper notes were used by Chinese merchants as certificates of exchange and, later, for paying taxes to the government. It was not until the eleventh century, also in China, that the notes were backed by deposits of silver and gold (called "hard money").

What was the **National Bank Act**?

The National Bank Act of 1863 was designed to create a national banking system, float federal war loans, and establish a national currency. Congress passed the act to help resolve the financial crisis that emerged during the early days of the American Civil War (1861-65); the fight with the South was expensive, and no effective tax program had been drawn up to finance it. In December 1861 banks suspended specie payments (payments in gold or silver coins for paper currency)—people could not convert bank notes into coins. The government responded by passing the Legal Tender Act (1862), issuing $150 million in national notes called greenbacks. But bank notes (paper bills issued by state banks) accounted for most of the currency in circulation.

To bring financial stability to the nation and fund the war effort, the National Bank Act of 1863 was introduced in the Senate in January of that year. Secretary of the

Treasury Salmon Chase (1808-1873), aided by Senator John Sherman (1823-1900) of Ohio, promoted it to the legislators. The bill was approved in the Senate by a close vote of 23 to 21. The House passed the legislation in February. National banks organized under the act were required to purchase government bonds as a condition of start-up. As soon as those bonds were deposited with the federal government, the bank could issue its own notes up to 90 percent of the market value of the bonds on deposit.

The National Bank Act improved but did not solve the nation's financial problems: Some of the 1,500 state banks, which had all been issuing bank notes, were converted to national banks by additional legislation (passed June 1864 to amend the original bank act). Other state banks were driven out of business or ceased to issue notes because of the 1865 passage of a 10 percent federal tax on notes they issued, making it unprofitable for them to print their own money. The legislation created $300 million in national currency—in the form of notes issued by the national banks. But since most of this money was distributed in the East, the money supply in other parts of the country remained precarious. The West demanded more money—an issue that would dominate American politics in the years after the American Civil War (1861-65). Nevertheless, the nation's banking system stayed largely the same—despite the Panic of 1873—until passage of the Federal Reserve Act in 1913.

What is the **Federal Reserve**?

It is the central banking system in the United States, created by a 1913 act of Congress, the Federal Reserve Act (sometimes called the Glass-Owens Bill). The legislation provided for a stable central banking system after the system set up by the National Bank Act of 1863 proved ineffective in managing the nation's currency, in responding to economic growth, or in exerting a controlling influence on the economy.

The Federal Reserve Act created 12 regional federal reserve banks: in Boston, Massachusetts; New York; Philadelphia, Pennsylvania; Cleveland, Ohio; Richmond, Virginia; Atlanta, Georgia; Chicago; St. Louis, Missouri; Minneapolis, Minnesota; Kansas City, Missouri; Dallas, Texas; and San Francisco, California. These institutions operate as "bankers' banks": member banks (commercial institutions) use their accounts with the Federal Reserve in the same way that consumers use their accounts on deposit at commercial banks. All national banks must be members of the Federal Reserve system; state banks may join the system upon meeting certain requirements. The Federal Reserve Act also established a Federal Reserve Board, now called the Board of Governors, to supervise the system. The board consists of seven members who are appointed by the president of the United States and are approved by the Senate. To reduce the possibility of nearsighted political influence, members serve staggered 14-year terms (one of the 14 terms expires every other year).

The duties of the Federal Reserve include lending money to commercial (member) banks, directing the reserve banks' purchase and sale of U.S. government securities on the open market, setting reserve requirements (for how much money needs to be in the U.S. Treasury), and regulating the discount rate (the interest rate the Federal Reserve charges commercial banks for loans), which is one of the system's principal influences on the economy. In performing these duties, the Federal Reserve (often called "the Fed" in financial circles) can expand (loosen) or contract (tighten) the supply of money in circulation. The Federal Reserve also issues the national currency and supervises and regulates the activities of banks and their holding companies. It began operation in November 1914.

The central bank systems of other developed nations include the Bank of Canada, Banque de France, and the Deutsche Bundesbank (of Germany).

When were **ATMs** introduced?

The ubiquitous automatic teller machine (ATM) was introduced in 1967 by Britain's Barclays Bank at a branch near London. Two years later, the Chemical Bank opened the first ATM in the United States, at Rockville Centre, New York. Self-service banking grew steadily in the 1980s and took off in the 1990s, when some banks began charging their customers for banking through tellers rather than ATMs.

When was the **euro** introduced?

The euro, the currency of the 12 European Union nations—Belgium, Germany, Greece, Spain, France, Ireland, Italy, Luxembourg, the Netherlands, Austria, Portugal, and Finland—went into circulation January 1, 2002, becoming part of daily life for more than 300 million people. The banknotes and coins replaced national currencies, making the franc, deutschmark, peseta, and lira, among others, history in the participating nations.

The euro's origins can be traced to a series of international agreements, beginning in 1978, which were made among the members of what was then called the European Community, or EC. In February 1986 the framework for the unified monetary system was agreed upon by nations who signed the Single European Act, creating "an area without internal frontiers in which the free movement of goods, persons, services, and capital is ensured." The 1989 Delors Report outlined a plan to introduce the currency in three phases. The final phase of that plan began on January 1, 1999, when the 11 countries (later to become 12) belonging to the European Union established the conversion rates between their respective national currencies and the euro, creating a monetary union with a single currency. A three-year transition phase followed, during which monetary transactions could be made in euro, but there was no requirement to do so. On January 1, 2002, the central banks of the 12 participating countries put into circulation about 7.8 billion euro notes and 40.4 billion euro coins, together worth 144 billion euros. Simultaneously each country began to withdraw its own currency from circulation. By February 28, 2002, the changeover was complete, meaning the national currencies were completely withdrawn and only the euro was in circulation.

When 10 new nations (Cyprus, Czech Republic, Estonia, Hungary, Latvia, Lithuania, Malta, Poland, Slovakia, and Slovenia) joined the EU on May 1, 2004, there was no timetable for their adoption of the euro. Previously, in 2003, Sweden voted against joining the euro area.

NATURAL RESOURCES

What was the biggest **gold rush**?

The greatest American gold rush began on January 24, 1848, when James Marshall discovered gold at Sutter's Mill in Coloma, California. Within a year, a large-scale gold rush was on. As the nearest port, the small town of San Francisco grew into a bustling city as fortune seekers arrived from around the world. Due to the influx, by 1850 California had enough people to qualify it for statehood. This pattern repeated itself elsewhere in the American West, including the Pikes Peak gold rush in 1859, which effectively launched the city of Denver, Colorado. The gold rush led to the discovery of copper, lead, silver, and other useful minerals. It also spawned related industry. One of the success stories is that of Levi Strauss (1829-1902), a Bavarian immigrant who in 1853 began making and selling sturdy clothing to miners in San Francisco.

In other countries, gold rushes had the same effect on the growth and development of regions: After the precious metal was discovered in Australia in 1851, the country's population almost tripled over the course of the next decade. The effect of an 1861 gold rush in nearby New Zealand was to double the country's population in six years' time. An 1886 discovery in South Africa led to the development of the city of Johannesburg. Just over a decade later, the infamous Yukon gold rush (in the Klondike region of Canada) spurred development there.

What is **"black gold"**?

Black gold is a term for oil or petroleum—*black* because of its appearance when it comes out of the ground, and *gold* because it made prospectors, drillers, and oil industry men rich. The oil industry in the United States began in 1859 when retired railroad conductor Edwin L. Drake (1819-1880) drilled a well near Titusville, Pennsylvania. His drill, powered by an old steam engine, struck oil. Oil from animal tallow and whales, had been used as a lubricant since colonial times. The discovery of a process for deriv-

Miners in Colorado, 1880. Gold rushes led to a mass migration of prospectors to the American West and spurred the growth of such cities as San Francisco and Denver.

ing kerosene, a clean-burning and easy-lighting fuel, from coal oil had been patented in 1854. After Drake's Titusville well produced shale oil, the substance was analyzed for its properties and it, too, was determined to be an excellent source of kerosene. Soon others began prospecting for "rock oil." Western Pennsylvania became an important oil-producing region. Wagons and river barges transported barrels to market; later, the railroad reached into the region; and by 1875 a pipeline was built to carry the oil directly to Pittsburgh. Petroleum products soon replaced whale oil as a fluid for illumination. During the 1880s, Ohio, Kentucky, Illinois, and Indiana also produced oil. In 1901 the famous Spindletop Field in eastern Texas produced the nation's first "gusher"—oil literally sprang out of the earth. During the next decade, California and Oklahoma joined Texas to lead the nation's oil production. Between 1859 and 1900, U.S. oil production boomed: Just 2,000 barrels were produced the year it was discovered in Pennsylvania; more than 64 million barrels were produced annually by the turn of the century.

The second half of the 1800s saw the oil industry boom: The fuel was used for lighting, heating, and lubrication (principally of machinery and tools). But the advent of the automobile and its central role in the life of twentieth-century America made the oil industry richer yet. Demand soon exceeded the nation's supply of petroleum, prompting the United States to increasingly rely on imported oil for fuel.

When did **diamond mining** begin in Africa?

An 1867 discovery of a "pretty pebble" along the banks of the Orange River in South Africa led to the finding of a rich diamond field near present-day Kimberley (the city was founded as a result of the mining, in 1871). Similar to the California gold rush roughly a decade and a half earlier, the finding in central South Africa prompted people from Britain and other countries to flock to the area. However, the ultimate outcome was conflict: Since both the British and the Boers (who were Dutch descendants living in South Africa) claimed the Kimberley area, the first Boer War ensued in 1880.

INDUSTRIAL REVOLUTION

How were **finished goods** produced **before the Industrial Revolution**?

Before the factory and machine age ushered in by the Industrial Revolution, people made many of their own finished goods, bought them from small-scale producers (who manufactured the goods largely by hand), or bought them from merchants who contracted homeworkers to produce goods. The putting-out system was a production method that was used in New England from the mid-1700s to the early 1800s. It worked this way: Merchants supplied raw materials (cotton, for example) to families, especially women and young girls, who would make partially finished goods (thread) or fully finished goods (cloth) for the merchant. These manufactured goods were then sold by the merchant. Homeworkers, who "put out" goods, provided the needed manufacturing labor of the day.

How did the **textile industry** begin?

The large-scale factory production of textiles began in the late 1700s, becoming established first in Great Britain, where a cotton-spinning machine was invented in 1783 by Richard Arkwright (1732-1792). Spinning mills were introduced to the United States in 1790 by English-born mechanist and businessman Samuel Slater (1768-1835). The 21-year-old had worked as a textile laborer for more than six years in an English mill where he learned the workings of Arkwright's machine, which the British considered the cornerstone of their booming textiles industry; laws prevented anyone with knowledge of the mill from leaving the country. In 1789 Slater, determined he could recreate the spinning mill and eager to seek his own fortune, disguised himself to evade the authorities and leave the country, sailing from England for American shores. Arriving in Providence, Rhode Island, he formed a partnership with the textiles firm Almy and

Young girls work in a basket factory, 1908. Child labor was rampant in the United States until the Fair Labor Standards Act of 1938 brought reforms.

Brown. Slater began building a spinning mill based on the Arkwright machine. This he did from memory. The spinning mill was debuted December 20, 1790, in the village of Pawtucket, Rhode Island, where the wheels of the mill were turned by the waters of the Blackstone River. The machine was a success and soon revolutionized the American textiles industry, which previously relied on cottage workers (the putting-out system) to manufacture thread and yarn.

Slater's innovation, which would earn him the title Father of the American Textiles Industry, spawned the factory system in the United States. By 1815 there were 165 cotton mills in New England, all working to capacity. The early mills were not large-scale, however, and for a time after Slaters's introductions, New England mills and merchants continued to rely on homeworkers to weave threads (now produced by the mills) into cloth.

In 1813 the Boston Manufacturing Company opened the first textile factory, where laborers ran spinning and weaving machines to produce woven cloth from start to finish. The advent of machinery had given rise to the factory system. And laborers were shifted from working in their homes to working in factories. While native New Englanders continued to provide the labor for the textile industry for the next two decades, an influx of immigrants in the mid-1800s provided the hungry manufacturers with a steady supply of laborers who were willing to work for less money and longer hours. Within the first three decades of the 1800s, New England became the center of the nation's textiles industry. The region's ample rivers and streams provided the necessary water power, and the commercial centers of Boston and New York City readily received the finished products. Labor proved to be in ample supply as well: Since the mill machinery was not complicated, children could operate it and did. Slater hired children ages 7 to 14 to run the mill, a practice that other New England textile factories also adopted. The Jefferson Embargo of 1807, which prohibited importing textiles, also aided the industry. New England's mills provided the model for the American factory system. Slater had brought the Industrial Revolution to America.

How did Eli Whitney invent the **cotton gin**?

American inventor Eli Whitney (1765-1825) is credited with developing the cotton gin, a machine that removes cottonseeds from cotton fibers. A simple cotton gin (called the *churka*) dates back to ancient India (300 B.C.). But Whitney's gin would prove to be far superior. In 1792 Whitney, who had recently graduated from Yale University, was visiting the Georgia plantation owned by Catharine Littlefield Greene, widow of American Revolution (1775-83) hero General Nathanael Greene (1742-1786). Whitney observed that short-staple (or upland) cotton, which has green seeds that are difficult to separate from the fiber, differs from long-staple (also called Sea Island) cotton, which has black seeds that are easily separated. The latter was the staple of American commerce at the time. In 1793 Whitney, who is described as a mechanical genius, completed an invention that could be used to clean bolls of short-staple cotton of their seeds; he patented it the next year.

The machine worked by turning a crank, which caused a cylinder covered with wire teeth to revolve; the teeth pulled the cotton fiber, carrying it through slots in the cylinder as it revolved; since the slots were too small for the seeds, they were left behind; a roller with brushes then removed the fibers from the wire teeth. The cotton gin revolutionized the American textiles industry, which was then but a fledgling concern. The increase in cotton production was as much as fiftyfold: One large gin could process 50 times the cotton that a (slave) laborer could in a day. Soon plantations and farms were supplying huge amounts of cotton to textile mills in the Northeast, where in 1790 another inventor, British-born industrialist Samuel Slater (1768-1835), had built the first successful water-powered machines for spinning cotton. Together the inventions founded the American cotton industry. Whitney struggled to protect his patent, but imitations of his invention were already in production, prompting the U.S. government to allow his patent to expire. Though he did not profit from his cotton gin, he went on to devise a system of interchangeable parts, which introduced the idea of mass production and revolutionized manufacturing.

Why was the **invention of the reaper** important to the U.S. economy?

Reapers, machines developed in the early 1800s to help farmers harvest grain such as wheat, dramatically increased overall grain production and consumption in the United States and the rest of the world. The first commercially successful reaper was built in 1831 by Virginia-born inventor Cyrus Hall McCormick (1809-1884), who patented it in 1834 and first sold it in 1840 in Virginia. The McCormick reaper was horse-drawn and replaced the use of sickles and scythes in the fields; it also reduced the amount of manual labor required to harvest grain crops. It worked in this way: A straight blade (protected by guards) was linked to a drive wheel; as the drive wheel turned, the blade moved back and forth in a sawing motion, cutting through the stalks of grain, which were held straight by rods; the cut grain stalks then fell onto a platform and were collected with a rake by a worker. The device increased average production from two or three acres a day to ten acres a day. McCormick's reaper was soon in wide use, and the inventor was on his way to becoming an industrialist.

In 1847 he moved his business to Chicago, were he could transport reapers via the Great Lakes and connected waterways to the East and to the South. Within five years McCormick's business had become the largest farm implement factory in the world. Sales and distribution of the equipment increased further during the 1850s as Chicago became a center for the nation's then-expanding rail system. In 1879 Cyrus McCormick's business became the McCormick Harvesting Machine Company, with the inventor himself as president (until 1884, when he was succeeded by his son). The reaper was improved over time: in the 1850s a self-raking feature was added, further reducing the amount of labor required to harvest grain; in the 1870s a binder was added, which bound the sheaves of grain and dropped them to the ground to be collected. In the 1920s the reaper (or harvester) was joined with another invention, the thresher, which separates grains from the stalks. The new reaper-thresher machine was called a combine. Today's combines still use the basic features present in McCormick's revolutionary 1831 invention. His company later became International Harvester (1902) and today is known as Navistar Corporation.

When did the American **cattle industry** begin?

As a large-scale commercial endeavor, the beef industry had its beginnings in the decades following the American Civil War (1861-65). Longhorn cattle, a breed of cattle descended from cows and bulls left by early Spanish settlers in the American Southwest, spurred the growth of the industry. Named for their long horns, which span about four feet, by the 1860s they had multiplied and great numbers of them roamed freely across the open range of the West. Ranchers in Texas bred the longhorns with other cattle breeds such as Hereford and Angus to produce quality meat. With beef in demand in the eastern United States, shrewd businessmen capitalized on the business opportunity, buying cattle for $3 to $5 a head and selling them in eastern and northern markets for as much as $25 to $60 a head. Ranchers hired cowboys to round up, sort out, and drive their herds to railheads in places like Abilene and Dodge City, Kansas, which became famous as "cow towns," raucous boom towns where saloons and brothels proliferated. After the long trail drive, the cattle were loaded onto rail cars and shipped live to local butchers who slaughtered the livestock and prepared the beef. For a 20-year period the plentiful longhorn cattle sustained a booming livestock industry in the West: at least 6 million Texas longhorns were driven across Oklahoma to the cow towns of Kansas.

By 1890 the complexion of the industry changed. Farmers and ranchers in the West used a new material, barbed wire, to fence in their lands, closing the open range; railroads were extended, bringing an end to the long, hard, and much-glorified cattle drives; the role of the cowboy changed, making him little more than a hired hand; and big business took over the industry. Among the entrepreneurs who capitalized on beef's place in the American diet was New England-born Gustavus Swift (1839-1903), who in 1877 began a large-scale slaughterhouse operation in Chicago, shipping ready-packed meat via refrigerated railcars to markets in the East.

Why was the **introduction of canning** important?

The advent of canned foods not only created an industry, but it altered the average American diet, helped usher in the consumer age, and saved time. Canning, a process for preserving food (vegetables, fruits, meats, and fish) by heating and sealing it in airtight containers, was developed by French candymaker Nicolas-François Appert (c. 1750-1841) in 1809, though he did not understand why the process worked. Some 50 years later, the pioneering work of French chemist and microbiologist Louis Pasteur (1822-1895) explained that heating is necessary to the canning process since it kills bacteria (microorganisms) that would otherwise spoil the food. Canning was introduced to American consumers in stages. In 1821 the William Underwood Company began a canning operation in Boston, Massachusetts; in the 1840s oyster canning began in Baltimore, Maryland; in 1853 American inventor Gail Borden (1801-1874) developed a way to condense and preserve milk in a can, founding the Borden Company four years later; and in 1858 American inventor John Landis Mason (1832-1902) developed a glass jar and lid suited to home canning.

Though early commercial canning methods did not ensure a safe product and many American women avoided the convenience foods, the canning industry grew rapidly, at least in part due to the male market, which included cowboys in the West. Between 1860 and 1870 the U.S. canning industry increased output from 5 million to 30 million cans. Improvements in the process during the 1870s helped eliminate the chance that cans would burst (a problem early on). And though the canning process changes food flavor, color, and texture, the convenience and long shelf life of canned foods helped them catch on: By the end of the 1800s a wide variety of canned foods, which had also come down in price, were common to the urban American diet. Companies such as Franco-American advertised in women's magazines, promoting their "delicacies in tins." An outbreak of botulism in the 1920s prompted the American canning industry to make further improvements to its process.

When did **chain stores** begin?

The innovation of the chain store, technically defined as two or more retail outlets operated by the same company and which sell the same kind of merchandise, was made by American businessmen George Gilman (c. 1830-1901) and George Huntington Hartford (1833-1917), who in 1859 set up the Great Atlantic & Pacific Tea Company in New York City. Better known as A&P, the stores proliferated rapidly, and other chain stores, such as W. P. Woolworth (established 1879) and J. C. Penney (1902) opened their doors for business. The early twentieth century saw tremendous growth of the chain stores: Between 1910 and 1931, the number of A&P stores grew from 200 to more than 15,000. While the department stores, also a byproduct of the late 1800s, catered to middle- and upper-class customers, the chain stores, including Woolworth's "five-and-dimes" (which sold many items at such low price points), served lower-income consumers.

Chain stores, which operate within all major retailing categories (including grocery stores, department stores, and drugstores, as well as apparel and food outlets), offer consumers many advantages. Their system of centralized and mass buying allow them to acquire merchandise from manufacturers and wholesalers at reduced costs; this savings is passed along to the consumer, who pays less for the item. Further, they experience economies of advertising: A single ad placement promotes all the stores within the chain. In the 1920s independent retailers rallied against the chain stores, citing they had unfair advantages. This argument has resurfaced off and on throughout the twentieth century, as chain stores entered into more and more retailing sectors, including hardware, jewelry, furniture, music, and books. But the only federal legislation that constructively attempted to regulate the chain stores came in 1936: The Robinson-Patman Act tried to control competition. Today chain stores account for roughly one-third of all American retail sales.

When did **department stores** begin?

Department stores, which offer a wide variety of goods for sale in various departments, emerged in the mid-1800s. Many evolved out of general stores (which offered a variety of goods but not divided into departments), while others evolved out of dry-goods stores (which sold textiles and related merchandise). The first bona fide department store was established in Paris: the Bon Marché (French meaning "good bargain") opened its doors in 1838. Between the 1850s and 1880s, numerous department stores opened in American cities—including Jordan Marsh, founded 1851 in Boston, Massachusetts; R. H. Macy's, founded 1858 in New York City (the store was known for its creative advertisements); Wanamaker's, founded 1861 in Philadelphia, Pennsylvania (it successfully implemented

Shoppers in a crowded Woolworth's. Department stores emerged in the mid-1800s.

fixed pricing so that customers no longer haggled over price); and Marshall Field, founded 1881 in Chicago (within 25 years it became the world's largest wholesale and retail dry goods store). These pioneer department stores, multistoried enterprises located in downtown areas, introduced many innovations to merchandising, including the policy of returnable or exchangeable goods, ready-made apparel, clearly marked prices, and window displays. By the early 1900s department stores could be found throughout the country. The timing was right for their emergence. Urban centers grew rapidly at the end of the century, giving department stores a ready clientele; the advent of the telephone, electric lighting, and billing machines helped retailers conduct business efficiently; transportation improvements allowed for the shipment of large quantities of goods; and a variety of finished goods were mass-produced, increasing supply and lowering cost of production as well as the price to the consumer. By the 1910s the stores were part of a new mass culture, which centered in American cities. During the twentieth century, department store sales typically ranged between 6 and 12 percent of total annual retail sales.

What was the first **mail-order** company?

The mail-order business was pioneered by retailer Montgomery Ward & Company, founded in 1872 in Chicago when American merchant Aaron Montgomery Ward

(1843-1913) set up shop over a livery stable and printed a one-sheet "catalog" of bargains. Midwestern farmers, hurt by low farm prices and rising costs, were a ready market for the value-priced goods, which were shipped by rail to rural customers. Originally called "The Original Grange Supply House," Montgomery Ward offered 30 dry goods priced at $1 or less and provided special terms of sale for Grange members (the Grange is an association of farmers). Ward bought merchandise directly from wholesalers and, since he did not maintain a store building, overhead was low. By 1876 Ward's catalog had grown to 150 pages; in 1884 it was 240 pages and offered nearly 10,000 products, including household items (such as furniture, cutlery, and writing paper), farm implements (such as harnesses and tools), and fashions (such as ready-made apparel and parasols). Ward offered customers "satisfaction or your money back." In 1886 American Richard W. Sears (1863-1914) entered the mail-order business, opening operations in Minneapolis, Minnesota. He moved the business to Chicago the following year and sold it in 1889. In 1893 he joined with Alvah C. Roebuck (1864-1948) to found Sears, Roebuck and Company. The Sears catalog, which soon consisted of hundreds of pages and thousands of items, became popularly known as the "Wish Book."

Montgomery Ward and Sears Roebuck were aided by the U.S. Postal Service's expansion into remote areas: Beginning in 1896 mail could be delivered via the RFD, Rural Free Delivery. In 1913 parcel post was added to the postal service's offerings, further benefiting the mail-order houses and their growing lists of customers. Montgomery Ward and Sears Roebuck offered rural America more than merchandise; the mail-order houses were farm families' link to the greater consumer society that was emerging at the turn of the century. Regardless of geography, rural Americans could purchase "store-bought" goods, manufactured goods that were mass-produced in factories. The mail-order houses offered customers convenience (since customer purchases no longer had to be deferred for the next trip to a town), variety (since catalogers catered to a nationwide customer base, on-hand inventory included a multitude of products), and low prices (the mail-order houses bought merchandise at reduced rates from the wholesalers). Fashions were no longer restricted to the middle- and upper-class city dwellers who had access to department stores; rural customers became aware of new styles each time the Montgomery Ward and Sears Roebuck catalogs were delivered, which, by the early 1900s, was twice a year.

Though both Montgomery Ward and Sears Roebuck exited the mail-order business to concentrate efforts on their chain store retail operations later in the century, they set the standard for modern mail-order houses through their early policies addressing merchandise returns, competitive pricing, flexible payment methods, and shipping terms.

Who were the **"robber barons"**?

They were the industrial and financial tycoons of the late nineteenth century, the early builders of American business. Some called them the captains of industry. The "robber

What was Black Friday?

The term refers to one of two Fridays in the second half of the 1800s when severe market drops precipitated financial crises in the United States. The first Black Friday was September 24, 1869: Financiers Jay Gould (1836-1892) and James Fisk (1834-1872) had conspired to raise the market price of gold by buying it in huge quantities (leaving less supply on the open market, which would, theoretically, increase demand and therefore price). Having caused the price to increase, the businessmen planned to sell their gold supplies at a profit. While they did make out handsomely, clearing some $11 million, a panic resulted when the price of gold rose sharply: Businesses that needed gold to meet their obligations were forced to pay exorbitant prices for it. The government responded to the crisis by selling off $4 million of its gold reserves, causing gold prices to tumble. Speculators were hit hard, but Gould and Fisk came out unscathed, selling off their gold supplies before the price plummeted.

Four years later, another Friday turned dark when the investment banking firm of Jay Cooke & Company failed after it had invested too heavily in railroad securities, which had since declined. When news of the company's collapse was released on September 19, 1873, it affected the entire stock market, and prices fell sharply. The so-called Panic of 1873 signaled the beginning of a depression that persisted through most of the 1870s.

barons" included bankers J. Pierpont Morgan (1837-1913) and Jay Cooke (1821-1905); oil industrialist John D. Rockefeller (1839-1937); steel mogul Andrew Carnegie (1835-1919); financiers James J. Hill (1838-1916), James Fisk (1834-1872), Edward Harriman (1848-1909), and Jay Gould (1836-1892); and rail magnates Cornelius Vanderbilt (1794-1877) and Collis Huntington (1821-1900). These influential businessmen were hailed for expanding and modernizing the capitalist system and lauded for their philanthropic contributions to the arts and education. But they were also viewed as opportunistic, exploitative, and unethical.

Many factors converged to make the robber baron possible. The new nation was rich in natural resources, including iron, coal, and oil; technological advances steadily improved manufacturing machinery and processes; the population growth, fed by an influx of immigrants, provided a steady workforce, often willing to work for a low wage; the government turned over the building and operation of the nation's railways to private interests; and, adhering to the philosophy of laissez-faire (noninterference in the private sector), the government also provided a favorable environment in which to conduct business. Shrewd businessmen turned these factors to their advantage, amassing great empires. Reinvesting profits into their businesses, fortunes grew. The robber barons, especially the railroad men and the financiers who gained control of rail compa-

Illustration of the "robber barons" of the late nineteenth century: James J. Hill, Andrew Carnegie, Cornelius Vanderbilt, John D. Rockefeller, J. Pierpont Morgan, Edward H. Harriman, and Jay Gould. (Original lithograph by Bernarda Bryson.)

nies through stock buy-outs, hired lobbyists who worked on their behalf to gain the corporations subsidies, land grants, and even tax relief at both the federal and state levels.

The robber barons converted their business prowess into political might. In Washington, politicians grew tired of the advantage-seeking representatives of the nation's business leaders. Reform-minded progressives complained that the robber barons lived in opulent luxury while their workers barely eked out a living, their families teetering on despair.

After dominating the American economy for decades, changes around the turn of the century worked to curb the influence of the robber barons. In 1890 the federal government passed the Sherman Anti-Trust Act, making trusts (combinations of firms or corporations formed to limit competition and monopolize a market) illegal; workers continued to organize in labor unions, with which corporations were increasingly compelled to negotiate; the Interstate Commerce Commission (ICC) was established in 1887 to prevent abusive practices; and in 1913 the Sixteenth Amendment was ratified, allowing the federal government to collect a graduated income tax. Though many American businessmen and women would make great fortunes in the twentieth century, by the end of the 1920s the era of the robber barons had drawn to a close.

MODERN INDUSTRY

When was the **New York Stock Exchange** founded?

The oldest and largest stock exchange in the United States, the New York Stock Exchange (NYSE) had its origins on May 17, 1792, when local brokers who had been buying and selling securities under a designated tree agreed to formalize their business transactions. The NYSE that most people would recognize today opened for business in 1825 at 11 Wall Street, New York City. At the time most shares traded were in canal, turnpike, mining, and gaslight companies. Though a few industrial securities were first traded on the New York Stock Exchange as early as 1831, it was another 40 years before the complexion of trading changed to a more industrial nature. As the nation became increasingly manufacturing oriented, the companies listed on the exchange reflected the economic shift. Today, if corporations wish to list their stocks on the NYSE, they must have a minimum of 2,000 shareholders, each of those original shareholders must have 100 or more shares, the corporation must be able to issue at least 1 million shares of stock, and it must also provide a record of earnings for the previous three-year period. The board of the stock exchange can make exceptions to these guidelines. Corporations may be listed with other stock exchanges (such as the American Stock Exchange) or they may allow stock in their company to be traded as unlisted stocks, which are bought and sold in over-the-counter (OTC) trading. Companies that do not allow shares to be publicly traded are called private corporations.

When was the ***Wall Street Journal*** first published?

The newspaper, considered one of the world's best and certainly the preeminent American financial periodical, was first published in 1889, seven years after the Dow, Jones and Company (the comma between the two names was later dropped) was founded by financial reporters Charles Henry Dow (1851-1902) and Edward Davis Jones (1856-1920). Since the founding of the New York Stock Exchange (NYSE) in 1792, business reporting had been largely based on rumor or speculation. Dow and Jones were determined to provide American businesspeople and investors with up-to-date and accurate reporting on the stock market. In its first seven years of business, their publishing company grew from six employees to a staff of 50. In 1889 Dow and Jones expanded their two-page daily newspaper, titled *Customers' Afternoon Letter,* into the *Wall Street Journal.* The paper's stated goal was to give full and fair information regarding fluctuations in the prices of stocks, bonds, and some commodities. Further, the focus was to be on news rather than opinion. The paper began publishing composite lists of major stocks in 1884. In the decades since, it has expanded coverage to include all facets of the business and economic world and now caters to the leisure interests of businesspeople by publishing reports on the arts, travel, sports, and other recreational activities.

What is the history of the **Dow Jones Industrial Average**?

A measure of stock prices of important industrial companies, the Dow Jones Industrial Average (DJIA) was first printed in the *Wall Street Journal* in 1897. The average is an indicator of the market overall and is used, along with other indexes, by investors, stockbrokers, and analysts to make investment forecasts and decisions. "The Dow," as it has come to be called, was conceived of as a summary measure of the stock market, an index that could be used to analyze past trends, indicate current trends, and even predict future ones. The first DJIA averaged the prices of 12 major companies. The list had been expanded since: in 1916 it averaged the stock prices of 20 companies; in 1928, 30. Adjustments have been made as the result of company mergers and dissolutions. Though it is a measure only of the New York Stock Exchange, the Dow Jones Average has been called a barometer of the stock market. News of fluctuations in the DJIA can affect market prices around the world.

Who invented the **assembly line**?

Ford Motor Company founder Henry Ford (1863-1947) is credited with the creation of the assembly line, an industrial innovation that allowed cars to be produced quickly and efficiently. In 1913, 10 years after founding Ford Motor Company, Henry Ford installed the first moving assembly line in one of his Model T manufacturing plants. The innovation proved to be the beginning of the consumer age: The assembly line allowed greater efficiencies in auto production, which, in turn, reduced the price of a quality car, putting it in reach of the ordinary person. Soon, manufactured goods of every variety would be mass produced.

Why was **Ford's Model T** important?

The enormous success of the Model T, a Ford Motor Company car introduced in 1908 and manufactured until 1927, has been the source of extensive analysis and commentary by historians, sociologists, economists, business writers, and pop culture experts. The Model T has been credited with not only changing America but with defining it. When Ford Motor Company founder and president Henry Ford (1863-1947) unveiled the prize Model T in October 1908, he hailed it as "a motor car for the great multitude." The product lived up to the promise. The internal combustion vehicle had been in production in the United States only since the 1890s, but in the decade preceding the Model T's debut, manufacturers and consumers alike had come to regard the "horseless carriage" as a luxury item, custom made for wealthy Americans. Ford had conceived of a different and, as the company would advertise throughout the century, a better idea: A car that was simple to operate, easy to service, comfortable, *and* affordable.

The Model T had a wooden body on a steel frame; four-cylinder, 20-horsepower engine; tank capacity of 10 gallons (in the "touring sedan") or 16 gallons (in the "run-

A 1914 Ford Model T. The vehicle, which was nicknamed "Tin Lizzie," became the symbol of low-cost, reliable transportation.

about"); and a completely enclosed power plant and transmission. It was also lighter than other models. Through large-scale production, based on a system of interchangeable parts, the Model T took 728 minutes (just more than 12 hours) to build and sold for $850, lower than the price of other automobiles, but still beyond the reach of the average American. Nevertheless, 17,000 Model Ts were bought by American consumers the year they were introduced. Ford improved production methods to realize greater economies and lower the price each year; sales steadily rose. The company raised eyebrows in the business community when it offered workers an eight-hour day for $5 a day—twice what other factory workers were earning. Ford explained that this was merely good business practice. By raising the wages of his factory workers, Ford enlarged the potential market for his Model T.

In 1914 Ford implemented the moving assembly line. It used the principles of scientific management, where each job has one "best way" of being accomplished, to bring unprecedented efficiency to manufacturing. Assembly time per car dropped to just 90 minutes. That year the Ford plant in Highland Park, Michigan, produced almost 250,000 Model Ts. To keep up with ever-rising demand, operations were sped up and capacity increased to the point that one day in 1925, Ford produced one Model T every 10 seconds. That year the car retailed for just $295, making the so-called "Tin Lizzie" (or the "Flivver") accessible to working-class families. By 1927, when Ford retired the Model T so the company could respond to consumer demand for cars with better per-

Ford workers on a flywheel assembly line, 1913. Henry Ford is credited with the creation of the assembly line, an industrial innovation that allowed cars to be produced quickly and efficiently.

formance, power, and styling, the company had turned out 15 million Tin Lizzies. Ford's innovative Model T, a reliable, no-nonsense, mass-produced automobile, manufactured on a moving assembly line, brought mobility within the reach of the average American. It had changed consumer mind-set to view the car as a necessity.

What was **Black Tuesday**?

It was the day the stock market crashed—Tuesday, October 29, 1929, signaling the beginning of the worldwide economic downturn called the Great Depression (1929-39).

On Thursday, October 24, 1929, stock values declined rapidly following a five-year period in which the average price of common stocks on the New York Stock Exchange had more than doubled. The prosperity of the 1920s and the widespread sale and purchase of Liberty Bonds (U.S. government bonds) to help finance World War I (1914-18) had encouraged many Americans to invest in the stock market: With the market robust, timing seemed right for speculation and America's experience with Liberty Bonds had made many people comfortable with and interested in investments. So when the stock market dropped precipitously on that fateful October day in 1929, the effects were felt by many. On the following Monday prices again plummeted; on Tuesday, October 29, stockholders panicked, selling off more than 16.4 million shares, and prices nose-dived. Institutions were also affected: Banks, also investors, lost huge sums of money, forcing many to close their doors. News of the stock market failure and bank closures caused many Americans to try to withdraw their money from their deposit accounts, leading to the famous run on the banks. The late-October financial crises marked the beginning of a decade of hard times.

What was the **New Deal**?

While the Great Depression began with the stock market crash on Black Tuesday, October 29, 1929, many factors contributed to the financial crisis, including overproduction, limited foreign markets (due to war debts that prevented trading), and overexpansion of credit, as well as stock market speculation. Soon the country was in the grips of a severe economic downturn that affected most every American. Some were harder hit than others: many lost their jobs (16 million people were unemployed at the depth of the crisis, accounting for about a third of the workforce); families were unable to make their mortgage payments and lost their homes; hunger was widespread, since there was no money to buy food. The sight of people waiting in bread lines was a common one.

It was amidst this crisis, which was soon felt overseas, that Franklin D. Roosevelt (1882-1945) took office as president in 1933. In his inaugural address, he called for faith in America's future, saying, "The only thing we have to fear is fear itself." Roosevelt soon rolled out a program of domestic reforms called the New Deal. For the first time in American history, the federal government took a central role in organizing business and agriculture. Roosevelt initiated aid programs and directed relief in the form of public works programs that would put people back to work. The new government agencies that were set up included the Public Works Administration, Federal Deposit Insurance Corporation, Security and Exchange Commission, National Labor Relations Board, Tennessee Valley Association, the National Recovery Administration, and the Civilian Conservation Corps. These government organizations soon become known by their initials (PWA, FDIC, SEC, NLRB, TVA, NRA, CCC). Roosevelt's critics charged him with giving the federal government too much power and began calling his New Deal "alphabet soup." The president became widely known as FDR.

Though the New Deal measures alleviated the situation and did put some Americans back to work, the country did not pull out of the Depression until industry was called upon to step up production in order to provide arms, aircraft, vehicles, and supplies for the war effort. It was during the early days of World War II (1939-45), the economy buoyed by military spending, that the nation finally recovered. Many New Deal agencies are still part of the federal government today.

Shacks serve as homes for men and women in a Seattle, Washington, "Hooverville." Such villages popped up during the Great Depression and were sarcastically named after President Herbert Hoover.

Why did the **auto industry boom** in the postwar era?

In the years following World War II (1939-45), auto ownership in the United States soared from 27.5 million registered vehicles in 1940 to 61.5 million in 1960. Americans had resumed their love affair with the automobile, inextricably linking the car with the U.S. history of the postwar era. Many factors combined to bring about the automobile's widespread popularity.

During World War II the car manufacturers curtailed auto production, converting factories to military production and turning out some $29 billion in materials, including trucks, jeeps, tanks, aircraft, engines, artillery, and ammunition. With the conflict ended, automakers stepped up production to fulfill the unmet demand of the war years, and soon found themselves working to meet new demand, created by an increase in consumer spending and the growth of the suburbs. The overall prosperity of the late 1940s and 1950s produced a new spirit of consumerism: Government regulations (brought about through the efforts of the labor unions) resulted in increased wages and improved benefits—meaning Americans, for the most part, had more disposable income. Advertisers took advantage of the new medium of television to reach wide—and eager—audiences. The housing industry, largely dormant during World

War II, built new neighborhoods around the edges of American cities, making the automobile a necessity rather than a luxury. The Big Three (GM, Ford, and Chrysler) increased capacity to meet the tremendous demand, setting new records for production in 1949 and 1950. By 1960 more than three out of every four American families owned at least one car. The infrastructure raced to keep pace with a nation on wheels. Superhighways were built (covering some 10,000 miles of road); motels and fast-food restaurants went up along roadsides; and shopping centers were built outside city centers. While imports would challenge the American automakers in the decades to come, it was the U.S. manufacturers that defined the postwar era.

Why was the **introduction of plastic** important to industry?

Pioneered in the early 1900s, plastic—which is any synthetic organic material that can be molded under heat and pressure to retain a shape—affected every industry and every consumer. As a malleable material, plastic could quite literally be molded for countless uses, both for the production of goods and as a material in finished goods. In 1909 Bakelite plastic was introduced, and over the next three decades the plastics industry grew, developing acrylic, nylon, polystyrene, and vinyl (polyvinyl chloride or PVC) in the 1930s, and polyesters in the 1940s. The applications seemed endless: from household items such as hosiery, clocks, radios, toys, flooring, food containers, bags, electric plugs, and garden hoses, to commercial uses such as automobile bodies and parts, airplane windows, boat hulls, packaging, and building materials. The space industry and medicine have also found critical uses for plastic products. Scientists have continued to find new applications for plastics—in products such as compact disks (CDs), computer diskettes, outdoor furniture, and personal computers (PCs). The material has become essential to modern life.

When did **IBM** enter the personal computer business?

IBM (International Business Machines, organized in 1924) had long been an industry leader in developing and producing computers for business and science, but in August 1981, the company jumped into the consumer business, competing with upstart Apple for a share in the personal computer (PC) business. The PC introduced by IBM used a Microsoft disk-operating system (MS-DOS) and soon captured 75 percent of the market. Observing the company's enormous success, other firms began producing IBM "clones," which could use the same software as the IBM PC.

When was **Microsoft** founded?

It wasn't all that long ago, 1975, that computer whiz Bill Gates (1955-) founded what is now the dominant manufacturer of computer software (so dominant that the company has faced antitrust allegations from the federal government). Gates was only 19 years old when he founded the business with his friend Paul Gardner Allen, and he had dropped out of Harvard to do so. It paid off: Gates was a billionaire by age 30. Though he's undoubtedly a math ace (he scored a perfect 800 in math on his SATs and began writing computer programs when he was all of 13), Gates has more than once credited the success of Microsoft to not his own programming skills—but to hiring the best programming talent for the Redmond, Washington-based company.

ECONOMIC LEGISLATION

What was the **Embargo Act**?

On December 22, 1807, President Thomas Jefferson (1743-1826) signed the Embargo Act, prohibiting ships that were destined for foreign ports from leaving the United States. The legislation had been drawn up in an effort to pressure France and Britain, which were then at war and had been seizing U.S. merchant ships to prevent each other from receiving American goods. The situation began after the French navy was crushed by the British under Admiral Horatio Nelson (1758-1805) at the Battle of Trafalgar (October 1805). French ruler Napoleon Bonaparte (1769-1821) turned to economic warfare in his long struggle with the British, directing all countries under French control not to trade with Britain. Its economy dependent on trade, Britain struck back by imposing a naval blockade on France, which soon interfered with U.S. shipping. Ever since the struggle between the two European powers had begun in 1793, the United States had tried to remain neutral. But the interruption of shipping to and from the Continent and the search and seizure of ships posed significant problems to the American export business. The Embargo Act was an attempt to solve these problems without getting involved in the conflict. But the effort failed. The embargo made sales of U.S. farm surpluses impossible. New England shippers protested the act and were joined by southern cotton and tobacco planters in their opposition. Nevertheless, the embargo remained in effect for 14 months, during which the American economy suffered and many ships resorted to smuggling. In 1809 Congress passed the Non-Intercourse Act, which limited the shipping embargo to France and Britain; all other foreign ports were again open to U.S. ships. Three years later, the United States was drawn into the conflict, fighting the British in the War of 1812 (1812-14).

What was the **Tariff of Abominations**?

In 1828 the U.S. Congress passed a bill putting high tariffs (government taxes) on imported goods. The measure was intended to protect the burgeoning industries of New England, where numerous factories had opened during the first three decades of the century and the manufacture of finished goods defined the region's economy. Congress figured that by placing high taxes on goods from other countries, Americans would buy American-made products. But southern farmers had come to rely on cheaper imported goods. Believing the 1828 legislation was overly protective of the nation's industrial interests, southerners dubbed it the "tariff of abominations." Vice President John C. Calhoun (1782-1850), from South Carolina, openly and strongly criticized the tax, pronouncing that any state could declare null a federal law it deemed unconstitutional. In response, Congress took measures to lower the tariffs, but not eliminate them. South Carolina remained dissatisfied with the legislation, and in 1832 the state declared the tariff act null and void. Further, it threatened secession from the Union. President Andrew Jackson (1767-1845), unwilling to tolerate such rebelliousness and determined to enforce the federal law at all costs, asked Congress to pass the Force Bill—legislation allowing the nation's armed forces to collect the tariffs. Jackson's move inspired tremendous opposition in Congress. The Senate leader of the anti-Jackson contingency was Henry Clay (1777-1852) of Kentucky. Clay, who had earned himself the nickname "Great Pacificator" for his work in crafting the Missouri Compromise (1820), presented another compromise in 1833. He proposed that duties on certain goods could remain high but others should be gradually reduced over time. The Compromise Tariff authored by Clay averted an all-out conflict in the nation. The measure was passed and thereafter tariffs were adjusted depending on the prevailing economic conditions. But the fury over the Tariff of Abominations further revealed the North-South differences and the federal-government-versus-states'-rights issues that would inspire the southern states—led by South Carolina—to secede from the Union in 1860 and 1861, bringing on the American Civil War (1861-65).

How old is the U.S. **income tax**?

It dates to 1913. Proposed in Congress on July 12, 1909, and ratified February 3, 1913, the Sixteenth Amendment to the U.S. Constitution gives the federal government (specifically, the U.S. Congress) authority to levy and collect income taxes. The language of the amendment states that incomes "from whatever sources derived" may be taxed—and without regard to a census. In other words, it is up to Congress to determine the level at which citizens of the country are taxed, and this may be done without apportionment among the individual states.

One hundred years before the Sixteenth Amendment was approved, Congress had begun eyeing income tax as a way to collect funds for government use. Lawmakers first considered levying an income tax to help pay for the War of 1812 (1812-14), which the new republic fought against Great Britain over shipping disputes. During the American Civil War (1861-65), Congress imposed an income tax for the first time, charging workers and businessmen between 3 and 5 percent of their earnings and establishing (in 1862) a Bureau of Internal Revenue to administer the tax program. Once the war was over, income taxes were phased out. In 1894, responding to increasing economic and political pressures, the legislature again passed an income tax law (2 percent on all incomes over $4,000), as part of the Wilson-Gorman Tariff Act. But it was struck down by the U.S. Supreme Court, which declared it unconstitutional in the case of *Pollock* v. *Farmers' Loan and Trust Company* (1898). In the early 1900s, the idea of an income tax received widespread political support for the first time. Progressive politicians could see that the nation's wealth was poorly distributed, the gap between rich and poor growing wider. Conservative politicians worried that the government would not be able to respond to a national emergency if it lacked resources. These political factions found a single voice in favor of a graduated income tax (a tax based on level of income: those who earn more pay higher taxes). To circumvent the U.S. Supreme Court, it was necessary for Congress to propose an amendment to the Constitution. In ratifying the amendment, the states gave Congress the authority to set rates and collect income tax.

Tax rates have fluctuated ever since the passage of the Sixteenth Amendment, reaching their highest mark during World War II (1939-45) when the rate soared to 91 percent. The war effort also brought the innovation of automatic withholdings: Taxes were deducted directly from paychecks. In 1953 the Bureau of Internal Revenue was dramatically reorganized to create the Internal Revenue Service (IRS). Over the decades, tax laws (collectively called the Tax Code) have become increasingly complex, prompting a recent movement in favor of a flat (versus the graduated) tax, where all taxpayers are charged at the same rate.

When was the **Interstate Commerce Commission** formed?

The Interstate Commerce Commission (ICC) was established by act of Congress in 1887. The agency is responsible for regulating the rates and services of specified carriers that transport freight (goods, whether raw or finished) and passengers between states. Its jurisdiction, expanded by subsequent acts of Congress, includes trucking, bus services, water carriers, expedited delivery services, and even oil pipelines. The regulatory agency, the nation's first such body, was borne out of necessity in the late 1800s, as farmers in particular charged the railroads with discriminatory freight practices. With rail lines crisscrossing the nation, the question of who would control rates and monitor practices had become an increasingly difficult one to answer. Many states, particularly in the Midwest, set up their own regulatory boards, but because the rail companies operated between states, enforcing state laws on them proved cumbersome and impractical. Meanwhile the railroads, operating without the purview of any effective regulatory body, set their own standards and practices, which resulted in many abuses.

In an 1877 U.S. Supreme Court ruling, in the case of *Munn* v. *Illinois,* the authority of the state boards to regulate the railroads was upheld. But less than a decade later, in the case of *Wabash, St. Louis and Pacific Railway Company* v. *Illinois,* the high court invalidated its earlier decision and proclaimed that only the U.S. Congress has the right to regulate interstate commerce. Citing Section 8 of Article 1 of the U.S.

Constitution (1790), which states that "Congress shall have the power...to regulate commerce with foreign nations, and among the several states, and with the Indian tribes," the Interstate Commerce Act was passed in 1887, setting up the Interstate Commerce Commission to regulate the interstate railroads. The agency's purview was later expanded to include all ground and water carriers that operate on an interstate basis. In addition to controlling rates, the agency also enforces laws against discrimination. The ICC's authority was strengthened by congressional legislation including the Hepburn Act (1906) and the Mann-Elkins Act (1910).

What is the **Sherman Anti-Trust Act**?

Passed by Congress in 1890, the Sherman Anti-Trust Act was an attempt to break up corporate trusts (combinations of firms or corporations formed to limit competition and monopolize a market). The legislation stated that "every contract, combination in the form of trust or otherwise, or conspiracy in the restraint of trade" is illegal. While the act made clear that anyone found to be in violation of restraining trade would face fines, jail terms, and the payment of damages, the language lacked clear definitions of what exactly constituted restraint of trade. The nation's courts were left with the responsibility of interpreting the Sherman Anti-Trust Act, and the justices proved as reluctant to take on big business as Congress had been.

The legislation was introduced in Congress by Senator John Sherman (1823-1900) of Ohio, in response to increasing outcry from state governments and the public for the passage of national antitrust laws. Many states had passed their own antitrust bills or had made constitutional provisions prohibiting trusts, but the statutes proved difficult to enforce and big business found ways around them. When the legislation proposed by Sherman reached the Senate, conservative congressmen rewrote it; many charged that the Senators had made it deliberately vague. In the decade after its passage, the federal government prosecuted only 18 antitrust cases and court decisions did little to break up monopolies. But after the turn of the century, a progressive spirit in the nation grew; among progressive reformers' demands was that government regulate business. In 1911 the U.S. Justice Department won key victories against monopolies, breaking up John D. Rockefeller's Standard Oil Company of New Jersey and James B. Duke's American Tobacco Company. The decisions set a precedent for how the Sherman Anti-Trust Act would be enforced and demonstrated a national intolerance toward monopolistic trade practices. In 1914 national antitrust legislation was strengthened by the passage of the Clayton Anti-Trust Act, which outlawed price fixing (the practice of pricing below cost to eliminate a competitive product), made it illegal for the same executives to manage two or more competing companies (a practice called interlocking directorates), and prohibited any corporation from owning stock in a competing corporation. The creation of the Federal Trade Commission (FTC) that same year provided further insurance that U.S. corporations engaging in unfair practices would be investigated by the government.

Between 1880 and the early 1900s corporate trusts proliferated in the United States, becoming powerful business forces. The vague language of the Sherman Anti-Trust legislation and the courts' reluctance to prosecute big business based on that act did little to break up the monopolistic giants. The tide turned against corporate trusts when Theodore Roosevelt (1858-1919) became president in September 1901, after President William McKinley (1843-1901) was assassinated. Roosevelt launched a "trust-busting" campaign, initiating, through the attorney general's office, some 40 lawsuits against American corporations such as American Tobacco Company, Standard Oil Company, and American Telephone and Telegraph (AT&T). Government efforts to break up the monopolies were strengthened in 1914, during the presidency of Woodrow Wilson (1856-1924), when Congress passed the Clayton Anti-Trust legislation and created the Federal Trade Commission (FTC), which is responsible for keeping business competition free and fair. Trust-busting declined during the prosperity of the 1920s, but was again vigorously pursued in the 1930s, during the administration of Franklin D. Roosevelt (1882-1945).

What is **NAFTA**?

NAFTA is the North American Free Trade Agreement, signed on December 17, 1992, by U.S. president George H. W. Bush (1924-), Canadian prime minister Brian Mulroney (1939-), and Mexican president Carlos Salinas de Gortari (1948-). It went into effect January 1, 1994. Inspired by the success of the European Community's open-trade agreement, the architects of NAFTA aimed to create free trade among North America's three largest countries. A 1988 pact between the United States and Canada had already lifted numerous barriers to trade between the two nations; that agreement was expanded to include Mexico through a series of negotiations that were preliminarily approved in August 1992 and were concluded with the signing of NAFTA later that year. The agreement removes trade barriers, including customs duties and tariffs, over the course of 15 years, allowing commodities and manufactured goods to be freely traded among the three nations. NAFTA also includes provisions that allow American and Canadian service companies to expand their markets into Mexico.

MATH, NUMBERS, AND MEASUREMENTS

NUMBERS

When and where did the concept of "**numbers**" and **counting** first develop?

The human adult (including some of the higher animals) can discern the numbers one through four without any training. After that people must learn to count. To count requires a system of number manipulation skills, a scheme to name the numbers, and some way to record the numbers. Early people began with fingers and toes, and progressed to shells and pebbles. In the fourth millennium B.C.E. in Elam (near what is today Iran along the Persian Gulf), accountants began using unbaked clay tokens instead of pebbles. Each represented one order in a numbering system: a stick shape for the number one, a pellet for ten, a ball for 100, and so on. During the same period, another clay-based civilization in Sumer in lower Mesopotamia invented the same system.

When was a symbol for the concept **zero** first used?

Surprisingly, the symbol for zero emerged later than the concept for the other numbers. The ancient Greeks, for instance, conceived of logic and geometry, concepts providing the foundation for all mathematics, yet they never had a symbol for zero. Hindu mathematicians are usually given credit for developing a symbol for the concept "zero"; it appears in an inscription at Gwalior dated 870 C.E. It is certainly older than that; it is found in inscriptions dating from the seventh century in Cambodia, Sumatra, and Bangka Island (off Sumatra). While there is no documented evidence for the zero in China before 1247, some historians believe that it originated there and arrived in India via Indochina.

What is a perfect number?

A perfect number is a number equal to the sum of all its proper divisors (divisors smaller than the number) including 1. The number 6 is the smallest perfect number; the sum of its divisors 1, 2, and 3 equals 6. The next three perfect numbers are 28, 496, and 8,126. No odd perfect numbers are known. The largest known perfect number is

$$2^{13466916}(2^{13466917}-1).$$

It was discovered in 2001.

What are **Roman numerals**?

Roman numerals are symbols that stand for numbers. They are written using seven basic symbols: I (1), V (5), × (10), L (50), C (100), D (500), and M (1,000). Sometimes a bar is place over a numeral to multiply it by 1,000. A smaller numeral appearing before a larger numeral indicates that the smaller numeral is subtracted from the larger one. This notation is generally used for 4s and 9s; for example, 4 is written IV, 9 is IX, 40 is XL, and 90 is XC.

What are **Fibonacci numbers**?

Fibonacci numbers are a series of numbers where each, after the second term, is the sum of the two preceding numbers—for example, 1, 1, 2, 3, 5, 8, 13, 21 .... (1+1=2, 1+2=3, 2+3=5, 3+5=8, 5+8=13, 8+13=21, and so on). They were first described by Leonardo Fibonacci (ca. 1180-ca. 1250), also known as Leonard of Pisa, as part of a thesis on series in his most famous book *Liber abaci* (*The Book of the Calculator*), published in 1202 and later revised by him.

What is the **largest prime number** presently known?

A prime number is one that is evenly divisible only by itself and 1. The integers 1, 2, 3, 5, 7, 11, 13, 17, and 19 are prime numbers. Euclid (ca. 300 B.C.E.) proved that there is no "largest prime number," because any attempt to define the largest results in a paradox. If there is a largest prime number (P), adding 1 to the product of all primes up to and including P, 1 + (1 × 2 × 3 × 5 × ... × P), yields a number that is itself a prime number, because it cannot be divided evenly by any of the known primes. In 2008, the 45th and 46th prime numbers were discovered to be $2^{37156667-1}$ and $2^{43112609-1}$ respectively. They are both prime numbers that are part of a special class of prime numbers called Mersenne Primes (named after Marin Mersenne,

1588-1648, a French monk who did the first work in this area). Mersenne primes occur where 2^{n-1} is prime.

There is no apparent pattern to the sequence of primes. Mathematicians have been trying to find a formula since the days of Euclid, without success. The 39th prime was discovered on a personal computer as part of the GIMPS effort (the Great Internet Mersenne Prime Search), which was formed in January 1996 to discover new world-record-size prime numbers. GIMPS relies on the computing efforts of thousands of small, personal computers across the planet. Interested participants can become involved in the search for primes by pointing their browsers to: http://www.mersenne.org/prime.htm.

How are names for large and small **quantities constructed** in the **metric system**?

Each prefix listed below can be used in the metric system and with some customary units. For example, centi + meter = centimeter, meaning one-hundredth of a meter.

Prefix	Power	Numerals
Exa-	10^{18}	1,000,000,000,000,000,000
Peta-	10^{15}	1,000,000,000,000,000
Tera-	10^{12}	1,000,000,000,000
Giga-	10^{9}	1,000,000,000
Mega-	10^{6}	1,000,000
Myria-	10^{5}	100,000
Kilo-	10^{3}	1,000
Hecto-	10^{2}	100
Deca-	10^{1}	10
Deci-	10^{-1}	0.1
Centi-	10^{-2}	0.01
Milli-	10^{-3}	0.001
Micro-	10^{-6}	0.000001
Nano-	10^{-9}	0.000000001
Pico-	10^{-12}	0.000000000001
Femto-	10^{-15}	0.000000000000001
Atto-	10^{-18}	0.000000000000000001

Why is the number **ten** considered **important**?

One reason is that the metric system is based on the number ten. The metric system emerged in the late-eighteenth century out of a need to bring standardization to measurement, which had up to then been fickle, depending upon the preference of the ruler of the day. But ten was important well before the metric system. Nicomachus of Gerasa, a second-century neo-Pythagorean from Judea, considered ten a "perfect" number, the figure of divinity present in creation with mankind's fingers and toes. Pythagoreans believed ten to be "the first-born of the numbers, the mother of them all, the one that never wavers and gives the key to all things." And shepherds of West Africa counted sheep in their flocks by colored shells based on ten, and ten had evolved as a "base" of most numbering schemes. Some scholars believe the reason ten developed as a base number had more to do with ease: ten is easily counted on fingers and the rules of addition, subtraction, multiplication, and division for the number ten are easily memorized.

What are some **very large numbers**?

Name	Value in powers of 10	Number of 0's	Number of groups of three 0's after 1,000
Billion	10^{9}	9	2
Trillion	10^{12}	12	3
Quadrillion	10^{15}	15	4
Quintillion	10^{18}	18	5
Sextillion	10^{21}	21	6
Septillion	10^{24}	24	7
Octillion	10^{27}	27	8
Nonillion	10^{30}	30	9
Decillion	10^{33}	33	10
Undecillion	10^{36}	36	11
Duodecillion	10^{39}	39	12
Tredecillion	10^{42}	42	13
Quattuor-decillion	10^{45}	45	14
Quindecillion	10^{48}	48	15
Sexdecillion	10^{51}	51	16
Septen-decillion	10^{54}	54	17
Octodecillion	10^{57}	57	18
Novemdecillion	10^{60}	60	19
Vigintillion	10^{63}	63	20
Centillion	10^{303}	303	100

The British, French, and Germans use a different system for naming denominations above one million. The googol and googolplex are rarely used outside the United States.

How large is a **googol**?

A googol is 10^{100} (the number 1 followed by 100 zeros). Unlike most other names for numbers, it does not relate to any other numbering scale. The American mathematician

Edward Kasner first used the term in 1938; when searching for a term for this large number, Kasner asked his nephew, Milton Sirotta, then about nine years old, to suggest a name. The googolplex is 10 followed by a googol of zeros, represented as 10^{googol}. The popular Web search engine Google.com is named after the concept of a googol.

What is an **irrational number**?

Numbers that cannot be expressed as an exact ratio are called irrational numbers; numbers that can be expressed as an exact ratio are called rational numbers. For instance, 1/2 (one half, or 50 percent of something) is rational. 1.61803 (θ), 3.14159 (π), 1.41421 ($\sqrt{2}$), are irrational. History claims that Pythagoras in the sixth century B.C.E. first used the term when he discovered that the square root of 2 could not be expressed as a fraction.

What are **imaginary numbers**?

Imaginary numbers are the square roots of negative numbers. Since the square is the product of two equal numbers with like signs it is always positive. Therefore, no number multiplied by itself can give a negative real number. The symbol *i* is used to indicate an imaginary number.

What is the **value of pi** out to 30 digits past the decimal point?

Pi (π) represents the ratio of the circumference of a circle to its diameter, used in calculating the area of a circle (πr^2) and the volume of a cylinder ($\pi r^2 h$) or cone. It is a "transcendental number," an irrational number with an exact value that can be measured to any degree of accuracy, but that can't be expressed as the ratio of two integers. In theory, the decimal extends into infinity, though it is generally rounded to 3.1416. The Welsh-born mathematician William Jones selected the Greek symbol (π) for Pi. Rounded to 30 digits past the decimal point, it equals 3.141592653589793238462643383279. In 1989, Gregory and David Chudnovsky at Columbia University in New York City calculated the value of pi to 1,011,961,691 decimal places. They performed the calculation twice on an IBM 3090 mainframe and on a CRAY-2 supercomputer with matching results. In 1991, they calculated pi to 2,260,321,336 decimal places. In 1999, Yasumasa Kanada and Daisuke Takahashi of the University of Tokyo calculated pi out to 206,158,430,000 digits. Mathematicians have also calculated pi in binary format (i.e. 0s and 1s). The five trillionth binary digit of pi was computed by Colin Percival and 25 others at Simon Fraser University. The computation took over 13,500 hours of computer time.

Why is **seven** considered a **supernatural number**?

In magical lore and mysticism, all numbers are ascribed certain properties and energies. Seven is a number of great power, a magical number, a lucky number, a number of psychic and mystical powers, of secrecy and the search for inner truth. The origin of belief in seven's power lies in the lunar cycle. Each of the moon's four phases lasts about seven days. The Sumerians, who based their calendar on the moon, gave the week seven days and declared the seventh and last day of each week to be uncanny. Life cycles on Earth also have phases demarcated by seven. Furthermore, there are said to be seven years to each stage of human growth; there are seven colors to the rainbow; and seven notes are in the musical scale. The seventh son of a seventh son is said to be born with formidable magical and psychic powers. The number seven is widely held to be a lucky number, especially in matters of love and money, and it also carries great prominence in the old and new testaments. Here are a few examples: the Lord rested on the seventh day; there were seven years of plenty and seven years of famine in Egypt in the story of Joseph; God commanded Joshua to have seven priests carry trumpets, and on the seventh day they were to march around Jericho seven times; Solomon built the temple in seven years; and there are seven petitions of the Lord's Prayer.

What are some examples of **numbers** and **mathematical concepts** in **nature**?

The world can be articulated with numbers and mathematics. Some numbers are especially prominent. The number six is ubiquitous: every normal snowflake has six sides; every honeybee colony's combs are six-sided hexagons. The curved, gradually decreasing chambers of a nautilus shell are propagating spirals of the Golden Section and the Fibonacci sequence of numbers. Pine cones also rely on the Fibonacci sequence, as do many plants and flowers in their seed and stem arrangements. Fractals are evident in shorelines, blood vessels, and mountains.

MATHEMATICS

How is **arithmetic** different from **mathematics**?

Arithmetic is the study of positive integers (i.e. 1, 2, 3, 4, 5, ...) manipulated with addition, subtraction, multiplication, and division, and the use of the results in daily life. Mathematics is the study of shape, arrangement, and quantity. It is traditionally viewed as consisting of three fields: algebra, analysis, and geometry. But any lines of division have evaporated because the fields are now so interrelated.

Who invented **calculus**?

The German mathematician Gottfried Wilhelm Leibniz published the first paper on calculus in 1684. Most historians agree that Isaac Newton invented calculus eight to ten years earlier, but he was typically very late in publishing his works. The invention of calculus marked the beginning of higher mathematics. It provided scientists and mathematicians with a tool to solve problems that had been too complicated to attempt previously.

Gottfried Wilhelm Leibniz made important contributions to the science of calculus and designed early manifestations of the computer.

What is the most **enduring mathematical work** of all time?

The Elements of Euclid (fl. about 300 B.C.E.) has been the most enduring and influential mathematical work of all time. In it, the ancient Greek mathematician presented the work of earlier mathematicians and included many of his own innovations. The *Elements* is divided into 13 books: the first six cover plane geometry; seven to nine address arithmetic and number theory; 10 treats irrational numbers; and 11 to 13 discuss solid geometry. In presenting his theorems, Euclid used the synthetic approach, in which one proceeds from the known to the unknown by logical steps. This method became the standard procedure for scientific investigation for many centuries, and the *Elements* probably had a greater influence on scientific thinking than any other work.

Is it possible to **count** to **infinity**?

No. Very large finite numbers are not the same as infinite numbers. Infinite numbers are defined as being unbounded, or without limit. Any number that can be reached by counting or by representation of a number followed by billions of zeros is a finite number.

How long has the **abacus** been used? Is it still used?

The abacus grew out of early counting boards, with hollows in a board holding pebbles or beads used to calculate. It has been documented in Mesopotamia back to around 3500 B.C.E.. The current form, with beads sliding on rods, dates back at least to 15th-century China. Before the use of decimal number systems, which allowed the familiar paper-and-pencil methods of calculation, the abacus was essential for almost all multiplication and division. The abacus is still used in many countries where modern calculators are not available. It is also still used in countries, such as Japan and China, that have long traditions of abacus use. As recently as the mid-1970s, most Japanese shop-

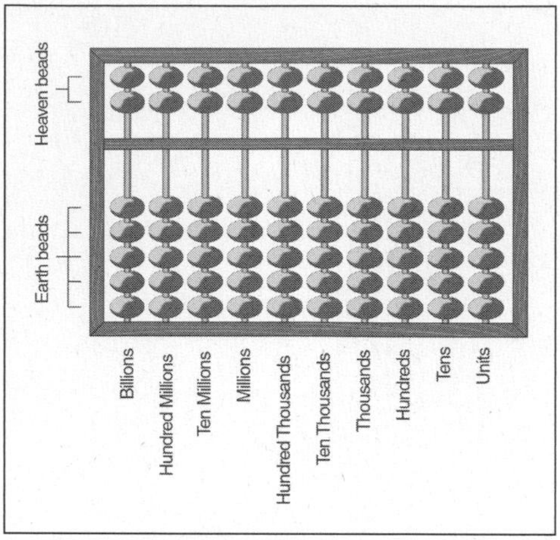

A Chinese abacus called a suan pan.

John Napier, the Scottish mathematician known for a device called "Napier's bones," devised the use of the decimal point when writing numbers.

keepers used abaci for totaling customers' bills. While the calculator is now more widely used, many people still prefer to check the results on an abacus. At least one manufacturer offers calculators with small, built-in abaci.

What are **Napier's bones**?

In the 16th century, the Scottish mathematician John Napier (1550-1617), Baron of Merchiston, developed a method of simplifying the processes of multiplication and division, using exponents of 10, which Napier called logarithms (commonly abbreviated as logs). Using this system, multiplication is reduced to addition and division to subtraction. For example, the log of 100 (10^2) is 2; the log of 1000 (10^3) is 3; the multiplication of 100 by 1000, $100 \times 1000 = 100{,}000$, can be accomplished by adding their logs: $\log[(100)(1000)] = \log(100) + \log(1000) = 2 + 3 = 5 = \log(100{,}000)$. Napier published his methodology in *A Description of the Admirable Table of Logarithms* in 1614. In 1617 he published a method of using a device, made up of a series of rods in a frame, marked with the digits 1 through 9, to multiply and divide using the principles of logarithms. This device was commonly called "Napier's bones" or "Napier's rods."

What is a **slide rule**, and who invented it?

Up until about 1974, most engineering and design calculations for buildings, bridges, automobiles, airplanes, and roads were done on a slide rule. A slide rule is an apparatus with moveable scales based on logarithms, which were invented by John Napier (1550-1617), Baron of Merchiston, and published in 1614. The slide rule can, among other things, quickly multiply, divide, square root, or find the logarithm of a number. In 1620, Edmund Gunter (1581-1626) of Gresham College, London, England, described an immediate forerunner of the slide rule, his "logarithmic line of numbers." William Oughtred (1574-1660), rector of Aldbury, England, made the first rectilinear slide rule in 1621. This slide rule consisted of two logarithmic scales that could be manipulated together for calculation. His former pupil, Richard Delamain, published a description of a circular slide rule in 1630 (and received a patent about that time for it), three years before Oughtred published a description of his invention (at least one source says that Delamain published in 1620). Oughtred accused Delamain of stealing his idea, but evidence indicates that the inventions were probably arrived at independently.

The earliest existing straight slide rule using the modern design of a slider moving in a fixed stock dates from 1654. A wide variety of specialized slide rules were developed by the end of the 17th century for trades such as masonry, carpentry, and excise tax collecting. Peter Mark Roget (1779-1869), best known for his *Thesaurus of English Words and Phrases,* invented a log-log slide rule for calculating the roots and powers of numbers in 1814. In 1967, Hewlett-Packard (now known as HP) produced the first pocket calculators. Within a decade, slide rules became the subject of science trivia and collector's books.

What is the difference between a **median** and a **mean**?

If a string of numbers is arranged in numerical order, the median is the middle value of the string. If there is an even number of values in the string, the median is found by adding the two middle values and dividing by two. The arithmetic mean, also known as the simple average, is found by taking the sum of the numbers in the string and dividing by the number of items in the string. While easy to calculate for relatively short strings, the arithmetic mean can be misleading, as very large or very small values in the string can distort it. For example, the mean of the salaries of a professional football team would be skewed if one of the players was a high-earning superstar; it could be well above the salaries of any of the other players. The mode is the number in a string that appears most often.

For the string 111222234455667, for example, the median is the middle number of the series: 3. The arithmetic mean is the sum of numbers divided by the number of numbers in the series, $51 \div 15 = 3.4$. The mode is the number that occurs most often, 2.

When does **0** $\times$ **0** = **1**?

Factorials are the product of a given number and all the factors less than that number. The notation n! is used to express this idea. For example, 5! (five factorial) is $5 \times 4 \times 3 \times 2 \times 1 = 120$. For completeness, 0! is assigned the value 1, so $0 \times 0 = 1$.

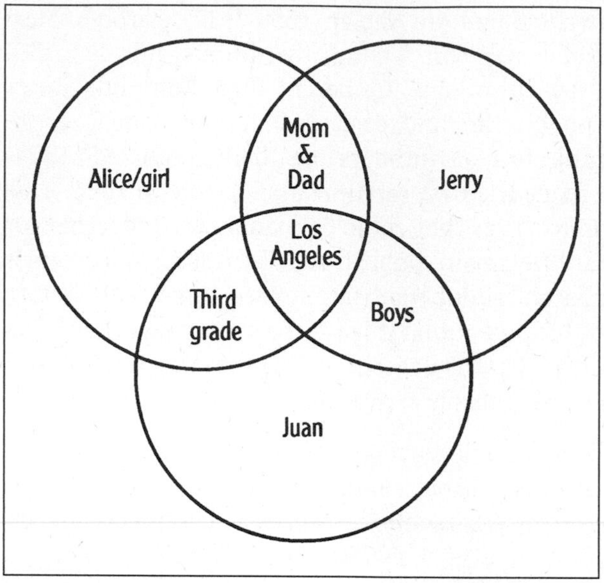

Example of a Venn diagram.

When did the concept of **square root** originate?

A square root of a number is a number that, when multiplied by itself, equals the given number. For instance, the square root of 25 is 5 ($5 \times 5 = 25$). The concept of the square root has been in existence for many thousands of years. Exactly how it was discovered is not known, but several different methods of exacting square roots were used by early mathematicians. Babylonian clay tablets from 1900 to 1600 B.C.E. contain the squares and cubes of integers 1-30. The early Egyptians used square roots around 1700 B.C.E., and during the Greek Classical Period (600 to 300 B.C.E.) better arithmetic methods improved square root operations. In the 16th century, French mathematician René Descartes was the first to use the square root symbol, called "the radical sign," $\sqrt{\ }$.

What are **Venn diagrams**?

Venn diagrams are graphical representations of set theory, which use circles to show the logical relationships of the elements of different sets, using the logical operators (also called in computer parlance "Boolean Operators") *and, or,* and *not.* John Venn (1834-1923) first used them in his 1881 Symbolic Logic, in which he interpreted and corrected the work of George Boole (1815-1864) and Augustus de Morgan (1806-1871). While his attempts to clarify perceived inconsistencies and ambiguities in Boole's work are not widely accepted, the new method of diagraming is considered to be an improvement. Venn used shading to better illustrate inclusion and exclusion. Charles Dodgson (1832-1898), better known as Lewis Carroll, refined Venn's system, in particular by enclosing the diagram to represent the universal set.

What are the common **mathematical formulas** for **volume**?

Volume of a sphere:

Volume = 4/3 times pi times the cube of the radius

$V = 4/3 \times \pi r^3$

Volume of a pyramid:

Volume = 1/3 times the area of the base times the height

$V = 1/3bh$

Volume of a cylinder:

Volume = area of the base times the height

$V = Ah$

Volume of a circular cylinder (with circular base):

Volume = pi times the square of the radius of the base times the height

$V = \pi r^2 h$

Volume of a cube:

Volume = the length of one side cubed

$V = S^3$

Volume of a cone:

Volume = 1/3 times pi times the square of the radius of the base times the height.

$V = 1/3\ \pi r^2 h$

Volume of a rectangular solid:

Volume = length times width times height

$V = lwh$

How many feet are on each side of an **acre** that is square?

An acre that is square in shape has about 208.7 feet (64 meters) on each side.

What are the common mathematical formulas for **area**?

Area of a rectangle:

Area = length times width

$A = lw$

Area = altitude times base

$A = ab$

Area of a circle:

Area = pi times the radius squared

$A = \pi r^2$ or $A = 1/4\pi d^2$

Area of a triangle:

Area = one half the altitude times the base

$A = 1/2ab$

Area of the surface of a sphere:

Area = four times pi times the radius squared

$A = 4\pi r^2$ or $A = \pi d^2$

Area of a square:

Area = length times width, or length of one side squared

$A = s^2$

Area of a cube:

Area = square of the length of one side times 6

$A = 6s^2$

Area of an ellipse:

Area = long diameter times short diameter times 0.7854.

How is **Pascal's triangle** used?

Pascal's triangle is an array of numbers, arranged so that every number is equal to the sum of the two numbers above it on either side. It can be represented in several slightly different triangles, but this is the most common form:

$$
\begin{array}{ccccccccccc}
 & & & & & 1 & & & & & \\
 & & & & 1 & & 1 & & & & \\
 & & & 1 & & 2 & & 1 & & & \\
 & & 1 & & 3 & & 3 & & 1 & & \\
 & 1 & & 4 & & 6 & & 4 & & 1 & \\
1 & & 5 & & 10 & & 10 & & 5 & & 1
\end{array}
$$

French mathematician and scientist Blaise Pascal (1623–1662) uncovered a relationship between numbers in Pascal's triangle.

The triangle is used to determine the numerical coefficients resulting from the computation of higher powers of a binomial (two numbers added together). When a binomial is raised to a higher power, the result is expanded, using the numbers in that row of the triangle. For example, $(a + b)^1 = a^1 + b^1$, using the coefficients in the second line of the triangle. $(a + b)^2 = a^2 + 2ab + b^2$, using the coefficients in the next line of the triangle. (The first line of the triangle correlates to $(a + b)^0$.) While the calculation of coefficients is fairly straightforward, the triangle is useful in calculating them for the higher powers without needing to multiply them out. Binomial coefficients

What is the ancient Greek problem of squaring the circle?

This problem was to construct, with a straight-edge and compass, a square having the same area as a given circle. The Greeks were unable to solve the problem because the task is impossible, as was shown by the German mathematician Ferdinand von Lindemann (1852-1939) in 1882.

are useful in calculating probabilities; Blaise Pascal was one of the pioneers in developing laws of probability.

As with many other mathematical developments, there is some evidence of a previous appearance of the triangle in China. Around 1100 C.E., the Chinese mathematician Chia Hsien wrote about "the tabulation system for unlocking binomial coefficients"; the first publication of the triangle was probably in a book called *Piling-Up Powers and Unlocking Coefficients,* by Liu Ju-Hsieh.

Who discovered the formula for the **area of a triangle**?

Heron (or Hero) of Alexandria (first century B.C.E.) is best known in the history of mathematics for the formula that bears his name. This formula calculates the area of a triangle with sides a, b, and c, with s = half the perimeter: $A = \sqrt{[s\ (2 - a)(s - b)(s - c)]}$. The Arab mathematicians who preserved and transmitted the mathematics of the Greeks reported that this formula was known earlier to Archimedes (ca. 287-212 B.C.E.), but the earliest proof now known is that appearing in Heron's Metrica.

What is the **Pythagorean theorem**?

In a right triangle (one where two of the sides meet in a 90-degree angle), the hypotenuse is the side opposite the right angle. The Pythagorean theorem, also known as the rule of Pythagoras, states that the square of the length of the hypotenuse is equal to the sum of the squares of the other two sides ($h^2 = a^2 + b^2$). If the lengths of the sides are: h = 5 inches, a = 4 inches, and b = 3 inches, then

$$h = \sqrt{a^2 + b^2} = \sqrt{4^2 + 3^2} = \sqrt{16 + 9} = \sqrt{25} = 5$$

The theorem is named for the Greek philosopher and mathematician Pythagoras (ca. 580-ca. 500 B.C.E.). Pythagoras is credited with the theory of the functional significance of numbers in the objective world and numerical theories of musical pitch. As he left no writings, the Pythagorean theorem may actually have been formulated by one of his disciples.

What are the **Platonic solids**?

The Platonic solids are the five regular polyhedra: the four-sided tetrahedron, the six-sided cube or hexahedron, the eight-sided octahedron, the twelve-sided dodecahedron, and the twenty-sided icosahedron. While they had been studied as long ago as the time of Pythagorus (around 500 B.C.E.), they are called the Platonic solids because they were first described in detail by Plato around 400 B.C.E. The ancient Greeks gave mystical significance to the Platonic solids: the tetrahedron represented fire, the icosahedron represented water, the stable cube represented the Earth, the octahedron represented the air. The twelve faces of the dodecahedron corresponded to the twelve signs of the zodiac, and this figure represented the entire universe.

What is a **golden section**?

Golden section, also called the divine proportion, is the division of a line segment so that the ratio of the whole segment to the larger part is equal to the ratio of the larger part to the smaller part. The ratio is approximately 1.61803 to 1. The number 1.61803 is called the Golden Number (also called Phi [with a capital P]). The golden number is the limit of the ratios of consecutive Fibonacci numbers, such as, for instance, 21/13, and 34/21. A golden rectangle is one whose length and width correspond to this ratio. The ancient Greeks thought this shape had the most pleasing proportions. Many famous painters have used the Golden Rectangle in their paintings, and architects have used it in their design of buildings, the most famous example being the Greek Parthenon.

What is a **Möbius strip**?

A Möbius strip is a surface with only one side, usually made by connecting the two ends of a rectangular strip of paper after putting a half-twist (180 degrees relative to the opposite side) in the strip. Cutting a Möbius strip in half down the center of the length of the strip results in a single band with four half-twists. Devised by the German mathematician August Ferdinand Möbius (1790-1868) to illustrate the properties of one-sided surfaces, it was presented in a paper that was not discovered or published until after his death. Another 19th-century German mathematician, Johann Benedict Listing, developed the idea independently at the same time.

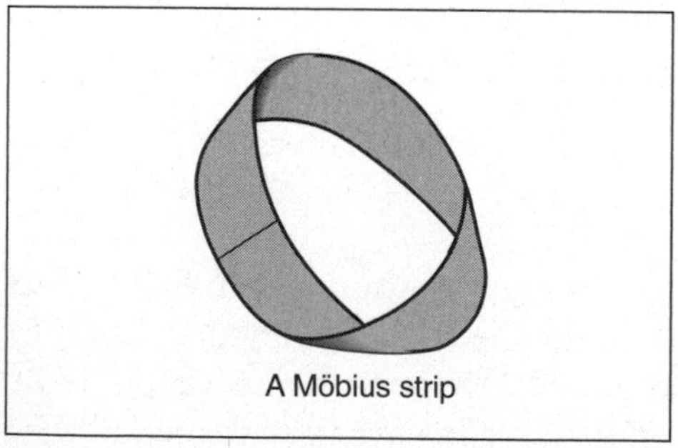

A Möbius strip.

What are **fractals**?

A fractal is a set of points that is too irregular to be described by traditional geometric terms, but that often have some degree of self-similarity; that is, they are made of parts that resemble the whole. They are used in image processing to compress data and to depict apparently chaotic objects in nature such as mountains or coastlines. Scientists also use fractals to better comprehend rainfall trends, patterns formed by clouds and waves, and the distribution of vegetation. Fractals are also used to create computer-generated art.

How is **percent of increase** calculated?

To find the percent of increase, divide the amount of increase by the base amount. Multiply the result by 100 percent. For example, a raise in salary from \$10,000 to \$12,000 would have percent of increase = (2,000 ÷ 10,000) × 100% = 20%.

What is the difference between **simple interest** and **compound interest**?

Simple interest is calculated on the amount of principal only. Compound interest is calculated on the amount of principal plus any previous interest already earned. For example, \$100 invested at a rate of 5 percent for 1 year will earn \$5.00 after one year earning simple interest. The same \$100 will earn \$5.12 if compounded monthly.

If 30 people are chosen at random, what is the probability that at least two of them have their **birthday on the same day**?

The probability that at least two people in a group of 30 share the same birthday is about 70 percent.

What is the **law of very large numbers**?

Formulated by Persi Diaconis (1945-) and Frederick Mosteller (1916-) of Harvard University, this long-understood law of statistics states that "with a large enough sample, any outrageous thing is apt to happen." Therefore, seemingly amazing coincidences can actually be expected if given sufficient time or a large enough pool of subjects. For example, when a New Jersey woman won the lottery twice in four months, the media publicized it as an incredible long shot of 1 in 17 trillion. However, when statisticians looked beyond this individual's chances and asked what were the odds of the same happening to any person buying a lottery ticket in the United States over a six-month period, the number dropped dramatically to 1 in 30. According to researchers, coincidences arise often in statistical work, but some have hidden causes and therefore are not coincidences at all. Many are simply chance events reflecting the luck of the draw.

What is the **Königsberg Bridge Problem**?

The city of Königsberg was located in Prussia on the Pregel River. Two islands in the river were connected by seven bridges. By the eighteenth century, it had become a

Representation of the Königsberg Bridge Problem.

tradition for the citizens of Königsberg to go for a walk through the town trying to cross each bridge only once. No one was able to succeed, and the question was asked whether it was possible to do so. In 1736, Leonhard Euler (1707-1783) proved that it was not possible to cross the Königsberg bridges only once. Euler's solution led to the development of two new areas of mathematics: graph theory, which deals with questions about networks of points that are connected by lines, and topology, which is the study of those aspects of the shape of an object that do not depend on length measurements.

What is **Zeno's paradox**?

Zeno of Elea (ca. 490-ca. 425 B.C.E.), a Greek philosopher and mathematician, is famous for his paradoxes, which deal with the continuity of motion. One form of the paradox is: If an object moves with constant speed along a straight line from point 0 to point 1, the object must first cover half the distance (1/2), then half the remaining distance (1/4), then half the remaining distance (1/8), and so on without end. The conclusion is that the object never reaches point 1. Because there is always some distance to be covered, motion is impossible. In another approach to this paradox, Zeno used an allegory telling of a race between a tortoise and Achilles (who could run 100 times as fast), where the tortoise started running 10 rods in front of Achilles. Because the tortoise always advanced 1/100 of the distance that Achilles advanced in the same time period, it was theoretically impossible for Achilles to pass him. The English mathematician and writer Charles Dodgson (1832-1898), better known as Lewis Carroll, used the characters of Achilles and the tortoise to illustrate his paradox of infinity.

WEIGHTS, MEASURES, AND MEASUREMENT

What is the **SI system** of measurement?

French scientists as far back as the 17th and 18th centuries questioned the hodgepodge of the many illogical and imprecise standards used for measurement, and so began a crusade to make a comprehensive, logical, precise, and universal measurement system called Système Internationale d'Unités, or SI for short. It uses the metric system as its base. Since all the units are in multiples of 10, calculations are simplified. Today all countries except the United States, Burma, and Liberia use this system. However, some elements within American society do use SI—scientists, exporting/importing industries, and federal agencies (as of November 30, 1992).

The SI or metric system has seven fundamental standards: the meter (for length), the kilogram (for mass), the second (for time), the ampere (for electric current), the kelvin (for temperature), the candela (for luminous intensity), and the mole (for amount of substance). In addition, two supplementary units, the radian (plane angle) and steradian (solid angle), and a large number of derived units compose the current system, which is still evolving. Some derived units, which use special names, are the hertz, newton, pascal, joule, watt, coulomb, volt, farad, ohm, siemens, weber, tesla, henry, lumen, lux, becquerel, gray, and sievert. Its unit of volume or capacity is the cubic decimeter, but many still use "liter" in its place. Very large or very small dimensions are expressed through a series of prefixes, which increase or decrease in multiples of ten. For example, a decimeter is 1/10 of a meter; a centimeter is 1/100 of a meter, and a millimeter is 1/1000 of a meter. A dekameter is 10 meters, a hectometer is 100 meters, and a kilometer is 1,000 meters. The use of these prefixes enable the system to express these units in an orderly way and avoid inventing new names and new relationships.

How was the length of a **meter** originally determined?

It was originally intended that the meter should represent one ten-millionth of the distance along the meridian running from the North Pole to the equator through Dunkirk, France, and Barcelona, Spain. French scientists determined this distance, working nearly six years to complete the task in November 1798. They decided to use a platinum-iridium bar as the physical replica of the meter. Although the surveyors made an error of about two miles, the error was not discovered until much later. Rather than change the length of the meter to conform to the actual distance, scientists in 1889 chose the platinum-iridium bar as the international prototype. It was used until 1960. Numerous copies of it are in other parts of the world, including the United States National Bureau of Standards.

How is the **length of a meter** presently determined?

The meter is equal to 39.37 inches. It is presently defined as the distance traveled by light in a vacuum during 1/299,792,458 of a second. From 1960 to 1983, the length of a meter had been defined as 1,650,763.73 times the wavelength of the orange light emitted when a gas consisting of the pure krypton isotope of mass number 86 is excited in an electrical discharge.

How did the **yard** as a unit of measurement originate?

In early times the natural way to measure lengths was to use various portions of the body (the foot, the thumb, the forearm, etc.). According to tradition, a yard measured on King Henry I (1068-1135) of England became the standard yard still used today. It was the distance from his nose to the middle fingertip of his extended arm.

Other measures were derived from physical activity such as a pace, a league (distance that equaled an hour's walking), an acre (amount plowed in a day), a furlong (length of a plowed ditch), etc., but obviously these units were unreliable. The ell, based on the distance between the elbow and index fingertip, was used to measure out cloth. It ranged from 0.513 to 2.322 meters depending on the locality where it was used and even on the type of goods measured.

Below are listed some linear measurements that evolved from this old reckoning into U.S. customary measures:

U.S. customary linear measures

1 hand	=	4 inches
1 foot	=	12 inches
1 yard	=	3 feet
1 rod (pole or perch)	=	16.5 feet
1 fathom	=	6 feet
1 furlong	=	220 yards or 660 feet or 40 rods
1 (statute) mile	=	1,760 yards or 5,280 feet or 8 furlongs
1 league	=	5,280 yards or 15,840 feet or 3 miles
1 international nautical mile	=	6,076.1 feet

Conversion to metric

1 inch	=	2.54 centimeters
1 foot	=	0.304 meters
1 yard	=	0.9144 meters
1 fathom	=	1.83 meters
1 rod	=	5.029 meters
1 furlong	=	201.168 meters
1 league	=	4.828 kilometers

Conversion to metric

1 mile	=	1.609 kilometers
1 international nautical mile	=	1.852 kilometers

Why is a **nautical mile** different from a **statute mile**?

Queen Elizabeth I established the statute mile as 5,280 feet (1,609 meters). This measure, based on walking distance, originated with the Romans, who designated 1,000 paces as a land mile.

The nautical mile is not based on human locomotion, but on the circumference of the Earth. There was wide disagreement on the precise measurement, but by 1954 the United States adopted the international nautical mile of 1,852 meters (6,076 feet). It is the length on the Earth's surface of one minute of arc.

1 nautical mile (Int.) = 1.1508 statute miles

1 statute mile = 0.868976 nautical miles

How are U.S. customary measures **converted** to metric measures and vice versa?

Listed below is the conversion process for common units of measure:

To convert from	To	Multiply by
acres	meters, square	4,046.856
centimeters	inches	0.394
centimeters	feet	0.0328
centimeters, cubic	inches, cubic	0.06
centimeters, square	inches, square	0.155
feet	meters	0.305
feet, square	meters, square	0.093
gallons, U.S.	liters	3.785
grams	ounces (avoirdupois)	0.035
hectares	kilometers, square	0.01
hectares	miles, square	0.004
inches	centimeters	2.54
inches	millimeters	25.4
inches, cubic	centimeters, cubic	16.387
inches, cubic	liters	0.016387
inches, cubic	meters, cubic	0.0000164
inches, square	centimeters, square	6.4516
inches, square	meters, square	0.0006452
kilograms	ounces, troy	32.15075

To convert from	To	Multiply by
kilograms	pounds (avoirdupois)	2.205
kilograms	tons, metric	0.001
kilometers	feet	3,280.8
kilometers	miles	0.621
kilometers, square	hectares	100
knots	miles per hour	1.151
liters	fluid ounces	33.815
liters	gallons	0.264
liters	pints	2.113
liters	quarts	1.057
meters	feet	3.281
meters	yards	1.094
meters, cubic	yards, cubic	1.308
meters, cubic	feet, cubic	35.315
meters, square	feet, square	10.764
meters, square	yards, square	1.196
miles, nautical	kilometers	1.852
miles, square	hectares	258.999
miles, square	kilometers, square	2.59
miles (statute)	meters	1,609.344
miles (statute)	kilometers	1.609344
ounces (avoirdupois)	grams	28.35
ounces (avoirdupois)	kilograms	0.0283495
ounces, fluid	liters	0.03
pints, liquid	liters	0.473
pounds (avoirdupois)	grams	453.592
pounds (avoirdupois)	kilograms	0.454
quarts	liters	0.946
tons (short/U.S.)	tonne	0.907
ton, long	tonne	1.016
tonne	ton(short/U.S.)	1.102
tonne ton,	long	0.984
yards	meters	0.914
yards, square	meters, square	0.836
yards, cubic	meters, cubic	0.765

Which **countries** of the world have not formally begun **converting** to the metric system?

The United States, Burma, and Liberia are the only countries that have not formally converted to the metric system. As early as 1790, Thomas Jefferson, then Secretary of

State, proposed adoption of the metric system. It was not implemented because Great Britain, America's major trading source, had not yet begun to use the system.

What are the equivalents for **dry** and **liquid measures**?

U.S. customary dry measures

1 pint	=	33.6 cubic inches
1 quart	=	2 pints or 67.2006 cubic inches
1 peck	=	8 quarts or 16 pints or 537.605 cubic inches
1 bushel	=	4 pecks or 2,150.42 cubic inches or 32 quarts
1 barrel	=	105 quarts or 7,056 cubic inches
1 pint, dry	=	0.551 liter
1 quart, dry	=	1.101 liters
1 bushel	=	35.239 liters

U.S. customary liquid measures

1 tablespoon	=	4 fluid drams or 0.5 fluid ounce
1 cup	=	0.5 pint or 8 fluid ounces
1 gill	=	4 fluid ounces
4 gills	=	1 pint or 28.875 cubic inches
1 pint	=	2 cups or 16 fluid ounces
2 pints	=	1 quart or 57.75 cubic ounces
1 quart	=	2 pints or 4 cups or 32 fluid ounces
4 quarts	=	1 gallon or 231 cubic inches or 8 pints or 32 gills or 0.833 British quart
1 gallon	=	16 cups or 231 cubic inches or 128 fluid ounces
1 bushel	=	8 gallons or 32 quarts

Conversion to metric

1 fluid ounce	=	29.57 milliliters or 0.029 liter
1 gill	=	0.118 liter
1 cup	=	0.236 liter
1 pint	=	0.473 liter
1 U.S. quart	=	0.833 British quart or 0.946 liter
1 U.S. gallon	=	0.833 British gallon or 3.785 liters

What is the difference between a **short ton**, a **long ton**, and a **metric ton**?

A short ton or U.S. ton or net ton (sometimes just "ton") equals 2,000 pounds; a long ton or an avoirdupois ton is 2,240 pounds; and a metric ton or tonne is 2,204.62 pounds. Other weights are compared below:

U.S. customary measure

1 ounce	=	16 drams or 437.5 grains
1 pound	=	16 ounces or 7,000 grains or 256 drams
1 (short) hundredweight	=	100 pounds
1 long hundredweight	=	112 pounds
1 (short) ton	=	20 hundredweights or 2,000 pounds
1 long ton	=	20 long hundredweights or 2,240 pounds

Conversion to metric

1 grain	=	65 milligrams
1 dram	=	1.77 grams
1 ounce	=	28.3 grams
1 pound	=	453.5 grams
1 metric ton (tonne)	=	2,204.6 pounds

What are the U.S. and metric units of measurement for **area**?

U.S. customary area measures

1 square foot	=	144 square inches
1 square yard	=	9 square feet or 1,296 square miles
1 square rod or pole or perch	=	30.25 square yards or 272.5 square feet
1 rood	=	40 square rods
1 acre	=	160 square rods or 4,840 square yards or 43,460 square feet
1 section	=	1 mile square or 640 acres
1 township	=	6 miles square or 36 square miles or 36 sections
1 square mile	=	640 acres or 4 roods, or 1 section

International area measures

1 square millimeter	=	1,000,000 square microns
1 square centimeter	=	100 square millimeters
1 square meter	=	10,000 square centimeters
1 are	=	100 square meters
1 hectare	=	100 ares or 10,000 square meters
1 square kilometer	=	100 hectares or 1,000,000 square meters

How much does **water** weigh?

U.S. customary measures

1 gallon	=	4 quarts

Which is heavier—a pound of gold or a pound of feathers?

A pound of feathers is heavier than a pound of gold because gold is measured in troy pounds, while feathers are measured in avoirdupois pounds. Troy pounds have 12 ounces; avoirdupois pounds have 16 ounces. A troy pound contains 372 grams in the metric system; an avoirdupois pound contains 454 grams. Each troy ounce is heavier than an avoirdupois ounce.

U.S. customary measures

1 gallon	=	231 cubic inches
1 gallon	=	8.34 pounds
1 gallon	=	0.134 cubic foot
1 cubic foot	=	7.48 gallons
1 cubic inch	=	.0360 pound
12 cubic inches	=	.433 pound

British measures

1 liter	=	1 kilogram
1 cubic meter	=	1 tonne (metric ton)
1 imperial gallon	=	10.022 pounds
1 imperial gallon salt water	=	10.3 pounds

How are **avoirdupois** measurements converted to **troy measurements** and how do the measures differ?

Troy weight is a system of mass units used primarily to measure gold and silver. A troy ounce is 480 grains or 31.1 grams. Avoirdupois weight is a system of units that is used to measure mass, except for precious metals, precious stones, and drugs. It is based on the pound, which is approximately 454 grams. In both systems, the weight of a grain is the same—65 milligrams. The two systems do not contain the same weights for other units, however, even though they use the same name for the unit.

Troy

1 grain = 65 milligrams
1 ounce = 480 grains = 31.1 grams
1 pound = 12 ounce = 5760 grains = 373 grams

Avoirdupois

1 grain = 65 milligrams
1 ounce = 437.5 grains = 28.3 grams
1 pound = 16 ounces = 7000 grains = 454 grams

To convert from	To	Multiply by
pounds avdp	ounces troy	14.583
pounds avdp	pounds troy	1.215
pounds troy	ounces avdp	1.097
pounds troy	pounds avdp	0.069
ounces avdp	ounces troy	0.911
ounces troy	ounces avdp	1.097

How is the distance to the **horizon** measured?

Distance to the horizon depends on the height of the observer's eyes. To determine that, take the distance (in feet) from sea level to eye level and multiply by three, then divide by two and take the square root of the answer. The result is the number of miles to the horizon. For example, if eye level is at a height of six feet above sea level, the horizon is almost three miles away. If eye level were exactly at sea level, there would be no distance seen at all; the horizon would be directly in front of the viewer.

What is a **bench mark**?

A bench mark is a permanent, recognizable point that lies at a known elevation. It may be an existing object, such as the top of a fire hydrant, or it may be a brass plate placed on top of a concrete post. Surveyors and engineers use bench marks to find the elevation of objects by reading, through a level telescope, the distance a point lies above some already established bench mark.

What is a **theodolite**?

This optical surveying instrument used to measure angles and directions is mounted on an adjustable tripod and has a spirit level to show when it is horizontal. Similar to the more commonly used transit, the theodolite gives more precise readings; angles can be read to fractions of a degree. It is comprised of a telescope that sights the main target, a horizontal plate to provide readings around the horizon, and a vertical plate and scale for vertical readings. The surveyor uses the geometry of triangles to calculate the distance from the angles measured by the theodolite. Such triangulation is used in road- and tunnel-building and other civil engineering work. One of the earliest forms of this surveying instrument was described by Englishman Leonard Digges (d. 1571?) in his 1571 work, *Geometrical Treatise Named Pantometria*.

TIME

How is **time** measured?

The passage of time can be measured in three ways. Rotational time is based on the unit of the mean solar day (the average length of time it takes the Earth to complete one rotation on its axis). Dynamic time, the second way to measure time, uses the motion of the moon and planets to determine time and avoids the problem of the Earth's varying rotation. The first dynamic time scale was Ephemeris Time, proposed in 1896 and modified in 1960.

Atomic time is a third way to measure time. This method, using an atomic clock, is based on the extremely regular oscillations that occur within atoms. In 1967, the atomic second (the length of time in which 9,192,631,770 vibrations are emitted by a hot cesium atom) was adopted as the basic unit of time. Atomic clocks are now used as international time standards.

But time has also been measured in other less scientific terms. Listed below are some other "timely" expressions.

Twilight—The first soft glow of sunlight; the sun is still below the horizon; also the last glow of sunlight.

Midnight—12 a.m.; the point of time when one day becomes the next day and night becomes morning.

Daybreak—The first appearance of the sun.

Dawn—A gradual increase of sunlight.

Noon—12 p.m.; the point of time when morning becomes afternoon.

Dusk—The gradual dimming of sunlight.

Sunset—The last diffused glow of sunlight; the sun is below the horizon.

Evening—A term with wide meaning, evening is generally the period between sunset and bedtime.

Night—The period of darkness, lasting from sunset to midnight.

What is the basis for **modern timekeeping**?

Mankind has typically associated the durations of the year, month, week, and day on the earth and moon cycles. The modern clock, however, is based on the number 60. The Sumerians around 3000 B.C.E. employed a base ten counting system and also a base 60 counting system. The timekeeping system inherited this pattern with 60 seconds per minute and 60 minutes per hour. Ten and sixty fit together to form the notion of time: 10 hours is 600 minutes; 10 minutes is 600 seconds; one minute is 60 seconds. One second is not related to any of these factors; instead, scientists based the duration of one second on cesium-133, an isotope of the metal cesium. Officially, one second is the amount of time it takes for a cesium-133 atom to vibrate 9,192,631,770 times.

What is the exact length of a **calendar year**?

The calendar year is defined as the time between two successive crossings of the celestial equator by the sun at the vernal equinox. It is exactly 365 days, 5 hours, 48 minutes, 46 seconds. The fact that the year is not a whole number of days has affected the development of calendars, which over time generate an accumulative error. The current calendar used, the Gregorian calendar, named after Pope Gregory XII (1502-1585), attempts to compensate by adding an extra day to the month of February every four years. A "leap year" is one with the extra day added.

When does a **century begin**?

A century has 100 consecutive calendar years. The first century consisted of years 1 through 100. The 20th century started with 1901 and ended with 2000. The 21st century began on January 1, 2001.

When did **January 1** become the first day of the **new year**?

When Julius Caesar (100-44 B.C.E.) reorganized the Roman calendar and made it solar rather than lunar in the year 45 B.C.E., he moved the beginning of the year to January 1. When the Gregorian calendar was introduced in 1582, January 1 continued to be recognized as the first day of the year in most places. In England and the American colonies, however, March 25, intended to represent the spring equinox, was the beginning of the year. Under this system, March 24, 1700, was followed by March 25, 1701. In 1752, the British government changed the beginning date of the year to January 1.

Besides the Gregorian calendar, what **other kinds of calendars** have been used?

Babylonian calendar—A lunar calendar composed of alternating 29-day and 30-day months to equal roughly 354 lunar days. When the calendar became too misaligned with astronomical events, an extra month was added. In addition, three extra months were added every eight years to coordinate this calendar with the solar year.

Chinese calendar—A lunar month calendar of 12 periods having either 29 or 30 days (to compensate for the 29.5 days from new moon to new moon). The new year begins on the first new moon over China after the sun enters Aquarius (between January 21st and February 19th). Each year has both a number and a name (for example, the year 1992, or 4629 in the Chinese era, is the year of the monkey). The calendar is synchronized with the solar year by the addition of extra months at fixed intervals.

Muslim calendar—A lunar 12-month calendar with 30 and 29 days alternating every month for a total of 354 days. The calendar has a 30-year cycle with designated leap years of 355 days (one day added to the last month) in the 30-year period. The Islamic year does not attempt to relate to the solar year (the season). The dating of the beginning of the calendar is 622 C.E. (the date of Mohammed's flight from Mecca to Medina).

Jewish calendar—A blend of the solar and lunar calendar, this calendar adds an extra month (Adar Sheni, or the second Adar or Veadar) to keep the lunar and solar years in alignment. This occurs seven times during a 19-year cycle. When the extra 29-day month is inserted, the month Adar has 30 days instead of 29. In a usual year the 12 months alternately have 30, then 29 days.

Egyptian calendar—The ancient Egyptians were the first to use a solar calendar (about 4236 B.C.E. or 4242 B.C.E.), but their year started with the rising of Sirius, the brightest star in the sky. The year, composed of 365 days, was one-quarter day short of the true solar year, so eventually the Egyptian calendar did not coincide with the seasons. It used twelve 30-day months with five-day weeks and five dates of festival.

Coptic calendar—Still used in areas of Egypt and Ethiopia, it has a similar cycle to the Egyptian calendar: 12 months of 30 days followed by five complementary days. When a leap year occurs, usually preceding the Julian calendar leap year, the complementary days increase to six.

Roman calendar—Borrowing from the ancient Greek calendar, which had a four-year cycle based on the Olympic Games, the earliest Roman calendar (about 738 B.C.E.) had 304 days with 10 months. Every second year a short month of 22 or 23 days was added to coincide with the solar year. Eventually two more months were added at the end of the year (Januarius and Februarius) to increase the year to 354 days. The Roman republican calendar replaced this calendar during the reign of Tarquinius Priscus (616-579 B.C.E.). This new lunar calendar had 355 days, with the month of February having 28 days. The other months had either 29 or 31 days. To keep the calendar aligned with the seasons, an extra month was added every two years. By the time the Julian calendar replaced this one, the calendar was three months ahead of the season schedule.

Julian calendar—Julius Caesar, (100-44 B.C.E.) in 46 B.C.E., wishing to have one calendar in use for all the empire, had the astronomer Sosigenes develop a uniform solar calendar with a year of 365 days with one day ("leap day") added every fourth year to compensate for the true solar year of 365.25 days. The year had 12 months with 30 or 31 days except for February,

What is the World Calendar?

Following World War II, the United States led a movement in the United Nations to encourage the international community to adopt a common calendar. Called the World Calendar, it would self-adjust the irregular months, equalize the quarterly divisions of the years, and fix the sequence of weekdays and month dates so that days of the month would always fall on the same day of the week. This calendar would make the normal year 364 days long, divided into four quarters of 91 days each. The quarters could be segmented into three months of 31, 30, and 30 days. Every year would have 52 whole weeks; every quarter would begin with a Sunday and end with a Saturday. An extra day would need to be added to each year. This day, "World's Day," is formally called "W December," observed following the last day of December. Leap Year Day would be a similar insertion in the calendar every fourth year, following June 30, and would be called "W June." Although it was predicted that the calendar would be adopted in 1961, it has repeatedly failed passage in the United Nations.

which had 28 days (or 29 days in a leap year). The first of the year was moved from March 1 to January 1.

Gregorian calendar—Pope Gregory XIII (1502-1585) instituted calendrical reform in 1582 to realign the church celebration of Easter with the vernal equinox (the first day of spring). To better align this solar calendar with the seasons, the new calendar would not have leap year in the century years that were not divisible by 400. Because the solar year is shortening, today a one-second adjustment is made (usually on December 31 at midnight) when necessary to compensate.

Japanese calendar—It has the same structure as the Gregorian calendar in years, months, and weeks. But the years are enumerated in terms of the reigns of emperors as epochs. The last epoch (for Emperor Akihito) is Epoch Heisei, which started January 8, 1989.

Hindu calendars—The principal Indian calendars reckon their epochs from historical events, such as rulers' accessions or death dates, or a religious founder's dates. The Vikrama era (originally from Northern India and still used in western India) dates from February 23, 57 B.C.E., in the Gregorian calendar. The Saka era dates from March 3, 78 C.E., in the Gregorian calendar and is based on the solar year with 12 months of 365 days and 366 days in leap years. The first five months have 31 days; the last seven have 30 days. In leap years, the first six months have 31 days and the last six have

30. The Saka era is the national calendar of India (since 1957). The Buddhist era starts with 543 B.C.E. (believed to be the date of Buddha's death).

Three other secular calendars of note are the *Julian Day calendar* (a calendar astronomers use, which counts days within a 7,980-year period and must be used with a table), the *perpetual calendar* (which gives the days of the week for the Julian and Gregorian calendars as well), and the *world calendar*, which is similar to the perpetual calendar, having 12 months of 30 or 31 days, a year-day at the end of each year, and a leap-year-day before July 1 every four years.

There have been attempts to reform and simplify the calendar. One such example is the Thirteen-Month or International Fixed calendar, which would have 13 months of four weeks each. The month *Sol* would come before July; there would be a year-day at the end of each year and a leap-year-day every four years just before July 1. A radical reform was made in France when the French republican calendar (1793-1806) replaced the Gregorian calendar after the French Revolution. It had 12 months of 30 days and five supplementary days at the end of the year (six in a leap-year), and weeks were replaced with 10-day decades.

What is the **Julian Day Count**?

This system of counting days rather than years was developed by Joseph Justus Scaliger (1540-1609) in 1583. Still used by astronomers today, the Julian Day Count (named after Scaliger's father, Julius Caesar Scaliger) Julian Day (JD) 1 was January 1, 4113 B.C.E. On this date the Julian calendar, the ancient Roman tax calendar, and the lunar calendar all coincided. This event would not occur again until 7,980 years later. Each day within this 7,980-year period is numbered. December 31, 1991, at noon is the beginning of JD 2,448,622. The figure reflects the number of days that have passed since its inception. To convert Gregorian calendar dates into Julian Day, simple JD conversion tables have been devised for astronomers.

Do all calendars other than the Gregorian calendar use a **twelve-month cycle**?

No. Some calendars have a varying cycle of months, with their first month falling at a different time. Listed below are some variations with the beginning month of the year in italics:

Months of the year

Gregorian	Hebrew	Hindu
January	Shebat	Magha
February	Adar	Phalguna
March	Nisan	Caitra
April	Iyar	Vaisakha

Gregorian	Hebrew	Hindu
May	Sivan	Jyaistha
June	Tammuz	Asadhe
July	Ab	Sravana
August	Elul	Bhadrapada
September	Tishri	Asvina
October	Heshvan	Karttika
November	Kislev	Margasivsa
December	Tebet	Pansa
	Ve-Adar (13th month every three years)	

Muslim	Chinese	
Muharram	Li Chun	Li Qui
Safar	Yu Shui	Chu Shu
Rabi I	Jing Zhe	Bai Lu
Rabi II	Chun Fen	Qui Fen
Jumada I	Qing Ming	Han Lu
Jumada II	Gu Yu	Shuang Jiang
Rajab	Li Xia	Li Dong
Sha'ban	Xiao Man	Xiao Xue
Ramadan	Mang Zhong	Da Xue
Shawwal	Xia Zhi	Dong Zhi
Dhu'l-Qa'da	Xiao Shu	Xiao Han
Dhu'l-hijja	Da Shu	Da Han

Which animal designations have been given to the **Chinese years**?

There are 12 different names, always used in the same sequence: Rat, Ox, Tiger, Hare (Rabbit), Dragon, Snake, Horse, Sheep (Goat), Monkey, Rooster, Dog, and Pig. The following table shows this sequence.

Chinese year cycle

Rat	Ox	Tiger	Hare (Rabbit)	Dragon	Snake
1996	1997	1998	1999	2000	2001
2008	2009	2010	2011	2012	2013
2020	2021	2022	2023	2024	2025
Horse	**Sheep (Goat)**	**Monkey**	**Rooster**	**Dog**	**Pig**
2002	2003	2004	2005	2006	2007
2014	2015	2016	2017	2018	2019
2026	2027	2028	2029	2030	2031

The Chinese year of 354 days begins three to seven weeks into the western 365-day year, so the animal designation changes at that time, rather than on January 1.

When does **leap year** occur?

A leap year occurs when the year is exactly divisible by four, except for centenary years. A centenary year must be divisible by 400 to be a leap year. There was no February 29 in 1900, which was not a leap year. The year 2000 was a centenary leap year, and the next one will be 2400.

What is a **leap second**?

The Earth's rotation is slowing down, and to compensate for this lagging motion a leap second is added to a specified day. One leap second was used in 1992 to keep the calendar in close alignment with international atomic time. To complete this change, 23h 59m 59s universal time on June 30, 1992 was followed by 23h 59m 60s and this in turn was followed by 0h 0m 0s on July 1.

What were the **longest** and **shortest** years on record?

The longest year was 46 B.C.E. when Julius Caesar (100-44 B.C.E.) introduced his calendar, called the Julian calendar, which was used until 1582. He added two extra months and 23 extra days to February to make up for accumulated slippage in the Egyptian calendar. Thus, 46 B.C.E. was 455 days long. The shortest year was 1582, when Pope Gregory XIII (1502-1585) introduced his calendar, the Gregorian calendar. He decreed that October 5 would be October 15, eliminating 10 days, to make up for the accumulated error in the Julian calendar. Not everyone changed over to this new calendar at once. Catholic Europe adopted it within two years of its inception. Many Protestant continental countries did so in 1699-1700; England imposed it on its colonies in 1752 and Sweden in 1753. Many non-European countries adopted it in the 19th century, with China doing so in 1912, Turkey in 1917, and Russia in 1918. To change from the Julian to the Gregorian calendar, 10 days are added to dates October 5, 1582, through February 28, 1700; after that date add 11 days through February 28, 1800; 12 days through February 28, 1900; and 13 days through February 28, 2100.

Where do the names of the **days of the week** come from?

The English days of the week are named for a mixture of figures in Anglo-Saxon and Roman mythology.

Day	Named after
Sunday	The sun
Monday	The moon

Day	Named after
Tuesday	Tiu (the Anglo-Saxon god of war, equivalent to the Norse Tyr or the Roman Mars)
Wednesday	Woden (the Anglo-Saxon equivalent of Odin, the chief Norse god)
Thursday	Thor (the Norse god of thunder)
Friday	Frigg (the Norse god of love and fertility, the equivalent of the Roman Venus)
Saturday	Saturn (the Roman god of agriculture)

What is the **origin** of the **week**?

The week originated in the Babylonian calendar, where one day out of seven was devoted to rest.

How were the **months** of the year **named**?

The English names of the months of the current (Gregorian) calendar come from the Romans, who tended to honor their gods and commemorate specific events by designating them as month names:

January (*Januarius* in Latin), named after Janus, a Roman two-faced god, one face looking into the past, the other into the future.

February (*Februarium*) is from the Latin word *Februare*, meaning "to cleanse." At the time of year corresponding to our February, the Romans performed religious rites to purge themselves of sin.

March (*Martius*) is named in honor of Mars, the god of war.

April (*Aprilis*), after the Latin word *Aperio*, meaning "to open," because plants begin to grow in this month.

May (*Maius*), after the Roman goddess Maia, as well as from the Latin word *Maiores* meaning "elders," who were celebrated during this month.

June (*Junius*), after the goddess Juno and Latin word *iuniores*, meaning "young people."

July (*Iulius*) was, at first, known as *Quintilis* from the Latin word meaning five, since it was the fifth month in the early Roman calendar. Its name was changed to July, in honor of Julius Caesar (100-44 B.C.E.).

August (*Augustus*) is named in honor of the Emperor Octavian (63-14 B.C.E.), first Roman emperor, known as Augustus Caesar. Originally the month was known as *Sextilis* (sixth month of early Roman calendar).

September (*September*) was once the seventh month and accordingly took its name from *septem*, meaning "seven."

October (*October*) takes its name from *octo* (eight); at one time it was the eighth month.

November (*November*) from *novem,* meaning "nine," once the ninth month of the early Roman calendar.

December (*December*) from *decem,* meaning "ten," once the tenth month of the early Roman calendar.

Why are the **lengths of the seasons** not equal?

The lengths of the seasons are not exactly equal because the orbit of the Earth around the sun is elliptic rather than a circular. When the Earth is closest to the sun in January, gravitational forces cause the planet to move faster than it does in the summer months when it is far away from the sun. As a result, the autumn and winter seasons in the Northern Hemisphere are slightly shorter than spring and summer. The duration of the northern seasons are:

spring	92.76 days
summer	93.65 days
autumn	89.84 days
winter	88.99 days

How is the date for **Easter** determined?

The rule for establishing the date in the Christian Churches is that Easter always falls on the first Sunday after the first full moon that occurs on or just after the vernal equinox. The vernal equinox is the first day of spring in the Northern Hemisphere. Because the full moon can occur on any one of many dates after the vernal equinox, the date of Easter can be as early as March 22 and as late as April 25.

How is the date for **Passover** determined?

Passover (Pesah) begins at sundown on the evening before the 15th day of the Hebrew month of Nisan, which falls in March or April. Celebrated as a public holiday in Israel, the Passover commemorates the exodus of the Israelites from Egypt in 1290 B.C.E. The term "Passover" is a reference to the last of the 10 plagues that "passed over" the Israelite homes at the end of their captivity in Egypt.

Occasionally one sees a date expressed as "**B.P.** 6500" instead of "B.C. 6500". What does this signify?

Archaeologists use the B.P. or BP as an abbreviation for years before the present. This date is a rough generalization of the number of years before 1950, and is a date not necessarily based on radiocarbon dating methods.

How is **"local noon"** calculated?

Local noon, also called "the time of solar meridian passage," is the time of day when the sun is at its highest point in the sky. This is different from noon on clocks. To calculate local noon, first find the sunrise and sunset (readily available in larger newspapers), add the total amount of sunlight, divide this number by two, and add that to the sunrise. For instance, if sunrise is at 7:30 a.m. and sunset is at 8:40 p.m., the total sunlight is 13 hours and ten minutes, divided by two is 6 hours and 40 minutes (13 hours/2 = 6.5 hours plus 10 minutes), added to 7:30 a.m. equals a local noon of 1:40 p.m.

When is **Daylight Savings Time** observed in the United States?

In 1967, all states and possessions of the United States were to begin observing Daylight Savings Time at 2 a.m. on the first Sunday in April of every year. The clock would advance one hour at that time until 2 a.m. of the last Sunday of October, when the clock would be turned back one hour. In the intervening years, the length of this time period changed, but on July 8, 1986, the original starting and ending dates were reinstated. A 1972 amendment allowed some areas to be exempt. In 2005, the U.S. Congress established a law that took effect in 2007 and changed the dates for Daylight Savings Time. It now begins on the second Sunday of March (at 2:00 a.m. clocks are moved ahead one hour) and ends on the first Sunday in November (clocks are moved back an hour, again at 2:00 p.m.).

Which states and territories of the United States are **exempt from Daylight Savings Time**?

Arizona, Hawaii, Puerto Rico, the U.S. Virgin Islands, American Samoa, and most of Indiana are exempt from Daylight Savings Time.

How many **time zones** are there in the world?

There are 24 standard time zones that serially cover the Earth's surface at coincident intervals of 15 degrees longitude and 60 minutes Universal Time (UT), as agreed at the Washington Meridian Conference of 1884, thus accounting, respectively, for each of the 24 hours in a calendar day.

What is unusual about the observance of **time zones** in **Russia** and **China**?

Russia, which spans 11 time zones, is on "advanced time" year round, meaning that it maintains its Standard Time one hour faster than the zone designation. The country also observes Daylight Saving Time from the fourth Sunday in March until the fourth Sunday in September. China, though it lies across five time zones, keeps one time, which is eight hours faster than Greenwich Time.

Why do the minute and hour hands on a clock go "clockwise"?

Henry Fried, an expert on timekeeping, postulates that the clockwise motion of minute and hour hands has its origin in the use of sundials before the development of clocks. In the northern hemisphere, the shadow rotates in a clockwise direction, and clock inventors built the hands to copy the natural movement of the sun.

When traveling from Tokyo to Seattle and crossing the **International Date Line**, what day is it?

Traveling from west to east (Tokyo to Seattle), the calendar day is set back (e.g., Sunday becomes Saturday). Traveling east to west, the calendar day is advanced (e.g., Tuesday becomes Wednesday). The International Date Line is a zigzag line at approximately the 180th meridian, where the calendar days are separated.

What is meant by **Universal Time**?

On January 1, 1972, Universal Time (UT) replaced Greenwich Mean Time (GMT) as the time reference coordinate for scientific work. Universal Time is measured by an atomic clock and is seen as the logical development of the adoption of the atomic second in 1968. An advantage of UT is that the time at which an event takes place can be determined very readily without recourse to the time-consuming astronomical observations and calculations that were necessary before the advent of atomic clocks. Universal Time is also referred to as International Atomic Time. GMT is measured according to when the sun crosses the Greenwich Meridian (zero degrees longitude, which passes through the Greenwich Observatory).

Who establishes the **correct time** in the United States?

The United States National Institute of Standards and Technology (NIST) uses a cesium beam clock as its NIST atomic frequency standard to determine atomic time. It is possible to check the time by accessing the NIST Web site at http://www.nist.gov and selecting "check time" from the options. The clock is accurate to plus or minus one second. The atomic second was officially defined in 1967 by the 13th General Conference of Weights and Measures as 9,192,631,770 oscillations of the atom of cesium-133. This cesium-beam clock of the NIST is referred to as a primary clock because, independently of any other reference, it provides highly precise and accurate time.

What is the **United States Time Standard** signal?

Universal Time is announced in International Morse Code each five minutes by radio stations WWV (Fort Collins, Colorado) and WWVH (Puuene, Maui, Hawaii). These stations are under the direction of the U.S. National Institute of Standards and Technology (formerly called National Bureau of Standards). They transmit 24 hours a day on 2.5, 5, 10, 15, and 20 megahertz. The first radio station to transmit time signals regularly was the Eiffel Tower Radio Station in Paris in 1913.

What do the initials **a.m.** and **p.m.** mean?

The initials a.m. stand for *ante meridian,* Latin for "before noon." The initials p.m. stand for *post meridian,* Latin for "after noon."

How does a **sundial** work?

The sundial, one of the first instruments used in the measurement of time, works by simulating the movement of the sun. A gnomon is affixed to a time (or hour) scale and the time is read by observing the shadow of the gnomon on the scale. Sundials generally use the altitude of the sun to give the time, so certain modifications and interpretations must be made for seasonal variance.

How is **time** denoted at **sea**?

The day is divided into watches and bells. A watch equals four hours except for the time period between 4 p.m. and 8 p.m., which has two short watches. Within each watch there are eight bells—one stroke for each half hour, so that each watch ends on eight bells except the dog watches, which end at four bells. New Year's Day is marked with 16 bells.

Bell	Time equivalent		
1 bell	12:30 or	4:30	or 8:30 A.M. or P.M.
2 bells	1:00	5:00	9:00
3 bells	1:30	5:30	9:30
4 bells	2:00	6:00	10:00
5 bells	2:30	6:30	10:30
6 bells	3:00	7:00	11:00
7 bells	3:30	7:30	11:30
8 bells	4:00	8:00	12:00

What is the difference between a **quartz** watch and a **mechanical** watch?

Quartz watches and mechanical watches use the same gear mechanism for turning the hour and minute gear wheels. Mechanical watches are powered by a coiled spring known as the mainspring and regulated by a system called a lever escarpment. As the watch runs, the mainspring unwinds. Quartz watches are powered by a battery-powered electronic integrated circuit on a tiny piece of silicon chip and regulated by quartz crystals that vibrate and produce electric pulses at a fixed rate.

Who invented the **alarm clock**?

Levi Hutchins of Concord, New Hampshire, invented an alarm clock in 1787. His alarm clock, however, rang at only one time—4 a.m. He invented this device so that he would never sleep past his usual waking time. He never patented or manufactured it. The first modern alarm clock was made by Antoine Redier (1817-1892) in 1847. It was a mechanical device; the electric alarm clock was not invented until around 1890. The earliest mechanical clock was made in 725 C.E. in China by Yi Xing and Liang Lingzan.

What is **military time**?

Military time divides the day into one set of 24 hours, counting from midnight (0000) to midnight of the next day (2400). This is expressed without punctuation.

Midnight becomes 0000 (or 2400 of the next day)

1:00 a.m. becomes 0100 (pronounced oh-one hundred)

2:10 a.m. becomes 0210

Noon becomes 1200

6:00 p.m. becomes 1800

9:45 p.m. becomes 2145

To translate 24-hour time into familiar time, the a.m. times are obvious. For p.m. times, subtract 1200 from numbers larger than 1200; e.g., 1900 - 1200 is 7 p.m.

Who set a **doomsday clock** for nuclear annihilation?

The clock first appeared on the cover of the magazine *Bulletin of the Atomic Scientists* in 1947 and was set at 11:53 p.m. The clock, created by the magazine's board of directors, represents the threat of nuclear annihilation, with midnight as the time of destruction. The clock has been reset eighteen times in fifty-five years. In 1953, just after the United States tested the hydrogen bomb, it was set at 11:58 p.m., the closest to midnight ever. In 1991, following the collapse of the Soviet Union, it was moved back to 11:43 p.m., the farthest from midnight the clock has ever been. However, in 1995, the clock was shifted forward to 11:47, reflecting the instability of the post-Cold-War world. The clock was set at seven minutes to midnight (11:53 p.m.) in 2002 because little progress is being made on global nuclear disarmament, and because terrorists are seeking to acquire and use nuclear and biological weapons.

TECHNOLOGY

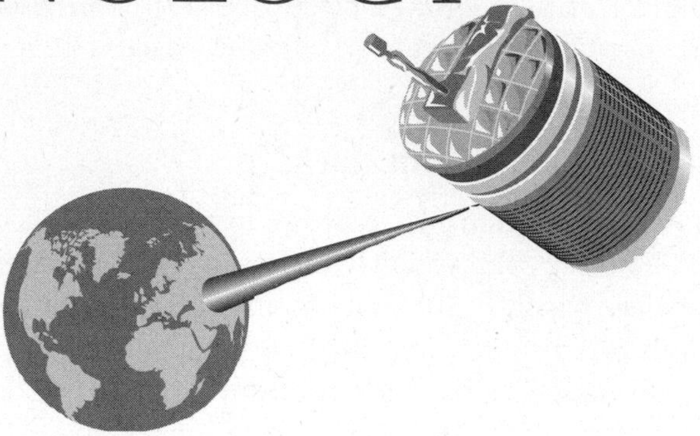

RADIO AND TELEVISION

Who invented **radio**?

Guglielmo Marconi (1874-1937), of Bologna, Italy, was the first to prove that radio signals could be sent over long distances. Radio is the radiation and detection of signals propagated through space as electromagnetic waves to convey information. It was first called wireless telegraphy because it duplicated the effect of telegraphy without using wires. On December 12, 1901, Marconi successfully sent Morse code signals from Newfoundland to England.

In 1906, the American inventor Lee de Forest (1873-1961) built what he called "the Audion," which became the basis for the radio amplifying vacuum tube. This device made voice radio practical, because it magnified the weak signals without distorting them. The next year, de Forest began regular radio broadcasts from Manhattan, New York. As there were still no home radio receivers, de Forest's only audience was ship wireless operators in New York City Harbor.

What was the first **radio broadcasting station**?

The identity of the "first" broadcasting station is a matter of debate since some pioneer AM broadcast stations developed from experimental operations begun before the institution of formal licensing practices. According to records of the Department of Commerce, which then supervised radio, WBZ in Springfield, Massachusetts, received the first regular broadcasting license on September 15, 1921. However, credit for the first radio broadcasting station has customarily gone to Westinghouse station KDKA in Pittsburgh for its broadcast of the Harding-Cox presidential election returns on November 2, 1920.

Senator Guglielmo Marconi, inventor of the wireless radio.

Unlike most other earlier radio transmissions, KDKA used electron tube technology to generate the transmitted signal and hence to have what could be described as broadcast quality. It was the first corporate-sponsored radio station and the first to have a well-defined commercial purpose—it was not a hobby or a publicity stunt. It was the first broadcast station to be licensed on a frequency outside the amateur bands. Altogether, it was the direct ancestor of modern broadcasting.

How are the **call letters** beginning with "K" or "W" assigned to **radio stations**?

These beginning call letters are assigned on a geographical basis. For the majority of radio stations located east of the Mississippi River, their call letters begin with the letter "W"; if the stations are west of the Mississippi, their first call letter is "K." There are exceptions to this rule. Stations founded before this rule went into effect kept their old letters. So, for example, KDKA in Pittsburgh has retained the first letter "K"; likewise, some western pioneer stations have retained the letter "W." Since many AM licensees also operate FM and TV stations, a common practice is to use the AM call letters followed by "-FM" or "-TV."

Why do **FM radio stations** have a limited broadcast range?

Usually radio waves higher in frequency than approximately 50 to 60 megahertz are not reflected by the Earth's ionosphere, but are lost in space. Television, FM radio, and high frequency communications systems are therefore limited to approximately line-of-sight ranges. The line-of-sight distance depends on the terrain and antenna height, but is usually limited to from 50 to 100 miles (80 to 161 kilometers). FM (frequency-modulation) radio uses a wider band than AM (amplitude-modulation) radio to give broadcasts high fidelity, especially noticeable in music—crystal clarity to high frequencies and rich resonance to base notes, all with a minimum of static and distortion. Invented by Edwin Howard Armstrong (1891-1954) in 1933, FM receivers became available in 1939.

With his invention of the FM receiver, Edward Howard Armstrong revolutionized the future of radio broadcasting.

Why do **AM stations** have a wider **broadcast range at night**?

This variation is caused by the nature of the ionosphere of the Earth. The ionosphere consists of several different layers of rarefied gases in the upper atmosphere that have become conductive through the bombardment of the atoms of the atmosphere by solar radiation, by electrons and protons emitted by the sun, and by cosmic rays. These layers, sometimes called the Kennelly-Heaviside layer, reflect AM radio signals, enabling AM broadcasts to be received by radios that are great distances from the transmitting antenna. With the coming of night, the ionosphere layers partially dissipate and become an excellent reflector of the short waveband AM radio waves. This causes distant AM stations to be heard more clearly at night.

Can **radio transmissions** between **space shuttles** and ground control be picked up by shortwave radio?

Amateur radio operators at Goddard Space Flight Center, Greenbelt, Maryland, retransmit shuttle space-to-ground radio conversations on shortwave frequencies. These retransmissions can be heard freely around the world. To hear astronauts talking with ground controllers during liftoff, flight, and landing, a shortwave radio capable of receiving single-sideband signals should be tuned to frequencies of 3.860, 7.185, 14.295, and 21.395 megahertz. British physics teacher Geoffrey Perry, at the Kettering Boys School, has taught his students how to obtain telemetry from orbiting Russian satellites. Since the early 1960s Perry's students have been monitoring Russian space signals using a simple taxicab radio, and using the data to calculate position and orbits of the spacecraft.

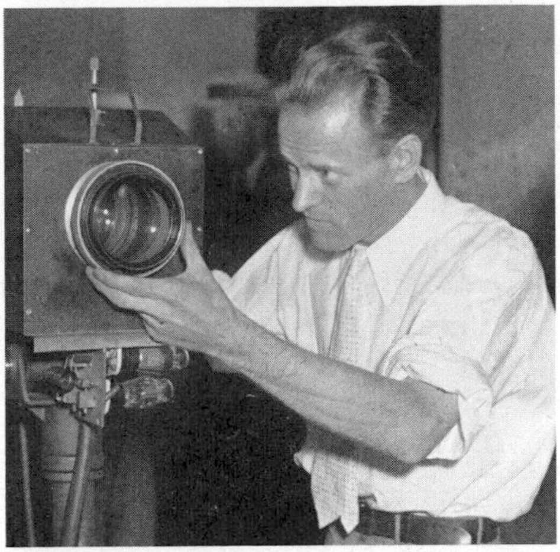

Philo T. Farnsworth played a key role in the development of television.

Who was the founder of **television**?

The idea of television (or "seeing by electricity," as it was called in 1880) was offered by several people over the years, and several individuals contributed a multiplicity of partial inventions. For example, in 1897 Ferdinand Braun (1850-1918) constructed the first cathode ray oscilloscope, a fundamental component to all television receivers. In 1907, Boris Rosing proposed using Braun's tube to receive images, and in the following year Alan Campbell-Swinton likewise suggested using the tube, now called the cathode-ray tube, for both transmission and receiving. The figure most frequently called the father of television, however, was a Russian-born American named Vladimir K. Zworykin (1889-1982). A former pupil of Rosing, he produced a practical method of amplifying the electron beam so that the light/dark pattern would produce a good image. In 1923, he patented the iconoscope (which would become the television camera), and in 1924 he patented the kinoscope (television tube). Both inventions rely on streams of electrons for both scanning and creating the image on a fluorescent screen. By 1938, after adding new and more sensitive photo cells, Zworykin demonstrated his first practical model.

Another "father" of television is the American Philo T. Farnsworth (1906-1971). He was the first person to propose that pictures could be televised electronically. He came up with the basic design for an apparatus in 1922 and discussed his ideas with his high school teacher. This documented his ideas one year before Zworykin and was critical in settling a patent dispute between Farnsworth and his competitor at the Radio Corporation of America. Farnsworth eventually licensed his television patents to the growing industry and let others refine and develop his basic inventions.

During the early 20th century others worked on different approaches to television. The best-known is John Logie Baird (1888-1946), who in 1936 used a mechanized scanning device to transmit the first recognizable picture of a human face. Limitations in his designs made any further improvements in the picture quality impossible.

What name is used for a **satellite dish** that picks up **TV broadcasts**?

Earth station is the term used for the complete satellite receiving or transmitting station. It includes the antenna, the electronics, and all associated equipment necessary to receive or transmit satellite signals. It can range from a simple, inexpensive, receive-only Earth station that can be purchased by the individual consumer, to elaborate, two-way communications stations that offer commercial access to the satellite's capacity. Signals are captured and focused by the antenna into a feedhorn and low noise amplifier. These are relayed by cable to a down converter and then into the satellite receiver/modulator.

Satellite television became widely available in the late 1970s when cable television stations, equipped with satellite dishes, received signals and sent them to their subscribers by coaxial cable. Taylor Howard designed the first satellite dish for personal use in 1976. By 1984 there were 500,000 installations, and in recent years that number has increased worldwide to 3.7 million.

How do **flat-panel displays** differ from traditional screens?

Flat-panel screens are different because they do not use the cathode-ray tube. Cathode-ray tube monitors—the monitors that are nearly omnipresent around the world—work by bombarding a phosphorescent screen with a ray of electrons. The electrons illuminate "phosphors" on the screen into the reds, greens, and blues that form the picture. In contrast, flat-panel displays use a grid of electrodes, crystals, or vinyl polymers to create the small dots that make up the picture. Flat-panel screens are not a new idea: LCD (short for liquid crystal display) watches and calculators going back decades have relied on crystal-based flat-panel displays. The newest flat-panel screens found on laptop computers use plasma display panels (or "PDPs"). They can be very wide—over a meter—but only a few centimeters thick. A PDP screen is made of a layer of picture elements in the three primary colors. Electrodes from a grid behind produce a charge that create ultraviolet rays. These rays illuminate the various picture elements and form the picture.

What is **high-definition television**?

The amount of detail shown in a television picture is limited by the number of lines that make it up and by the number of picture elements on each line. The latter is mostly determined by the width of the electron beam. To obtain pictures closer to the quality associated with 35-millimeter photography, a new television system, HDTV (high-definition television), will have more than twice the number of scan lines with a much smaller picture element. Currently, American and Japanese television has 525 scanning lines, while Europe uses 625 scanning lines. The Japanese are generally given credit for being pioneers in HDTV, ever since the Japanese broadcasting company NHK began research in 1968. In fact, the original pioneer was RCA's Otto Schade, who began his research after the end of World War II. Schade was ahead of his time, and decades passed before television pickup tubes and other components became available to take full advantage of his research.

HDTV cannot be used in the commercial broadcast bands until technical standards are approved by the United States Federal Communications Commission (FCC) or the various foreign regulating agencies. The more immediate problem, however, has been a technological one—HDTV needs to transmit five times more data than is currently assigned to each television channel. One approach is signal compression—squeezing the 30-megahertz bandwidth signal that HDTV requires into the six-megahertz bandwidth currently used for television broadcasting. The Japanese and Europeans have explored analog systems that use wavelike transmission, while the Americans based their HDTV development on digital transmission systems. In 1994, the television industry cleared this hurdle when it accepted a digital signal transmission system developed by Zenith.

The public can now enjoy HDTV: programming and television sets are available, albeit in limited broadcast areas and at a high cost. The programming is available through digital service for about 450 stations in 130 markets (almost every large city). Where digital HDTV service is not yet available, customers can order satellite service, but it requires a specialized dish and receiver. Television sets are also available, but as with any new technology prices are still high, starting at about $2,000 for an entry-level set with wide-screen models approaching $5,000.

TELECOMMUNICATIONS AND RECORDINGS

When was the first **commercial communications satellite** used?

In 1960 *Echo 1,* the first communications satellite, was launched. Two years later, on July 10, 1962, the first commercially funded satellite, *Telstar 1* (paid for by American Telephone and Telegraph), was launched into low Earth orbit. It was also the first true communications satellite, being able to relay not only data and voice, but television as well. The first broadcast, which was relayed from the United States to England, showed an American flag flapping in the breeze. The first commercial satellite (in which its operations are conducted like a business) was *Early Bird,* which went into regular service on June 10, 1965, with 240 telephone circuits. *Early Bird* was the first satellite launched for Intelsat (International Telecommunications Satellite Organization). Still in existence, the system is owned by member nations—each nation's contribution to the operating funds are based on its share of the system's annual traffic.

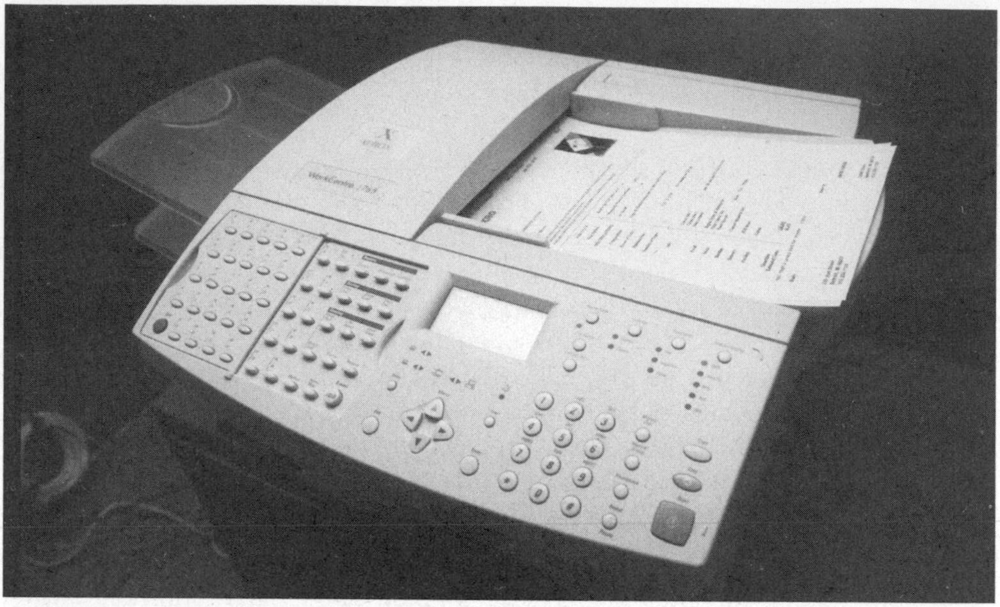

The telefacsimile, or fax machine, transmits information between locations by way of telephone lines.

How does a **fax** machine work?

Telefacsimile (also telefax or facsimile or fax) transmits graphic and textual information from one location to another through telephone lines. A transmitting machine uses either a digital or analog scanner to convert the black-and-white representations of the image into electrical signals that are transmitted through the telephone lines to a designated receiving machine. The receiving unit converts the transmission back to an image of the original and prints it. In its broadest definition, a facsimile terminal is simply a copier equipped to transmit and receive graphics images.

The fax was invented by Alexander Bain of Scotland in 1842. His crude device, along with scanning systems invented by Frederick Bakewell in 1848, evolved into several modern versions. In 1924, faxes were first used to transmit wire photos from Cleveland to New York, a boon to the newspaper industry.

Can a **fax** and an **answering machine** be used on the **same telephone line**?

Most fax machines come with an interface that allows it to work with an answering machine. The fax "listens" for the incoming call and sends it to the answering machine if no one picks up the phone. As the message is being recorded, the fax machine listens for a fax tone. If it hears the tone, it sends the fax through. If not, the answering machine continues to function as it normally would. Fax machines with built-in answering machines are also available, making such an interface unnecessary.

How does a **fiber-optic cable** work?

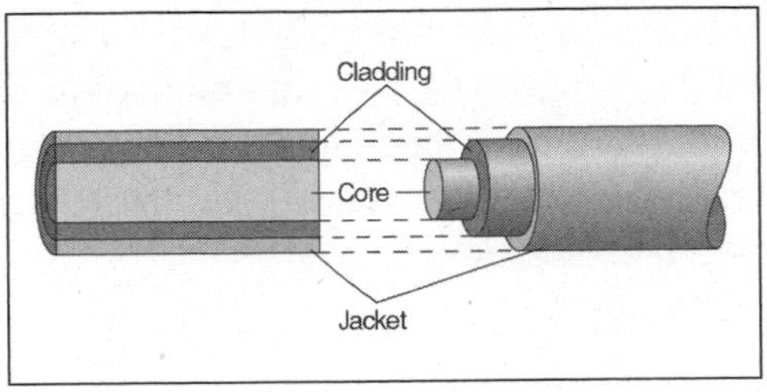

A cross section of a fiber-optic cable.

A fiber-optic cable is composed of many very thin strands of coated glass or plastic fibers that transmit light through the process of "cladding," in which total internal reflection of light is achieved by using material that has a lower refractive index. Once light enters the fiber, the cladding layer inside it prevents light loss as the beam of light zigzags inside the glass core. Glass fibers can transmit messages or images by directing beams of light inside itself over very short or very long distances up to 13,000 miles (20,917 kilometers) without significant distortion. The pattern of light waves forms a code that carries a message. At the receiving end, the light beams are converted back into electric current and decoded. Uses include telecommunications medical fiber-optic viewers, such as endoscopes and fiberscopes, to see internal organs; fiber-optic message devices in aircraft and space vehicles; and fiber-optic connections in automotive lighting systems.

Fiber-optic cables have greater "bandwidth": they can carry much more data than metal cable. Because fiber optics is based on light beams, the transmissions are more impervious to electrical noise and can also be carried greater distances before fading. The cables are thinner than metal wires. Fiber-optic cable delivers data in digital code instead of an analog signal, the delivery method of metal cables; computers are structured for digital, so there is a natural symbiosis. The main disadvantage is cost: fiber optics are much more expensive than traditional metal cable.

What is a **Clarke belt**?

Back in 1945, Arthur C. Clarke (b. 1917), the famous scientist and science fiction writer, predicted that an artificial satellite placed at a height of 22,248 miles (35,803 kilometers) directly above the equator would orbit the globe at the same speed with which the Earth was rotating. As a result, the satellite would remain stationary with respect to any point on the Earth's surface. This equatorial belt, rather like one of Saturn's rings, is affectionately known as the Clarke belt.

What is the difference between "**analog**" and "**digital**"?

The word analog is derived from "analogous," meaning something corresponds to something else. A picture of a mountain is a representation of the mountain. If the picture is on traditional color film it is called an analog picture and is characterized by different colors and range of color on the paper. However, if the photographer took the picture with a digital camera, the image is digital: it is stored as a series of numbers in the camera's memory. Its colors are discrete. In communications and computers, a range of continuous variables characterizes analog. Digital, in contrast, is characterized by measurements that happen at discrete intervals. Digital representations are, therefore, more precise. Common examples of analog media include records (music) and VCR tapes (movies). Counterpart examples of digital media include CD-ROM discs and DVD movies.

How have **cellular telephones** styles evolved?

The first and oldest variety of mobile cellular phones are permanently attached to an automobile and are powered by the car's battery. They also have an antenna that must be mounted outside the vehicle. The second type are transportable, or bag, cellular phones. These are essentially mobile phones with their own battery packs that allow owners to detach them from the car and carry them in a pouch. However, most weigh about five pounds (2.25 kilograms) and are not very practical when used this way. The third type is a portable cellular phone. Similar in appearance to a cordless phone handset, a portable generally weighs less than a pound and is the most versatile type of cellular phone. It is also the most expensive and has a transmitter of less power than a mobile or transportable cellular phone. Kits are available for some models, however, that boosts the transmitter's power. Despite claims that they may cause health problems or that they may distract drivers, cell phone use is more popular than ever: in 2000 about 100 million Americans routinely used mobile phones.

What is the latest type of **wireless** telephone?

The latest wireless telephone introduced in 1995 is called a PCS (personal communications services) phone. These are digital cellular telephones; they are digital because they convert the speech into a chain of numbers. This makes the transmission much clearer and enhances security by making eavesdropping more difficult. It also allows for computer integration. Users can send and receive e-mail and browse the web. They are cellular because antennas on metal towers—visible on the horizon of nearly every reasonably developed location in America—send and receive all calls within a geographical area. Transmissions are carried over microwave radiation. Wireless companies can use the same frequency over again in different cells (except for cells that are nearby) because each cell is small and therefore requires only a limited range signal. When users move across cells the signal is "handed off" to the next cell tower.

What is the **Dolby** noise reduction system?

The magnetic action of a tape produces a background hiss—a drawback in sound reproduction on tape. A noise reduction system known as Dolby—named after R. M. Dolby (b. 1933), its American inventor—is widely used to deal with the hiss. In quiet passages, electronic circuits automatically boost the signals before they reach the

On average, the expected life span of a CD-ROM disc is between three and five years.

recording head, drowning out the hiss. On playback, the signals are reduced to their correct levels. The hiss is reduced at the same time, becoming inaudible.

What is **digital audio tape** (DAT)?

DAT, a new concept in magnetic recording, produces a mathematical value for each sound based on the binary code. When the values are reconstructed during playback, the reconstructed sound is so much like the original that the human ear cannot distinguish the difference. The reproduction is so good that American record companies have lobbied lawmakers to prevent DAT from being sold in the United States, claiming that it could encourage illegal CD copying.

How are **compact discs** (CDs) made?

The master disc for a CD is an optically flat glass disc coated with a resist. The resist is a chemical that is impervious to an etchant that dissolves glass. The master is placed on a turntable. The digital signal to be recorded is fed to the laser, turning the laser off and on in response to the binary on-off signal. When the laser is on, it burns away a small amount of the resist on the disc. While the disc turns, the recording head moves across the disc, leaving a spiral track of elongated "burns" in the resist surface. After the recording is complete, the glass master is placed in the chemical etchant bath. This developing removes the glass only where the resist is burned away.

The spiral track now contains a series of small pits of varying length and constant depth. To play a recorded CD, a laser beam scans the three miles (five kilometers) of playing track and converts the "pits" and "lands" of the CD into binary codes. A photodiode converts these into a coded string of electrical impulses. In October 1982, the first CDs were marketed; they were invented by Phillips (Netherlands) Company and Sony in Japan in 1978.

What is the life span of a **CD-ROM** disc?

Although manufacturers claim that a CD-ROM disc will last 20 years, recent statements by the United States National Archives and Records Administration suggest that a life span of three to five years is more accurate. The main problem is that the aluminum substratum on which the data is recorded is vulnerable to oxidation.

COMPUTERS, THE INTERNET, AND ROBOTICS

What is an **algorithm**?

An algorithm is a set of clearly defined rules and instructions for the solution of a problem. It is not necessarily applied only in computers, but can be a step-by-step procedure for solving any particular kind of problem. A nearly 4,000-year-old Babylonian banking calculation inscribed on a tablet is an algorithm, as is a computer program that consists of step-by-step procedures for solving a problem.

The term is derived from the name of Muhammad ibn Musa al Kharizmi (ca. 780-ca. 850), a Baghdad mathematician who introduced Hindu numerals (including 0) and decimal calculation to the West. When his treatise was translated into Latin in the 12th century, the art of computation with Arabic (Hindu) numerals became known as algorism.

Who invented the **computer**?

Computers developed from calculating machines. One of the earliest mechanical devices for calculating, still widely used today, is the abacus—a frame carrying parallel rods on which beads or counters are strung. The abacus originated in Egypt in 2000 B.C.E.; it reached the Orient about a thousand years later, and arrived in Europe in about the year 300 C.E. In 1617, John Napier (1550-1617) invented "Napier's Bones"—marked pieces of ivory for multiples of numbers. In the middle of the same century, Blaise Pascal (1623-

1662) produced a simple mechanism for adding and subtracting. Multiplication by repeated addition was a feature of a stepped drum or wheel machine of 1694 invented by Gottfried Wilhelm Leibniz (1646-1716). In 1823, the English visionary Charles Babbage (1792-1871) persuaded the British government to finance an "analytical engine." This would have been a machine that could undertake any kind of calculation. It would have been driven by steam, but the most important innovation was that the entire program of operations was stored on a punched tape. Babbage's machine was not completed in his lifetime because the technology available to him was not sufficient to support his design. However, in 1991 a team led by Doron Swade at London's Science Museum built the "analytical engine" (sometimes called the "difference engine") based on Babbage's work. Measuring 10 feet (3 meters) wide by 6.5 feet (2 meters) tall, it weighed three tons and could calculate equations down to 31 digits. The feat proved that Babbage was way ahead of his time, even though the device was impractical because one had to turn a crank hundreds of times in order to generate a single calculation. Modern computers use electrons, which travel at nearly the speed of light.

Charles Babbage conceived his "analytical engine"—building upon a science that has produced today's modern computer.

Based on the concepts of British mathematician Alan M. Turing (1912-1954), the earliest programmable electronic computer was the 1,500-valve "Colossus," formulated by Max Newman (1897-1985), built by T. H. Flowers, and used by the British government in 1943 to crack the German codes generated by the coding machine "Enigma."

What is meant by **fifth-generation computers**? What are the other four generations?

The evolution of computers has advanced so much in the past few decades that "generations" are used to describe these important advances:

First-generation computer—a mammoth computer using vacuum tubes, drum memories, and programming in machine code as its basic technology. Univax 1, used in 1951, was one of the earliest of these vacuum-tube based electronic computers. The generation starts at the end of World War II and ends about 1957.

Second-generation computer—a computer using discrete transistors as its basic technology. Solid-state components replaced the vacuum tubes during this period from 1958 to 1963. Magnetic core memories store information. This era includes the development of high-level computer languages.

Third-generation computer—a computer having integrated circuits, semiconductor memories, and magnetic disk storage. New operating systems, minicomputer systems, virtual memory, and timesharing are the advancements of this period from 1963 to 1971.

Fourth-generation computer—a computer using microprocessors and large-scale integrated chips as its basic technology, which made computers accessible to a large segment of the population. Networking, improved memory, database management systems, and advanced languages mark the period from 1971 to the end of the 1980s.

Fifth-generation computer—a computer that uses inference to draw reasoned conclusions from a knowledge base and interacts with its users via an intelligent user interface to perform such functions as speech recognition, machine translation of natural languages, and robotic operations. These computers using artificial intelligence have been under development since the early 1980s, especially in Japan, as well as in the United States and Europe. In 1991, however, Japan began a new 10-year initiative to investigate neural networks, which will probably divert resources from development of the fifth generation as traditionally defined.

What was the **first computer game**?

Despite that computers were not invented for playing games, the idea that they could be used for games did not take long to emerge. Alan Turing proposed a famous game called "Imitation Game" in 1950. In 1952, Rand Air Defense Lab in Santa Monica created the first military simulation games. In 1953, Arthur Samuel created a checkers program on the new IBM 701. From these beginnings computer games have today become a multi-billion-dollar industry.

What was the first successful **video-arcade game**?

Pong, a simple electronic version of a tennis game, was the first successful video-arcade game. Although it was first marketed in 1972, Pong was actually invented 14 years earlier in 1958 by William Higinbotham, who headed instrumentation design at Brookhaven National Laboratory at the time. Invented to amuse visitors touring the laboratory, the game was so popular that visitors would stand in line for hours to play it. Higinbotham dismantled the system two years later, and, considering it a trifle, did not patent it. In 1972, Atari released Pong, an arcade version of Higinbotham's game, and Magnavox released Odyssey, a version that could be played on home televisions.

What was **"The Turk"**?

The Turk was the name for a famous chess-playing automaton. An automaton, such as a robot, is a mechanical figure constructed to act as if it moves by its own power. On a dare in 1770, a civil servant in the Vienna Imperial Court named Wolfgang von Kempelen created a chess-playing machine. This mustached, man-sized figure carved from wood wore a turban, trousers, and robe, and sat behind a desk. In one hand it held a long Turkish pipe, implying that it had just finished a pre-game smoke, and its innards were filled with gears, pulleys, and cams. The machine seemed a keen chess player and dumbfounded onlookers by defeating all the best human chess players. It was a farce, however: its moves were surreptitiously made by a man hiding inside. The Turk, so dubbed because of the audacious outfit, is regarded as a forerunner to the industrial revolution because it created a commotion over devices that could complete complex tasks. Historians argue that it inspired people to invent other early devices such as the power loom and the telephone, and it even was a precursor to concepts such as artificial intelligence and computerization. Today, however, computer chess games are so sophisticated that they can defeat even the world's best chess masters. In May 1997, the "Deep Blue" chess computer, an IBM RS/6000 SP that relied on 32 processors functioning as 512 to calculate 200 million chess moves per second, defeated World Champion Garry Kasparov.

What is a **silicon chip**?

A silicon chip is an almost pure piece of silicon, usually less than one centimeter square and about half a millimeter thick. It contains hundreds of thousands of microminiature electronic circuit components, mainly transistors, packed and interconnected in layers beneath the surface. These components can perform control, logic, and memory functions. There is a grid of thin metallic strips on the surface of the chip; these wires are used for electrical connections to other devices. The silicon chip was developed independently by two researchers: Jack Kilby of Texas Instruments in 1958, and Robert Noyce (b. 1927) of Fairchild Semiconductor in 1959.

While silicon chips are essential to most computer operation today, a myriad of other devices depend on them as well, including calculators, microwave ovens, automobile diagnostic equipment, and VCRs.

Are any devices being developed to **replace** silicon chips?

When transistors were introduced in 1948, they demanded less power than fragile, high-temperature vacuum tubes; allowed electronic equipment to become smaller, faster, and more dependable; and generated less heat. These developments made computers much more economical and accessible; they also made portable radios practical. However, the smaller components were harder to wire together, and hand wiring was both expensive and error-prone.

In the early 1960s, circuits on silicon chips allowed manufacturers to build increased power, speed, and memory storage into smaller packages, which required less electricity to operate and generated even less heat. While through most of the 1970s manufacturers could count on doubling the components on a chip every year without increasing the size of the chip, the size limitations of silicon chips are becoming more restrictive. Though components continue to grow smaller, the same rate of shrinking cannot be maintained.

Researchers are investigating different materials to use in making circuit chips. Gallium arsenide is harder to handle in manufacturing, but it has potential for greatly increased switching speed. Organic polymers are potentially cheaper to manufacture and could be used for liquid-crystal and other flat-screen displays, which need to have their electronic circuits spread over a wide area. Unfortunately, organic polymers do not allow electricity to pass through as well as the silicons do. Several researchers are working on hybrid chips, which could combine the benefits of organic polymers with those of silicon. Researchers are also in the initial stages of developing integrated optical chips, which would use light rather than electric current. Optical chips would generate little or no heat, would allow faster switching, and would be immune to electrical noise.

What are **carbon nanotubes**?

Carbon nanotubes are structures of microscopic cylinders that scientists can create when electricity arcs between two carbon electrodes. The carbon atoms become arranged in a lattice that forms a tiny tube a few nanometers long (a nanometer is a billionth of a meter). Scientists can then position them to act as transmitters. The benefit of such a structure is that they are a hundred times smaller than transistors now used on computer chips. Carbon nanotubes may eventually replace the standard silicon computer chip, allowing increased performance in a smaller size.

What is **Moore's Law**?

Gordon Moore, cofounder of Intel, a top microchip manufacturer, observed in 1965 that the number of transistors per microchip—and hence a chip's processing power—would double about every year and a half. The press dubbed this Moore's Law. Despite claims that this ever-increasing trend cannot perpetuate, history has shown that microchip advances are, indeed, keeping pace with Moore's prediction.

Who invented the computer **mouse**?

A computer "mouse" is a hand-held input device that, when rolled across a flat surface, causes a cursor to move in a corresponding way on a display screen. A prototype mouse was part of an input console demonstrated by Douglas C. Englehart in 1968 at the Fall Joint Computer Conference in San Francisco. Popularized in 1984 by the

Who was the first programmer?

According to historical accounts, Lord Byron's daughter, Augusta Ada Byron, the Countess of Lovelace, was the first person to write a computer program for Charles Babbage's (1792-1871) "analytical engine." This machine was to work by means of punched cards that could store partial answers that could later be retrieved for additional operations and would then print the results. Her work with Babbage and the essays she wrote about the possibilities of the "engine" established her as a "patron saint," if not a founding parent, of the art and science of programming. The programming language called "Ada" was named in her honor by the United States Department of Defense. In modern times the honor goes to Commodore Grace Murray Hopper (1906-1992) of the United States Navy. She wrote the first program for the Mark I computer.

Macintosh from Apple Computer, the mouse was the result of 15 years devoted to exploring ways to make communicating with computers simpler and more flexible.

The physical appearance of the small box with the dangling, tail-like wire suggested the name of "mouse."

What is **Hopper's rule**?

Electricity travels one foot in a nanosecond (a billionth of a second). This is one of a number of rules compiled for the convenience of computer programmers; it is also considered to be a fundamental limitation on the possible speed of a computer—signals in an electrical circuit cannot move any faster.

Is an **assembly language** the same thing as a **machine language**?

While the two terms are often used interchangeably, an assembly language is a more "user friendly" translation of a machine language. A machine language is the collection of patterns of bits recognized by a central processing unit (CPU) as instructions. Each particular CPU design has its own machine language. The machine language of the CPU of a microcomputer generally includes about 75 instructions; the machine language of the CPU of a large mainframe computer may include hundreds of instructions. Each of these instructions is a pattern of 1's and 0's that tells the CPU to perform a specific operation.

An assembly language is a collection of symbolic, mnemonic names for each instruction in the machine language of its CPU. Like the machine language, the assembly language is tied to a particular CPU design. Programming in assembly language requires intimate familiarity with the CPU's architecture, and assembly language programs are difficult to maintain and require extensive documentation.

The computer language C, developed in the late 1980s, is now frequently used instead of assembly language. It is a high-level programming language that can be compiled into machine languages for almost all computers, from microcomputers to mainframes, because of its functional structure.

What are the **generations** of **programming languages**?

Computer scientists use the following abbreviations to grade computer languages in steps or evolutions:

1GL—A first-generation language is called a "machine language," the set of instructions that the programmer writes for the processor to perform. It appears in binary form. It is written in 0s and 1s.

2GL—A second-generation language is termed an "assembly" language, because an assembler converts it into machine language for the processor.

3GL—A third-generation language is called a "high-level" programming language. Java and C++ are 3GL languages. A compiler then converts it into machine language, typically written like this:

```
if (chLetter ≥ 'B')
Console.WriteLine ("Usage: one argument");
return 1; // sample code
```

4GL—A fourth-generation language resembles plain language. Relational databases use this language. An example is the following:

FIND All Titles FROM Books WHERE Title begins with "Handy"

5GL—A fifth-generation language uses a graphical design interface that allows a 3GL or 4GL compiler to translate the language. This is similar to HTML text editors because it allows drag and drop of icons and visual display of hierarchies.

Who invented the **COBOL** computer language?

COBOL (common business oriented language) is a prominent computer language designed specifically for commercial uses, created in 1960 by a team drawn from several computer makers and the Pentagon. The best-known individual associated with COBOL was then-Lieutenant Grace Murray Hopper (1906-1992) who made fundamental contributions to the United States Navy standardization of COBOL. COBOL excels at the most common kinds of data processing for business—simple arithmetic operations performed on huge files of data. The language endures because its syntax is very much like English and because a program written in COBOL for one kind of computer can run on many others without alteration.

Who invented the **PASCAL** computer language?

Niklaus Wirth (b. 1934), a Swiss computer programmer, created the PASCAL computer language.

What's the difference between a **"bit"** and a **"byte"**?

A byte, a common unit of computer storage, holds the equivalent of a single character, such as a letter ("A"), a number ("2"), a symbol ("$"), a decimal point, or a space. It is usually equivalent to eight "data bits" and one "parity bit." A bit (a binary digit), the smallest unit of information in a digital computer, is equivalent to a single "0" or "1". The parity bit is used to check for errors in the bits making up the byte. Although eight data bits per byte is the most common size, computer manufacturers are free to define a differing number of bits as a byte. Six data bits per byte is another common size.

What does it mean to **"boot"** a computer?

Booting a computer is starting it, in the sense of turning control over to the operating system. The term comes from bootstrap, because bootstraps allow an individual to pull on boots without help from anyone else. Some people prefer to think of the process in terms of using bootstraps to lift oneself off the ground, impossible in the physical sense, but a reasonable image for representing the process of searching for the operating system, loading it, and passing control to it. The commands to do this are embedded in a read-only memory (ROM) chip that is automatically executed when a microcomputer is turned on or reset. In mainframe or minicomputers, the process usually involves a great deal of operator input. A cold boot powers on the computer and passes control to the operating system; a warm boot resets the operating system without powering off the computer.

What is the correct way to **face a computer** screen?

Correct positioning of the body at a computer is essential to preventing physical problems such as carpal tunnel syndrome and back pain. You should sit so that your eyes are 18 to 24 inches (45 to 61 centimeters) from the screen, and at a height so that they are six to eight inches (15 to 20 centimeters) above the center of the screen. Your hands should be level with or slightly below the arms.

Correct posture is also necessary. You should sit upright, keeping the spine straight. Sit all the way back in the chair with the knees level with or below the thighs. Both feet should be on the floor. The arms may rest on the desk or chair arms, but make sure you do not slouch. If you need to bend or lean forward, do so from the waist.

What is virtual reality?

Virtual reality combines state-of-the-art imaging with computer technology to allow users to experience a simulated environment as reality. Several different technologies are integrated into a virtual reality system, including holography, which uses lasers to create three-dimensional images; liquid crystal displays; high-definition television; and multimedia techniques that combine various types of displays in a single computer terminal.

Where did the term **bug** originate?

The slang term bug is used to describe problems and errors occurring in computer programs. The term may have originated during the early 1940s at Harvard University, when computer pioneer Grace Murray Hopper (1906-1992) discovered that a dead moth had caused the breakdown of a machine on which she was working. When asked what she was doing while removing the corpse with tweezers, she replied, "I'm debugging the machine." The moth's carcass, taped to a page of notes, is preserved with the trouble log notebook at the Virginia Naval Museum.

How did the term **glitch** originate?

A glitch is a sudden interruption or fracture in a chain of events, such as in commands to a processor. The stability may or may not be salvageable. The word is thought to have evolved from the German *glitschen*, meaning "to slip," or by the Yiddish *glitshen,* to slide or skid.

One small glitch can lead to a cascade of failure along a network. For instance, in 1997 a small Internet service provider in Virginia unintentionally provided incorrect router (a router is the method by which the network determines the next location for information) information to a backbone operator (a backbone is a major network thoroughfare in which local and regional networks patch into for lengthy interconnections). Because many other Internet service providers rely on the backbone providers, the error echoed around the globe, causing temporary network failures.

What is a computer **virus** and how is it spread?

Taken from the obvious analogy with biological viruses, a computer "virus" is a program that searches out other programs and "infects" them by replicating itself in them. When the programs are executed, the embedded virus is executed too, thus propagating the "infection." This normally happens invisibly to the user. A virus cannot infect other computers, however, without assistance. It is spread when users communicate by computer, often when they trade programs. The virus might do nothing but propagate itself and then allow the program to run normally. Usually, however, after propagating silently for a while, it starts doing other things—possibly inserting "cute" messages or destroying all of the user's files. Computer "worms" and "logic bombs" are similar to viruses, but they do not replicate themselves within programs as viruses do. A logic bomb does its damage immediately—destroying data, inserting garbage into data files, or reformatting the hard disk; a worm can alter the program and database either immediately or over a period of time.

In the 1990s, viruses, worms, and logic bombs have become such a serious problem, especially among IBM PC and Macintosh users, that the production of special detection and "inoculation" software has become an industry.

What is a **fuzzy search**?

Fuzzy search is a feature of some software programs that allows a user to search for text that is similar to but not exactly the same as what he or she specifies. It can produce results when the exact spelling is unknown, or it can help users obtain information that is loosely related to a topic.

What is **GIGO**?

GIGO is not a computer language despite its similarity to the names of computer languages; instead it is an acronym for the truism that one gets out of something what one puts into it: GIGO stands for the phrase Garbage In, Garbage Out. This is a computer hacker term for when people input imprecise information and get imprecise results.

What is a **pixel**?

A pixel (from the words pix, for picture, and element) is the smallest element on a video display screen. A screen contains thousands of pixels, each of which can be made up of one or more dots or a cluster of dots. On a simple monochrome screen, a pixel is one dot; the two colors of image and background are created when the pixel is switched either on or off. Some monochrome screen pixels can be energized to create different light intensities to allow a range of shades from light to dark. On color screens, three dot colors are included in each pixel—red, green, and blue. The simplest screens have just one dot of each color, but more elaborate screens have pixels with clusters of each color. These more elaborate displays can show a large number of colors and intensities. On color screens, black is created by leaving all three colors off; white by all three colors on; and a range of grays by equal intensities of all the colors.

The most economical displays are monochrome, with one bit per pixel, with settings limited to on and off. High-resolution color screens, which can use a million pixels, with each color dot using four bytes of memory, would need to reserve many megabytes just to display the image.

What does **DOS** stand for?

DOS stands for "disk operating system," a program that controls the computer's transfer of data to and from a hard or floppy disk. Frequently, it is combined with the main operating system. The operating system was originally developed at Seattle Computer Products as SCP-DOS. When IBM decided to build a personal computer and needed an operating system, it chose the SCP-DOS after reaching an agreement with the Microsoft Corporation to produce the actual operating system. Under Microsoft, SCP-DOS became MS-DOS, which IBM referred to as PC-DOS (personal computer), and which everyone eventually simply called DOS.

What is the **information highway**?

A term originally coined by former Vice President Al Gore (1948-), the information highway is envisioned as an electronic communications network of the near future that would easily connect all users to one another and provide every type of electronic service possible, including shopping, electronic banking, education, medical diagnosis, video conferencing, and game playing. Initially implemented on a national scale, it would eventually become a global network.

The exact form of the information highway is a matter of some debate. Two principle views currently exist. One visualizes the highway as a more elaborate form of the Internet, the principle purpose of which would be to gather and exchange written information via a global electronic mail network. The other possibility centers around plans to create an enhanced interactive television network that would provide video services on demand.

What is the **Internet**?

The Internet is the world's largest computer network. It links computer terminals together via wires or telephone lines in a web of networks and shared software. With the proper equipment, an individual can access vast amounts of information and search databases on various computers connected to the Internet, or communicate with someone located anywhere in the world as long as he or she has the proper equipment.

Originally created in the late 1960s by the U.S. Department of Defense Advanced Research Projects Agency to share information with other researchers, the Internet mushroomed when scientists and academics using the network discovered its great value. Despite its origin, however, the Internet is not owned or funded by the U.S. government or any other organization or institution. A group of volunteers, the Internet Society, addresses such issues as daily operations and technical standards.

Which technology holds the most promise for keeping information sent over the **Internet secure**?

Public-key cryptography is a means for authenticating information sent over the Internet. The system works by encrypting and decrypting information through the use of a combination of "keys." One key is a published "public key"; the second is a "private key," which is kept secret. An algorithm is used to decipher each of the keys. The method is for the sender to encrypt the information using the public key, and the recipient to decrypt the information using the secret private key.

The strength of the system depends on the size of the key: a 128-bit encryption is about 3 × 1,026 times stronger than 40-bit encryption. No matter how complex the encryption, as with any code, keeping the secret aspects secret is the important part to safeguarding the information.

How many people **use the Internet**?

According to *Newsweek*, there are as of the year 2000 about 259 to 300 million people in 56 countries who are in some way using the Internet. About 111 million users are in the United States, followed by Japan with about 18 million, and then Britain with 14 million. Users are projected to reach one billion by 2005.

What is **e-mail**?

Electronic mail, also known as E mail or e-mail, uses communication facilities to transmit messages. Many systems use computers as transmitting and receiving interfaces, but fax communication is also a form of E mail. A user can send a message to a single recipient, or to many. Different systems offer different options for sending, receiving, manipulating text, and addressing. For example, a message can be "registered," so that the sender is notified when the recipient looks at the message (though there is no way to tell if the recipient has actually read the message). Many systems allow messages to be forwarded. Usually messages are stored in a simulated "mailbox" in the network server or host computer; some systems announce incoming mail if the recipient is logged onto the system. An organization (such as a corporation, university, or professional organization) can provide electronic mail facilities; national and international networks can provide them as well. In order to use e-mail, both sender and receiver must have accounts on the same system or on systems connected by a network.

Who sent the **first e-mail**?

In the early 1970s computer engineer Ray Tomlinson noticed that people working at the same mainframe computer could leave one another messages. He imagined great utility of this communication system if messages could be sent to different mainframes. So he wrote a software program over the period of about a week that used file-transfer protocols and send-and-receive features. It enabled people to send messages from one mainframe to another over the Arpanet, the network that became the Internet. To make sure the messages went to the right system he adopted the symbol because it was the least ambiguous keyboard symbol and because it was brief. As of April 2001, Hotmail(r)—just one of several e-mail providers—had over 70 million users and added about 100,000 e-mail accounts every day.

What is a **hacker**?

A hacker is a skilled computer user. The term originally denoted a skilled programmer, particularly one skilled in machine code and with a good knowledge of the machine and its operating system. The name arose from the fact that a good programmer could always hack an unsatisfactory system around until it worked.

The term later came to denote a user whose main interest is in defeating password systems. The term has thus acquired a pejorative sense, with the meaning of one who deliberately and sometimes criminally interferes with data available through telephone lines. The activities of such hackers have led to considerable efforts to tighten security of transmitted data. The "hacker ethic" is that information-sharing is the proper way of human dealing, and, indeed, it is the responsibility of hackers to liberally impart their wisdom to the software world by distributing information. Nefarious hacker attacks by people outside the company costs companies on average about $56,000 per attack.

What is a **kludge**?

A kludge (also spelled kluge) is a sloppy, crude, cumbersome solution to a problem. It refers to a makeshift solution as well as to any poorly designed product, or a product that becomes unmanageable over time.

Who coined the term **technobabble**?

John A. Barry used the term "technobabble" to mean the pervasive and indiscriminate use of computer terminology, especially as it is applied to situations that have nothing at all to do with technology. He first used it in the early 1980s.

How did the **Linux operating system** get its name?

The name Linux is combination of the first name of its principal programmer, Finland's Linus Torvalds (1970-), and the UNIX operating system. Linux (pronounced with a short "i") is an open source computer operating system that is comparable to more powerful, expansive, and usually costly UNIX systems, of which it resembles in form and function. Linux allows users to run an amalgam of reliable and hearty open-source software tools and interfaces, including powerful Web utilities such as the popular Apache server, on their home computers. Anyone can download Linux for free or can obtain it on disk for only a marginal fee. Torvalds created the kernel—or heart of the system—"just for fun," and released it freely to the world, where other programmers helped further its development. The world, in turn, has embraced Linux and made Torvalds into a folk hero.

What is the idea behind **"open-source-software"**?

Open-source software is computer software where the code (the rules governing its operation) is available for users to modify. This is in contrast to proprietary code, where the software vendor veils the code so users cannot view and, hence, manipulate (or steal) it. The software termed open source is not necessarily free—that is, without charge; authors can charge for its use, and some do, albeit nominal fees. According to the Free Software Foundation, "Free software" is a matter of liberty, not price. To understand the concept, you should think of "free" as in "free speech," not as in "free beer." Free software is a matter of the users' freedom to run, copy, distribute, study, change, and improve the software." Despite this statement, most of it is available without charge. Open-source software is usually protected under the notion of "copyleft," instead of "copyright" law. Copyleft does not mean releasing material to the public domain, nor does it mean near absolute prohibition from copying, like the federal copyright law. Instead, according to the Free Software Foundation, copyleft is a form of protection guaranteeing that whoever redistributes software, whether modified or not, "must pass along the freedom to further copy and share it." Open source has evolved into a movement of sharing, cooperation, and mutual innovation, ideas that many believe are necessary in today's cutthroat corporatization of software.

Who invented the **World Wide Web**?

Tim Berners-Lee (1955-) is considered the creator of the World Wide Web (WWW). The WWW is a massive collection of interlinked hypertext documents that travel over the Internet and are viewed through a browser. The Internet is a global network of computers developed in the 1960s and 1970s by the U.S. Department of Defense's Advanced Research Project Agency (hence the term "Arpanet"). The idea of the Internet was to provide redundancy of communications in case of a catastrophic event (like a nuclear blast), which might destroy a single connection or computer but not the entire network. The browser is used to translate the hypertext, usually written in Hypertext Markup Language (HTML), so it is human-readable on a computer screen. Along with Gutenberg's invention of the printing press, the inception of the WWW in 1990 and 1991, when Berners-Lee released the tools and protocols onto the Internet, is considered one of humanity's greatest communications achievements.

How does a **search engine** work?

Internet search engines are akin to computerized card catalogs at libraries. Viewed through a web browser with an Internet connection, they provide a hyperlinked listing of locations on the World Wide Web according to the requested keyword or pattern of words submitted by the searcher. A Web directory service provides the same service, but uses different methods to gather its source information. A Web directory service employs humans to "surf" Web sites and organize them into a hierarchical index by subject or some other category. A search engine, however, uses computer software called "spiders" or "bots" to search out, inventory, and index Web pages automatically. The spiders scan each Web page's content for words and the frequency of the words, then stores that information in a database. When the user submits words or terms, the search engine returns a list of sites from the database and ranks them according to the relevancy of the search terms.

How can a grocery store customer become involved in **data mining**?

Many grocery stores today offer a free card that allows instant price reductions that function like a plastic, reusable coupon. The only catch is the customer must sign up for the card and reveal demographic information, such as age and gender. The particulars of each sale are stored in a database each time the customer uses the card, including facts such as day and time of purchase and items purchased. The grocery store then uses "data mining" to better target its sales campaigns and position its in-store displays. Data mining, as its name implies, is a computer and statistical technology where computers sift through extensive data to extract patterns, identify relationships, and allow for predictions. For instance, if patterns show that diapers are purchased before 3 p.m. on weekends by men aged 26 to 35, and most wine is purchased after 3 p.m. by men aged 46 to 55, then the store can move diapers to a prominent, high-traffic location during the day and place items close by that men of the same age group also purchase. Then after 3 p.m. the store can move the diapers out and the wine into the same prominent location, along with items that men in the 46 to 55 age range also purchase.

In which industries are **robots** being used?

A robot is a device that can execute a wide range of maneuvers under the direction of a computer. Reacting to feedback from sensors or by reprogramming, a robot can alter its maneuvers to fit a changed task or situation. The worldwide population of robots is about 250,000, with approximately 65 percent being used in Japan and 14 percent being used in the United States (the second largest user).

Robots are used to do welding, painting, drilling, sanding, cutting, and moving tasks in manufacturing plants. Automobile factories account for more than 50 percent of robot use in the United States. Robots can work in environments that are extremely threatening to humans or in difficult physical environments. They clean up radioactive areas, extinguish fires, disarm bombs, and load and unload explosives and toxic chemicals. Robots can process light-sensitive materials, such as photographic films that require near darkness—a difficult task for human workers. They can perform a variety of tasks in underwater exploration and in mines (a hazardous, low-light environment). There are only 100 robots in mines, but they produce about one-third of the coal coming from these mines. In the military and security fields, robots are used to sense targets or as surveillance devices. In the printing industry, robots perform miscellaneous tasks, such as sorting and tying bundles of output material, delivering paper to the presses, and applying book covers. In research laboratories, small desktop robots prepare samples and mix compounds.

What **film** was the first to feature a **robot**?

In 1886, the French movie *l'Eve Futur* had a Thomas Edison-like mad scientist building a robot in the likeness of a woman. A British lord falls in love with her in a variation on the Pygmalion theme. True working robots, in contrast to these entertainment devices, are strictly functional in appearance, looking more like machines rather than human beings or animals. However, one early exception to this is the very human-looking "Scribe" built in 1773 by two French inventors, Pierre and Henri-Louis Jacquel-Droz, a father and son team, who produced "The Automaton" to dip a quill pen into an inkwell and write a text of 40 characters maximum.

Who was the founder of **cybernetics**?

Norbert Wiener (1894-1964) is considered the creator of cybernetics. Derived from the Greek word kubernetes, meaning steerman or helmsman, cybernetics is concerned with the common factors of control and communication in living organisms, automatic machines, or organizations. These factors are exemplified by the skill used in steering a boat, in which the helmsman uses continual judgment to maintain control. The principles of cybernetics are used today in control theory, automation theory, and computer programs to reduce many time-consuming computations and decision-making processes formerly done by people.

PHYSICS AND CHEMISTRY

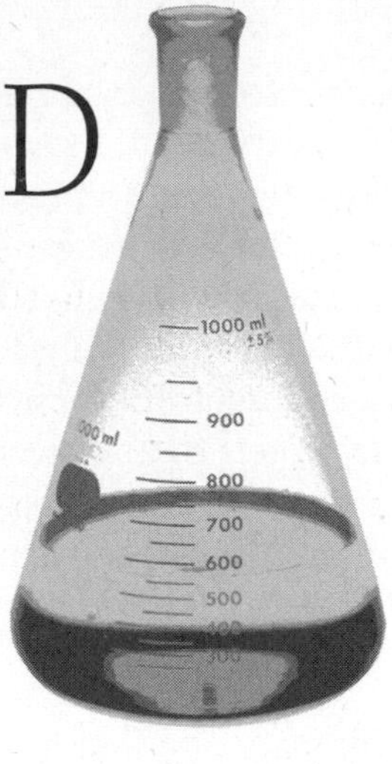

How is "**absolute zero**" defined?

Absolute zero is the theoretical temperature at which all substances have zero thermal energy. Originally conceived as the temperature at which an ideal gas at constant pressure would contract to zero volume, absolute zero is of great significance in thermodynamics and is used as the fixed point for absolute temperature scales. Absolute zero is equivalent to 0 K, -459.67°F, or -273.15°C.

The velocity of a substance's molecules determines its temperature; the faster the molecules move, the more volume they require, and the higher the temperature becomes. The lowest actual temperature ever reached was two-billionth of a degree above absolute zero (2×10^{-9}K) by a team at the Low Temperature Laboratory in the Helsinki University of Technology, Finland, in October 1989.

What is **superconductivity**?

Superconductivity is a condition in which many metals, alloys, organic compounds, and ceramics conduct electricity without resistance, usually at low temperatures. Heinke Kamerlingh Omnes, a Dutch physicist, discovered superconductivity in 1911. The modern theory regarding the phenomenon was developed by three American physicists—John Bardeen, Leon N. Cooper, and John Robert Schrieffer. Known as the BCS theory after the three scientists, it postulates that superconductivity occurs in certain materials because the electrons in them, rather than remaining free to collide with imperfections and scatter, form pairs that can flow easily around imperfections and do not lose their energy. Bardeen, Cooper, and Schrieffer received the Nobel Prize in Physics for their work in 1972. A further breakthrough in superconductivity was made in 1986 by J. Georg Bednorz and K. Alex Müller. Bednorz and Müller discovered a ceramic material consisting of lanthanum, barium, copper and oxygen which became superconductive at 35 K (-238°C)—much higher than any other material. Bednorz and Müller won the Nobel Prize in Physics in 1987. This was a significant accomplishment since in most situations the Nobel Prize is awarded for discoveries made as many as 20 to 40 years earlier.

What is the **string theory**?

A relatively recent theory in particle physics, the string theory conceives elementary particles not as points but as lines or loops. The idea of these "strings" is purely theoretical since no string has ever been detected experimentally. The ultimate expression of string theory may potentially require a new kind of geometry—perhaps one involving an infinity of dimensions.

In 1687, Isaac Newton published his *Philosophae Naturalis Principia Mathematica,* laying the foundation for the science of mechanics.

What is **inertia**?

Inertia is a tendency of all objects and matter in the universe to stay still, or, if moving, to continue moving in the same direction, unless acted on by some outside force. This forms the first law of motion formulated by Isaac Newton (1642-1727). To move a body at rest, enough external force must be used to overcome the object's inertia; the larger the object is, the more force is required to move it. In his *Philosophae Naturalis Principia Mathematica,* published in 1687, Newton sets forth all three laws of motion. Newton's second law is that the force to move a body is equal to its mass times its acceleration (F = MA), and the third law states that for every action there is an equal and opposite reaction.

What is **Maxwell's demon**?

An imaginary creature who, by opening and shutting a tiny door between two volumes of gases, could, in principle, concentrate slower molecules in one (making it colder) and faster molecules in the other (making it hotter), thus breaking the second law of thermodynamics. Essentially this law states that heat does not naturally flow from a colder body to a hotter body; work must be expended to make it do so. This hypothesis was formulated in 1871 by James C. Maxwell (1831-1879), who is considered to be the greatest theoretical physicist of the 19th century. The demon

William Gilbert first explained the connection between magnetism and electricity.

would bring about an effective flow of molecular kinetic energy. This excess energy would be useful to perform work and the system would be a perpetual motion machine. About 1950, the French physicist Léon Brillouin disproved Maxwell's hypothesis by demonstrating that the decrease in entropy resulting from the demon's actions would be exceeded by the increase in entropy in choosing between the fast and slow molecules.

Who is the founder of the science of **magnetism**?

The English scientist William Gilbert (1544-1603) regarded the Earth as a giant magnet and investigated its magnetic field terms of dip and variation. He explored many other magnetic and electrostatic phenomena. The Gilbert (symbol Gb), a unit of magnetism, is named for him.

John H. Van Vleck (1899-1980), an American physicist, made significant contributions to modern magnetic theory. He explained the magnetic, electrical, and optical properties of many elements and compounds with the ligand field theory, demonstrated the effect of temperature on paramagnetic materials (called Van Vleck paramagnetism), and developed a theory on the magnetic properties of atoms and their components.

When was **spontaneous combustion** first recognized?

Spontaneous combustion is the ignition of materials stored in bulk. This is due to internal heat build-up caused by oxidation (generally a reaction in which electrons are lost, specifically when oxygen is combined with a substance, or when hydrogen is removed from a compound). Because this oxidation heat cannot be dissipated into the surrounding air, the temperature of the material rises until the material reaches its ignition point and bursts into flame.

A Chinese text written before 290 C.E. recognized this phenomenon in a description of the ignition of stored oiled cloth. The first Western acknowledgment of spontaneous combustion was by J. P. F. Duhamel in 1757, when he discussed the gigantic conflagration of a stack of oil-soaked canvas sails drying in the July sun. Before spontaneous combustion was recognized, such events were usually blamed on arsonists.

What is the **kindling point of paper**?

Paper ignites at 451°F (230°C).

What is an **adiabatic process**?

It is any thermodynamic process in which no heat transfer takes place between a system and its surrounding environment.

Does **water running down a drain** rotate in a different direction in the Northern versus the Southern Hemisphere?

If water runs out from a perfectly symmetrical bathtub, basin, or toilet bowl in the Northern Hemisphere, it would swirl counterclockwise; in the Southern Hemisphere, the water would run out clockwise. This is due to the Coriolis effect (the Earth's rotation influencing any moving body of air or water). However, some scientists think that the effect does not work on small bodies of water. Exactly on the equator, the water would run straight down.

Who invented the **cyclotron**?

The cyclotron was invented by Ernest Lawrence (1901-1958) at the University of California, Berkeley, in 1934 to study the nuclear structure of the atom. The cyclotron produced high energy particles that were accelerated outwards in a spiral rather than through an extremely long, linear accelerator.

What is a **Leyden jar**?

A Leyden jar, the earliest form of capacitor, is a device for storing an electrical charge. First described in 1745 by E. Georg van Kleist (c. 1700-1748), it was also used by Pieter van Musschenbroek (1692-1761), a professor of physics at the University of Leyden. The device came to be known as a Leyden jar and was the first device that could store large amounts of electric charge. The jars contained an inner wire electrode in contact with water, mercury, or wire. The outer electrode was a human hand holding the jar. An improved version coated the jar inside and outside with separate metal foils with the inner foil connected to a conducting rod and terminated in a conducting sphere. This eliminated the need for the liquid electrolyte. In use, the jar was normally charged from an electrostatic generator. The Leyden jar is still used for classroom demonstrations of static electricity.

LIGHT, SOUND, AND OTHER WAVES

What is the **speed of light**?

The figure is 186,282 miles (299,792 kilometers) per second.

What are the **primary colors** in light?

Color is determined by the wavelength of visible light (the distance between one crest of the light wave and the next). Those colors that blend to form "white light" are, from shortest wave length to longest: red, orange, yellow, green, blue, indigo, and violet. All these monochromatic colors, except indigo, occupy large areas of the spectrum (the entire range of wavelengths produced when a beam of electromagnetic radiation is broken up). These colors can be seen when a light beam is refracted through a prism. Some consider the primary colors to be six monochromatic colors that occupy large areas of the spectrum: red, orange, yellow, green, blue, and violet. Many physicists recognize three primary colors: red, yellow, and blue; or red, green, and blue. All other colors can be made from these by adding two primary colors in various proportions. Within the spectrum, scientists have discovered 55 distinct hues. Infra-red and ultraviolet rays at each end of the spectrum are invisible to the human eye.

How do **polarized sunglasses** reduce glare?

Sunlight reflected from the horizontal surface of water, glass, and snow is partially polarized, with the direction of polarization chiefly in the horizontal plane. Such reflected light may be so intense as to cause glare. The Polaroid material in sunglasses will block light that is polarized in a direction perpendicular to the transmission axes; Polaroid sunglasses are made with the transmission axes of the lenses oriented vertically.

What were **Anders Ångström's** contributions to the development of **spectroscopy**?

Swedish physicist and astronomer Anders Jonas Ångström (1814-1874) was one of the founders of spectroscopy. His early work provided the foundation for spectrum analysis (analysis of the ranges of electromagnetic radiation emitted or absorbed). He investigated the sun spectra as well as that of the Aurora Borealis. In 1868, he established measurements for wavelengths of greater than 100 Frauenhofer. In 1907, the angstrom (Å, equal to 10^{-10}m), a unit of wavelength measurement, was officially adopted.

Why was the **Michelson-Morley** experiment important?

This experiment on light waves, first carried out in 1881 by physicists Albert A. Michelson (1852-1931) and E. W. Morley (1838-1923) in the United States, is one of the most historically significant experiments in physics and led to the development of Einstein's theory of relativity. The original experiment, using the Michelson interferometer, attempted to detect the velocity of the Earth with respect to the hypothetical "luminiferous ether," a medium in space proposed to carry light waves. The procedure measured the speed of light in the direction of the Earth and the speed of light at right angles to the Earth's motion. No difference was found. This result discredited the ether theory and ultimately led to the proposal by Albert Einstein (1879-1955) that the speed of light is a universal constant.

Who was the first person to break the **sound barrier**?

On October 14, 1947, Charles E. (Chuck) Yeager (b. 1923) was the first pilot to break the sound barrier. He flew a Bell X-1, attaining a speed of 750 miles (1,207 kilometers) per hour (Mach 1.06) and an altitude of 70,140 feet (21,379 meters) over the town of Victorville, California. The first woman to break the sound barrier was Jacqueline Cochran. On May 18, 1953, she flew a North American F-86 Saber over Edwards Air Force Base in California, attaining the speed of 760 miles (1,223 kilometers) per hour.

Why does a **double sonic boom** occur when the space shuttle enters the atmosphere?

As long as an airborne object, such as a plane, is moving below the speed of sound (called Mach 1), the disturbed air remains well in front of the craft. But as the craft passes Mach 1 and is flying at supersonic speeds, a sharp air pressure rise occurs in front of the craft. In a sense, the air molecules are crowded together and collectively impact. What is heard is a claplike thunder called a sonic boom or a supersonic bang. There are many shocks coming from a supersonic aircraft, but these shocks usually combine to form two main shocks, one coming from the nose and one from the aft end of the aircraft. Each of the shocks moves at a different velocity. If the time difference between the two shock waves is greater than 0.10 seconds apart, two sonic booms will be heard. This usually occurs when an aircraft ascends or descends quickly. If the aircraft moves more slowly, the two booms will sound like only one boom to the observer.

What is the **Doppler effect**?

The Austrian physicist Christian Doppler (1803-1853) in 1842 explained the phenomenon of the apparent change in wavelength of radiation—such as sound or light—emitted either by a moving body (source) or by the moving receiver. The frequency of the wavelengths increases and the wavelength becomes shorter as the moving source approaches, producing high-pitched sounds and bluish light (called blue shift). Likewise, as the source recedes from the receiver the frequency of the wavelengths decreases, the sound is pitched lower, and light appears reddish (called red shift). This

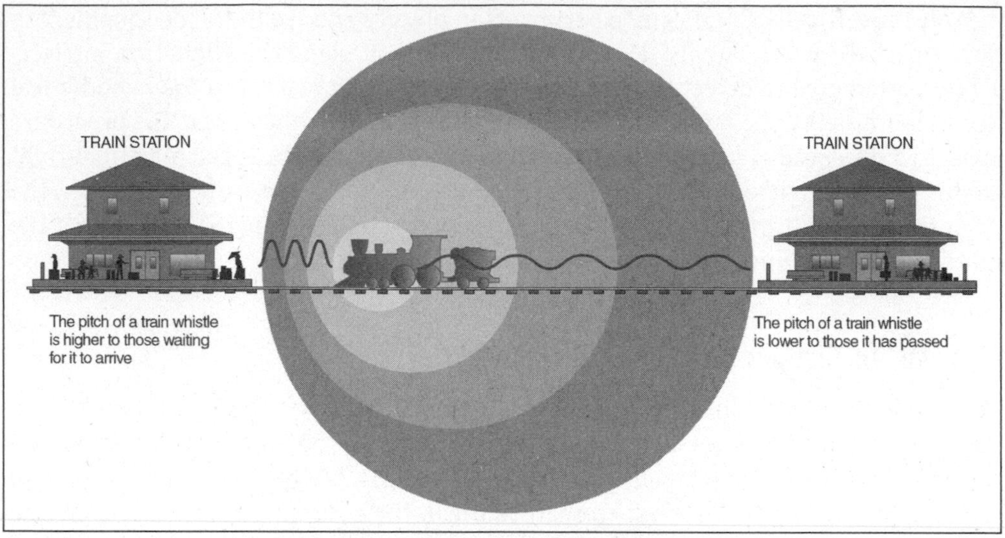

The Doppler effect.

Doppler effect is commonly demonstrated by the whistle of an approaching train or the roar of a jet aircraft.

There are three differences between acoustical (sound) and optical (light) Doppler effects: The optical frequency change is not dependent on which is moving—the source or observer—nor is it affected by the medium through which the waves are moving, but acoustical frequency is affected by such conditions. Optical frequency changes are affected if the source or observer moves at right angles to the line connecting the source and observer. Observed acoustical changes are not affected in such a situation. Applications of the Doppler phenomenon include the Doppler radar and the measurement by astronomers of the motion and direction of celestial bodies.

What is a **decibel**?

A decibel is a measure of the relative loudness or intensity of sound. A 20 decibel sound is 10 times louder than a 10 decibel sound; 30 decibels is 100 times louder, etc. One decibel is the smallest difference between sounds detectable by the human ear.

Decibel Level	Equivalent
10	Light whisper
20	Quiet conversation
30	Normal conversation
40	Light traffic
50	Loud conversation

Decibel Level	Equivalent
60	Noisy office
70	Normal traffic, quiet train
80	Rock music, subway
90	Heavy traffic, thunder
100	Jet plane at takeoff

What is the sound frequency of the **musical scale**?

EQUAL TEMPERED SCALE

Note	Frequency	Note	Frequency
C♭	261.63	G	392.00
C#	277.18	G#	415.31
D	293.67	A	440.00
D#	311.13	A#	466.16
E	329.63	B	493.88
F	349.23	Cn	523.25
F#	369.99		

Notes: ♭ indicates flat; # indicates sharp; n indicates return to natural.

The lowest frequency distinguishable as a note is about 20 hertz. The highest audible frequency is about 20,000 hertz. A hertz (symbol Hz) is a unit of frequency that measures the number of the wave cycles per second frequency of a periodic phenomenon whose periodic time is one second (cycles per second).

What is the **speed of sound**?

The speed of sound is not a constant; it varies depending on the medium in which it travels. The measurement of sound velocity in the medium of air must take into account many factors, including air temperature, pressure, and purity. At sea level and 32°F (0°C), scientists do not agree on a standard figure; estimates range from 740 to 741.5 miles (1,191.6 to 1,193.22 kilometers) per hour. As air temperature rises, sound velocity increases. Sound travels faster in water than in air and even faster in iron and steel. Sounds traveling a mile in air for five seconds will travel the same distance in one second underwater and one-third of a second in steel.

What are the characteristics of **alpha, beta**, and **gamma radiation**?

Radiation is a term that describes all the ways energy is emitted by the atom as X-rays, gamma rays, neutrons, or as charged particles. Most atoms, being stable, are nonradioactive; others are unstable and give off either particles or gamma radiation. Substances bombarded by radioactive particles can become radioactive and yield alpha particles, beta particles, and gamma rays.

Alpha particles, first identified by Antoine Henri Becquerel (1852-1908), have a positive electrical charge and consist of two protons and two neutrons. Because of their great mass, alpha particles can travel only a short distance, around two inches (five centimeters) in air, and can be stopped by a sheet of paper.

Beta particles, identified by Ernest Rutherford (1871-1937), are extremely high-speed electrons that move at the speed of light. They can travel far in air and can pass through solid matter several millimeters thick.

Gamma rays, identified by Marie (1867-1934) and Pierre Curie (1859-1906), are similar to X-rays, but they usually have a shorter wave length. These rays, which are bursts of photons, or very short-wave electromagnetic radiation, travel at the speed of light. They are much more penetrating than either the alpha or beta particles and can go through seven inches (18 centimeters) of lead.

MATTER

Who proposed the **theory of the atom**?

The modern theory of atomic structure was first proposed by the Japanese physicist Hantaro Nagaoka (1865-1950) in 1904. In his model, electrons rotated in rings around a small central nucleus. In 1911, Ernest Rutherford (1871-1937) discovered further evidence to prove that the nucleus of the atom is extremely small and dense and is surrounded by a much larger and less dense cloud of electrons. In 1913, the Danish physicist Niels Bohr (1885-1962) suggested that electrons orbit the nucleus in concentric quantum shells that correspond to the electron's energy levels.

What is the **fourth state of matter**?

Plasma, a mixture of free electrons and ions or atomic nuclei, is sometimes referred to as a "fourth state of matter." Plasmas occur in thermonuclear reactions as in the sun, in fluorescent lights, and in stars. When the temperature of gas is raised high enough, the collision of atoms becomes so violent that electrons are knocked loose from their nuclei. The result of a gas having loose, negatively charged electrons and heavier, positively charged nuclei is called a plasma.

All matter is made up of atoms. Animals and plants are organic matter; minerals and water are inorganic matter. Whether matter appears as a solid, liquid, or gas depends on how the molecules are held together in their chemical bonds. Solids have a rigid structure in the atoms of the molecules; in liquids the molecules are close together but not packed; in a gas, the molecules are widely spaced and move around, occasionally colliding but usually not interacting. These states—solid, liquid, and gas—are the first three states of matter.

What is the difference between **nuclear fission** and **nuclear fusion**?

Nuclear fission is the splitting of an atomic nucleus into at least two fragments. Nuclear fusion is a nuclear reaction in which the nuclei of atoms of low atomic number, such as hydrogen and helium, fuse to form a heavier nucleus. In both nuclear fission and nuclear fusion substantial amounts of energy are produced.

Who is generally regarded as the discoverer of the **electron**, the **proton**, and the **neutron**?

The British physicist Sir Joseph John Thomson (1856-1940) in 1897 researched electrical conduction in gases, which led to the important discovery that cathode rays consist of negatively charged particles called electrons. The discovery of the electron inaugurated the electrical theory of the atom, and this, along with other work, entitled Thomson to be regarded as the founder of modern atomic physics.

Ernest Rutherford (1871-1937) discovered the proton in 1919. He also predicted the existence of the neutron, later discovered by his colleague, James Chadwick (1891-1974). Chadwick was awarded the 1935 Nobel Prize for physics for this discovery.

How did a total **solar eclipse** confirm Einstein's **theory of general relativity**?

When formulating his theory of general relativity, Albert Einstein (1879-1955) proposed that the curvature of space near a massive object like the sun would bend light that passed close by. For example, a star seen near the edge of the sun during an eclipse would appear to have shifted by 1.75 arc seconds from its usual place. The British astronomer Arthur Eddington (1882-1944) confirmed Einstein's hypothesis during an eclipse on May 29, 1919. The subsequent attention given Eddington's findings helped establish Einstein's reputation as one of science's greatest figures.

How did the **quark** get its name?

This theoretical particle, considered to be the fundamental unit of matter, was named by Murray Gell-Mann (b. 1929) an American theoretical physicist and Nobel Prize winner.

Murray Gell-Mann theorized the existence of fundamental particles he called "quarks."

Its name was initially a playful tag that Gell-Mann invented, sounding something like "kwork." Later, Gell-Mann came across the line "Three quarks for Master Marks" in James Joyce's *Finnegan's Wake*, and the tag became known as a quark. There are six kinds or "flavors" (up, down, strange, charm, bottom, and top) of quarks, and each "flavor" has three varieties or "colors" (red, blue, and green). All eighteen types have different electric charges (a basic characteristic of all elementary particles). Three quarks form a proton (having one unit of positive electric charge) or a neutron (zero charge), and two quarks (a quark and an antiquark) form a meson. Like all known particles, a quark has its anti-matter opposite, known as an antiquark (having the same mass but opposite charge).

What was **Richard Feynman's** contribution to physics?

Richard Feynman (1918-1988) developed a theory of quantum electrodynamics that described the interaction of electrons, positrons, and photons, providing physicists a new way to work with electrons. He reconstructed quantum mechanics and electrodynamics in his own terms, formulating a matrix of measurable quantities visually represented by a series of graphs knows as the Feynman diagrams. Feynman was awarded the Nobel Prize in Physics in 1965.

What are the **subatomic particles**?

Subatomic particles are particles that are smaller than atoms. Historically, subatomic particles were considered to be electrons, protons, and neutrons. However, the definition of subatomic particles has now been expanded to include elementary particles, which are the particles so small that they do not appear to be made of more minute units. The physical study of such particles became possible only during the twentieth century with the development of increasingly sophisticated apparatus. Many new particles have been discovered in the last half of the twentieth century.

A number of proposals have been made to organize the particles by their spin, their mass, or their common properties. One system is now commonly known as the Standard Model. This system recognizes two basic types of fundamental particles: quarks and leptons. Other force-carrying particles are called bosons. Photons, gluons, and weakons are bosons. Leptons include electrons, muons, taus, and three kinds of neutrinos. Quarks never occur alone in nature. They always combine to form particles called hadrons. According to the Standard Model, all other subatomic particles consist of some combination of quarks and their antiparticles. A proton consists of three quarks.

What are **colligative properties**?

Colligative properties are properties of solutions that depend on the number of particles present in the solution and not on characteristics of the particles themselves. Colligative properties include depression of freezing point and elevation of boiling point. For living systems, perhaps the most important colligative property is osmotic pressure.

What substance, other than water, is **less dense as a solid** than as a liquid?

Only bismuth and water share this characteristic. Density (the mass per unit volume or mass/volume) refers to how compact or crowded a substance is. For instance, the density of water is 1 g/cm^3 (gram per cubic centimeter) or 1 kg/l (kilogram per liter); the density of a rock is 3.3 g/cm^3; pure iron is 7.9 g/cm^3; and the Earth (as a whole) is 5.5 g/cm^3 (average). Water as a solid (i.e., ice) floats, which is a good thing; otherwise, ice would sink to the bottom of every lake or stream.

Why is **liquid water** more dense than ice?

Pure liquid water is most dense at 39.2°F (3.98°C) and decreases in density as it freezes. The water molecules in ice are held in a relatively rigid geometric pattern by their hydrogen bonds, producing an open, porous structure. Liquid water has fewer bonds; therefore, more molecules can occupy the same space, making liquid water more dense than ice.

What does **half-life** mean?

Half-life is the time it takes for the number of radioactive nuclei originally present in a sample to decrease to one-half of their original number. Thus, if a sample has a half-life of one year, its radioactivity will be reduced to half its original amount at the end of a year and to one quarter at the end of two years. The half-life of a particular radionuclide is always the same, independent of temperature, chemical combination, or any other condition. Natural radiation was discovered in 1896 by the French physicist Antoine Henri Becquerel (1852-1908). His discovery initiated the science of nuclear physics.

What is a chemical garden and how is one made?

Mix four tablespoons of bluing, four tablespoons of salt, and one tablespoon household ammonia. Pour this mixture over pieces of coal or brick in a suitable dish or bowl. Put several drops of red or green ink or mercurochrome on various parts of the coal and leave undisturbed for several days.

A chemical garden—a dishful of crystals that grow like plants and look like coral—will begin to appear. How soon the crystals will begin to appear depends on the temperatures and humidity in the room. Before long, crystals will be growing all over the briquettes, on the side of the dish, and down onto the plate. The crystals will be pure white with a snow-like texture.

Who made the **first organic compound to be synthesized** from inorganic ingredients?

In 1828, Friedrich Wöhler (1800-1882) synthesized urea from ammonia and cyanic acid. This synthesis dealt a deathblow to the vital-force theory, which held that definite and fundamental differences existed between organic and inorganic compounds. The Swedish chemist Jöns Jakob Berzelius (1779-1848) proposed that the two classes of compounds were produced from their elements by entirely different laws. Organic compounds were produced under the influence of a vital force and so were incapable of being prepared artificially. This distinction ended with Wöhler's synthesis.

Who is known as the **founder** of **crystallography**?

The French priest and mineralogist René-Just Haüy (1743-1822) is called the father of crystallography. In 1781 Haüy had a fortunate accident when he dropped a piece of calcite and it broke into small fragments. He noticed that the fragments broke along straight planes that met at constant angles. Haüy hypothesized that each crystal was built from successive additions of what is now called a unit cell to form a simple geometric shape with constant angles. An identity or difference in crystalline form implied an identity or difference in chemical composition. This was the beginning of the science of crystallography.

By the early 1800s many physicists were experimenting with crystals; in particular, they were fascinated by their ability to bend light and separate it into its component colors. An important member of the emerging field of optical mineralogy was the British scientist David Brewster (1871-1868), who succeeded in classifying most known crystals according to their optical properties.

The work of French chemist Louis Pasteur (1822-1895) during the mid 1800s became the foundation for crystal polarimetry—a method by which light is polarized, or aligned to a single plane. Pierre Curie (1859-1906) and his brother Jacques (1855-1941) discovered another phenomenon displayed by certain crystals called piezoelectricity. It is the creation of an electrical potential by squeezing certain crystals.

Perhaps the most important application of crystals is in the science of X-ray crystallography. Experiments in this field were first conducted by the German physicist Max von Laue (1879-1960). This work was perfected by William Henry Bragg (1862-1942) and William Lawrence Bragg (1890-1971), who were awarded the Nobel Prize in physics for their work. The synthesis of penicillin and insulin were made possible by the use of X-ray crystallography.

CHEMICAL ELEMENTS, ETC.

Who are some of the **founders** of **modern chemistry**?

Several contenders share this honor:

Swedish chemist Jöns Jakob Berzelius (1779-1848) devised chemical symbols, determined atomic weights, contributed to the atomic theory, and discovered several new elements. Between 1810 and 1816, he described the preparation, purification, and analysis of 2,000 chemical compounds. Then he determined atomic weights for 40 elements. He simplified chemical symbols, introducing a notation—letters with numbers—that replaced the pictorial symbols his predecessors used, and that is still used today. He discovered cerium (in 1803, with Wilhelm Hisinger), selenium (1818), silicon (1824), and thorium (1829).

Robert Boyle (1627-1691), a British natural philosopher, is considered one of the founders of modern chemistry. Best known for his discovery of Boyle's Law (volume of a gas is inversely proportional to its pressure at constant temperature), he was a pioneer in the use of experiments and the scientific method. A founder of the Royal Society, he worked to remove the mystique of alchemy from chemistry to make it a pure science.

The French chemist Antoine-Laurent Lavoisier (1743-1794) is regarded as another founder of modern chemistry. His wide-ranging contributions include the discrediting of the phlogiston theory of combustion, which had been for so long a stumbling block to a true understanding of chemistry. He established modern terminology for chemical substances and did the first experiments in quantitative organic analysis. He is sometimes credited with having discovered or established the law of conservation of mass in chemical reactions.

John Dalton (1766-1844), an English chemist, proposed an atomic theory of matter that became a basic theory of modern chemistry. His theory, first proposed in

1803, states that each chemical element is composed of its own kind of atoms, all with the same relative weight.

Dmitry Ivanovich Mendeleyev, the Russian chemist renowned for developing the periodic table of elements.

Who developed the **periodic table**?

Dmitry Ivanovich Mendeleyev (1834-1907) was a Russian chemist whose name will always be linked with the development of the periodic table. He was the first chemist really to understand that all elements are related members of a single ordered system. He changed what had been a highly fragmented and speculative branch of chemistry into a true, logical science. His nomination for the 1906 Nobel Prize for chemistry failed by one vote, but his name became recorded in perpetuity 50 years later when element 101 was called mendelevium.

According to Mendeleyev, the properties of the elements, as well as those of their compounds, are periodic functions of their atomic weights (in the 1920s, it was discovered that atomic number was the key rather than weight). Mendeleyev compiled the first true periodic table listing all the 63 (then-known) elements. In order to make the table work, Mendeleyev had to leave gaps, and he predicted that further elements would eventually be discovered to fill them. Three were discovered in Mendeleyev's lifetime: gallium, scandium, and germanium.

There are 95 naturally occurring elements; of the remaining elements (elements 96 to 109), 10 are undisputed. There are aproximately 17 million chemical compounds registered with *Chemical Abstracts* that have been produced from these elements.

What was the **first element** to be discovered?

Phosphorus was first discovered by German chemist Hennig Brand in 1669 when he extracted a waxy white substance from urine that glowed in the dark. But Brand did not publish his findings. In 1680, phosphorus was rediscovered by the English chemist Robert Boyle.

Atomic number | 86 (222) | Atomic weight
Symbol | Rn
Name | radon

Period	1 I A	2 II A	3 III B	4 IV B	5 V B	6 VI B	7 VII B	8 VIII B	9 VIII B	10 VIII B	11 I B	12 II B	13 III A	14 IV A	15 V A	16 VI A	17 VII A	18 VIII A
1	1 1.00794 H hydrogen																	2 4.002602 He helium
2	3 6.941 Li lithium	4 9.012182 Be beryllium											5 10.811 B boron	6 12.011 C carbon	7 14.00674 N nitrogen	8 15.9994 O oxygen	9 18.9984032 F fluorine	10 20.1797 Ne neon
3	11 22.989768 Na sodium	12 24.3050 Mg magnesium											13 26.981539 Al aluminum	14 28.0855 Si silicon	15 30.973762 P phosphorus	16 32.066 S sulfur	17 35.4527 Cl chlorine	18 39.948 Ar argon
4	19 39.0983 K potassium	20 40.078 Ca calcium	21 44.955910 Sc scandium	22 47.88 Ti titanium	23 50.9415 V vanadium	24 51.9961 Cr chromium	25 54.9305 Mn manganese	26 55.847 Fe iron	27 58.93320 Co cobalt	28 58.69 Ni nickel	29 63.546 Cu copper	30 65.39 Zn zinc	31 69.723 Ga gallium	32 72.61 Ge germanium	33 74.92159 As arsenic	34 78.96 Se selenium	35 79.904 Br bromine	36 83.80 Kr krypton
5	37 85.4678 Rb rubidium	38 87.62 Sr strontium	39 88.90585 Y yttrium	40 91.224 Zr zirconium	41 92.90638 Nb niobium	42 95.94 Mo molybdenum	43 (98) Tc technetium	44 101.07 Ru ruthenium	45 102.90550 Rh rhodium	46 106.42 Pd palladium	47 107.8682 Ag silver	48 112.411 Cd cadmium	49 114.82 In indium	50 118.710 Sn tin	51 121.75 Sb antimony	52 127.60 Te tellurium	53 126.90447 I iodine	54 131.29 Xe xenon
6	55 132.90543 Cs cesium	56 137.327 Ba barium	57 138.9055 *La lanthanum	72 178.49 Hf hafnium	73 180.9479 Ta tantalum	74 183.85 W tungsten	75 186.207 Re rhenium	76 190.2 Os osmium	77 192.22 Ir iridium	78 195.08 Pt platinum	79 196.96654 Au gold	80 200.59 Hg mercury	81 204.3833 Tl thallium	82 207.2 Pb lead	83 208.98037 Bi bismuth	84 (209) Po polonium	85 (210) At astatine	86 (222) Rn radon
7	87 (223) Fr francium	88 (226) Ra radium	89 (227) †Ac actinium	104 (261) Rf rutherfordium	105 (262) Db dubnium	106 (263) Sg seaborgium	107 (262) Bh bohrium	108 (265) Hs hassium	109 (267) Mt meitnerium	110 (269) Uun ununnilium	111 (272) Uuu unununium	112 (277) Uub ununbiium						

Main-Group Elements: groups 1–2 and 13–18. Transition Metals: groups 3–12.

Inner-Transition Metals

*Lanthanides	58 140.115 Ce cerium	59 140.90765 Pr praseodymium	60 144.24 Nd neodymium	61 (145) Pm promethium	62 150.36 Sm samarium	63 151.965 Eu europium	64 157.25 Gd gadolinium	65 158.92534 Tb terbium	66 162.50 Dy dysprosium	67 164.93032 Ho holmium	68 167.26 Er erbium	69 168.93421 Tm thulium	70 173.04 Yb ytterbium	71 174.967 Lu lutetium
†Actinides	90 232.0381 Th thorium	91 (231) Pa protactinium	92 238.0289 U uranium	93 (237) Np neptunium	94 (244) Pu plutonium	95 (243) Am americium	96 (247) Cm curium	97 (247) Bk berkelium	98 (251) Cf californium	99 (252) Es einsteinium	100 (257) Fm fermium	101 (258) Md mendelevium	102 (259) No nobelium	103 (262) Lr lawrencium

The periodic table.

What are the **alkali metals**?

These are the elements at the left of the periodic table: lithium (Li, element 3), potassium (K, element 19), rubidium (Rb, element 37), cesium (Cs, element 55), francium (Fr, element 87), and sodium (Na, element 11). The alkali metals are sometimes called the sodium family of elements, or Group I elements. Because of their great chemical reactivity (they easily form positive ions), none exist in nature in the elemental state.

What are the **alkaline Earth metals**?

These are beryllium (Be, element 4), magnesium (Mg, element 12), calcium (Ca, element 20), strontium (Sr, element 38), barium (Ba, element 56), and radium (Ra, element 88). The alkaline Earth metals are also called Group II elements. Like the alkali metals, they are never found as free elements in nature and are moderately reactive metals. Harder and less volatile than the alkali metals, these elements all burn in air.

What are the **transition elements**?

The transition elements are the 10 subgroups of elements between Group II and Group XIII, starting with period 4. They include gold (Au, element 79), silver (Ag, element 47), platinum (Pt, element 78), iron (Fe, element 26), copper (Cu, element 29), and other metals. All transition elements are metals. Compared to alkali and alkaline Earth metals, they are usually harder and more brittle and have higher melting points. Transition metals are also good conductors of heat and electricity. They have variable valences, and compounds of transition elements are often colored. Transition elements are so named because they comprise a gradual shift from the strongly electropositive elements of Groups I and II to the electronegative elements of Groups VI and VII.

What are the **transuranic chemical elements** and the names for elements 102-109?

Transuranic elements are those elements in the periodic system with atomic numbers greater than 92. Many of these elements are ephemeral, do not exist naturally outside the laboratory, and are not stable.

Elements 93-109

Element Number	Name	Symbol
93	Neptunium	Np
94	Plutonium	Pu
95	Americum	Am
96	Curium	Cm
97	Berkelium	Bk
98	Californium	Cf
99	Einsteinium	Es
100	Fermium	Fm
101	Mendelevium	Md
102	Nobelium	No
103	Lawrencium	Lr
104	Rutherfordium	Rf
105	Dubnium	Db
106	Seaborgium	Sg
107	Bohrium	Bh
108	Hassium	Hs
109	Meitnerium	Mt

The names for elements 110-116 are under review by the International Union of Pure and Applied Chemistry.

Which are the only two **elements** in the periodic table **named after women**?

Curium, atomic number 96, was named after the pioneers of radioactive research Marie (1867-1934) and Pierre Curie (1859-1906). Meitnerium, atomic number 109, was named after Lise Meitner (1878-1968), one of the founders of nuclear fission.

What is a philosopher's stone?

A philosopher's stone was the name of a substance believed by medieval alchemists to have the power to change baser metals into gold or silver. It had, according to some, the power of prolonging life and of curing all injuries and diseases. The pursuit of it by alchemists led to the discovery of several chemical substances; however, the magical philosopher's stone has since proved fictitious.

Which elements are the **"noble metals"**?

The noble metals are gold (Au, element 79), silver (Ag, element 47), mercury (Hg, element 80), and the platinum group, which includes platinum (Pt, element 78), palladium (Pd, element 46), iridium (Ir, element 77), rhodium (Rh, element 45), ruthenium (Ru, element 44), and osmium (Os, element 76). The term refers to those metals highly resistant to chemical reaction or oxidation (resistant to corrosion) and is contrasted to "base" metals, which are not so resistant. The term has its origins in ancient alchemy whose goals of transformation and perfection were pursued through the different properties of metals and chemicals. The term is not synonymous with "precious metals," although a metal, like platinum, may be both.

The platinum group metals have a variety of uses. In the United States more than 95 percent of all platinum group metals are used for industrial purposes. While platinum is a coveted material for jewelry making, it is also used in the catalytic converters of automobiles to control exhaust emissions, as are rhodium and palladium. Rhodium can also be alloyed with platinum and palladium for use in furnace windings, thermocouple elements, and in aircraft spark-plug electrodes. Osmium is used in the manufacture of pharmaceuticals and in alloys for instrument pivots and long-life phonograph needles.

What is **Harkin's rule**?

Atoms having even atomic numbers are more abundant in the universe than are atoms having odd atomic numbers. Chemical properties of an element are determined by its atomic number, which is the number of protons in the atom's nucleus.

Which elements are **liquid at room temperature**?

Mercury ("liquid silver," Hg, element 80) and bromine (Br, element 35) are liquid at room temperature 68° to 70°F (20° to 21°C). Gallium (Ga, element 31) with a melting point of 85.6°F (29.8°C) and cesium (Cs, element 55) with a melting point of 83°F (28.4°C), are liquid at slightly above room temperature and pressure.

What are some chemical elements whose **symbols** are **not derived from their English names**?

Modern Name	Symbol	Older Name
antimony	Sb	stibium
copper	Cu	cuprum
gold	Au	aurum
iron	Fe	ferrum
lead	Pb	plumbum
mercury	Hg	hydrargyrum
potassium	K	kalium
silver	Ag	argentum
sodium	Na	natrium
tin	Sn	stannum
tungsten	W	wolfram

Which chemical element is the **most abundant in the universe**?

Hydrogen (H, element 1) makes up about 75 percent of the mass of the universe. It is estimated that more than 90 percent of all atoms in the universe are hydrogen atoms. Most of the rest are helium (He, element 2) atoms.

Which chemical elements are the **most abundant on Earth**?

Oxygen (O, element 8) is the most abundant element in the Earth's crust, waters, and atmosphere. It composes 49.5 percent of the total mass of these compounds. Silicon (Si, element 14) is the second most abundant element. Silicon dioxide and silicates make up about 87 percent of the materials in the Earth's crust.

Which elements are the **best** and **worst conductors** of electricity?

The element with the lowest electrical resistance (and thus the highest electrical conductivity) under standard conditions is silver, followed by copper, gold, and aluminum. The poorest conductors of electricity among the metals are manganese, gadolinium, and terbium.

How do **lead-acid batteries** work?

Lead-acid batteries consist of positive and negative lead plates suspended in a diluted sulfuric acid solution called an electrolyte. Everything is contained in a chemically and electrically inert case. As the cell discharges, sulfur molecules from the electrolyte bond with the lead plates, releasing excess electrons. The flow of electrons is called electricity.

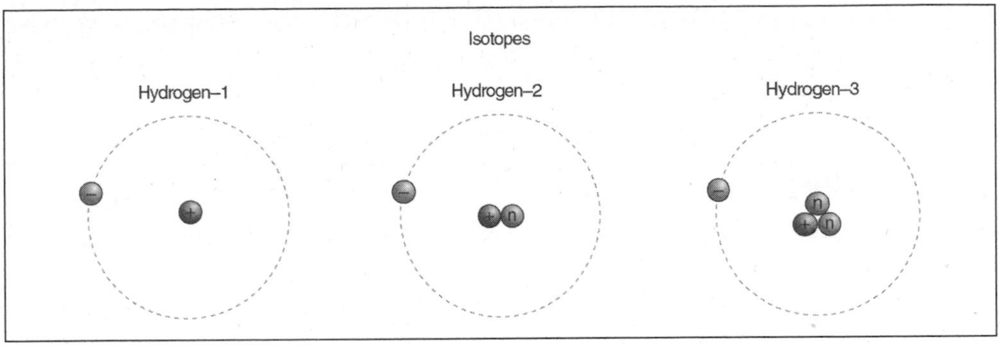

Hydrogen isotopes.

Which elements have the **most isotopes**?

The elements with the most isotopes, with 36 each, are xenon (Xe) with nine stable isotopes (identified from 1920 to 1922) and 27 radioactive isotopes (identified from 1939 to 1981), and cesium (Cs) with one stable isotope (identified in 1921) and 35 radioactive isotopes (identified from 1935 to 1983).

The element with the fewest number of isotopes is hydrogen (H), with three isotopes, including two stable ones—protium (identified in 1920) and deuterium (identified in 1931)—and one radioactive isotope—tritium (first identified in 1934, but later considered a radioactive isotope in 1939).

Which elements have the **highest** and **lowest boiling points**?

Helium has the lowest boiling point of all the elements at -452.074°F (-268.93°C) followed by hydrogen -423.16°F (-252.87°C). The highest boiling point for an element is that of rhenium 10,104.8°F (5,596°C) followed by tungsten 10,031°F (5,555°C).

Which element has the **highest density**?

Either osmium or iridium is the element with the highest density; however, scientists have yet to gather enough conclusive data to choose between the two. When traditional methods of measurement are employed, osmium generally appears to be the densest element. Yet, when calculations are made based upon the space lattice, which may be a more reliable method given the nature of these elements, the density of iridium is 22.65 compared to 22.61 for osmium.

Which elements are the **hardest** and **softest**?

Carbon is both the hardest and softest element occurring in two different forms as graphite and diamond. A single crystal of diamond scores the absolute maximum value on the Knoop hardness scale of 90. Based on the somewhat less informative abrasive hardness scale of Mohs, diamond has a hardness of 10. Graphite is an extremely soft material with a Mohs hardness of only 0.5 and a Knoop hardness of 0.12.

What are **isomers**?

Isomers are compounds with the same molecular formula but different structures due to the different arrangement of the atoms within the molecules. Structural isomers have atoms connected in different ways. Geometric isomers differ in their symmetry about a double bond. Optical isomers are mirror images of each other.

What are the **gas laws**?

The gas laws are physical laws concerning the behavior of gases. They include Boyle's law, which states that the volume of a given mass of gas at a constant temperature is inversely proportional to its pressure; and Charles's law, which states that the volume of a given mass of gas at constant pressure is directly proportional to its absolute temperature. These two laws can be combined to give the General or Universal gas law, which may be expressed as:

$$(\text{pressure} \times \text{volume})/\text{temperature} = \text{constant}$$

Avogadro's law states that equal volumes of all gases contain the same number of particles if they all have the same pressure and temperature.

The laws are not obeyed exactly by any real gas, but many common gases obey them under certain conditions, particularly at high temperatures and low pressures.

What is **heavy water**?

Heavy water, also called deuterium oxide (D_20), is composed of oxygen and two hydrogen atoms in the form of deuterium, which has about twice the mass of normal hydrogen. As a result, heavy water has a molecular weight of about 20, while ordinary water has a molecular weight of about 18. Approximately one part heavy water can be found in 6,500 parts of ordinary water, and it may be extracted by fractional distillation. It is used in thermonuclear weapons and nuclear reactors and as an isotopic tracer in studies of chemical and biochemical processes. Heavy water was discovered by Harold C. Urey in 1931.

What is a **Lewis acid**?

Named after the American chemist Gilbert Newton Lewis (1875-1946), the Lewis theory defines an acid as a species that can accept an electron pair from another atom, and a base as a species that can donate an electron pair to complete the valence shell of another atom. Hydrogen ion (proton) is the simplest substance that will do this, but Lewis acids include many compounds—such as boron trifluoride (BF_3) and aluminum chloride ($AlCl_3$)—that can react with ammonia, for example, to form an addition compound or Lewis salt.

Which chemical is **used in greater quantities** than any other?

Sodium chloride (NaCl), or salt, has over 14,000 uses, and is probably used in greater quantities and for more applications than any other chemical.

MEASUREMENT, METHODOLOGY, ETC.

What was the first **national physics society** organized in the United States?

The first national physics society in the United States was the American Physical Society, organized on May 20, 1899, at Columbia University in New York City. The first president was Henry Augustus Rowland.

What was the first **national chemical society** organized in the United States?

The first national chemical society in the United States was the American Chemical Society, organized in New York City on April 20, 1876. The first president was John William Draper (1811-1882).

What are the **four major divisions** of chemistry?

Chemistry has traditionally been divided into organic, inorganic, analytical, and physical chemistry. Organic chemistry is the study of compounds that contain carbon. More than 90 percent of all known chemicals are organic. Inorganic chemistry is the study of compounds of all elements except carbon. Analytical chemists determine the structure and composition of compounds and mixtures. They also develop and operate instruments and techniques for carrying out the analyses. Physical chemists use the principles of physics to understand chemical phenomena.

What were some of the leading contributions of **Albert Einstein**?

Albert Einstein (1879-1955) was the principal founder of modern theoretical physics; his theory of relativity (speed of light is a constant and not relative to the observer or

Albert Einstein revolutionized twentieth-century human understanding of the physical world.

source of light), and the relationship of mass and energy ($e = mc^2$), fundamentally changed human understanding of the physical world.

During a single year in 1905, he produced three landmark papers. These papers dealt with the nature of particle movement known as Brownian motion, the quantum nature of electromagnetic radiation as demonstrated by the photoelectric effect, and the special theory of relativity. Although Einstein is probably best known for the last of these works, it was for his quantum explanation of the photoelectric effect that he was awarded the 1921 Nobel Prize in physics.

His stature as a scientist, together with his strong humanitarian stance on major political and social issues, made him one of the outstanding men of the twentieth century.

What is **antimatter**?

Antimatter is the exact opposite of normal matter. Antimatter was predicted in a series of equations derived by Paul Dirac (1902-1984). He was attempting to combine the Theory of Relativity with equations governing the behavior of electrons. In order to make his equations work, he had to predict the existence of a particle that would be similar to the electron, but opposite in charge. This particle, discovered in 1932, was the antimatter equivalent of the electron and called the positron (electrons with a positive charge). Other antimatter particles would not be discovered until 1955 when particle accelerators were finally able to confirm the existence of the antineutron and antiproton (protons with a negative charge). Antiatoms (pairing of positrons and antiprotons) are other examples of antimatter.

Who is generally regarded as the founder of **quantum mechanics**?

The German mathematical physicist Werner Karl Heisenberg (1901-1976) is regarded as the father of quantum mechanics (the theory of small-scale physical phenomena). His theory of uncertainty in 1927 overturned traditional classical mechanics and electromagnetic theory regarding energy and motions when applied to subatomic particles such as electrons and parts of atomic nuclei. The theory states that while it is impossible to specify precisely both the position and the simultaneous momentum (mass $\times$ velocity) of a particle, they can only be predicted. This means that the result of an action can be expressed only in terms of probability that a certain effect will occur.

Who invented the **thermometer**?

The Greeks of Alexandria knew that air expanded as it was heated. Hero of Alexandria (first century C.E.) and Philo of Byzantium made simple "thermoscopes," but they were not real thermometers. In 1592, Galileo (1564-1642) made a kind of thermometer that also functioned as a barometer, and in 1612 his friend Santorio Santorio (1561-1636) adapted the air thermometer (a device in which a colored liquid was driven down by the expansion of air) to measure the body's temperature change during illness and recovery. Still, it was not until 1713 that Daniel Fahrenheit (1686-1736) began developing a thermometer with a fixed scale. He worked out his scale from two "fixed" points: the melting point of ice and the heat of the healthy human body. He realized that the melting point of ice was a constant temperature, whereas the freezing point of water varied. Fahrenheit put his thermometer into a mixture of ice, water, and salt (which he marked off as 0°) and using this as a starting point, marked off melting ice at 32° and blood heat at 96°. In 1835, it was discovered that normal blood measured 98.6°F. Sometimes Fahrenheit used spirit of wine as the liquid in the thermometer tube, but more often he used specially purified mercury. Later, the boiling point of water (212°F) became the upper fixed point.

What is the **pH scale**?

The pH scale is the measurement of the H^+ concentration (hydrogen ions) in a solution. It is used to measure the acidity or alkalinity of a solution. The pH scale ranges from 0 to 14. A neutral solution has a pH of 7, one with a pH greater than 7 is basic; or alkaline, and one with a pH less than 7 is acidic. The lower the pH below 7, the more acidic the solution. Each whole-number drop in pH represents a tenfold increase in acidity.

pH Value	Examples of Solutions
0	Hydrochloric acid (HCl), battery acid
1	Stomach acid (1.0-3.0)
2	Lemon juice (2.3)
3	Vinegar, wine soft drinks, beer, orange juice, some acid rain
4	Tomatoes, grapes, banana (4.6)
5	Black coffee, most shaving lotions, bread, normal rainwater
6	Urine (5-7), milk (6.6), saliva (6.2-7.4)
7	Pure water, blood (7.3-7.5)
8	Egg white (8.0), seawater (7.8-8.3)
9	Baking soda, phosphate detergents, Clorox, Tums
10	Soap solutions, milk of magnesia
11	Household ammonia (10.5-11.9), nonphosphate detergents
12	Washing soda (sodium carbonate)
13	Hair remover, oven cleaner
14	Sodium hydroxide (NaOH)

What is the **Kelvin** temperature scale?

Temperature is the level of heat in a gas, liquid, or solid. The freezing and boiling points of water are used as standard reference levels in both the metric (centigrade or Celsius) and the English system (Fahrenheit). In the metric system, the difference between freezing and boiling is divided into 100 equal intervals called degree Celsius or degree centigrade (°C). In the English system, the intervals are divided into 180 units, with one unit called degree Fahrenheit (°F). But temperature can be measured from absolute zero (no heat, no motion); this principle defines thermodynamic temperature and establishes a method to measure it upward. This scale of temperature is called the Kelvin temperature scale, after its inventor, William Thomson, Lord Kelvin (1824-1907), who devised it in 1848. The Kelvin (symbol K) has the same magnitude as the degree Celsius (the difference between freezing and boiling water is 100 degrees), but the two temperatures differ by 273.15 degrees (absolute zero, which is -273.15°C on the Celsius scale). Below is a comparison of the three temperatures:

Characteristic	K	°C	°F
Absolute zero	0	-273.15	-459.67
Freezing point of water	273.15	0	32
Normal human body temperature	310.15	37	98.6
Boiling point of water	373.15	100	212

To convert Celsius to Kelvin: Add 273.15 to the temperature($K = C + 273.15$). To convert Fahrenheit to Celsius: Subtract 32 from the temperature and multiply the difference by 5; then divide the product by 9 ($C = \frac{5}{9}[F - 32]$). To convert Celsius to Fahrenheit: Multiply the temperature by 1.8, then add 32 ($F = \frac{9}{5}C + 32$ or $F = 1.8C + 32$).

How are **Celsius** temperatures converted into **Fahrenheit** temperatures?

The formulas for converting Celsius temperatures into Fahrenheit (and the reverse) are as follows:

$$F = (C \times \tfrac{9}{5}) + 32$$
$$C = (F - 32) \times \tfrac{5}{9}$$

Some useful comparisons of the two scales:

Temperature	Fahrenheit	Celsius
Absolute zero	-459.67	-273.15
Point of equality	-40.0	-40.0
Zero Fahrenheit	0.0	-17.8
Freezing point of water	32.0	0.0
Normal human blood temperature	98.4	36.9
100 degrees F	100.0	37.8
Boiling point of water (at standard pressure)	212.0	100.0

Who invented **chromatography**?

Chromatography was invented by the Russian botanist Mikhail Tswett (1872-1919) in the early 1900s. The technique was first used to separate different plant pigments from one another. Chromatography has developed into a widely used method to separate various components of a substance from one another. Three types of chromatography are high-performance liquid chromatography (HPLC), gas chromatography, and paper chromatography. Different chromatography techniques are used in forensic science and analytical laboratories.

What is **nuclear magnetic resonance**?

Nuclear magnetic resonance (NMR) is a process in which the nuclei of certain atoms absorb energy from an external magnetic field. Analytical chemists use NMR spectroscopy to identify unknown compounds, check for impurities, and study the shapes of molecules. They use the knowledge that different atoms will absorb electromagnetic energy at slightly different frequencies.

What is **STP**?

The abbreviation STP is often used for standard temperature and pressure. As a matter of convenience, scientists have chosen a specific temperature and pressure as standards for comparing gas volumes. The standard temperature is 0°C (273 K) and the standard pressure is 760 torr (one atmosphere).

How did the electrical term **ampere** originate?

It was named for André Marie Ampère (1775-1836), the physicist who formulated the basic laws of the science of electrodynamics. The ampere (symbol A), often abbreviated as "amp," is the unit of electric current, defined at the constant current, that, maintained in two straight parallel infinite conductors placed one meter apart in a vacuum, would produce a force between the conductors of 2×10^{-7} newton per meter. For example, the amount of current flowing through a 100-watt light bulb is 1 amp; through a toaster, 10 amps; a TV set, 3 amps; a car battery, 50 amps (while cranking). A newton (symbol N) is defined as a unit of force needed to accelerate one kilogram by one meter second^{-2}, or 1 N = 1Kg^{MS-2}.

How did the electrical unit **volt** originate?

The unit of voltage is the volt, named after Alessandro Volta (1745-1827), the Italian scientist who built the first modern battery. (A battery, operating with a lead rod and vinegar, was also manufactured in ancient Egypt.) Voltage measures the force or "oomph" with which electrical charges are pushed through a material. Some common voltages are 1.5 volts for a flashlight battery; 12 volts for a car battery; 115 volts for ordinary household receptacles; and 230 volts for a heavy-duty household receptacle.

How did the electrical unit **watt** originate?

Named for the Scottish engineer and inventor James Watt (1736-1819), the watt is used to measure electric power. An electric device uses one watt when one volt of electric current drives one ampere of current through it.

What is a **mole** in chemistry?

A mole (symbol mol), a fundamental measuring unit for the amount of a substance, refers to either a gram atomic weight or a gram molecular weight of a substance. It is the quantity of a substance that contains 6.02×10^{23} atoms, molecules, or formula units of that substance. This number is called Avogadro's number or constant after Amadeo Avogadro (1776-1856), who is considered to be one of the founders of physical science.

How does **gram atomic weight** differ from **gram formula weight**?

Gram atomic weight is the amount of an element (substance made up of atoms having the same atomic number) equal to its atomic weight in grams. Gram formula weight is an amount of a compound (a combination of elements) equal to its formula weight in grams.

SPACE

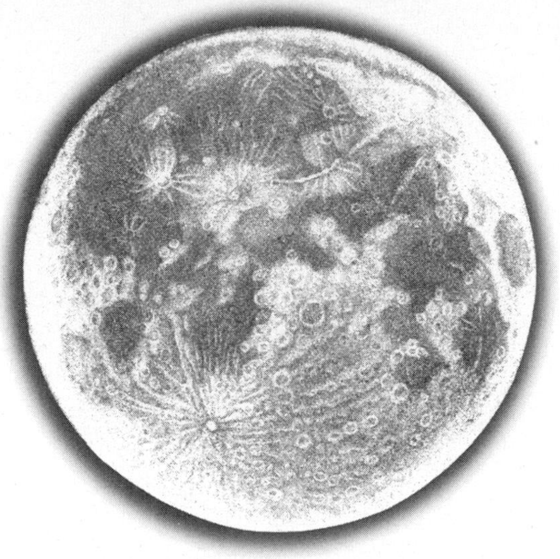

UNIVERSE

What was the **Big Bang**?

The Big Bang theory is the explanation most commonly accepted by astronomers for the origin of the universe. It proposes that the universe began as the result of an explosion—the Big Bang—15 to 20 billion years ago. Two observations form the basis of this cosmology. First, as Edwin Hubble (1889-1953) demonstrated, the universe is expanding uniformly, with objects at greater distances receding at greater velocities. Secondly, the Earth is bathed in a glow of radiation that has the characteristics expected from a remnant of a hot primeval fireball. This radiation was discovered by Arno A. Penzias (b. 1933) and Robert W. Wilson (b. 1936) of Bell Telephone Laboratories. In time, the matter created by the Big Bang came together in huge clumps to form the galaxies. Smaller clumps within the galaxies formed stars. Parts of at least one clump became a group of planets—our solar system.

What is the **Big Crunch** theory?

According to the Big Crunch theory, at some point in the very distant future, all matter will reverse direction and crunch back into the single point from which it began. Two other theories predict the future of the universe: the Big Bore theory and the Plateau theory. The Big Bore theory, named because it has nothing exciting to describe, claims that all matter will continue to move away from all other matter and the universe will expand forever. According to the Plateau theory, expansion of the universe will slow to the point where it will nearly cease, at which time the universe will reach a plateau and remain essentially the same.

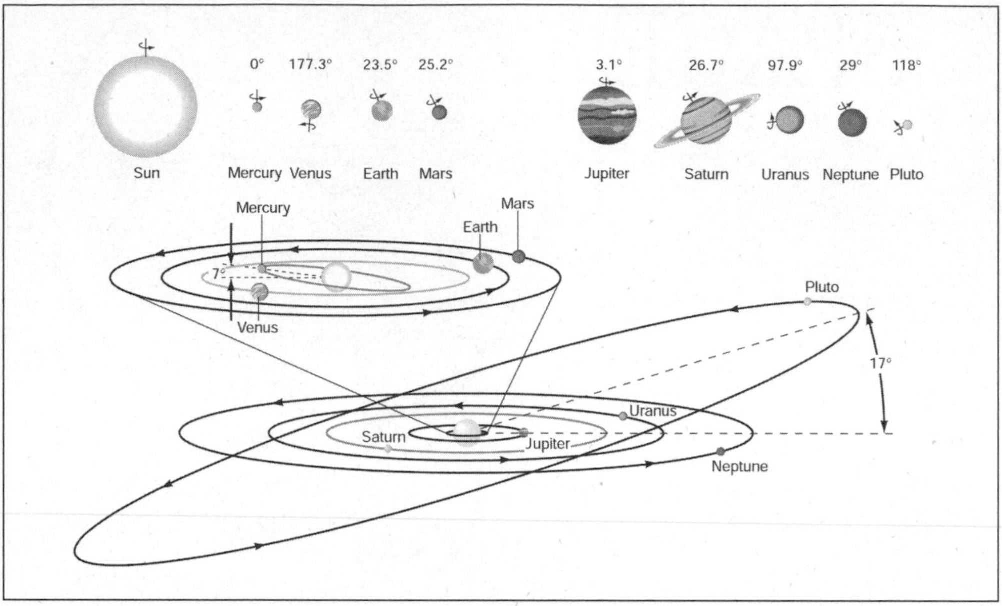

Schematic of the present-day solar system.

How **old** is the **universe**?

Recent data collected by the Hubble Space Telescope suggests that the universe may only be eight billion years old. This contradicts the previous belief the universe was somewhere between 13 billion and 20 billion years old. The earlier figure was derived from the concept that the universe has been expanding at the same rate since its birth at the Big Bang. The rate of expansion is a ratio known as Hubble's constant. It is calculated by dividing the speed at which the galaxy is moving away from the Earth by its distance from the Earth. By inverting Hubble's Constant—that is, dividing the distance of a galaxy by its recessional speed—the age of the universe can be calculated. The estimates of both the velocity and distance of galaxies from the Earth are subject to uncertainties, and not all scientists accept that the universe has always expanded at the same rate. Therefore, many still hold that the age of the universe is open to question.

How **large** is the **solar system**?

The size of the solar system can be visualized by imagining the sun (864,000 miles in diameter; 1,380,000 km) shrunk to a diameter of one inch (about the size of a ping-pong ball). Using the same size scale, the Earth would be a speck 0.01 inches (0.25 mm) in diameter and about nine feet (2.7 meters) away from the ping-pong ball sized sun. Our moon would have a diameter of 0.0025 inches (0.06 mm; the thickness of a human hair) and only a little over one-quarter inch (6.3 mm) from the Earth. Jupiter, the largest planet in the solar system, appears as the size of a small pea (0.1 inches [2.5 mm] in diameter) and 46 feet (14 meters) from the sun. Pluto, the smallest planet in the solar system, appears as a nearly invisible speck (0.00083 inches [0.02 mm] in diameter) and 355 feet (108 meters) from the sun.

Stephen Hawking, often recognized as the greatest theoretical physicist of the late 20th century.

Who is **Stephen Hawking**?

Hawking (b. 1943), a British physicist and mathematician, is considered to be the greatest theoretical physicist of the late 20th century. In spite of being severely handicapped by amyotrophic lateral sclerosis (ALS), he has made major contributions to scientific knowledge about black holes and the origin and evolution of the universe though his research into the nature of space-time and its anomalies. For instance, Hawking proposed that a black hole could emit thermal radiation, and he predicted that a black hole would disappear after all its mass has been converted into radiation (called "Hawking's radiation"). A current objective of Hawking is to synthesize quantum mechanics and relativity theory into a theory of quantum gravity. He is also the author of several books, including the popular best-selling work *A Brief History of Time*.

What are **quasars**?

The name quasar originated as a contraction of "quasi-stellar" radio source. Quasars appear to be star like, but they have large red shifts in their spectra indicating that they are receding from the Earth at great speeds, some at up to 90 percent of the speed of light. Their exact nature is still unknown, but many believe quasars to be the cores of distant galaxies, the most distant objects yet seen. Quasars, also called quasi-stellar objects or QSOs, were first identified in 1963 by astronomers at the Palomar Observatory in California.

What is a **syzygy**?

A syzygy (*sizz*-eh-jee) is a configuration that occurs when three celestial bodies lie in a straight line, such as the sun, Earth, and Moon during a solar or lunar eclipse. The particular syzygy when a planet is on the opposite side of the Earth from the sun is called an opposition.

Which **galaxy** is **closest** to us?

The Andromeda Galaxy is the galaxy closest to the Milky Way galaxy, where Earth is located. It is estimated to be 2.2 million light years away from Earth. Bigger than the Milky Way, Andromeda is a spiral-shaped galaxy that is also the brightest in Earth's sky.

STARS

What is a **supernova**?

A supernova is the death explosion of a massive star. Immediately after the explosion, the brightness of the star can outshine the entire galaxy, followed by a gradual fading. A supernova is a fairly rare event. The last supernova observed in our galaxy was in 1604. In February 1987, Supernova 1987A appeared in the Large Magellanic Cloud, a nearby galaxy.

What are the **four types** of **nebulae**?

The four types of nebulae are: emission, reflection, dark, and planetary. Primarily the birth place of stars, nebulae are clouds of gas and dust in space. Emission nebulae and reflection nebulae are bright nebulae. Emission nebulae are colorful and self-luminous. The Orion nebula, visible with the naked eye, is an example of an emission nebula. Reflection nebulae are cool clouds of dust and gas. They are illuminated by the light from nearby stars rather than by their own energy. Dark nebulae, also known as absorption nebulae, are not illuminated and appear as holes in the sky. The Horsehead nebula in the constellation Orion is an example of a dark nebula. Planetary nebulae are the remnants of the death of a star.

What is a **binary star**?

A binary star is a pair of stars revolving around a common center of gravity. About half of all stars are members of either binary star systems or multiple star systems, which contain more than two stars.

The bright star Sirius, about 8.6 light years away, is composed of two stars: one about 2.3 times the mass of the sun, the other a white dwarf star about 980 times the mass of Jupiter. Alpha Centauri, the nearest star to Earth after the sun, is actually three stars: Alpha Centauri A and Alpha Centauri B, two sunlike stars, orbit each other, and Alpha Centauri C, a low-mass red star, orbits around them.

What is a **black hole**?

When a star with a mass greater than about four times that of the sun collapses even the neutrons cannot stop the force of gravity. There is nothing to stop the contraction, and the star collapses forever. The material is so dense that nothing—not even light—can escape. The American physicist John Wheeler gave this phenomenon the name "black hole" in 1967. Since no light escapes from a black hole, it cannot be observed directly. However, if a black hole existed near another star, it would draw matter from the other star into itself and, in effect, produce X-rays. In the constellation of Cygnus, there is a strong X-ray source named Cygnus X-1. It is near a star, and the two revolve around each other. The unseen X-ray source has the gravitational pull of at least 10 suns and is believed to be a black hole. Another type of black hole, a primordial black hole, may also exist dating from the time of the Big Bang, when regions of gas and dust were highly compressed. Recently, astronomers observed a brief pulse of X-rays from Sagittarius A, a region near the center of the Milky Way Galaxy. The origin of this pulse and its behavior led scientists to conclude that there is probably a black hole in the center of our galaxy.

There are four other possible black holes: a Schwarzschild black hole has no charge and no angular momentum; a Reissner-Nordstrom black hole has charge but no angular momentum; a Kerr black hole has angular momentum but no charge; and a Kerr-Newman black hole has charge and angular momentum.

What is a **pulsar**?

A pulsar is a rotating neutron star that gives off sharp regular pulses of radio waves at rates ranging from 0.001 to four seconds. Stars burn by fusing hydrogen into helium. When they use up their hydrogen, their interiors begin to contract. During this contraction, energy is released and the outer layers of the star are pushed out. These layers are large and cool; the star is now a red giant. A star with more than twice the mass of the sun will continue to expand, becoming a supergiant. At that point, it may blow up in an explosion called a supernova. After a supernova, the remaining material of the star's core may be so compressed that the electrons and protons become neutrons. A star 1.4 to four times the mass of the sun can be compressed into a neutron star only about 12 miles (20 kilometers) across. Neutron stars rotate very fast. The neutron star at the center of the Crab Nebula spins 30 times per second.

A pulsar is formed by the collapse of a star with 1.4 to four times the mass of the sun. Some of these neutron stars emit radio signals from their magnetic poles in a direction that reaches Earth. These signals were first detected by Jocelyn Bell (b. 1943) of Cambridge University in 1967. Because of their regularity some people speculated that they were extraterrestrial beacons constructed by alien civilizations. This theory was eventually ruled out and the rotating neutron star came to be accepted as the explanation for these pulsating radio sources, or pulsars.

What does the **color** of a **star** indicate?

The color of a star gives an indication of its temperature and age. Stars are classified by their spectral type. From oldest to youngest and hottest to coolest, the types of stars are:

Type	Color	Temperature (°F)	Temperature (°C)
O	Blue	45,000-75,000	25,000-40,000
B	Blue	20,000-45,000	11,000-25,000
A	Blue-White	13,500-20,000	7,500-11,000
F	White	10,800-13,500	6,000-7,500
G	Yellow	9,000-10,800	5,000-6,000
K	Orange	6,300-9,000	3,500-5,000
M	Red	5,400-6,300	3,000-3,500

Each type is further subdivided on a scale of 0-9. The sun is a type G2 star.

Which **stars** are the **brightest**?

The brightness of a star is called its magnitude. Apparent magnitude is how bright a star appears to the naked eye. The lower the magnitude, the brighter the star. On a clear night, stars of about magnitude +6 can be seen with the naked eye. Large telescopes can detect objects as faint as +27. Very bright objects have negative magnitudes; the sun is -26.8.

Star	Constellation	Apparent Magnitude
Sirius	Canis Major	-1.47
Canopus	Carina	-0.72
Arcturus	Boötes	-0.06
Rigil Kentaurus	Centaurus	+0.01

The constellation Ursa Major, known as the greater bear, contains the cluster of seven stars that make up the Big Dipper.

Star	Constellation	Apparent Magnitude
Vega	Lyra	+0.04
Capella	Auriga	+0.05
Rigel	Orion	+0.14
Procyon	Canis Minor	+0.37
Betelgeuse	Orion	+0.41
Achernar	Eridanus	+0.51

What is the **Milky Way**?

The Milky Way is a hazy band of light that can be seen encircling the night sky. This light comes from the stars that make up the Milky Way galaxy, the galaxy to which the sun and the Earth belong. Galaxies are huge systems of stars separated from one another by largely empty space. Astronomers estimate that the Milky Way galaxy contains at least 100 billion stars and is about 100,000 light years in diameter. The galaxy is shaped like a compact disk with a central bulge, or nucleus, and spiral arms curving out from the center.

What is the **Big Dipper**?

The Big Dipper is a group of seven stars that are part of the constellation Ursa Major. They appear to form a sort of spoon with a long handle. The group is known as the Plough in

Great Britain. The Big Dipper is almost always visible in the northern hemisphere. It serves as a convenient reference point when locating other stars; for example, an imaginary line drawn from the two end stars of the dipper leads to Polaris, the North Star.

Where is the **North Star**?

If an imaginary line is drawn from the North Pole into space, it will reach a star called Polaris, or the North Star, less than one degree away from the line. As the Earth rotates on its axis, Polaris acts as a pivot-point around which all the stars visible in the northern hemisphere appear to move, while Polaris itself remains motionless.

Was **Polaris** always the **North Star**?

The Earth has had several North Stars. The Earth slowly wobbles on its axis as it spins. This motion is called precession. The Earth traces a circle in the sky over a period of 26,000 years. In Pharonic times the North Star was Thuban; today it is Polaris; around 14,000 C.E. it will be Vega.

What is the **summer triangle**?

The summer triangle is the triangle formed by the stars Deneb, Vega, and Altair as seen in the summer Milky Way.

How many **constellations** are there and how were they named?

Constellations are groups of stars that seem to form some particular shape, such as that of a person, animal, or object. They only appear to form this shape and be close to each other from Earth; in actuality, the stars in a constellation are often very distant from each other. There are 88 recognized constellations whose boundaries were defined in the 1920s by the International Astronomical Union.

Various cultures in all parts of the world have had their own constellations. However, because modern science is predominantly a product of Western culture, many of the constellations represent characters from Greek and Roman mythology. When Europeans began to explore the southern hemisphere in the 16th and 17th centuries, they derived some of the new star patterns from the technological wonders of their time, such as the microscope.

Names of constellations are usually given in Latin. Individual stars in a constellation are usually designated with Greek letters in the order of brightness; the brightest star is alpha, the second brightest is beta, and so on. The genitive, or possessive, form of the constellation name is used, thus Alpha Orionis is the brightest star of the constellation Orion.

Constellation	Genitive	Abbreviation	Meaning
Andromeda	Andromedae	And	Chained Maiden
Antlia	Antliae	Ant	Air Pump
Apus	Apodis	Aps	Bird of Paradise
Aquarius	Aquarii	Aqr	Water Bearer
Aquila	Aquilae	Aql	Eagle
Ara	Arae	Ara	Altar
Aries	Arietis	Ari	Ram
Auriga	Aurigae	Aur	Charioteer
Boötes	Boötis	Boo	Herdsman
Caelum	Caeli	Cae	Chisel
Camelopardalis	Camelopardalis	Cam	Giraffe
Cancer	Cancri	Cnc	Crab
Canes Venatici	Canum Venaticorum	CVn	Hunting Dogs
Canis Major	Canis Majoris	CMa	Big Dog
Canis Minor	Canis Minoris	CMi	Little Dog
Capricornus	Capricorni	Cap	Goat
Carina	Carinae	Car	Ship's Keel
Cassiopeia	Cassiopeiae	Cas	Queen of Ethiopia
Centaurus	Centauri	Cen	Centaur
Cepheus	Cephei	Cep	King of Ethiopia
Cetus	Ceti	Cet	Whale
Chamaeleon	Chamaeleonis	Cha	Chameleon
Circinus	Circini	Cir	Compass
Columba	Columbae	Col	Dove
Coma Berenices	Comae Berenices	Com	Berenice's Hair
Corona Australis	Coronae Australis	CrA	Southern Crown
Corona Borealis	Coronae Borealis	CrB	Northern Crown
Corvus	Corvi	Crv	Crow
Crater	Crateris	Crt	Cup
Crux	Crucis	Cru	Southern Cross
Cygnus	Cygni	Cyg	Swan
Delphinus	Delphini	Del	Dolphin
Dorado	Doradus	Dor	Goldfish
Draco	Draconis	Dra	Dragon
Equuleus	Equulei	Equ	Little Horse
Eridanus	Eridani	Eri	River Eridanus
Fornax	Fornacis	For	Furnace
Gemini	Geminorum	Gem	Twins
Grus	Gruis	Gru	Crane
Hercules	Herculis	Her	Hercules
Horologium	Horologii	Hor	Clock
Hydra	Hydrae	Hya	Hydra, Greek monster
Hydrus	Hydri	Hyi	Sea Serpent
Indus	Indi	Ind	Indian
Lacerta	Lacertae	Lac	Lizard
Leo	Leonis	Leo	Lion
Leo Minor	Leonis Minoris	LMi	Little Lion

Constellation	Genitive	Abbreviation	Meaning
Lepus	Leporis	Lep	Hare
Libra	Librae	Lib	Scales
Lupus	Lupi	Lup	Wolf
Lynx	Lyncis	Lyn	Lynx
Lyra	Lyrae	Lyr	Lyre or Harp
Mensa	Mensae	Men	Table Mountain
Microscopium	Microscopii	Mic	Microscope
Monoceros	Monocerotis	Mon	Unicorn
Musca	Muscae	Mus	Fly
Norma	Normae	Nor	Carpenter's Square
Octans	Octanis	Oct	Octant
Ophiuchus	Ophiuchi	Oph	Serpent Bearer
Orion	Orionis	Ori	Orion, the Hunter
Pavo	Pavonis	Pav	Peacock
Pegasus	Pegasi	Peg	Winged Horse
Perseus	Persei	Per	Perseus, a Greek hero
Phoenix	Phoenicis	Phe	Phoenix
Pictor	Pictoris	Pic	Painter
Pisces	Piscium	Psc	Fish
Piscis Austrinus	Piscis Austrini	PsA	Southern Fish
Puppis	Puppis	Pup	Ship's Stern
Pyxis	Pyxidis	Pyx	Ship's Compass
Reticulum	Reticuli	Ret	Net
Sagitta	Sagittae	Sge	Arrow
Sagittarius	Sagittarii	Sgr	Archer
Scorpius	Scorpii	Sco	Scorpion
Sculptor	Sculptoris	Scl	Sculptor
Scutum	Scuti	Sct	Shield
Serpens	Serpentis	Ser	Serpent
Sextans	Sextantis	Sex	Sextant
Taurus	Tauri	Tau	Bull
Telescopium	Telescopii	Tel	Telescope
Triangulum	Trianguli	Tri	Triangle
Triangulum	Triangli Australis	TrA	Southern Australe Triangle
Tucana	Tucanae	Tuc	Toucan
Ursa Major	Ursae Majoris	UMa	Big Bear
Ursa Minor	Ursae Minoris	UMi	Little Bear
Vela	Velorum	Vel	Ship's Sail
Virgo	Virginis	Vir	Virgin
Volans	Volantis	Vol	Flying Fish
Vulpecula	Vulpeculae	Vul	Little Fox

Which **star** is the **closest to Earth**?

The sun, at a distance of 92,955,900 miles (149,598,000 kilometers), is the closest star to the Earth. After the sun, the closest stars are the members of the triple star system known as Alpha Centauri (Alpha Centauri A, Alpha Centauri B, and Alpha Centauri C, sometimes called Proxima Centauri). They are 4.3 light years away.

How **hot** is the sun?

The center of the sun is about 27,000,000°F (15,000,000°C). The surface, or photosphere, of the sun is about 10,000°F (5,500°C). Magnetic anomalies in the photosphere cause cooler regions that appear to be darker than the surrounding surface. These sunspots are about 6,700°F (4,000°C). The sun's layer of lower atmosphere, the chromosphere, is only a few thousand miles thick. At the base, the chromosphere is about 7,800°F (4,300°C), but its temperature rises with altitude to the corona, the sun's outer layer of atmosphere, which has a temperature of about 1,800,000°F (1,000,000°C).

What is the **sun** made of?

The sun is an incandescent ball of gases. Its mass is 1.8 × 1027 tons or 1.8 octillion tons (a mass 330,000 times as great as the Earth).

Element	% of mass
Hydrogen	73.46
Helium	24.85
Oxygen	0.77
Carbon	0.29
Iron	0.16
Neon	0.12
Nitrogen	0.09
Silicon	0.07
Magnesium	0.05
Sulfur	0.04
Other	0.10

When will the **sun die**?

The sun is approximately 4.5 billion years old. About five billion years from now, the sun will have burned all of its hydrogen fuel into helium. As this process occurs, the sun will change from the yellow dwarf as we know it to a red giant. Its diameter will extend well beyond the orbit of Venus, and even possibly beyond the orbit of Earth. In either case, the Earth will be burned to a cinder.

What is the **ecliptic**?

Ecliptic refers to the apparent yearly path of the sun through the sky with respect to the stars. In the spring, the ecliptic in the northern hemisphere is angled high in the evening sky. In fall, the ecliptic lies much closer to the horizon.

How long does it take **light from the sun** to **reach the Earth**?

Sunlight takes about eight minutes and 20 seconds to reach the Earth, traveling at 186,282 miles (299,792 kilometers) per second, although it varies with the position of the Earth in its orbit. In January the light takes about 495 seconds to reach the Earth; in July the trip takes about 505 seconds.

How long is a **solar cycle**?

The solar cycle is the periodic change in the number of sunspots. The cycle is taken as the interval between successive minima and is about 11.1 years long. During an entire cycle, solar flares, sunspots, and other magnetic phenomena move from intense activity to relative calm and back again. The solar cycle is one area of study to be carried out by up to 10 ATLAS space missions designed to probe the chemistry and physics of the atmosphere. These studies of the solar cycle will yield a more detailed picture of the Earth's atmosphere and its response to changes in the sun.

What is the **sunspot cycle**?

It is the fluctuating number of sunspots on the sun during an 11-year period. The variation in the number of sunspots seems to correspond with the increase or decrease in the number of solar flares. An increased number of sunspots means an increased number of solar flares.

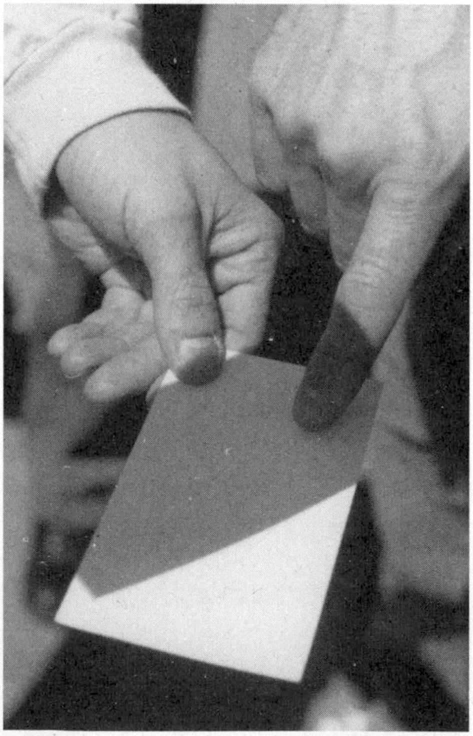

A simple pinhole camera can be used to focus the image of a solar eclipse for safe viewing.

When do **solar eclipses** happen?

A solar eclipse occurs when the moon passes between the Earth and the sun and all three bodies are aligned in the same plane. When the moon completely blocks Earth's view of the sun and the umbra, or dark part of the moon's shadow, reaches the Earth, a total eclipse occurs. A total eclipse happens only along a narrow path 100 to 200 miles (160 to 320 kilometers) wide called the track of totality. Just before totality, the only parts of the sun that are visible are a few points of light called Baily's beads shining through valleys on the moon's surface. Sometimes, a

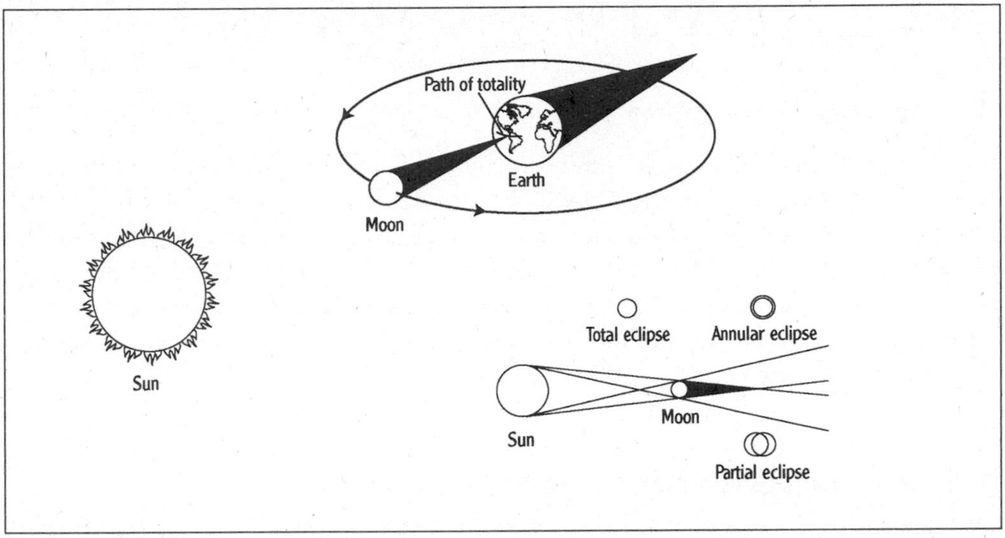

Solar eclipse.

last bright flash of sunlight is seen—the diamond ring effect. During totality, which averages 2.5 minutes but may last up to 7.5 minutes, the sky is dark and stars and other planets are easily seen. The corona, the sun's outer atmosphere, is also visible.

If the moon does not appear large enough in the sky to completely cover the sun, it appears silhouetted against the sun with a ring of sunlight showing around it. This is an annular eclipse. Because the sun is not completely covered, its corona cannot be seen, and although the sky may darken it will not be dark enough to see the stars.

During a partial eclipse of the sun, the penumbra of the moon's shadow strikes the Earth. A partial eclipse can also be seen on either side of the track of totality of an annular or total eclipse. The moon will cover part of the sun and the sky will not darken noticeably during a partial eclipse.

What is **solar wind**?

Solar wind is caused by the expansion of gases in the sun's outermost atmosphere, the corona. Because of the corona's extremely high temperature of 1,800,000°F (1,000,000°C), the gases heat up and their atoms start to collide. The atoms lose electrons and become electrically charged ions. These ions create the solar wind. Solar wind has a velocity of 310 miles (500 kilometers) per second, and its density is approximately 82 ions per cubic inch (five ions per cubic centimeter). Because the Earth is surrounded by strong magnetic forces, its magnetosphere, it is protected from the solar wind particles. In 1959, the Soviet spacecraft *Luna 2* acknowledged the existence of solar wind and made the first measurements of its properties.

PLANETS AND MOONS

How **old** is the **solar system**?

It is currently believed to be 4.5 billion years old. The Earth and the rest of the solar system formed from an immense cloud of gas and dust. Gravity and rotational forces caused the cloud to flatten into a disc and much of the cloud's mass to drift into the center. This material became the sun. The leftover parts of the cloud formed small bodies called planetesimals. These planetesimals collided with each other, gradually forming larger and larger bodies, some of which became the planets. This process is thought to have taken about 25 million years.

How **far** are the **planets** from the sun?

The planets revolve around the sun in elliptical orbits, with the sun at one focus of the ellipse. Thus, a planet is at times closer to the sun than at other times. The distances given below are the average distance from the sun, starting with Mercury, the planet closest to the sun, and moving outward.

Planet	Average distance (miles)	Average distance (km)
Mercury	35,983,000	57,909,100
Venus	67,237,700	108,208,600
Earth	92,955,900	149,598,000
Mars	141,634,800	227,939,200
Jupiter	483,612,200	778,298,400
Saturn	888,184,000	1,427,010,000
Uranus	1,782,000,000	2,869,600,000
Neptune	2,794,000,000	4,496,700,000
Pluto	3,666,000,000	5,913,490,000

Which **planets** have **rings**?

Jupiter, Saturn, Uranus, and Neptune all have rings. Jupiter's rings were discovered by Voyager 1 in March 1979. The rings extend 80,240 miles (129,130 kilometers) from the center of the planet. They are about 4,300 miles (7,000 kilometers) in width and less than 20 miles (30 kilometers) thick. A faint inner ring is believed to extend to the edge of Jupiter's atmosphere. Saturn has the largest, most spectacular set of rings in the solar system. That the planet is surrounded by a ring system was first recognized by the Dutch astronomer Christiaan Huygens (1629-1695) in 1659. Saturn's rings are 169,800 miles (273,200 kilometers) in diameter, but less

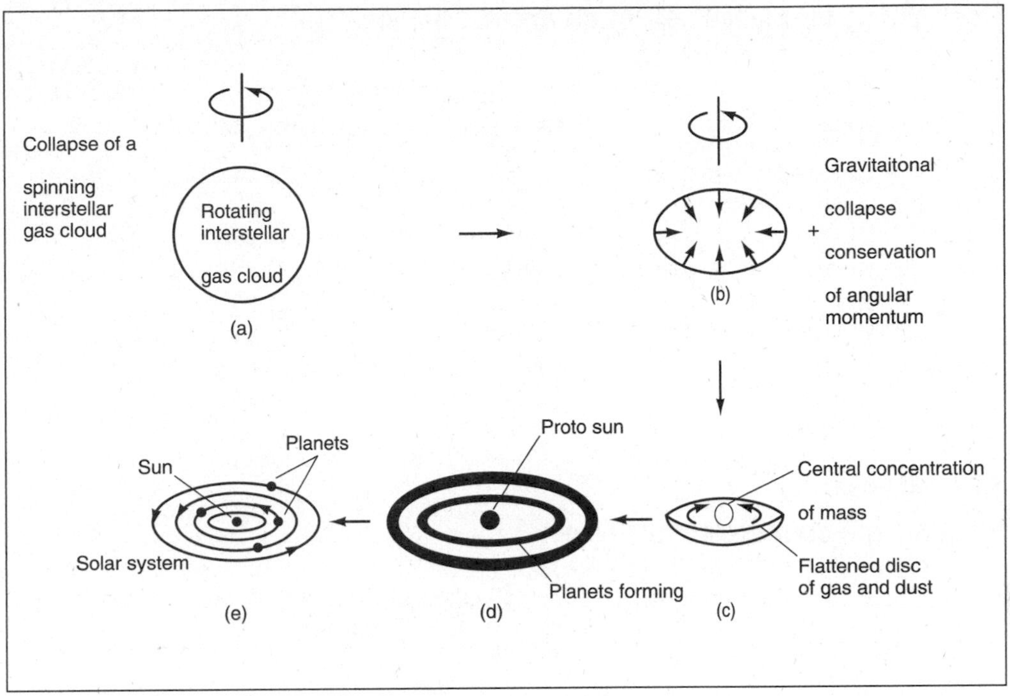

The evolution of the solar system from a gas cloud (a) to its present-day structure (e).

than 10 miles (16 kilometers) thick. There are six different rings, the largest of which appear to be divided into thousands of ringlets. The rings appear to be composed of pieces of water ice ranging in size from tiny grains to blocks several tens of yards in diameter.

In 1977 when Uranus occulted (passed in front of) a star, scientists observed that the light from the star flickered or winked several times before the planet itself covered the star. The same flickering occurred in reverse order after the occultation. The reason for this was determined to be a ring around Uranus. Nine rings were initially identified, and Voyager 2 observed two more in 1986. The rings are thin, narrow, and very dark.

Voyager 2 also discovered a series of at least four rings around Neptune in 1989. Some of the rings appear to have arcs, areas where there is a higher density of material than at other parts of the ring.

How **thick** are **Saturn's rings**?

Saturn's large rings are actually composed of thousands of smaller rings. The thickness of the rings varies, with some rings less than one hundred meters thick.

How long do the planets take **to go around the sun**?

Planet	Period of revolution Earth days	Earth years
Mercury	88	0.24
Venus	224.7	0.62
Earth	365.26	1.00
Mars	687	1.88
Jupiter	4,332.6	11.86
Saturn	10,759.2	29.46
Uranus	30,685.4	84.01
Neptune	60,189	164.8
Pluto	90,777.6	248.53

What are the **diameters** of the planets?

Planet	Diameter Miles	Kilometers
Mercury	3,031	4,878
Venus	7,520	12,104
Earth	7,926	12,756
Mars	4,221	6,794
Jupiter	88,846	142,984
Saturn	74,898	120,536
Uranus	31,763	51,118
Neptune	31,329	50,530
Pluto	1,423	2,290

Note: All diameters are as measured at the planet's equator.

What are the **colors** of the **planets**?

Planet	Color
Mercury	Orange
Venus	Yellow
Earth	Blue, brown, green
Mars	Red
Jupiter	Yellow, red, brown, white
Saturn	Yellow
Uranus	Green
Neptune	Blue
Pluto	Yellow

Who discovered Saturn's rings?

In 1610, Galileo was probably the first to discover Saturn's rings. Because his telescope was small, Galileo could not see the rings properly and assumed they were satellites. In 1656, Christiaan Huygens discovered a ring around Saturn with a more powerful telescope. Later, in 1675, Jean Domenique Cassini distinguished two rings around Saturn. Still later, more rings were discovered and, as recently as 1980, ringlets were observed.

What is the **gravitational force** on each of the planets, the moon, and the sun relative to the Earth?

If the gravitational force on the Earth is taken as 1, the comparative forces are:

Sun	27.9
Mercury	0.37
Venus	0.88
Earth	1.00
Moon	0.16
Mars	0.38
Jupiter	2.64
Saturn	1.15
Uranus	0.93
Neptune	1.22
Pluto	0.06

Weight comparisons can be made by using this table. If a person weighed 100 pounds (45.36 kilograms) on Earth, then the weight of the person on the Moon would be 16 pounds (7.26 kilograms) or 100×0.16.

What is **sidereal time**?

Sidereal time is measured by considering the rotation of the Earth relative to the distant stars (rather than the sun, which is the basis of civil time). A sidereal day is 23 hours, 56 minutes, and 4 seconds, nearly 4 minutes shorter than mean solar time.

Is a **day** the same on all the planets?

No. A day, the period of time it takes for a planet to make one complete turn on its axis, varies from planet to planet. Venus, Uranus, and Pluto display retrograde motion;

that is to say, they rotate in the opposite direction from the other planets. The table below lists the length of the day for each planet.

Planet	Earth days	Length of day Hours	Minutes
Mercury	58	15	30
Venus	243		32
Earth		23	56
Mars		24	37
Jupiter		9	50
Saturn		10	39
Uranus		17	14
Neptune		16	3
Pluto	6	9	18

What are the **Jovian** and **terrestrial planets**?

Jupiter, Saturn, Uranus, and Neptune are the Jovian (the adjectival form for the word "Jupiter"), or Jupiter-like, planets. They are giant planets, composed primarily of light elements such as hydrogen and helium.

Mercury, Venus, Earth, and Mars are the terrestrial (derived from "terra," the Latin word for "earth"), or Earth-like, planets. They are small in size, have solid surfaces, and are composed of rocks and iron. Pluto appears to be a terrestrial-type planet as well, but it may have a different origin from the other planets.

What is unique about the **rotation** of the **planet Venus**?

Unlike Earth and most of the other planets, Venus rotates in a retrograde, or opposite, direction with relation to its orbital motion about the sun. It rotates so slowly that only two sunrises and sunsets occur each Venusian year. Uranus and Pluto's rotation are also retrograde.

Is it true that the **rotation speed of the Earth** varies?

The rotation speed is at its maximum in late July and early August and at its minimum in April; the difference in the length of the day is about 0.0012 second. Since about 1900 the Earth's rotation has been slowing at a rate of approximately 1.7 seconds per year. In the geologic past the Earth's rotational period was much faster; days were shorter and there were more days in the year. About 350 million years ago, the year had 400 to 410 days; 280 million years ago, a year was 390 days long.

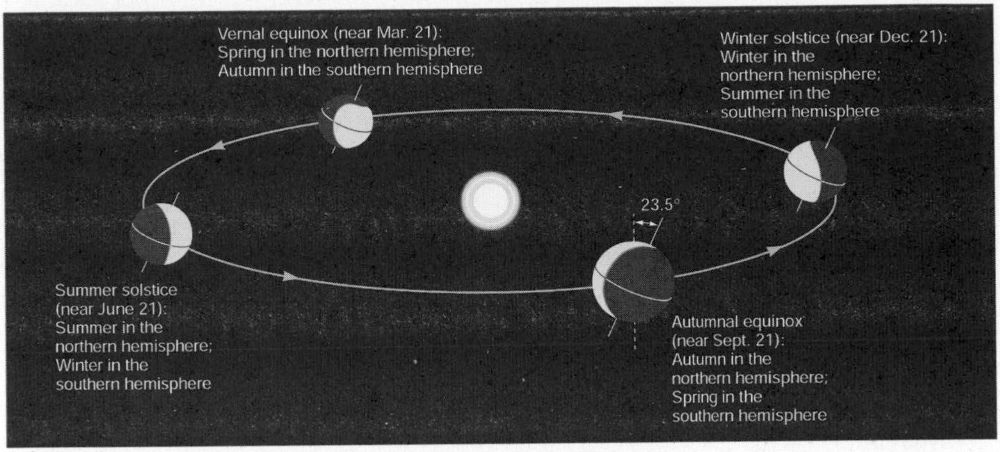

The seasons.

Is it true that the **Earth is closer to the sun in winter** than in summer in the northern hemisphere?

Yes. However, the Earth's axis, the line around which the planet rotates, is tipped 23.5° with respect to the plane of revolution around the sun. When the Earth is closest to the sun (its perihelion, about January 3), the northern hemisphere is tilted away from the sun. This causes winter in the northern hemisphere while the southern hemisphere is having summer. When the Earth is farthest from the sun (its aphelion, around July 4), the situation is reversed, with the northern hemisphere tilted towards the sun. At this time, it is summer in the northern hemisphere and winter in the southern hemisphere.

What is the **circumference** of the **Earth**?

The Earth is an oblate ellipsoid—a sphere slightly flattened at the poles and bulging at the equator. The distance around the Earth at the equator is 24,902 miles (40,075 kilometers). The distance around the Earth through the poles is 24,860 miles (40,008 kilometers).

What is the **precession** of the **equinoxes**?

The "precession of the equinoxes" is the 26,000-year circular movement of the Earth's axis. It is caused by the bulging at the equator, which makes the Earth's axis twist in such a way that the North and South Poles complete a circle every 26,000 years. Every year when the sun crosses the equator at the time of the equinox, it is in a slightly different position than the previous year. This movement proceeds eastward until a circle is completed.

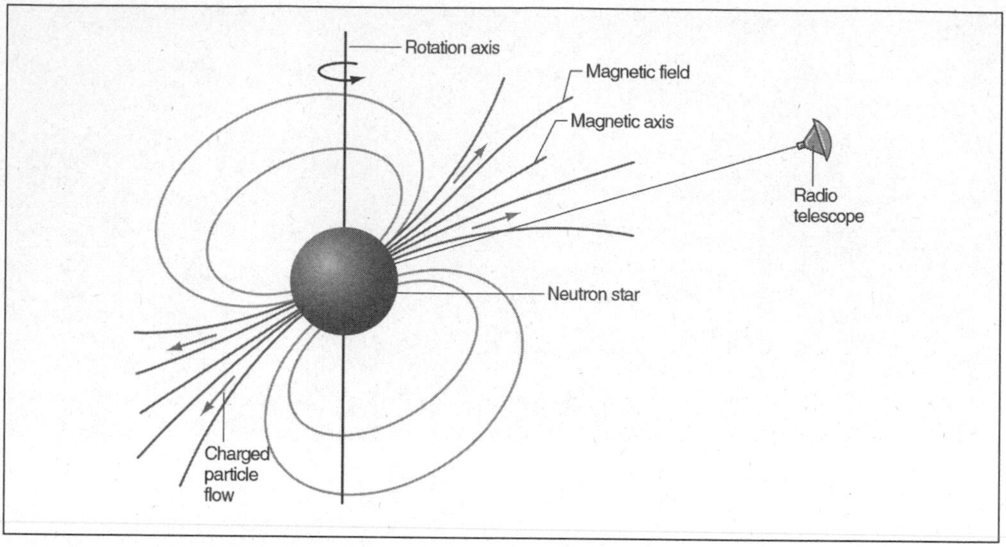

The precessional motion of the Earth.

Is it true that **Pluto** is not always the **outermost planet** in the solar system?

Pluto's very eccentric orbit carried it inside Neptune's orbit on January 23, 1979. It remained there until March 15, 1999. During that time, Neptune was the outermost planet in the solar system. However, because they are so far apart, the planets are in no danger of colliding with one another.

Pluto, discovered in 1930 by American astronomer Clyde Tombaugh (b. 1906), was considered the smallest planet in the solar system until it was recategorized as a planetoid in 2006. It is composed of rock and ice, with methane ice on the surface and a thin methane atmosphere. Pluto's single moon, Charon, discovered by James Christy in 1978, has a diameter of 741 miles (1,192 kilometers). This makes Charon, at half the size of Pluto, a very large moon relative to the planet. Some astronomers consider Pluto and Charon to be a double planet system.

What is **Planet X**?

Astronomers have observed perturbations, or disturbances, in the orbits of Uranus and Neptune since the discoveries of both planets. They speculated that Uranus and Neptune were being influenced by the gravity of another celestial body. Pluto, discovered in 1930, does not appear to be large enough to cause these disturbances. The existence of another planet, known as Planet X, orbiting beyond Pluto, has been proposed. As yet there have been no sightings of this tenth planet, but the search continues. There is a possibility that the unmanned space probes Pioneer 10 & 11 and Voyager 1 & 2, now heading out of the solar system, will be able to locate this elusive object.

What does it mean when a **planet** is said to be **in opposition**?

A body in the solar system is in opposition when its longitude differs from the sun by 180°. In that position, it is exactly opposite the sun in the sky and it crosses the meridian at midnight.

How **far** is the **moon** from the Earth?

Since the moon's orbit is elliptical, its distance varies from about 221,463 miles (356,334 kilometers) at perigee (closest approach to Earth), to 251,968 miles (405,503 kilometers) at apogee (farthest point), with the average distance being 238,857 miles (384,392 kilometers).

How many **moons** does each planet have?

Planet	Number of moons	Names of some of the moons
Mercury	0	
Venus	0	
Earth	1	The Moon (sometimes called Luna)
Mars	2	Phobos, Deimos
Jupiter	39	Metis, Adrastea, Amalthea, Thebe, Io, Europa, Ganymede, Callisto, Leda, Himalia, Lysithia, Elara, Ananke, Carme, Pasiphae, Sinope
Saturn	30	Epimetheus, Janus, Mimas, Enceladus, Tethys, Telesto, Calypso, Dione, Helene, Rhea, Titan, Hyperion, Iapetus, Phoebe
Uranus	20	Cordelia, Ophelia, Bianca, Cressida, Desdemona, Juliet, Portia, Rosalind, Belinda, Puck, Miranda, Ariel, Umbriel, Titania, Oberon
Neptune	8	Naiad, Thalassa, Despina, Galatea, Larissa, Proteus, Triton, Nereid
Pluto	1	Charon

Jupiter has the greatest number of moons. As scientists continue to explore Jupiter they expect to find even more moons. Its four largest moons—Io, Europa, Calisto, and Ganymede—were discovered by Galileo in 1610.

Does the **moon** have an **atmosphere**?

The moon does have an atmosphere; however it is very slight, having a density of about 50 atoms per cubic centimeter.

What are the **diameter** and **circumference** of the **moon**?

The moon's diameter is 2,159 miles (3,475 kilometers) and its circumference is 6,790 miles (10,864 kilometers). The moon is 27 percent the size of the Earth.

What are the **phases of the moon**?

The phases of the moon are changes in the moon's appearance during the month, which are caused by the moon's turning different portions of its illuminated hemisphere towards the Earth. When the moon is between the Earth and the sun, its daylight side is turned away from the Earth, so it is not seen. This is called the new moon. As the moon continues its revolution around the Earth, more and more of its surface becomes visible. This is called the waxing crescent phase. About a week after the new moon, half the moon is visible—the first quarter phase. During the next week, more than half of the moon is seen; this is called the waxing gibbous phase. Finally, about two weeks after the new moon, the moon and sun are on opposite sides of the Earth. The side of the moon facing the sun is also facing the Earth, and all the moon's illuminated side is seen as a full moon. In the next two weeks the moon goes through the same phases, but in reverse from a waning gibbous to third or last quarter to waning crescent phase. Gradually, less and less of the moon is visible until a new moon occurs again.

Why does the **moon** always keep the **same face toward the Earth**?

Only one side of the moon is seen because it always rotates in exactly the same length of time that it takes to revolve about the Earth. This combination of motions (called "captured rotation") means that it always keeps the same side toward the Earth.

Is the moon really blue during a **blue moon**?

The term "blue moon," the second full moon in a single month, does not refer to the color of the moon. A blue moon occurs, on average, every 2.72 years. Since 29.53 days pass between full moons (a synodial month), there is never a blue moon in February. On rare occasions, a blue moon can be seen twice in one year, but only in certain parts of the world. Blue moons will next occur:

Upcoming Blue Moons

December 31, 2009	October 31, 2020
August 31, 2012	August 31, 2023
July 31, 2015	May 31, 2026
January 31, 2018	December 31, 2028
March 31, 2018	

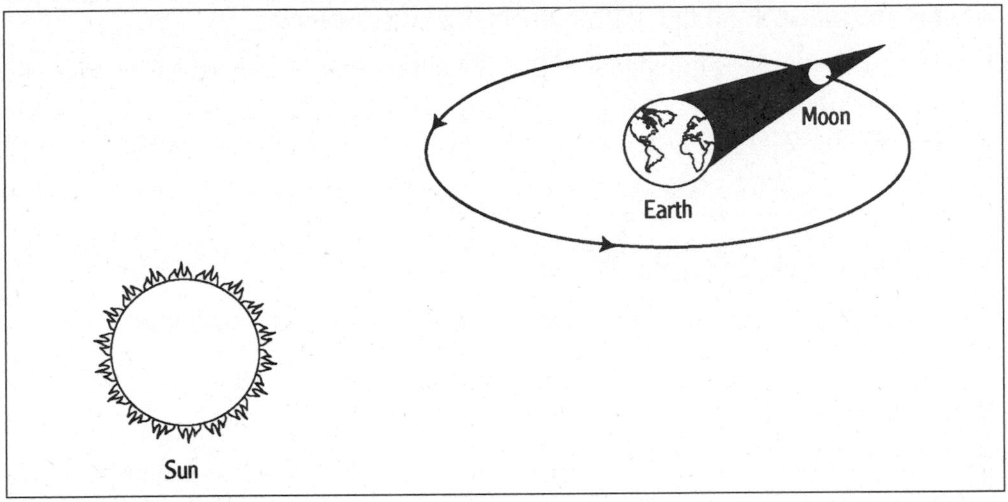

Lunar eclipse.

A bluish-looking moon can result from effects of the Earth's atmosphere. For example, the phenomenon was widely observed in North America on September 26, 1950, due to Canadian forest fires that had scattered high-altitude dust.

What is the difference between a **hunter's moon** and a **harvest moon**?

The harvest moon is the full moon nearest the autumnal equinox (on or about September 23). It is followed by a period of several successive days when the moon rises soon after sunset. In the southern hemisphere the harvest moon is the full moon closest to the vernal equinox (on or about March 21). This gives farmers extra hours of light for harvesting crops. The next full moon after the harvest moon is called the hunter's moon.

Why do **lunar eclipses** happen?

A lunar eclipse occurs only during a full moon when the moon is on one side of the Earth, the sun is on the opposite side, and all three bodies are aligned in the same plane. In this alignment the Earth blocks the sun's rays to cast a shadow on the moon. In a total lunar eclipse the moon seems to disappear from the sky when the whole moon passes through the umbra, or total shadow, created by the Earth. A total lunar eclipse may last up to one hour and 40 minutes. If only part of the moon enters the umbra, a partial eclipse occurs. A penumbral eclipse takes place if all or part of the moon passes through the penumbra (partial shadow or "shade") without touching the umbra. It is difficult to detect this type of eclipse from Earth. From the moon one could see that the Earth blocked only part of the sun.

What is the **moon's tail** that astronomers have discovered?

A glowing 15,000 mile (24,000 kilometer) long tail of sodium atoms streams from the moon. The faint, orange glow of sodium cannot be seen by the naked eye but it is detectable with the use of instruments. Astronomers are not certain of the source of these sodium atoms.

What is the **largest crater** on the moon?

The largest crater on the moon is Bailly. Its diameter is 184 miles (296 km).

What is the **Genesis rock**?

The Genesis rock is a lunar rock brought to Earth by Apollo 15. It is approximately 4.15 billion years old, which is only 0.5 billion years younger than the generally accepted age of the moon.

COMETS, METEORITES, ETC.

Where are **asteroids** found?

The asteroids, also called the minor planets, are smaller than any of the nine major planets in the solar system and are not satellites of any major planet. The term asteroid means "starlike" because asteroids appear to be points of light when seen through a telescope.

Most asteroids are located between Mars and Jupiter, between 2.1 and 3.3 AUs (astronomical units) from the sun. Ceres, the largest and first to be discovered, was found by Giuseppe Piazzi on January 1, 1801, and has a diameter of 582 miles (936 kilometers). A second asteroid, Pallas, was discovered in 1802. Since then, astronomers have identified more than 18,000 asteroids and have established orbits for about 5,000 of them. Some of these have diameters of only 0.62 mile (one kilometer). Originally, astronomers thought the asteroids were remnants of a planet that had been destroyed; now they believe asteroids to be material that never became a planet, possibly because it was affected by Jupiter's strong gravity.

Not all asteroids are in this main asteroid belt. Three groups reside in the inner solar system. The Aten asteroids have orbits that lie primarily inside Earth's orbit. However, at their farthest point from the sun, these asteroids may cross Earth's orbit. The Apollo asteroids cross Earth's orbit; some come even closer than the moon. The Amor asteroids cross the orbit of Mars, and some come close to Earth's orbit. The Trojan asteroids move in virtually the same orbit as Jupiter but at points 60° ahead or 60°

behind the planet. In 1977 Charles Kowal discovered an object now known as Chiron orbiting between Saturn and Uranus. Originally cataloged as an asteroid, Chiron was later observed to have a coma (a gaseous halo), and it may be reclassified as a comet.

What was the **Tunguska Event**?

On June 30, 1908, a violent explosion occurred in the atmosphere over the Podkamennaya Tunguska River in a remote part of central Siberia. The blast's consequences were similar to an H-bomb going off, leveling thousands of square miles of forest. The shock of the explosion was heard more than 600 miles (960 kilometers) away. A number of theories have been proposed to account for this event.

Some people thought that a large meteorite or a piece of anti-matter had fallen to Earth. But a meteorite, composed of rock and metal, would have created a crater and none was found at the impact site. There are no high radiation levels in the area that would have resulted from the collision of anti-matter and matter. Two other theories include a mini-black hole striking the Earth or the crash of an extraterrestrial spaceship. However, a mini-black hole would have passed through the Earth and there is no record of a corresponding explosion on the other side of the world. As for the spaceship, no wreckage of such a craft was ever found.

The most likely cause of the explosion was the entry into the atmosphere of a piece of a comet, which would have produced a large fireball and blast wave. Since a comet is composed primarily of ice, the fragment would have melted during its passage through the Earth's atmosphere, leaving no impact crater and no debris. Since the Tunguska Event coincided with the Earth's passage through the orbit of Comet Encke, the explosion could have been caused by a piece of that comet.

From where do **comets** originate?

According to a theory developed by Dutch astronomer Jan Oort, there is a large cloud of gas, dust, and comets orbiting beyond Pluto out to perhaps 100,000 astronomical units (AU). Occasional stars passing close to this cloud disturb some of the comets from their orbits. Some fall inwards towards the sun.

Comets, sometimes called "dirty snowballs," are made up mostly of ice, with some dust mixed in. When a comet moves closer to the sun, the dust and ice of the core, or nucleus, heats up, producing a tail of material that trails along behind it. The tail is pushed out by the solar wind and almost always points away from the sun.

Most comets have highly elliptical orbits that carry them around the sun and then fling them back out to the outer reaches of the solar system, never to return. Occasionally, however, a close passage by a comet near one of the planets can alter a comet's orbit, making it stay in the middle or inner solar system. Such a comet is called a short-period comet because it passes close to the sun at regular intervals. The

Edmund Halley observed the comet that bears his name in 1682 and predicted its return every 76 years based upon earlier recorded sightings.

most famous short-period comet is Comet Halley, which reaches perihelion (the point in its orbit that is closest to the sun) about every 76 years. Comet Encke, with an orbital period of 3.3 years, is another short-period comet.

When will **Halley's comet** return?

Halley's comet returns about every 76 years. It was most recently seen in 1985/1986 and is predicted to appear again in 2061, then in 2134. Every appearance of what is now known as Comet Halley has been noted by astronomers since the year 239 B.C.E.

The comet is named for Edmund Halley (1656-1742), England's second Astronomer Royal. In 1682 he observed a bright comet and noted that it was moving in an orbit similar to comets seen in 1531 and 1607. He concluded that the three comets were actually one and the same and that the comet had an orbit of 76 years. In 1705 Halley published *A Synopsis of the Astronomy of Comets,* in which he predicted that the comet seen in 1531, 1607, and 1682 would return in 1758. On Christmas night, 1758, a German farmer and amateur astronomer named Johann Palitzsch spotted the comet in just the area of the sky that Halley had foretold.

Prior to Halley, comets appeared at irregular intervals and were often thought to be harbingers of disaster and signs of divine wrath. Halley proved that they are natural objects subject to the laws of gravity.

How does a **meteorite** differ from a **meteoroid**?

A meteorite is a natural object of extraterrestrial origin that survives passage through the Earth's atmosphere and hits the Earth's surface. A meteorite is often confused with a meteoroid or a meteor. A meteoroid is a small object in outer space, generally less than 30 feet (10 meters) in diameter. A meteor (sometimes called a shooting star) is the flash of light seen when an object passes through Earth's atmosphere and burns as a result of heating caused by friction. A meteoroid becomes a meteor when it enters the Earth's atmosphere; if any portion of a meteoroid lands on Earth, it is a meteorite.

There are three kinds of meteorites. Irons contain 85 percent to 95 percent iron; the rest of their mass is mostly nickel. Stony irons are relatively rare meteorites composed of about 50 percent iron and 50 percent silicates. Stones are made up mostly of silicates and other stony materials.

When do **meteor showers** occur?

There are a number of groups of meteoroids orbiting the sun just as the Earth is. When Earth's orbit intercepts the path of one of these swarms of meteoroids, some of them enter Earth's atmosphere. When friction with the air causes a meteoroid to burn up, the streak, or shooting star, that is produced is called a meteor. Large numbers of meteors can produce a spectacular shower of light in the night sky. Meteor showers are named for the constellation that occupies the area of the sky from which they originate. Listed below are 10 meteor showers and the dates during the year during which they can be seen.

Name of Shower	Dates
Quadrantids	January 1-6
Lyrids	April 19-24
Eta Aquarids	May 1-8
Perseids	July 25-August 18
Orionids	October 16-26
Taurids	October 20-November 20
Leonids	November 13-17
Phoenicids	December 4-5
Geminids	December 7-15
Ursids	December 17-24

What are the **largest meteorites** that have been found in the world?

The famous Willamette (Oregon) iron, displayed at the American Museum of Natural History in New York, is the largest specimen found in the United States. It is 10 feet (3.048 meters) long and five feet (1.524 meters) high.

		Weight	
Name	Location	Tons	Tonnes
Hoba West	Namibia	66.1	60
Ahnighito (The Tent)	Greenland	33.5	30.4
Bacuberito	Mexico	29.8	27
Mbosi	Tanzania	28.7	26
Agpalik	Greenland	22.2	20.1
Armanty	Outer Mongolia	22	20
Willamette	Oregon, USA	15.4	14
Chupaderos	Mexico	15.4	14

Name	Location	Weight Tons	Tonnes
Campo del Cielo	Argentina	14.3	13
Mundrabilla	Western Australia	13.2	12
Morito	Mexico	12.1	11

How do scientists know that some **meteorites** that were found in Antarctica came **from the Moon**?

Because of the high-quality reference collection of lunar rocks collected during space flights to the moon, the original 1979 meteorite find in Antarctica and the 10 subsequent findings were verified as lunar in origin.

OBSERVATION AND MEASUREMENT

Who is considered the founder of **systematic astronomy**?

The Greek scientist Hipparchus (fl. 146-127 B.C.E.) is considered to be the father of systematic astronomy. He measured as accurately as possible the directions of objects in the sky. He compiled the first catalog of stars, containing about 850 entries, and designated each star's celestial coordinates, indicating its position in the sky. Hipparchus also divided the stars according to their apparent brightness or magnitudes.

What is a **light year**?

A light year is a measure of distance, not time. It is the distance that light, which travels in a vacuum at the rate of 186,282 miles (299,792 kilometers) per second, can travel in a year (365.25 days). This is equal to 5.87 trillion miles (9.46 trillion kilometers).

Besides the light year, what other units are used to measure **distances in astronomy**?

The astronomical unit (AU) is often used to measure distances within the solar system. One AU is equal to the average distance between the Earth and the sun, or 92,955,630 miles (149,597,870 kilometers). The parsec is equal to 3.26 light years, or about 19.18 trillion miles (30.82 trillion kilometers).

What is widely considered to be one of the earliest celestial observatories?

Built in England over a period of years between 2500 and 1700 B.C.E., Stonehenge is one of the earliest observatories or observatory-temples. It is widely believed that its primary function was to observe the mid-summer and mid-winter solstices.

How are **new celestial objects named**?

Many stars and planets have names that date back to antiquity. The International Astronomical Union (IAU), the professional astronomers organization, has attempted, in this century, to standardize names given to newly discovered celestial objects and their surface features.

Stars are generally called by their traditional names, most of which are of Greek, Roman, or Arabic origin. They are also identified by the constellation in which they appear, designated in order of brightness by Greek letters. Thus Sirius is also called alpha Canis Majoris, which means it is the brightest star in the constellation Canis Major. Other stars are called by catalog numbers, which include the star's coordinates. To the horror of many astronomers, several commercial star registries exist, and for a fee you can submit a star name to them. These names are not officially recognized by the IAU.

The IAU has made some recommendations for naming the surface features of the planets and their satellites. For example, features on Mercury are named for composers, poets, and writers; features of Venus for women; and features on Saturn's moon Mimas for people and places in Arthurian legend.

Comets are named for their discoverers. Newly discovered asteroids are first given a temporary designation consisting of the year of discovery plus two letters. The first letter indicates the half-month of discovery (A=first half of January, B=second half of January, etc.) and the second the order of discovery in that half-month. Thus asteroid 2002EM was the 13th (M) asteroid discovered in the first half of March (E) in 2002. After an asteroid's orbit is determined, it is given a permanent number and its discoverer is given the honor of naming it. Asteroids have been named after such diverse things as mythological figures (Ceres, Vesta), an airline (Swissair), and the Beatles (Lennon, McCartney, Harrison, Starr).

What is an **astrolabe**?

Invented by the Greeks or Alexandrians around 100 B.C.E. or before, an astrolabe is a two-dimensional working model of the heavens, with sights for observations. It consists of two concentric, flat disks, one fixed, representing the observer on Earth, the other moving, which can be rotated to represent the appearance of the celestial sphere at a given moment. Given latitude, date, and time, the observer can read off the altitude and azimuth of the sun, the brightest stars, and the planets. By measuring the altitude of a particular body, one can find the time. The astrolabe can also be used to find times of sunrise, sunset, twilight, or the height of a tower or depth of a well. After 1600, it was replaced by the sextant and other more accurate instruments.

Who invented the **telescope**?

Hans Lippershey (ca. 1570-1619), a German-Dutch lens grinder and spectacle maker, is generally credited with inventing the telescope in 1608 because he was the first scientist to apply for a patent. Two other inventors, Zacharias Janssen and Jacob Metius, also developed telescopes. Modern historians consider Lippershey and Janssen as the two likely candidates for the title of inventor of the telescope, with Lippershey possessing the strongest claim. Lippershey used his telescope for observing grounded objects from a distance.

In 1609, Galileo also developed his own refractor telescope for astronomical studies. Although small by today's standards, the telescope enabled Galileo to observe the Milky Way and to identify blemishes on the moon's surface as craters.

What are the differences between **reflecting** and **refracting telescopes**?

Reflecting telescopes capture light using a mirror while refracting telescopes capture light with a lens. The advantages of reflecting telescopes are: 1) they collect light with a mirror so there is no color fringing, and 2) since a mirror can be supported at the back there is no size limit. In an effort to alleviate the problem of color fringing always associated with lenses, Newton built a reflecting telescope in 1668 that collected light with mirrors.

What is the **Very Large Array** (VLA) and what information have we learned from it?

The Very Large Array (VLA) is one of the world's premier astronomical radio observatories. The VLA consists of 27 antennas arranged in a huge Y pattern up to 36km (22 miles) across—roughly one-and-a-half times the size of Washington, D.C. Each antenna is 25 meters (81 feet) in diameter; they are combined electronically to give the resolution of an antenna 36km (22 miles) across, with the sensitivity of a dish 130 meters (422 feet) in diameter. Each of the 27 radio telescopes in the VLA is the size of a house and can be moved on train tracks. In its twenty-second year of operation, the VLA has been one of the most productive observatories with more than 2,200 scientists using it for more than 10,000 separate observing projects. The VLA has been used to discover water on the planet Mercury, radio-bright coronae around ordinary stars, micro-

A series of radio telescope dishes make up the Very Large Array in New Mexico.

quasars in our galaxy, gravitationally induced Einstein rings around distant galaxies, and radio counterparts to cosmologically distant gamma-ray bursts. The vast size of the VLA has allowed astronomers to study the details of super-fast cosmic jets, and even map the center of our galaxy.

Who is the **Hubble** for whom the **space telescope** is named?

Edwin Powell Hubble (1889-1953) was an American astronomer known for his studies of galaxies. His study of nebulae, or clouds—the faint, unresolved luminous patches in the sky—showed that some of them were large groups of many stars. Hubble classified galaxies by their shapes as being spiral, elliptical, or irregular.

Hubble's Law establishes a relationship between the velocity of recession of a galaxy and its distance. The speed at which a galaxy is moving away from our solar system (measured by its redshift, the shift of its light to longer wavelengths, presumed to be caused by the Doppler effect) is directly proportional to the galaxy's distance from it.

The Hubble Space Telescope was deployed by the space shuttle Discovery on April 25, 1990. The telescope, which would be free of distortions caused by the Earth's atmosphere, was designed to see deeper into space than any telescope on land. However, on June 27, 1990, the National Aeronautics and Space Administration announced that the telescope had a defect in one of its mirrors that prevented it from properly focusing. Although other instruments, including one designed to make observations in ultraviolet light, were still operating, nearly 40 percent of the telescope's experiments had to be postponed until repairs were made. On December 2, 1993, astronauts were able to make the necessary repairs. Four of Hubble's six gyroscopes were replaced as well as two solar panels. Hubble's primary camera, which had a flawed mirror, was also replaced. Since that mission four other servicing missions have been conducted, dramatically improving the HST's capabilities.

EXPLORATION

Who was the first person to propose **space rockets**?

In 1903, Konstantin E. Tsiolkovsky, a Russian high school teacher, completed the first scientific paper on the use of rockets for space travel. Several years later, Robert H. Goddard of the United States and Herman Oberth of Germany awakened wider scientific interest in space travel. These three men worked individually on many of the technical problems of rocketry and space travel. They are known, therefore, as the "fathers of space flight." In 1919, Goddard wrote the paper, "A Method of Reaching Extreme Altitudes," which explained how rockets could be used to explore the upper atmosphere and described a way to send a rocket to the moon. During the 1920s Tsiolkovsky wrote a series of new studies that included detailed descriptions of multi-stage rockets. In 1923, Oberth wrote "The Rocket into Interplanetary Space," which discussed the technical problems of space flight and also described what a spaceship would be like.

What is the difference between **zero-gravity** and **microgravity**?

Zero-gravity is the absence of gravity; a condition in which the effects of gravity are not felt; weightlessness. Microgravity is a condition of very low gravity, especially approaching weightlessness. On a spaceship, while in zero- or microgravity, objects would fall freely and float weightlessly. Both terms, however, are technically incorrect. The gravitation in orbit is only slightly less than the gravitation on the earth. A spacecraft and its contents continuously fall toward earth. It is the spacecraft's immense forward speed that appears to make the earth's surface curve away as the vehicle falls toward it. The continuous falling seems to eliminate the weight of everything inside the spacecraft. For this reason, the condition is sometimes referred to as weightlessness or zero-gravity.

What is meant by the phrase **"greening of the galaxy"**?

The expression means the spreading of human life, technology, and culture through interstellar space and eventually across the entire Milky Way galaxy, the Earth's home galaxy.

Is anyone looking for extraterrestrial life?

A program called SETI (the Search for Extraterrestrial Intelligence) began in 1960, when American astronomer Frank Drake (b. 1930) spent three months at the National Radio Astronomy Observatory in Green Bank, West Virginia, searching for radio signals coming from the nearby stars Tau Ceti and Epsilon Eridani. Although no signals were detected and scientists interested in SETI have often been ridiculed, support for the idea of seeking out intelligent life in the universe has grown.

Project Sentinel, which used a radio dish at Harvard University's Oak Ridge Observatory in Massachusetts, could monitor 128,000 channels at a time. This project was upgraded in 1985 to META (Megachannel Extraterrestrial Assay), thanks in part to a donation by filmmaker Steven Spielberg. Project META is capable of receiving 8.4 million channels. NASA began a 10-year search in 1992 using radio telescopes in Arecibo, Puerto Rico, and Barstow, California.

Scientists are searching for radio signals that stand out from the random noises caused by natural objects. Such signals might repeat at regular intervals or contain mathematical sequences. There are millions of radio channels and a lot of sky to be examined. As of October 1995, Project BETA (Billion-channel Extraterrestrial Assay) has been scanning a quarter of a billion channels. This new design improves upon Project META 300-fold, making the challenge of scanning millions of radio channels seem less daunting. SETI has since developed other projects, some "piggybacking" on radio telescopes while engaged in regular uses. A program launched in 1999, SETI@HOME, uses the power of home computers while they are at rest.

When was the **Outer Space Treaty** signed?

The United Nations Outer Space Treaty was signed on January 23, 1967. The treaty provides a framework for the exploration and sharing of outer space. It governs the outer space activities of nations that wish to exploit and make use of space, the moon, and other celestial bodies. It is based on a humanist and pacifist philosophy and on the principle of the nonappropriation of space and the freedom that all nations have to explore and use space. A very large number of countries have signed this agreement, including those from the Western alliance, the former Eastern bloc, and non-aligned countries.

Space law, or those rules governing the space activities of various countries, international organizations, and private industries, has been evolving since 1957, when the General Assembly of the United Nations created the Committee on the Peaceful Uses of Outer Space (COPUOS). One of its subcommittees was instrumental in drawing up the 1967 Outer Space Treaty.

Russian Air Force Major Yuri Gagarin became the first man in space on April 12, 1961.

Who was the **first man in space**?

Yuri Gagarin (1934-1968), a Soviet cosmonaut, became the first man in space when he made a full orbit of the Earth in *Vostok I* on April 12, 1961. Gagarin's flight lasted only one hour and 48 minutes, but as the first man in space, he became an international hero. Partly because of this Soviet success, U.S. President John F. Kennedy (1917-1963) announced on May 25, 1961, that the United States would land a man on the moon before the end of the decade. The United States took its first step toward that goal when it launched the first American into orbit on February 20, 1962. Astronaut John H. Glenn Jr. (b. 1921) completed three orbits in *Friendship 7* and traveled about 81,000 miles (130,329 kilometers). Prior to this, on May 5, 1961, Alan B. Shepard Jr. (b. 1923) became the first American to pilot a spaceflight, aboard *Freedom 7.* This suborbital flight reached an altitude of 116.5 miles (187.45 kilometers).

What did NASA mean when it said ***Voyager 1*** and ***2*** would take a "grand tour" of the planets?

Once every 176 years the giant outer planets—Jupiter, Saturn, Uranus, and Neptune—align themselves in such a pattern that a spacecraft launched from Earth to Jupiter at just the right time might be able to visit the other three planets on the same mission. A technique called "gravity assist" used each planet's gravity as a power boost to point *Voyager* toward the next planet. The first opportune year for the "grand tour" was 1977.

Which astronauts have **walked on the moon**?

Twelve astronauts have walked on the moon. Each Apollo flight had a crew of three. One crew member remained in orbit in the command service module (CSM) while the other two actually landed on the moon.

Apollo 11, July 16-24, 1969

Neil A. Armstrong
Edwin E. Aldrin, Jr.
Michael Collins (CSM pilot, did not walk on the moon)

Apollo 12, November 14-24, 1969
- Charles P. Conrad
- Alan L. Bean
- Richard F. Gordon, Jr. (CSM pilot, did not walk on the moon)

Apollo 14, January 31-February 9, 1971
- Alan B. Shepard, Jr.
- Edgar D. Mitchell
- Stuart A. Roosa (CSM pilot, did not walk on the moon)

Apollo 15, July 26-August 7, 1971
- David R. Scott
- James B. Irwin
- Alfred M. Worden (CSM pilot, did not walk on the moon)

Apollo 16, April 16-27, 1972
- John W. Young
- Charles M. Duke, Jr.
- Thomas K. Mattingly, II (CSM pilot, did not walk on the moon)

Apollo 17, December 7-19, 1972
- Eugene A. Cernan
- Harrison H. Schmitt
- Ronald E. Evans (CSM pilot, did not walk on the moon)

When and what was the **first animal** sent into orbit?

A small female dog named Laika, aboard the Soviet *Sputnik 2,* launched November 3, 1957, was the first animal sent into orbit. This event followed the successful Soviet launch on October 4, 1957, of *Sputnik 1,* the first man-made satellite ever placed in orbit. Laika was placed in a pressurized compartment within a capsule that weighed 1,103 pounds (500 kilograms). After a few days in orbit, she died, and *Sputnik 2* reentered the Earth's atmosphere on April 14, 1958. Some sources list the dog as a Russian samoyed laika named "Kudyavka" or "Limonchik."

What were the **first monkeys** and **chimpanzees** in space?

On a United States *Jupiter* flight on December 12, 1958, a squirrel monkey named Old Reliable was sent into space, but not into orbit. The monkey drowned during recovery.

On another *Jupiter* flight, on May 28, 1959, two female monkeys were sent 300 miles (482.7 kilometers) high. Able was a six-pound (2.7-kilogram) rhesus monkey and Baker was an 11-ounce (0.3-kilogram) squirrel monkey. Both were recovered alive.

Laika made history as the first living creature to orbit the Earth aboard the Soviet *Sputnik 2.*

A chimpanzee named Ham was used on a *Mercury* flight on January 31, 1961. Ham was launched to a height of 157 miles (253 kilometers) into space but did not go into orbit. His capsule reached a maximum speed of 5,857 miles (9,426 kilometers) per hour and landed 422 miles (679 kilometers) downrange in the Atlantic Ocean, where he was recovered unharmed.

On November 29, 1961, the United States placed a chimpanzee named Enos into orbit and recovered him alive after two complete orbits around the Earth. Like the Soviets, who usually used dogs, the United States had to obtain information on the effects of space flight on living beings before they could actually launch a human into space.

Who were the first man and woman to **walk in space**?

On March 18, 1965, the Soviet cosmonaut Alexei Leonov (b. 1934) became the first person to walk in space when he spent 10 minutes outside his *Voskhod 2* spacecraft. The first woman to walk in space was Soviet cosmonaut Svetlana Savitskaya (b. 1947), who, during her second flight aboard the *Soyuz T-12* (July 17, 1984), performed 3.5 hours of extravehicular activity.

The first American to walk in space was Edward White II (1930-1967) from the spacecraft *Gemini 4* on June 3, 1965. White spent 22 minutes floating free attached to the *Gemini* by a lifeline. The photos of White floating in space are perhaps some of the most familiar of all space shots. Kathryn D. Sullivan (b. 1951) became the first American woman to walk in space when she spent 3.5 hours outside the *Challenger* orbiter during the space shuttle mission 41G on October 11, 1984.

American astronaut Bruce McCandless II (b. 1937) performed the first untethered space walk from the space shuttle *Challenger* on February 7, 1984, using an MMU (manual maneuvering unit) backpack.

Who was the **first woman** in space?

Valentina V. Tereshkova-Nikolaeva (b. 1937), a Soviet cosmonaut, was the first woman in space. She was aboard the *Vostok 6,* launched June 16, 1963. She spent three days circling the Earth, completing 48 orbits. Although she had little cosmonaut training, she was an accomplished parachutist and was especially fit for the rigors of space travel.

The United States space program did not put a woman in space until 20 years later when, on June 18, 1983, Sally K. Ride (b. 1951) flew aboard the space shuttle *Challenger* mission STS-7. In 1987, she moved to the administrative side of NASA and was instrumental in issuing the "Ride Report," which recommended future missions and direction for NASA. She retired from NASA in August 1987 to become a research fellow at Stanford University after serving on the Presidential Commission that investigated the *Challenger* disaster. At present, she is the director of the California Space Institute at the University of California San Diego.

What were the **first words spoken** by an astronaut after touchdown of the lunar module on the ***Apollo 11*** flight, and by an astronaut standing on the moon?

On July 20, 1969, at 4:17:43 p.m. Eastern Daylight Time (20:17:43 Greenwich Mean Time), Neil A. Armstrong (b. 1930) and Edwin E. Aldrin Jr. (b. 1930) landed the lunar module *Eagle* on the moon's Sea of Tranquility, and Armstrong radioed: "Houston, Tranquility Base here. The *Eagle* has landed." Several hours later, when Armstrong descended the lunar module ladder and made the small jump between the *Eagle* and the lunar surface, he announced: "That's one small step for man, one giant leap for mankind." The article "a" was missing in the live voice transmission, and was later inserted in the record to amend the message to "one small step for a man."

What are some of the accomplishments of **female astronauts**?

First American woman in space: Sally K. Ride—June 18, 1983, aboard *Challenger* STS-7.

First American woman to walk in space: Kathryn D. Sullivan—October 11, 1984, aboard *Challenger* STS 41G.

Astronaut Sally K. Ride became the first U.S. woman in space on June 18, 1983.

First woman to make three spaceflights: Shannon W. Lucid—June 17, 1985; October 18, 1989; and August 2, 1991.

First African American woman in space: Mae Carol Jemison—September 12, 1992, aboard *Endeavour*.

First American woman space shuttle pilot: Eileen M. Collins—February 3, 1995, aboard *Discovery*.

Who was the **first African American** in space?

Guion S. Bluford, Jr. (b. 1942), became the first African American to fly in space during the space shuttle *Challenger* mission STS-8 (August 30-September 5, 1983). Astronaut Bluford, who holds a Ph.D. in aerospace engineering, made a second shuttle flight aboard *Challenger* mission STS-61-A/Spacelab D1 (October 30-November 6, 1985). The first black man to fly in space was Cuban cosmonaut Arnaldo Tamayo-Mendez, who was aboard *Soyuz 38* and spent eight days aboard the Soviet space station *Salyut 6* during September 1980. Dr. Mae C. Jemison became the first African American woman in space on September 12, 1992 aboard the space shuttle *Endeavour* mission Spacelab-J.

Who were the **first married couple** to go into space together?

Astronauts Jan Davis and Mark Lee were the first married couple in space. They flew aboard the space shuttle *Endeavor* on an eight-day mission that began on September 12, 1992. Ordinarily, NASA bars married couples from flying together. An exception was made for Davis and Lee because they had no children and had begun training for the mission long before they got married.

Who has spent the **most time in space**?

As of December 31, 2001, cosmonaut Sergei Vasilyevich Avdeyev has accumulated the most spaceflight time—747.6 days in three flights.

When was the **first United States satellite** launched?

Explorer 1, launched January 31, 1958, by the U.S. Army, was the first United States satellite launched into orbit. This 31-pound (14.06-kilogram) satellite carried instrumentation that led to the discovery of the Earth's radiation belts, which would be named after University of Iowa scientist James A. Van Allen. It followed four months after the launching of the world's first satellite, the Soviet Union's *Sputnik 1.* On October 3, 1957, the Soviet Union placed the large 184-pound (83.5-kilogram) satellite into low Earth orbit. It carried instrumentation to study the density and temperature of the upper atmosphere, and its launch was the event that opened the age of space.

What is the mission of the ***Galileo*** spacecraft?

Galileo, launched October 18, 1989, required almost six years to reach Jupiter after looping past Venus once and the Earth twice. The *Galileo* spacecraft was designed to make a detailed study of Jupiter and its rings and moons over a period of years. On December 7, 1995, it released a probe to analyze the different layers of Jupiter's atmosphere. *Galileo* recorded a multitude of measurements of the planet, its four largest moons, and its mammoth magnetic field. The mission was originally scheduled to continue until the end of 1997, but, since it has continued to operate successfully, missions exploring Jupiter's moons were added in 1997, 1999, and 2001. *Galileo* is scheduled to plunge into Jupiter's atmosphere in September 2003.

Who was the **founder** of the **Soviet space program**?

Sergei P. Korolev (1907-1966) made enormous contributions to the development of Soviet manned space flight, and his name is linked with their most significant space achievements. Trained as an aeronautical engineer, he directed the Moscow group studying the principles of rocket propulsion, and in 1946 took over the Soviet program to develop long-range ballistic rockets. Under Korolev, the Soviets used these rockets for space projects and launched the world's first satellite on October 4, 1957. Besides a vigorous, unmanned, interplanetary research program, Korolev's goal was to place men in space, and following tests with animals his manned space flight program was initiated when Yuri Gagarin (1934-1968) was successfully launched into Earth's orbit.

What were some of the accomplishments of the **first nine *Challenger* spaceflights**?

First American woman in space—Sally Ride

First African American man in space—Guion S. Bluford Jr.

First American woman to spacewalk—Kathryn Sullivan

First shuttle spacewalk—Donald Peterson and Story Musgrave

First untethered spacewalk—Robert Stewart and Bruce McCandless

First satellite repair in orbit—Pinky Nelson and Ox Van Hoften

First Coke and Pepsi in orbit—1985

What is the composition of the **tiles** on the **underside of the space shuttle** and how hot do they get?

The 20,000 tiles are composed of a low-density, high purity silica fiber insulator hardened by ceramic bonding. Bonded to a Nomex fiber felt pad, each tile is directly bonded to the shuttle exterior. The maximum surface temperature can reach up to 922K to 978K (649°C to 704°C or 1,200°F to 1,300°F).

What are the **liquid fuels** used by the space shuttles?

Liquid hydrogen is used as a fuel, with liquid oxygen used to burn it. These two fuels are stored in chambers separately and then mixed to combust the two. Because oxygen must be kept below -183°C to remain a liquid, and hydrogen must be at -253°C to remain a liquid, they are both difficult to handle, but make useful rocket fuel.

EARTH

AIR

What is the **composition** of the **Earth's atmosphere**?

The Earth's atmosphere, apart from water vapor and pollutants, is composed of 78 percent nitrogen, 21 percent oxygen, and less than 1 percent each of argon and carbon dioxide. There are also traces of hydrogen, neon, helium, krypton, xenon, methane, and ozone. The Earth's original atmosphere was probably composed of ammonia and methane; 20 million years ago the air started to contain a broader variety of elements.

How many **layers** does the **Earth's atmosphere** contain?

The atmosphere, the "skin" of gas that surrounds the Earth, consists of five layers that are differentiated by temperature:

The troposphere is the lowest level; it averages about seven miles (11 kilometers) in thickness, varying from five miles (eight kilometers) at the poles to 10 miles (16 kilometers) at the equator. Most clouds and weather form in this layer. Temperature decreases with altitude in the troposphere.

The stratosphere ranges between seven and 30 miles (11 to 48 kilometers) above the Earth's surface. The ozone layer, important because it absorbs most of the sun's harmful ultraviolet radiation, is located in this band. Temperatures rise slightly with altitude to a maximum of about 32°F (0°C).

The mesosphere (above the stratosphere) extends from 30 to 55 miles (48 to 85 kilometers) above the Earth. Temperatures decrease with altitude to -130°F (-90°C).

The thermosphere (also known as the hetereosphere) is between 55 to 435 miles (85 to 700 kilometers). Temperatures in this layer range to 2696°F (1475°C).

The exosphere, beyond the thermosphere, applies to anything above 435 miles (700 kilometers). In this layer, temperature no longer has any meaning.

The ionosphere is a region of the atmosphere that overlaps the others, reaching from 30 to 250 miles (48 to 402 kilometers). In this region, the air becomes ionized (electrified) from the sun's ultraviolet rays, etc. This area affects the transmission and reflection of radio waves. It is divided into three regions: the D region (at 35 to 55 miles [56 to 88 kilometers]), the E Region (Heaviside-Kennelly Layer, 55 to 95 miles [88 to 153 kilometers]), and the F Region (Appleton Layer, 95 to 250 miles [153 to 402 kilometers]).

What are the **Van Allen belts**?

The Van Allen belts (or zones) are two regions of highly charged particles above the Earth's equator trapped by the magnetic field that surrounds the Earth. Also called the magnetosphere, the first belt extends from a few hundred to about 2,000 miles (3,200 kilometers) above the Earth's surface and the second is between 9,000 and 12,000 miles (14,500 to 19,000 kilometers). The particles, mainly protons and electrons, come from the solar wind and cosmic rays. The belts are named in honor of James Van Allen (b. 1914), the American physicist who discovered them in 1958 and 1959 with the aid of radiation counters carried aboard the artificial satellites, *Explorer I* (1958) and *Pioneer 3* (1959).

In May 1998 there were a series of large, solar disturbances that caused a new Van Allen belt to form in the so-called "slot region" between the inner and outer Van Allen belts. The new belt eventually disappeared once the solar activity subsided. There were also a number of satellite upsets around the same time involving the *Galaxy IV* satellite, Iridium satellites, and others. This is not the first time that a temporary new belt has been observed to form in the same region, but it takes a prolonged period of solar storm activity to populate this region with particles.

Why is the **sky blue**?

The sunlight interacting with the Earth's atmosphere makes the sky blue. In outer space the astronauts see blackness because outer space has no atmosphere. Sunlight consists of light waves of varying wavelengths, each of which is seen as a different color. The minute particles of matter and molecules of air in the atmosphere intercept and scatter the white light of the sun. A larger portion of the blue color in white light is scattered, more so than any other color because the blue wavelengths

James Van Allen discovered two regions of highly charged particles above the Earth's equator. Van Allen appears here (center) with William Pickering and Wernher von Braun, holding a model of the first successfully launched U.S. satellite, *Explorer.*

are the shortest. When the size of atmospheric particles are smaller than the wavelengths of the colors, selective scattering occurs—the particles only scatter one color and the atmosphere will appear to be that color. Blue wavelengths especially are affected, bouncing off the air particles to become visible. This is why the sun looks yellow (yellow equals white minus blue). At sunset, the sky changes color because as the sun drops to the horizon, sunlight has more atmosphere to pass through and loses more of its blue wavelengths. The orange and red, having the longer wavelengths and making up more of sunlight at this distance, are most likely to be scattered by the air particles.

PHYSICAL CHARACTERISTICS, ETC.

What is the **mass** of the **Earth**?

The mass of the Earth is estimated to be 6 sextillion, 588 quintillion short tons (6.6 sextillion short tons) or 5.97×10^{24} kilograms, with the Earth's mean density being 5.515 times that of water (the standard). This is calculated from using the parameters of an ellipsoid adopted by the International Astronomical Union in 1964 and recognized by the International Union of Geodesy and Geophysics in 1967.

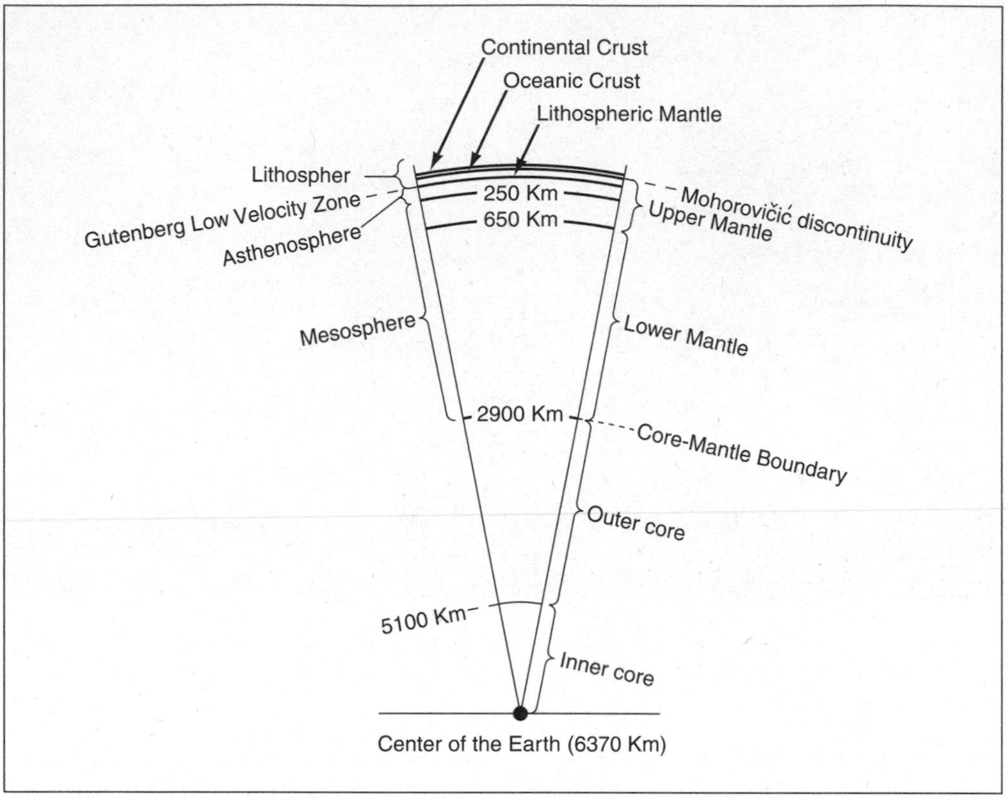

A diagram of the interior of the Earth.

What is the **interior of the Earth** like?

The Earth is divided into a number of layers. The topmost layer is the crust, which contains about 0.6 percent of the Earth's volume. The depth of the crust varies from 3.5 to five miles (five to nine kilometers) beneath the oceans to 50 miles (80 kilometers) beneath some mountain ranges. The crust is formed primarily of rocks such as granite and basalt.

Between the crust and the mantle is a boundary known as the Mohorovičić discontinuity (or Moho for short), named for the Croatian seismologist, Andrija Mohorovičić (1857-1936), who discovered it in 1909. Below the Moho is the mantle, extending down about 1,800 miles (2,900 kilometers). The mantle is composed mostly of oxygen, iron, silicon, and magnesium, and accounts for about 82 percent of the Earth's volume. Although mostly solid, the upper part of the mantle, called the asthenosphere, is partially liquid.

The core-mantle boundary, also called the Gutenberg discontinuity for the German-American seismologist, Beno Gutenberg (1889-1960), separates the mantle from the core. Made up primarily of nickel and iron, the core contains about 17 percent of the Earth's volume. The outer core is liquid and extends from the base of the mantle to a depth of about 3,200 miles (5,155 kilometers). The solid inner core reaches from the bottom of the outer core to the center of the Earth, about 3,956 miles (6,371 kilometers) deep. The temperature of the inner core is estimated to be about 7,000°F (3,850°C).

What is at the **center of the Earth**?

Geophysicists have held since the 1940s that the Earth's interior core is a partly crystallized sphere of iron and nickel that is gradually cooling and expanding. As it cools, this inner core releases energy to an outer core called the fluid core, which is composed of iron, nickel, and lighter elements, including sulfur and oxygen. Another model called the "nuclear earth model" holds that there is a small core, perhaps five miles wide, of uranium and plutonium surrounded by a nickel-silicon compound. The uranium and plutonium work as a natural nuclear reactor, generating radiating energy in the form of heat, which in turn drives charged particles to create the Earth's magnetic field. The traditional model of the Earth's core is still dominant; however, scientists have yet to disprove the nuclear earth model.

How does the **temperature of the Earth** change as one goes deeper underground?

The Earth's temperature increases with depth. Measurements made in deep mines and drill-holes indicate that the rate of temperature increase varies from place to place in the world, ranging from 59° to 167°F (15 to 75°C) per kilometer in depth. Actual temperature measurements cannot be made beyond the deepest drill-holes, which are a little more than 6.2 miles (10 kilometers) deep. Estimates suggest that the temperatures at the Earth's center can reach values of 5,000°F (2,760°C) or higher.

What are the **highest** and **lowest** points on Earth?

The highest point on land is the top of Mt. Everest (in the Himalayas on the Nepal-Tibet border) at 29,028 feet (8,848 meters) above sea level, plus or minus 10 feet (three meters) because of snow. This height was established by the Surveyor General of India in 1954 and accepted by the National Geographic Society. Prior to that the height was taken to be 29,002 feet (8,840 meters). Satellite measurements taken in 1987 indicate that Mt. Everest is 29,864 feet (9,102 meters) high, but this measurement has not been adopted by the National Geographic Society.

The lowest point on land is the Dead Sea between Israel and Jordan, which is 1,312 feet (399 meters) below sea level. The lowest point on the Earth's surface is thought to be in the Marianas Trench in the western Pacific Ocean, extending from southeast of Guam to northwest of the Marianas Islands. It has been measured as 36,198 feet (11,034 meters) below sea level.

Which elements are contained in the **Earth's crust**?

The most abundant elements in the Earth's crust are listed in the table below. In addition, nickel, copper, lead, zinc, tin, and silver account for less than 0.02 percent with all other elements comprising 0.48 percent.

Element	Percentage
Oxygen	47.0
Silicon	28.0
Aluminum	8.0
Iron	4.5
Calcium	3.5
Magnesium	2.5
Sodium	2.5
Potassium	2.5
Titanium	0.4
Hydrogen	0.2
Carbon	0.2
Phosphorus	0.1
Sulfur	0.1

What are the **highest** and **lowest elevations** in the **United States**?

Named in honor of U.S. president William McKinley (1843-1901), Mt. McKinley, Alaska, at 20,320 feet (6,194 meters), is the highest point in the United States and North America. Located in central Alaska, it is part of the Alaska Range. Its south peak measures 20,320 feet (6,194 meters) high and the north peak is 19,470 feet (5,931 meters) high. It boasts one of the world's largest unbroken precipices and is the main scenic attraction at Denali National Park. Denali means the "high one" or the "great one" and is a native American name sometimes used for Mt. McKinley. Mt. Whitney, California, at 14,494 feet (4,421 meters), is the highest point in the continental United States. Death Valley, California, at 282 feet (86 meters) below sea level, is the lowest point in the United States and in the western hemisphere.

WATER

Does **ocean water circulate**?

Ocean water is in a constant state of movement. Horizontal movements are called currents while vertical movements are called upwelling and downwelling. Wind, tidal motion, and differences in density due to temperature or salinity are the main causes

How much of the Earth's surface is land and how much is water?

Approximately 30 percent of the Earth's surface is land. This is about 57,259,000 square miles (148,300,000 square kilometers). The area of the Earth's water surface is approximately 139,692,000 square miles (361,800,000 square kilometers), or 70 percent of the total surface area.

of ocean circulation. Temperature differentials arise from the equatorial water being warmer than water in the polar regions. In the Northern Hemisphere the currents circulate in a clockwise direction while in the Southern Hemisphere the currents circulate in a counter-clockwise direction. In the equatorial regions the currents move in opposite directions—from left to right in the north and from right to left in the south. Currents moving north and south from equatorial regions carry warm water while those in polar regions carry cold water.

Major Cold Currents	Major Warm Currents
California	North Atlantic (Gulf Stream)
Humboldt	South Atlantic
Labrador	South Indian Ocean
Canaries	South Pacific
Benguela	North Pacific
Falkland	Monsoons
West Australian	Okhotsk

If you **melted all the ice** in the world, how high would the oceans rise?

If you melted all the ice in the world, some 5.5 million cubic miles (23 million cubic kilometers) in all, the oceans would rise 1.7 percent or about 180 feet (60 meters), which is enough, for example, for 20 stories of the Empire State Building to be underwater.

What fraction of an **iceberg** shows above water?

Only one seventh to one-tenth of an iceberg's mass shows above water.

What is an **aquifer**?

Some rocks of the upper part of the Earth's crust contain many small holes, or pores. When these holes are large or are joined together so that water can flow through them easily, the rock is considered to be permeable. A large body of permeable rock in which water is stored and flows through is called an aquifer (from the Latin for "water" and "to bear"). Sandstones and gravels are excellent examples of permeable rock.

As water reservoirs, aquifers provide about 60 percent of American drinking water. The huge Ogallala Aquifer, underlying about two million acres of the Great Plains, is a major source of water for the central United States. It has been estimated that after oceans (containing 850 million cubic miles [1,370 million cubic kilometers] of water), aquifers, with an estimated 31 million cubic miles (50 million cubic kilometers), are the second largest store of water. Water is purified as it is filtered through the rock, but it can be polluted by spills, dumps, acid rain, and other causes. In addition, recharging of water by rainfall often cannot keep up with the volume removed by heavy pumping. The Ogallala Aquifer's supply of water could be depleted by 25 percent in the year 2020.

What is the **chemical composition** of the **ocean**?

The ocean contains every known naturally occurring element plus various gases, chemical compounds, and minerals. Below is a sampling of the most abundant chemicals.

Constituent	Concentration (parts per million)
Chloride	18,980
Sodium	10,560
Sulfate	2,560
Magnesium	1,272
Calcium	400
Potassium	380
Bicarbonate	142
Bromide	65
Strontium	13
Boron	4.6
Fluoride	1.4

What causes **waves** in the ocean?

The most common cause of surface waves is air movement (the wind). Waves within the ocean can be caused by tides, interactions among waves, submarine earthquakes or volcanic activity, and atmospheric disturbances. Wave size depends on wind speed, wind duration, and the distance of water over which the wind blows. The longer the distance the wind travels over water, or the harder it blows, the higher the waves. As the wind blows over water it tries to drag the surface of the water with it. The surface cannot move as fast as air, so it rises. When it rises, gravity pulls the water back, carrying the falling water's momentum below the surface. Water pressure from below pushes this swell back up again. The tug of war between gravity and water pressure constitutes wave motion. Capillary waves are caused by breezes of less than two knots. At 13 knots the waves grow taller and faster than they grow longer, and their steepness cause them to break, forming whitecaps. For a whitecap to form, the wave height must be one-seventh the distance between wave crests.

How **deep** is the ocean?

The average depth of the ocean floor is 13,124 feet (4,000 meters). The average depth of the four major oceans is given below:

	Average depth	
Ocean	**Feet**	**Meters**
Pacific	13,740	4,188
Atlantic	12,254	3,735
Indian	12,740	3,872
Arctic	3,407	1,038

There are great variations in depth because the ocean floor is often very rugged. The greatest depth variations occur in deep, narrow depressions known as trenches along the margins of the continental plates. The deepest measurements made—36,198 feet (11,034 meters), deeper than the height of the world's tallest mountains—was taken in Mariana Trench east of the Mariana Islands. In January 1960, the French oceanographer Jacques Piccard, together with the United States Navy Lieutenant David Walsh, took the bathyscaphe *Trieste* to the bottom of the Mariana Trench.

		Depth	
Ocean	**Deepest point**	**Feet**	**Meters**
Pacific	Mariana Trench	36,200	11,033
Atlantic	Puerto Rico Trench	28,374	8,648
Indian	Java Trench	25,344	7,725
Arctic	Eurasia Basin	17,881	5,450

What is a **tidal bore**?

A tidal bore is a large, turbulent, wall-like wave of water that moves inland or upriver as an incoming tidal current surges against the flow of a more narrow and shallow river, bay, or estuary. It can be 10 to 16 feet (three to five meters) high and move rapidly (10 to 15 knots) upstream with and faster than the rising tide.

Where are the **world's highest tides**?

The Bay of Fundy (New Brunswick, Canada) has the world's highest tides. They average about 45 feet (14 meters) high in the northern part of the bay, far surpassing the world average of 2.5 feet (0.8 meter).

What is the difference between an **ocean** and a **sea**?

There is no neatly defined distinction between ocean and sea. One definition says the ocean is a great body of interconnecting salt water that covers 71 percent of the Earth's surface. There are four major oceans—the Arctic, Atlantic, Indian, and Pacific—but some sources do not include the Arctic Ocean, calling it a marginal sea. The terms "ocean" and "sea" are often used interchangeably but a sea is generally considered to be smaller than an ocean. The name is often given to saltwater areas on the margins of an ocean, such as the Mediterranean Sea.

How much salt is in **brackish water**?

Brackish water has a saline (salt) content between that of fresh water and sea water. It is neither fresh nor salty, but somewhere in between. Brackish waters are usually regarded as those containing 0.5 to 30 parts per thousand salt, while the average saltiness of seawater is 35 parts per thousand.

How **salty** is seawater?

Seawater is, on average, 3.3 to 3.7 percent salt. The amount of salt varies from place to place. In areas where large quantities of fresh water are supplied by melting ice, rivers, or rainfall, such as the Arctic or Antarctic, the level of salinity is lower. Areas such as the Persian Gulf and the Red Sea have salt contents over 4.2 percent. If all the salt in the ocean were dried, it would form a mass of solid salt the size of Africa. Most of the ocean salt comes from processes of dissolving and leaking from the solid Earth over hundreds of millions of years. Some is the result of salty volcanic rock that flows up from a giant rift that runs through all the ocean's basins.

Is the **Dead Sea** really dead?

Because the Dead Sea, on the boundary between Israel and Jordan, is the lowest body of water on the Earth's surface, any water that flows into it has no outflow. It is called "dead" because its extreme salinity makes impossible any animal or vegetable life except bacteria. Fish introduced into the sea by the Jordan River or by smaller streams die instantly. The only plant life consists primarily of halophytes (plants that grow in salty or alkaline soil). The concentration of salt increases toward the bottom of the lake. The water also has such a high density that bathers float on the surface easily.

Where is the world's **deepest lake**?

Lake Baikal, located in southeast Siberia, Russia, is approximately 5,371 feet (1,638 meters) deep at its maximum depth, Olkhon Crevice, making it the deepest lake in the world. Lake Tanganyika in Tanzania and Zaire is the second deepest lake, with a depth of 4,708 feet (1,435 meters).

What are rip tides and why are they so dangerous?

At points along a coast where waves are high, a substantial buildup of water is created near the shore. This mass of water moves along the shore until it reaches an area of lower waves. At this point, it may burst through the low waves and move out from shore as a strong surface current moving at an abnormally rapid speed known as a rip current. Swimmers who become exhausted in a rip current may drown unless they swim parallel to the shore. Rip currents are sometimes incorrectly called rip tides.

Where are the **five largest lakes** in the world located?

Location	Area		Length		Depth	
	Square miles	Square Km[a]	Miles	Km[a]	Feet	Meters
Caspian Sea,[b] Asia-Europe	143,244	370,922	760	1,225	3,363	1,025
Superior, North America	31,700	82,103	350	560	1,330	406
Victoria, Africa	26,828	69,464	250	360	270	85
Aral[b], Asia	24,904	64,501	280	450	220	67
Huron, North America	23,010	59,600	206	330	750	229

[a] = Kilometers — [b] = Salt water lake

What is a **yazoo**?

A yazoo is a tributary of a river that runs parallel to the river, being prevented from joining the river because the river has built up high banks. The name is derived from the Yazoo River, a tributary of the Mississippi River, which demonstrates this effect.

Which of the **Great Lakes** is the largest?

Lake	Surface area		Maximum depth	
	Square miles	Square kilometers	Feet	Meters
Superior	31,700	82,103	1,333	406
Huron	23,010	59,600	750	229
Michigan	22,300	57,757	923	281
Erie	9,910	25,667	210	64
Ontario	7,540	9,529	802	244

Lake Superior is the largest of the Great Lakes. The North American Great Lakes form a single watershed with one common outlet to the sea—the St. Lawrence Seaway. The total volume of all five basins is 6,000 trillion gallons (22.7 trillion liters) equivalent to about 20 percent of the world's freshwater. Only Lake Michigan lies wholly within the United States' borders; the others share their boundaries with Canada. Some believe that Lake Huron and Lake Michigan are two lobes of one lake, since they are the same elevation and are connected by the 120-foot (36.5-meter) deep Strait of Mackinac, which is 3.6 to five miles (six to eight kilometers) wide. Gage records indicate that they both have similar water level regimes and mean long-term behavior, so that hydrologically they act as one lake. Historically they were considered two by the explorers who named them, but this is considered a misnomer by some.

What are the **longest rivers** in the world?

The two longest rivers in the world are the Nile in Africa and the Amazon in South America. However, which is the longest is a matter of some debate. The Amazon has several mouths that widen toward the South Atlantic, so the exact point where the river ends is uncertain. If the Pará estuary (the most distant mouth) is counted, its length is approximately 4,195 miles (6,750 kilometers). The length of the Nile as surveyed before the loss of a few miles of meanders due to the formation of Lake Nasser behind the Aswan Dam was 4,145 miles (6,670 kilometers). The table below lists the five longest river systems in the world.

River	Length	
	Miles	Kilometers
Nile (Africa)	4,145	6,670
Amazon (South America)*	4,000	6,404
Chang jiang-Yangtze (Asia)	3,964	6,378
Mississippi-Missouri river system (North America)	3,740	6,021
Yenisei-Angara river system (Asia)	3,442	5,540

*excluding Pará estuary

What is the world's **highest waterfall**?

Angel Falls, named after the explorer and bush pilot Jimmy Angel, on the Carrao tributary in Venezuela is the highest waterfall in the world. It has a total height of 3,212 feet (979 meters) with its longest unbroken drop being 2,648 feet (807 meters).

It is difficult to determine the height of a waterfall because many are composed of several sections rather than one straight drop. The highest waterfall in the United States is Yosemite Falls on a tributary of the Merced River in Yosemite National Park, California, with a total drop of 2,425 feet (739 meters). There are three sections to the

> **When will Niagara Falls disappear?**
>
> The water dropping over Niagara Falls digs great plunge pools at the base, undermining the shale cliff and causing the hard limestone cap to cave in. Niagara has eaten itself seven miles (11 kilometers) upstream since it was formed 10,000 years ago. At this rate, it will disappear into Lake Erie in 22,800 years. The Niagara River connects Lake Erie with Lake Ontario, and marks the U.S.-Canada boundary (New York-Ontario).

Yosemite Falls: Upper Yosemite is 1,430 feet (435 meters), Cascades (middle portion) is 675 feet (205 meters), and Lower Yosemite is 320 feet (97 meters).

LAND

Are there **tides** in the **solid part** of the Earth as well as in its waters?

The solid Earth is distorted about 4.5 to 14 inches (11.4 to 35.6 centimeters) by the gravitational pull of the sun and moon. It is the same gravitational pull that creates the tides of the waters. When the moon's gravity pulls water on the side of the Earth near to it, it pulls the solid body of the Earth on the opposite side away from the water to create bulges on both sides, and causing high tides. These occur every 12.5 hours. Low tides occur in those places from which the water is drained to flow into the two high-tide bulges. The sun causes tides on the Earth that are about 33 to 46 percent as high as those due to the moon. During a new moon or a full moon when the sun and moon are in a straight line, the tides of the moon and the sun reinforce each other to make high tides higher; these are called spring tides. At the quarter moons, the sun and moon are out of step (at right angles), the tides are less extreme than usual; these are called neap tides. Smaller bodies of water, such as lakes, have no tides because the whole body of water is raised all at once, along with the land beneath it.

Do the **continents move**?

In 1912, a German geologist, Alfred Lothar Wegener (1880-1930), theorized that the continents had drifted or floated apart to their present locations and that once all the continents had been a single land mass near Antarctica, which is called Pangaea (from the Greek word meaning *all-earth*). Pangaea then broke apart some 200 mil-

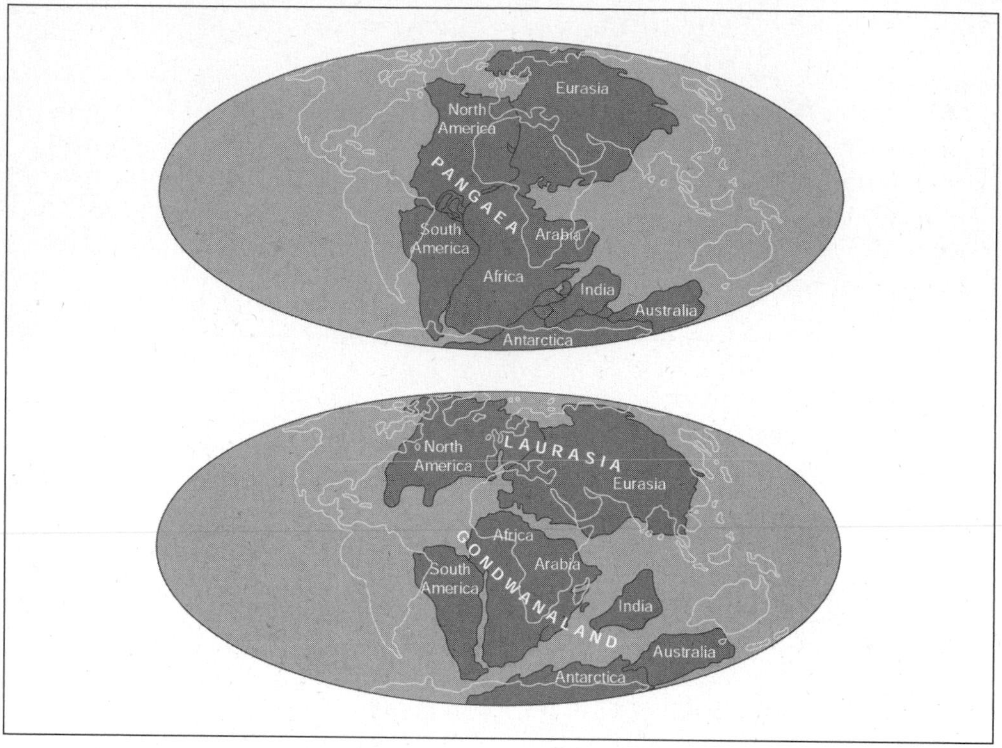

The Pangaea supercontinent (top) and its breakup into Laurasia and Gondwanaland.

lion years ago into two major continents called Laurasia and Gondwanaland. These two continents continued drifting and separating until the continents evolved their present shapes and positions. Wegener's theory was discounted, but it has since been found that the continents do move sideways (not drift) at an estimated 0.75 inch (19 millimeters) annually because of the action of plate tectonics. American geologist William Maurice Ewing (1906-1974) and Harry Hammond Hess (1906-1969) proposed that the Earth's crust is not a solid mass, but composed of eight major and seven minor plates that can move apart, slide by each other, collide, or override each other. Where these plates meet are major areas of mountain-building, earthquakes, and volcanoes.

How much of the **Earth's surface** is **permanently frozen**?

About one-fifth of the Earth's land is permafrost, or ground that is permanently frozen. This classification is based entirely on temperature and disregards the composition of the land. It can include bedrock, sod, ice, sand, gravel, or any other type of material in which the temperature has been below freezing for over two years. Nearly all permafrost is thousands of years old.

Where are the **northernmost** and **southernmost points of land**?

The most northern point of land is Cape Morris K. Jesup on the northeastern extremity of Greenland. It is at 83 degrees, 39 minutes north latitude and is 440 miles (708 kilometers) from the North Pole. However, the *Guinness Book of Records* reports that an islet of 100 feet (30 meters) across, called Oodaq, is more northerly at 83 degrees, 40 minutes north latitude and 438.9 miles (706 kilometers) from the North Pole. The southernmost point of land is the South Pole (since the South Pole, unlike the North Pole, is on land).

In the United States, the northernmost point of land is Point Barrow, Alaska (71 degrees, 23 minutes north latitude), and the southernmost point of land is Ka Lae or South Cape (18 degrees, 55 minutes north latitude) on the island of Hawaii. In the 48 contiguous states, the northernmost point is Northwest Angle, Minnesota (49 degrees, 23 minutes north latitude); the southernmost point is Key West, Florida (24 degrees, 33 minutes north latitude).

How **thick** is the ice that covers **Antarctica**?

The ice that covers Antarctica is 15,700 feet (4,785 meters) in depth at its thickest point. This is about ten times taller than the Sears Tower in Chicago. However, the average thickness is 7,100 feet (2,164 meters).

Who was the **first person on Antarctica**?

Historians are unsure who first set foot on Antarctica, the fifth largest continent covering 10 percent of the Earth's surface with its area of 5.4 million square miles (14 million square kilometers). In 1773-1775 British Captain James Cook (1728-1779) circumnavigated the continent. American explorer Nathaniel Palmer (1799-1877) discovered Palmer Peninsula in 1820, without realizing that this was a continent. That same year, Fabian Gottlieb von Bellingshausen (1779-1852) sighted the Antarctic continent. American sealer John Davis went ashore at Hughes Bay on February 7, 1821. In 1823, sealer James Weddell (1787-1834) traveled the farthest south (74 degrees south) that anyone had until that time and entered what is now called the Weddell Sea. In 1840, American Charles Wilkes (1798-1877), who followed the coast for 1,500 miles, announced the existence of Antarctica as a continent. In 1841, Sir James Clark Ross (1800-1862) discovered Victoria Land, Ross Island, Mount Erebus, and the Ross Ice Shelf. In 1895, the whaler Henryk Bull landed on the Antarctic continent. Norwegian explorer Roald Amundsen (1872-1928) was the first to reach the South Pole on December 14, 1911. Thirty-four days later, Amundsen's rival Robert Falcon Scott (1868-1912) stood at the South Pole, the second to do so, but he and his companions died upon their return trip.

The 200-foot oceanic face of Antarctica's Ross Ice Shelf stretches straight across the horizon, dwarfed in the midst of Mount Erebus.

When was the **Ice Age**?

Ice ages, or glacial periods, have occurred at irregular intervals for over 2.3 billion years. During an ice age, sheets of ice cover large portions of the continents. The exact reasons for the changes in the Earth's climate are not known, although some think they are caused by changes in the Earth's orbit around the sun.

The Great Ice Age occurred during the Pleistocene Epoch, which began about two million years ago and lasted until 11,000 years ago. At its height, about 27 percent of the world's present land area was covered by ice. In North America, the ice covered Canada and moved southward to New Jersey; in the Midwest, it reached as far south as St. Louis. Small glaciers and ice caps also covered the western mountains. Greenland was covered in ice as it is today. In Europe, ice moved down from Scandinavia into Germany and Poland; the British Isles and the Alps also had ice caps. Glaciers also covered the northern plains of Russia, the plateaus of Central Asia, Siberia, and the Kamchetka Peninsula.

The glaciers' effect on the United States can still be seen. The drainage of the Ohio River and the position of the Great Lakes were influenced by the glaciers. The rich soil of the Midwest is mostly glacial in origin. Rainfall in areas south of the glaciers formed large lakes in Utah, Nevada, and California. The Great Salt Lake in Utah is a remnant of one of these lakes. The large ice sheets locked up a lot of water; sea level fell about 450 feet (137 meters) below what it is today. As a result, some states, such as Florida, were much larger during the ice age.

The glaciers of the last ice age retreated about 11,000 years ago. Some believe that the ice age is not over yet; the glaciers follow a cycle of advance and retreat many times. There are still areas of the Earth covered by ice, and this may be a time in between glacial advances.

What is a **moraine**?

A moraine is a mound, ridge, or any other distinct accumulation of unsorted, unstratified material or drift, deposited chiefly by direct action of glacier ice.

What is a **hoodoo**?

A hoodoo is a fanciful name for a grotesque rock pinnacle or pedestal, usually of sandstone, that is the result of weathering in a semi-arid region. An outstanding example of hoodoos occurs in the Wasatch Formation at Bryce Canyon, Utah.

Hoodoo formations at Chirichua National Monument in Arizona.

What are **sand dunes** and how are they formed?

Mounds of wind-blown sand in deserts and coastal areas are called dunes. Winds transport grains of sand until it accumulates around obstacles to form ridges and mounds. Wind direction, the type of sand, and the amount of vegetation determine the type of dune. Dunes are named either for their shape (e.g. star dunes and parabolic dunes) or according to their alignment with the wind (e.g. longitudinal dunes and transverse dunes).

Which are the world's **largest deserts**?

A desert is an area that receives little precipitation and has little plant cover. Many deserts form a band north and south of the equator at about 20 degrees latitude

These sand dunes in California present a landscape of varying shapes, sizes and textures.

because moisture-bearing winds do not release their rain over these areas. As the moisture-bearing winds from the higher latitudes approach the equator, their temperatures increase and they rise higher and higher in the atmosphere. When the winds arrive over the equatorial areas and come in contact with the colder parts of the Earth's atmosphere, they cool down and release all their water to create the tropical rain forests near the equator.

The Sahara Desert, the world's largest, is three times the size of the Mediterranean Sea. In the United States, the largest desert is the Mojave Desert in southern California with an area of 15,000 square miles (38,900 square kilometers).

Desert	Location	Area: Square miles	Area: Square kilometers
Sahara	North Africa	3,500,000	9,065,000
Arabian	Arabian Peninsula	900,000	2,330,000
Australian	Australia	600,000	1,554,000
Gobi	Mongolia & China	500,000	1,295,000
Libyan	Libya, SW Egypt, Sudan	450,000	1,165,500

What is **quicksand**?

Quicksand is a mass of sand and mud that contains a large amount of water. A thin film separates individual grains of sand so the mixture has the characteristics of a liq-

What is the difference between spelunking and speleology?

Spelunking, or sport caving, is exploring caves as a hobby or for recreation. Speleology is the scientific study of caves and related phenomena, such as the world's deepest cave, Réseau Jean Bernard, in Haute Savoie, France, with a depth of 5,256 feet (1,602 meters), or the world's longest cave system, Mammoth Cave in Kentucky, with a length of 348 miles (560 kilometers).

uid. Quicksand is found at the mouths of large rivers or other areas that have a constant source of water. Heavy objects, including humans, can sink when encountering quicksand and the mixture collapses. However, since the density of the sand/water mix is slightly greater than the density of the human body, most humans can actually float on quicksand.

Are all **craters** part of a volcano?

No, not all craters are of volcanic origin. A crater is a nearly circular area of deformed sedimentary rocks, with a central, ventlike depression. Some craters are caused by the collapse of the surface when underground salt or limestone dissolves. The withdrawal of groundwater and the melting of glacial ice can also cause the surface to collapse, forming a crater.

Craters are also caused by large meteorites, comets, and asteroids that hit the Earth. A notable impact crater is Meteor Crater near Winslow, Arizona. It is 4,000 feet (1,219 meters) in diameter, 600 feet (183 meters) deep and is estimated to have been formed 30,000 to 50,000 years ago.

How are **caves** formed?

Water erosion creates most caves found along coastal areas. Waves crashing against the rock over years wears away part of the rock forming a cave. Inland caves are also formed by water erosion—in particular, groundwater eroding limestone. As the limestone dissolves, underground passageways and caverns are formed.

How is **speleothem** defined?

Speleothem is a term given to those cave features that form after a cave itself has formed. They are secondary mineral deposits that are created by the solidification of fluids or from chemical solutions. These mineral deposits usually contain calcium carbonate ($CaCO_3$) or limestone, but gypsum or silica may also be found. Stalactites, stalagmites, soda straws, cave coral, boxwork and cave pearls are all types of speleothems.

A massive stalactite and stalagmite column takes center stage in South Africa's Cango Caves.

What is a **tufa**?

It is a general name for calcium carbonate ($CaCO_3$) deposits or spongy porous limestone found at springs in limestone areas, or in caves as massive stalactite or stalagmite deposits. Tufa, derived from the Italian word for "soft rock," is formed by the precipitation of calcite from the water of streams and springs.

Which is the **deepest cave** in the United States?

Lechuguilla Cave, in Carlsbad Caverns National Park, New Mexico is the deepest cave in the United States. Its depth is 1,565 feet (477 meters). Unlike most caves in which carbon dioxide mixes with rainwater to produce carbonic acid, Carlsbad Caverns was shaped by sulfuric acid. The sulfuric acid was a result of a reaction between oxygen that was dissolved in groundwater and hydrogen sulfide that emanated from far below the cave's surface.

How does a **stalactite** differ from a **stalagmite**?

A stalactite is a conical or cylindrical calcite ($CaCO_3$) formation hanging from a cave roof. It forms from the centuries-long buildup of mineral deposits resulting from the seepage of water from the limestone rock above the cave. This water containing calcium bicarbonate evaporates, losing some carbon dioxide, to deposit small quantities of calcium carbonate (carbonate of lime), which eventually forms a stalactite.

A stalagmite is a stone formation that develops upward from the cave floor and resembles an icicle upside down. Formed from water containing calcite that drips from the limestone walls and roof of the cave, it sometimes joins a stalactite to form a column.

What and where is the **continental divide** of North America?

The Continental Divide, also known as the Great Divide, is a continuous ridge of peaks in the Rocky Mountains that marks the watershed separating easterly flowing waters from westerly flowing waters in North America. To the east of the Continental Divide, water drains into Hudson Bay or the Mississippi River before reaching the Atlantic Ocean. To the west, water generally flows through the Columbia River or the Colorado River on its way to the Pacific Ocean.

How long is the **Grand Canyon**?

The Grand Canyon, cut out by the Colorado River over a period of 15 million years in the northwest corner of Arizona, is the largest land gorge in the world. It is four to 13 miles (6.4 to 21 kilometers) wide at its brim, 4,000 to 5,500 feet (1,219 to 1,676 meters) deep, and 217 miles (349 kilometers) long, extending from the mouth of the Little Colorado River to Grand Wash Cliffs (and 277 miles, 600 feet [445.88 kilometers] if Marble Canyon is included).

However, it is not the deepest canyon in the United States; that distinction belongs to Kings Canyon, which runs through the Sierra and Sequoia National Forests near East Fresno, California, with its deepest point being 8,200 feet (2,500 meters). Hell's Canyon of the Snake River between Idaho and Oregon is the deepest United States canyon in low-relief territory. Also called the Grand Canyon of the Snake, it plunges 7,900 feet (2,408 meters) down from Devil Mountain to the Snake River.

What are the **LaBrea Tar Pits**?

The tar pits are located in an area of Los Angeles, California, formerly known as Rancho LaBrea. Heavy, sticky tar oozed out of the Earth there, the scum from great petroleum reservoirs far underground. The pools were cruel traps for uncounted numbers of animals. Today, the tar pits are a part of Hancock Park, where many fossil remains are displayed along with life-sized reconstructions of these prehistoric species.

The tar pits were first recognized as a fossil site in 1875. However, scientists did not systematically excavate the area until 1901. By comparing Rancho La Brea's fossil specimens with their nearest living relatives, paleontologists have a greater understanding of the climate, vegetation, and animal life in the area during the Ice Age. Perhaps the most impressive fossil bones recovered belong to such large extinct mammals as the imperial mammoth and the saber-toothed cat. Paleontologists have even found the remains of the western horse and the camel, which originated in North America, migrated to other parts of the world, and became extinct in North America at the end of the Ice Age.

VOLCANOES AND EARTHQUAKES

Which is the **most famous volcano**?

The eruption of Mt. Vesuvius in Italy on August 79 C.E. is perhaps the most famous historical volcanic eruption. Vesuvius had been dormant for generations. When it erupted, entire cities were destroyed, including Pompeii, Stabiae, and Herculaneum. Pompeii and Stabiae were buried under ashes while Herculaneum was buried under a mud flow.

How many **kinds of volcanoes** are there?

Volcanoes are usually cone-shaped hills or mountains built around a vent connecting to reservoirs of molten rock, or magma, below the surface of the Earth. At times the molten rock is forced upwards by gas pressure until it breaks through weak spots in the Earth's crust. The magma erupts forth as lava flows or shoots into the air as clouds of lava fragments, ash, and dust. The accumulation of debris from eruptions cause the volcano to grow in size. There are four kinds of volcanoes:

Cinder cones are built of lava fragments. They have slopes of 30 degrees to 40 degrees and seldom exceed 1,640 feet (500 meters) in height. Sunset Crater in Arizona and Paricutin in Mexico are examples of cinder cones.

Composite cones are made of alternating layers of lava and ash. They are characterized by slopes of up to 30 degrees at the summit, tapering off to five degrees at the base. Mount Fuji in Japan and Mount St. Helens in Washington are composite cone volcanoes.

Shield volcanoes are built primarily of lava flows. Their slopes are seldom more than 10 degrees at the summit and two degrees at the base. The Hawaiian Islands are clusters of shield volcanoes. Mauna Loa is the world's largest active volcano, rising 13,653 feet (4,161 meters) above sea level.

Lava domes are made of viscous, pasty lava squeezed like toothpaste from a tube. Examples of lava domes are Lassen Peak and Mono Dome in California.

How do we determine when **ancient volcanic eruptions** occurred?

The most common method used to date ancient volcanic eruptions is carbon dating. Carbon dating relies on the rate of radioactive decay of carbon 14. It is used to date eruptions

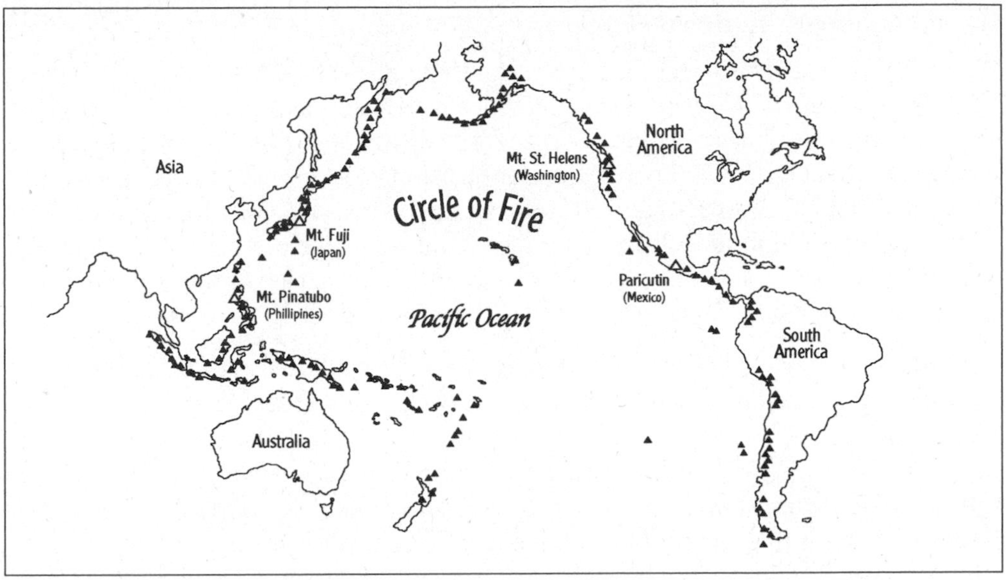

The Circle of Fire is a belt of volcanoes bordering the Pacific Ocean.

that took place more than 200 years ago. Charcoal from trees burned during a volcanic eruption is almost pure carbon and is ideal for tracing the tiny amounts of carbon 14.

Where is the **Circle of Fire**?

The belt of volcanoes bordering the Pacific Ocean is often called the "Circle of Fire" or the "Ring of Fire." The Earth's crust is composed of 15 pieces, called plates, which "float" on the partially molten layer below them. Most volcanoes, earthquakes, and mountain building occur along the unstable plate boundaries. The Circle of Fire marks the boundary between the plate underlying the Pacific Ocean and the surrounding plates. It runs up the west coast of the Americas from Chile to Alaska (through the Andes Mountains, Central America, Mexico, California, the Cascade Mountains, and the Aleutian Islands) then down the east coast of Asia from Siberia to New Zealand (through Kamchatka, the Kurile Islands, Japan, the Philippines, Celebes, New Guinea, the Solomon Islands, New Caledonia, and New Zealand). Of the 850 active volcanoes in the world, over 75 percent of them are part of the Circle of Fire.

Which **volcanoes** in the **contiguous 48 states** are considered **active**?

Seven major volcanoes in the contiguous 48 states are considered active: three in California—Cinder Cone, Lassen Peak, and Mt. Shasta; three in Washington—Mt. Baker, Mt. Rainier, and Mt. St. Helens; and one in Oregon—Mt. Hood.

When did **Mount St. Helens** erupt?

Mount St. Helens, located in southwestern Washington state in the Cascades mountain range, erupted on May 18, 1980. Sixty-one people died as a result of the eruption. This was the first known eruption in the 48 contiguous United States to claim a human life. Geologists call Mount St. Helens a composite volcano (a steep-sided, often symmetrical cone constructed of alternating layers of lava flows, ash, and other volcanic debris). Composite volcanoes tend to erupt explosively. Mount St. Helens and the other active volcanoes in the Cascade Mountains are a part of the "Ring of Fire," the Pacific zone having frequent and destructive volcanic activity.

Volcanoes have not only been active in Washington, but also in three other U.S. states: California, Alaska, and Hawaii. Lassen Peak is one of several volcanoes in the Cascade Range. It last erupted in 1921. Mount Katmai in Alaska had an eruption in 1912 in which the flood of hot ash formed the Valley of Ten Thousand Smokes 15 miles (24 kilometers) away. And Hawaii has its famed Mauna Loa, which is the world's largest volcano, being 60 miles (97 kilometers) in width at its base.

Which **volcanoes** have been the **most destructive**?

The five most destructive eruptions from volcanoes since 1700 are as follows:

Volcano	Date of eruption	Number killed	Lethal agent
Mt. Tambora, Indonesia	April 5, 1815	92,000	10,000 directly by the volcano, 82,000 from starvationafterwards
Karkatoa, Indonesia	Aug. 26, 1883	36,417	90% killed by a tsunami
Mt. Pelee, Martinque	Aug. 30, 1902	29,025	Pyroclastic flows
Nevada del Ruiz, Colombia	Nov. 13, 1985	23,000	Mud flow
Unzen, Japan	1792	14,300	70% killed by cone collapse; 30% by a tsunami

What is a **tsunami**?

A tsunami is a giant wave set in motion by a large earthquake occurring under or near the ocean that causes the ocean floor to shift vertically. This vertical shift pushes the water ahead of it, starting a tsunami. These are very long waves (100 to 200 miles [161 to 322 kilometers]) with high speeds (500 mph [805 kph]) that, when approaching shallow water, can grow into a 100-foot (30.5-meter) high wave as its wavelength is reduced abruptly. Ocean earthquakes below a magnitude of 6.5 on the Richter scale, and those that shift the sea floor only horizontally, do not produce these destructive waves. The highest recorded tsunami was 1,719 feet (524 meters) high along Lituya Bay, Alaska, on July 9, 1958. Caused by a giant landslip, it moved at

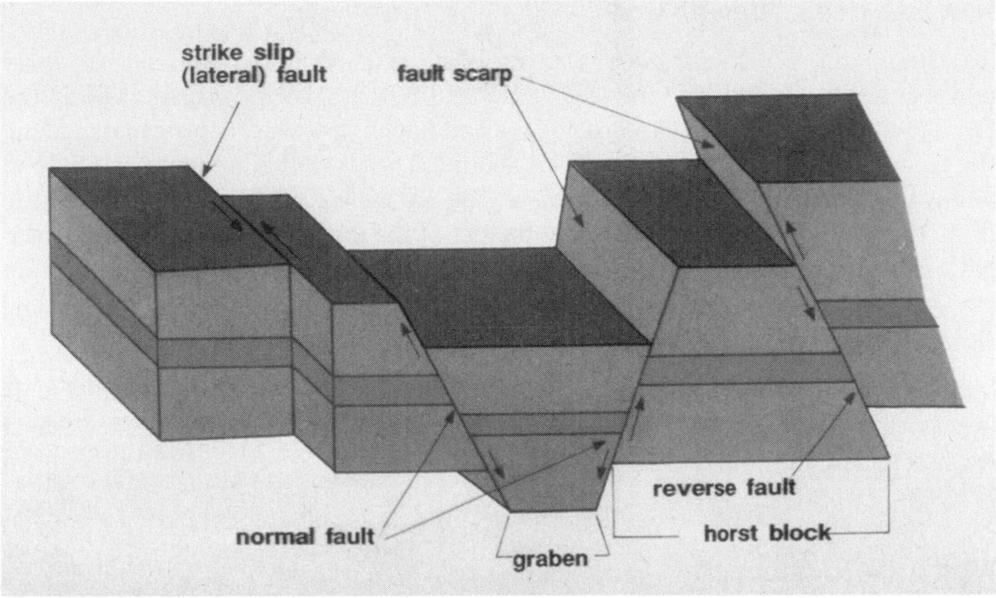

An illustration of three main types of fault motion.

100 miles per hour. This wave would have swamped the Petronas Towers in Kuala Lumpur, Malaysia, which are 1,483 feet (452 meters) high and are recognized as the tallest in the world.

How many different kinds of **faults** have been identified?

Faults are fractures in the Earth's crust. Faults are classified as normal, reverse or strike-slip. Normal faults occur when the end of one plate slides vertically down the end of another. Reverse faults occur when one plate slides vertically up the end of another. A strike-slip fault occurs when two plate ends slide past each other horizontally. In an oblique fault there is plate movement vertically and horizontally at the same time.

Where is the **San Andreas Fault**?

Perhaps the most famous fault in the world, the San Andreas Fault extends from Mexico north through most of California. The San Andreas Fault is not a single fault, but rather a system of faults. The northern half of the fault, near San Francisco, has reverse faults and is mostly mountainous. The southern half, near Los Angeles, has mostly normal faults. Land development has made it difficult to see the fault except in a few locations, notably near Lake San Andreas south of San Francisco. The fault was named in honor of Andrew Lawson (1861-1952), a geologist who studied the 1906 San Francisco earthquake.

How does a **seismograph** work?

A seismograph records earthquake waves. When an earthquake occurs, three types of waves are generated. The first two, the P and S waves, are propagated within the Earth, while the third, consisting of Love and Rayleigh waves, is propagated along the planet's surface. The P wave travels about 3.5 miles (5.6 kilometers) per second and is the first wave to reach the surface. The S wave travels at a velocity of a little more than half of the P waves. If the velocities of the different modes of wave propagation are known, the distance between the earthquake and an observation station may be deduced by measuring the time interval between the arrival of the faster and slower waves.

When the ground shakes, the suspended weight of the seismograph, because of its inertia, scarcely moves, but the shaking motion is transmitted to the marker, which leaves a record on the drum.

What is the **Richter scale**?

On a machine called a seismograph, the Richter scale measures the magnitude of an earthquake, i.e., the size of the ground waves generated at the earthquake's source. The scale was devised by American geologist Charles W. Richter (1900-1985) in 1935. Every increase of one number means a tenfold increase in magnitude.

Richter Scale

Magnitude	Possible effects
1	Detectable only by instruments
2	Barely detectable, even near the epicenter
3	Felt indoors
4	Felt by most people; slight damage
5	Felt by all; damage minor to to moderate
6	Moderately destructive
7	Major damage
8	Total and major damage

What is the **modified Mercalli Scale**?

The modified Mercalli Scale is a means of measuring the intesity of an earthquake. Unlike the Richter Scale, which uses mathematical calculation to measure seismic waves, the modified Mercalli Scale uses the effects of an earthquake on the people and structures in a given area to determine its intensity. It was invented by Guiseppe Mercalli (1850-1914) in 1902 and modified by Harry Wood and Frank Neumann in the 1930s to take into consideration such modern inventions as the automobile and the skyscraper.

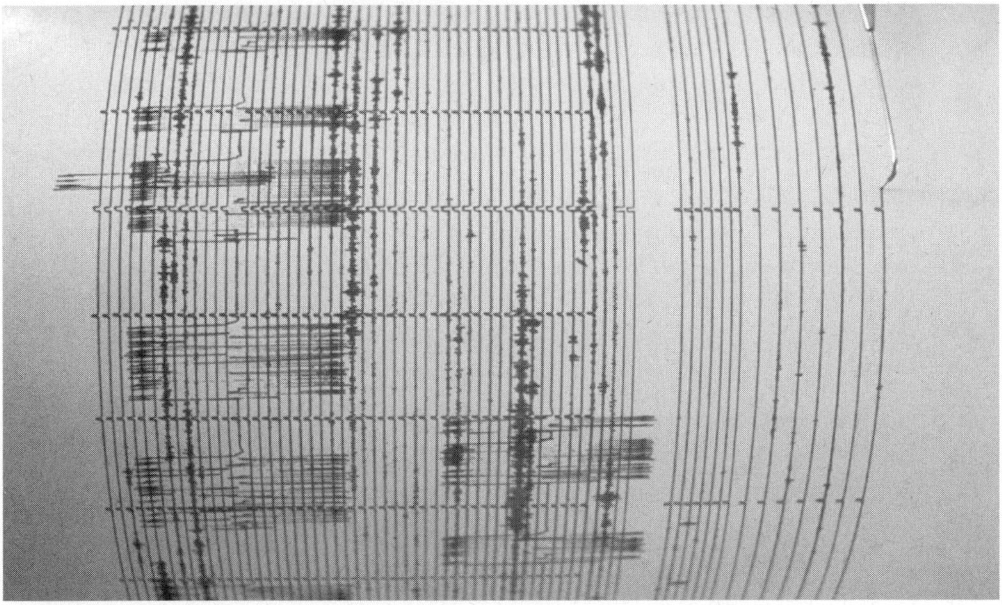

A seismograph records seismic activity in the Philippines.

The Modified Mercalli Scale

I. Only felt by a few under especially favorable circumstances.

II. Felt only by a few sleeping persons, particularly on upper floors of buildings. Some suspended objects may swing.

III. Felt quite noticeably indoors, especially on upper floors of buildings, but may not be recognized as an earthquake. Standing automobiles may rock slightly. Vibration like passing of truck.

IV. During the day felt indoors by many, outdoors by few. At night some awakened. Dishes, windows, doors disturbed; walls make creaking sound. Sensation like heavy truck striking building. Standing automobiles rocked noticeably.

V. Felt by nearly everyone, many awakened. Some dishes, windows, and so on broken; cracked plaster in a few places; unstable objects overturned. Disturbances of trees, poles, and other tall objects sometimes noticed. Pendulum clocks may stop.

VI. Felt by all; many frightened and run outdoors. Some heavy furniture moved; a few instances of fallen plaster and damaged chimneys. Damage slight.

VII. Everybody runs outdoors. Damage negligible in buildings of good design and construction; slight to moderate in well-built ordinary structures; considerable in poorly built or badly designed structures; some chimneys broken. Noticed by persons driving cars.

VIII. Damage slight in specially designed structures; considerable in ordinary substantial buildings with partial collapse; great in poorly built structures. Panel walls thrown out of frame structures. Fall of chimneys, factory stacks, columns, monuments, walls. Heavy furniture overturned. Sand and mud ejected in small amounts. Changes in well water. Persons driving cars disturbed.

IX. Damage considerable in specially designed structures; well-designed frame structures thrown out of plumb; great in substantial buildings, with partial collapse. Building shifted off foundations. Ground cracked conspicuously. Underground pipes broken.

X. Some well-built wooden structures destroyed; most masonry and frame structures destroyed with foundations; ground badly cracked. Rails bent. Landslides considerable from river banks and steel slopes. Shifted sand and mud. Water splashed, slopped over banks.

XI. Few, if any, (masonry) structures remain standing. Bridges destroyed. Broad fissures in ground. Underground pipelines completely out of service. Earth slumps and landslips in soft ground. Rails bent greatly.

XII. Damage total. Waves seen on ground surface. Lines of sight and level distorted. Objects thrown into the air.

When did the **most severe earthquake** in **American history** occur?

The New Madrid series of earthquakes (a series of quakes starting on December 16, 1811, and lasting until March 1812) is considered to be the most severe earthquake event in United States history. It shook more than two-thirds of the United States and was felt in Canada. It changed the level of land by as much as 20 feet (six meters), altered the course of the Mississippi River, and created new lakes, such as Lake St. Francis west of the Mississippi and Reelfoot Lake in Tennessee. Because the area was so sparsely populated, no known loss of life occurred. Scientists agree that at least three, and possibly five, of the quakes had surface wave magnitudes of 8.0 or greater. The largest was probably a magnitude of 8.8, which is larger than any quake yet experienced in California.

Of what magnitude was the **earthquake** that hit **San Francisco** on April 18, 1906?

The historic 1906 San Francisco earthquake took a mighty toll on the city and surrounding area. Over 700 people were killed; the newly constructed $6 million city hall was ruined; the Sonoma Wine Company collapsed, destroying 15 million gallons (57 million liters) of wine. The quake registered 8.3 on the Richter scale and lasted 75 seconds total. Many poorly constructed buildings built on landfills were flattened and the quake destroyed almost all of the gas and water mains. Fires broke out shortly after the quake, and when they were finally eliminated, 3,000 acres of the city, the equivalent of 520 blocks, were charred. Damage was estimated to be $500 million, and many insurance agencies went bankrupt after paying out the claims.

Another large earthquake hit San Francisco on October 17, 1989. It measured 7.1 on the Richter scale, killed 67 people, and caused billions of dollars worth of damage.

ROCKS AND MINERALS

How do **rocks** differ?

Rocks can be conveniently placed into one of three groups—igneous, sedimentary, and metamorphic.

Igneous rocks, such as granite, pegmatite, rhyolite, obsidian, gabbro, and basalt, are formed by the solidification of molten magma that emerges through the Earth's crust via volcanic activity. The nature and properties of the crystals vary greatly, depending in part on the composition of the original magma and partly on the conditions under which the magma solidified. There are thousands of different igneous rock types. For example, granite is formed by slow cooling of molten material (within the Earth). It has large crystals of quartz, feldspars, and mica.

Sedimentary rocks, such as brecchia, sandstone, shale, limestone, chert, and coals, are produced by the accumulation of sediments. These are fine rock particles or fragments, skeletons of microscopic organisms, or minerals leached from rocks that have accumulated from weathering. These sediments are then redeposited under water and later compressed in layers over time. The most common sedimentary rock is sandstone, which is predominantly quartz crystals.

Metamorphic rocks, such as marble, slate, schist, gneiss, quartzite, and hornsfel, are formed by the alteration of igneous and sedimentary rocks through heat and/or pressure. One example of these physical and chemical changes is the formation of marble from thermal changes in limestone.

What is **petrology** and what does a **petrologist** do?

Petrology is the science of rocks. A petrologist is a person who studies the mineralogy of rocks and the record of the geological past contained within rocks. From rocks, a petrologist can learn about past climates and geography, past and present composition of the Earth, and the conditions that prevail within the interior of the Earth.

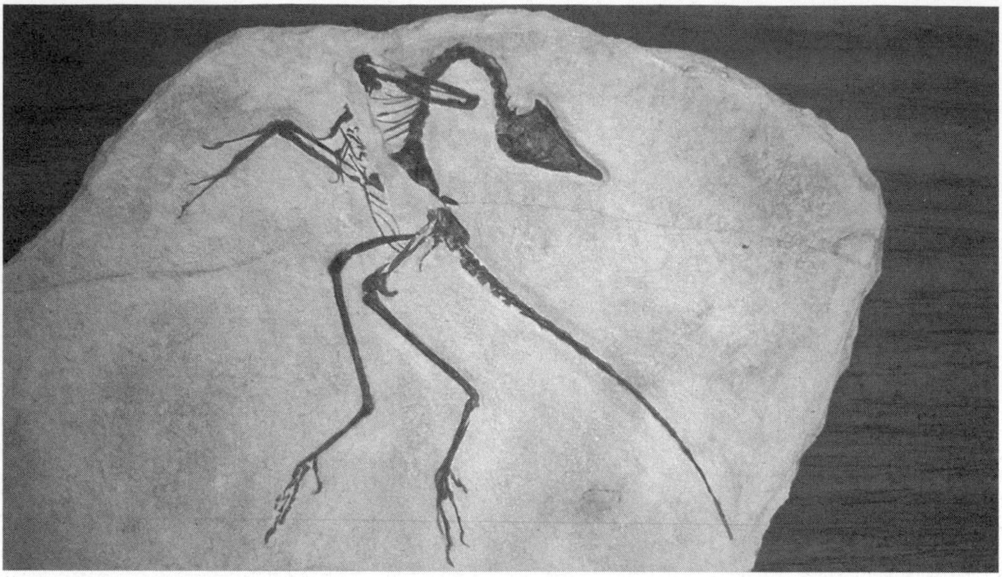

The fossilized remains of an archaeopteryx.

How are **fossils formed**?

Fossils are the remains of animals or plants that were preserved in rock before the beginning of recorded history. It is unusual for complete organisms to be preserved; fossils usually represent the hard parts such as bones or shells of animals and leaves, seeds, or woody parts of plants.

Some fossils are simply the bones, teeth, or shells themselves, which can be preserved for a relatively short period of time. Another type of fossil is the imprint of a buried plant or animal that decomposes, leaving a film of carbon that retains the form of the organism.

Some buried material is replaced by silica and other materials that permeate the organism and replace the original material in a process called petrification. Some woods are replaced by agate or opal so completely that even the cellular structure is duplicated. The best examples of this can be found in the Petrified Forest National Park in Arizona.

Molds and casts are other very common fossils. A mold is made from an imprint, such as a dinosaur footprint, in soft mud or silt. This impression may harden, then be covered with other materials. The original footprint will have formed a mold and the sediments filling it will be a cast of the footprint.

How **old** are **fossils**?

The oldest known fossils are of bacteria that left their impressions approximately 3.5 billion years ago. The oldest animal fossils are of invertebrates that lived approximately 700 million years ago. The largest number of fossils come from the Cambrian period of 590-505 million years ago, when living organisms began to develop skeletons and hard parts. Since these parts tended to last longer than ordinary tissue, they were more likely to be preserved in clay and become fossilized.

What is a **tektite**?

Tektites are silica-rich glass objects (rocks) found scattered in selected regions of the Earth's surface. They are generally black, oblong, teardrop or dumbbell-shaped, and several centimeters in length. They are formed from molten rock resulting when a meteorite, asteroid, or comet fragment impacts the Earth's surface. The molten rock is hurled high into atmosphere, where it rapidly cools into its unique shape and physical characteristics. Their mode of formation is considered indisputable evidence of such impacts. Tektites range from 0.7 to 35 million years in age.

What is **cinnabar**?

Cinnabar is the main ore of the mineral mercury. Its cinnamon to scarlet-red color makes it a colorful mineral. It is produced primarily in the United States (California, Oregon, Texas and Arkansas), Spain, Italy, and Mexico. It is often used as a pigment.

What are **Indian Dollars**?

They are six-sided, disk-shaped, twin crystals of aragonite ($CaCO_3$), which have altered to calcite but retained their outer form. They occur in large numbers in northern Colorado, where they are known as "Indian Dollars." In New Mexico they are called "Aztec Money" and in western Kansas they are called "Pioneer Dollars."

How does a **rock** differ from a **mineral**?

Mineralogists use the term "mineral" for a substance that has all four of the following features: it must be found in nature; it must be made up of substances that were never alive (organic); it has the same chemical makeup wherever it is found; and its atoms are arranged in a regular pattern to form solid crystals.

While "rocks" are sometimes described as an aggregate or combination of one or more minerals, geologists extend the definition to include clay, loose sand, and certain limestones.

What is the **Mohs scale**?

The Mohs scale is a standard of 10 minerals by which the hardness of a mineral is rated. It was introduced in 1812 by the German mineralogist Friedrich Mohs (1773-

If diamond is the hardest substance, what is the next hardest substance?

Cubic boron nitride, which is the hardest ceramic, is the second hardest substance in the world.

1839). The minerals are arranged from softest to hardest. Harder minerals, with higher numbers, can scratch those with a lower number.

Hardness	Mineral	Comment
1	Talc	Hardness 1-2 can be scratched by a fingernail
2	Gypsum	Hardness 2-3 can be scratched by a copper coin
3	Calcite	Hardness 3-6 can be scratched by a steel pocket knife
4	Fluorite	
5	Apatite	
6	Orthoclase	Hardness 6-7 will not scratch glass
7	Quartz	
8	Topaz	Hardness 8-10 will scratch glass
9	Corundum	
10	Diamond	

Who was the first person to attempt a **color standardization** scheme for minerals?

The German mineralogist Abraham Gottlob Werner (c.1750-1817) devised a method of describing minerals by their external characteristics, including color. He worked out an arrangement of colors and color names, illustrated by an actual set of minerals.

What is **pitchblende**?

Pitchblende is a massive variety of uraninite, or uranium oxide, found in metallic veins. It is a radioactive material and the most important ore of uranium. In 1898, Marie and Pierre Curie discovered that pitchblende contained radium, a rare element that has since been used in medicine and the sciences.

What is **galena**?

Galena is a lead sulphide (PbS) and the most common ore of lead, containing 86.6 percent lead. Lead-gray in color, with a brilliant metallic luster, galena has a specific gravity of 7.5 and a hardness of 2.5 on the Mohs scale, and usually occurs as cubes or a

> **What is fool's gold?**
>
> Iron pyrite (FeS_2) is a mineral popularly known as "fool's gold." Because of its metallic luster and pale brass yellow color, it is often mistaken for gold. Real gold is much heavier, softer, not brittle, and not grooved.

modification of an octahedral form. Mined in Australia, it is also found in Canada, China, Mexico, Peru, and the United States (Missouri, Kansas, Oklahoma, Colorado, Montana, and Idaho).

What is **stibnite**?

Stibnite is a lead-gray mineral (Sb_2S_3) with a metallic luster. It is the most important ore of antimony, and is also known as antimony glance. One of the few minerals that fuse easily in a match flame (977°F or 525°C), stibnite has a hardness of two on the Mohs scale and a specific gravity of 4.5 to 4.6. It is commonly found in hydrothermal veins or hot springs deposits. Stibnite is mined in Germany, Romania, France, Bolivia, Peru, and Mexico. The Yellow Pine mine at Stibnite, Idaho, is the largest producer in the United States, but California and Nevada also have deposits.

What are **Cape May diamonds**?

They are pure quartz crystals of many sizes and colors, found in the vicinity of the Coast Guard station in Cape May, New Jersey. When polished and faceted, these crystals have the appearance of real diamonds. Prior to the development of modern gem examination equipment, many people were fooled by these quartz crystals. The possibility of finding a Cape May diamond on one's own, and the availability of already-polished faceted stones, has been a long-standing tourist attractions in the Cape May area.

How can a **genuine diamond** be identified?

There are several tests that can be performed without the aid of tools. A knowledgeable person can recognize the surface lustre, straightness and flatness of facets, and high light reflectivity. Diamonds become warm in a warm room and cool if the surroundings are cool. A simple test that can be done is exposing the stones to warmth and cold and then touching them to one's lips to determine their appropriate temperature. This is especially effective when the results of this test are compared to the results of the test done on a diamond known to be genuine. Another test is to pick up

A miner holds the Cullinan diamond—the largest ever discovered—pieces of which were later used in the British Crown and Sceptre.

the stone with a moistened fingertip. If this can be done, then the stone is likely to be a diamond. The majority of other stones cannot be picked up in this way.

The water test is another simple test. A drop of water is placed on a table. A perfectly clean diamond has the ability to almost "magnetize" water and will keep the water from spreading. An instrument called a diamond probe can detect even the most sophisticated fakes. Gemologists always use this as part of their inspection.

What are the **four "C"s of diamonds**?

The four "C"s are cut, color, clarity, and carat. Cut refers to the proportions, finish, symmetry, and polish of the diamond. These factors determine the brilliance of a diamond. Color describes the amount of color the diamond contains. Color ranges from colorless to yellow with tints of yellow, gray, or brown. Colors can also range from intense yellow to the more rare blue, green, pink, and red. Clarity describes the cleanness or purity of a diamond as determined by the number and size of imperfections. Carat is the weight of the diamond.

How are **diamonds weighed**?

The basic unit is a carat, which is set at 200 milligrams (0.00704 ounces or 1/142 of an avoirdupois ounce). A well-cut, round diamond of one carat measures almost exactly 0.25 inch (6.3 millimeters) in diameter. Another unit commonly used is the point, which is one hundredth of a carat. A stone of one carat weighs 100 points. "Carat" as a unit of weight should not be confused with the term "karat" used to indicate purity of the gold into which gems are mounted.

Which **diamond** is the **world's largest**?

The Cullinan Diamond, weighing 3,106 carats, is the world's largest. It was discovered on January 25, 1905, at the Premier Diamond Mine, Transvaal, South Africa. Named for Sir Thomas M. Cullinan, chairman of the Premier Diamond Company, it was cut into nine major stones and 96 smaller brilliants. The total weight of the cut stones was 1,063 carats, only 35 percent of the original weight.

Cullinan I, also known as the "Greater Star of Africa" or the "First Star of Africa," is a pear-shaped diamond weighing 530.2 carats. It is 2.12 inches (5.4 centimeters) long, 1.75 inches (4.4 centimeters) wide, and one inch (2.5 centimeters) thick at its deepest point. It was presented to Britain's King Edward VII in 1907, and was set in the British monarch's sceptre with the cross. It is still the largest cut diamond in the world.

Cullinan II, also know as the "Second Star of Africa," is an oblong stone that weighs 317.4 carats. It is set in the British Imperial State Crown.

What are the **common cuts** of **gemstones**?

Modern gem cutting uses faceted cutting for most transparent gems. In faceted cutting, numerous facets—geometrically disposed to bring out the beauty of light and color to the best advantage—are cut. The four most common cuts are the brilliant, the rose, the baguette, and the step or trap cut. The step or trap cut is also known as the emerald cut and is used for emeralds. The brilliant and rose cuts are often used for diamonds.

What is **cubic zirconium**?

Cubic zirconium was discovered in 1937 by two German mineralogists. It became popular with jewelry designers in the 1970s after Soviet scientists learned how to "grow" the mineral in a laboratory. Most of the cubic zirconium on the market is chemically comprised of zirconium oxide and yttrium oxide. The two compounds are melted together at a very high temperature (almost 5,000°F) (2,760°C) using the skull melt method. This method uses a radio-frequency generator to heat the zirconium oxide. A careful cooling of the mixture produces the flawless crystals that become cubic zirconia gemstones.

What is the difference between **cubic zirconium** and **diamonds**?

Cubic zirconium is a gemstone material that is an imitation of diamonds. The word "imitation" is key. The U.S. Federal Trade Commission defines imitation materials as resembling the natural material in appearance only. Cubic zirconia may be cut the same way as diamonds. It is very dense and solid, weighing 1.7 times more than a diamond of the same millimeter size.

Besides the Cullinan diamonds, what are the **largest precious stones**?

The largest ruby is a 8,500 carat stone that is 5.5 inches (14 centimeters) tall, carved to resemble the Liberty Bell. The largest star ruby is the 6,465 carat "Eminent Star" from India that has a six-line star. The largest cut emerald was found in Carnaiba, Brazil, in August 1974. It is 86,136 carats. A 2,302 carat sapphire from Anakie, Queensland, Australia, was carved into a 1,318 carat head of Abraham Lincoln, making it the largest carved sapphire. "The Lone Star," at 9,719.5 carats, is the largest star sapphire. The largest natural pearl is the "Pearl of Lao-tze," also called the "Pearl of Allah." Found in May 1934 in the shell of a giant clam at Palawan, Philippines, the pearl weighs 14 pounds, 1 ounce (6.4 kilograms).

How does the **emerald** get its color?

Emerald is a variety of green beryl ($Be_3Al_2Si_6O_{18}$) that is colored by a trace of chromium (Cr), which replaces the aluminum (Al) in the beryl structure. Other green beryls exist; but if no chromium is present, they are, technically speaking, not emeralds.

How is the star in **star sapphires** produced?

Sapphires are composed of gem-quality corundum (Al_2O_3). Color appears in sapphires when small amounts of iron and titanium are present. Star stapphires contain needles of the mineral rutile that will display as a six-ray star figure when cut in the unfaceted cabochon (dome or convex) form. The most highly prized star sapphires are blue. Black or white star sapphires are less valuble. Since a ruby is simply the red variety of corundum, star rubies also exist.

What is a **tiger's eye**?

Tiger's eye is a semiprecious quartz gem that has a vertical luminescent band like that of a cat's eye. To achieve the effect of a cat's eye, veins of parallel blue asbestos fibers are first altered to iron oxides and then replaced by silica. The gem has a rich yellow to yellow-brown or brown color.

METALS

Which **metallic element** is the **most abundant**?

Aluminum is the most abundant metallic element on the surface of the Earth and moon; it comprises more than 8 percent of the Earth's crust. It is never free in nature, combining with oxygen, sand, iron, titanium, etc.; its ores are mainly bauxites (aluminum hydroxide). Nearly all rocks, particularly igneous rocks, contain aluminum as aluminosilicate minerals. Napoleon III (1808-1883) recognized that the physical characteristic of its lightness could revolutionize the arms industry, so he granted a large subsidy to French chemist Sainte-Claire Deville (1818-1881) to develop a method to make its commercial use feasible. In 1854, Deville obtained the first pure aluminum metal through the process of reduction of aluminum chloride. In 1886, the American Charles Martin Hall (1863-1914) and the Frenchman Paul Heroult (1863-1914) independently discovered an electrolytic process to produce aluminum from bauxite. Because of aluminum's resistance to corrosion, low density, and excellent heat-conducting property, the packaging industry uses a large percentage of the aluminum alloy that is produced for drink and food containers and covers, and foil pouches and wraps. It is a good conductor of electricity and is widely used in power and telephone cables, light bulbs, and electrical equipment. Large amounts of aluminum are used in the production of all types of vehicles; alloys have high tensile strengths and are of considerable industrial importance to the aerospace industry. The building construction industry uses aluminum alloys in such items as gutters, panels, siding, window frames, and roofing. Examples of the numerous other products containing aluminum and aluminum alloys are cookware, golf clubs, air conditioners, lawn furniture, license plates, paints, refrigerators, rocket fuel, and zippers.

What are the **noble metals**?

The noble metals are gold, silver, mercury, and the platinum group (including palladium, iridium, rhodium, ruthenium, and osmium). The term refers to those metals highly resistant to chemical reaction or corrosion and is contrasted with "base" metals, which are not so resistant. The term has its origins in ancient alchemy whose goals of transformation and perfection were pursued through the different properties of metals and chemicals. The term is not synonymous with "precious metals," although a metal, like platinium, may be both.

What are the **precious metals**?

This is a general term for expensive metals that are used for making coins, jewelry, and ornaments. The name is limited to gold, silver, and platinum. Expense or rarity does not make a metal precious, but rather it is a value set by law that states that the object made of these metals has a certain intrinsic value. The term is not synonymous with "noble metals," although a metal (such as platinum) may be both noble and precious.

What is **24 karat gold**?

The term "karat" refers to the percentage of gold versus the percentage of an alloy in a piece of jewelry or a decorative object. Gold is too soft to be usable in its purest form and has to be mixed with other metals. One karat is equal to one-24th part fine gold. Thus, 24 karat gold is 100 percent pure and 18 karat gold is 18/24 or 75 percent pure.

Is white gold really gold?

White gold is the name of a class of jeweler's white alloys used as substitutes for platinum. Different grades vary widely in composition, but usual alloys consist of from 20 percent to 50 percent nickel, with the balance gold. A superior class of white gold is made of 90 percent gold and 10 percent palladium. Other elements used include copper and zinc. The main use of these alloys is to give the gold a white color.

Karatage	Percentage of fine gold
24	100
22	91.75
18	75
14	58.5
12	50.25
10	42
9	37.8
8	33.75

How far can a **troy ounce of gold**, if formed into a thin wire, **be stretched** before it breaks?

Ductility is the characteristic of a substance to lend itself to shaping and stretching. A troy ounce of gold (31.1035 grams) can be drawn into a fine wire that is 50 miles (80 kilometers) long.

How thick is **gold leaf**?

Gold leaf is pure gold that is hammered or rolled into sheets or leaves so extremely thin that it can take 300,000 units to make a stack one inch high. The thickness of a single gold leaf is typically 0.0000035 inch (3.5 millionths of an inch), although this may vary widely according to which manufacturer makes it. Also called gold foil, it is used for architectural coverings and for hot-embossed printing on leather.

What is **sterling silver**?

Sterling silver is a high-grade alloy that contains a minimum of 925 parts in 1,000 of silver (92.5 percent silver and 7.5 percent of another metal—usually copper).

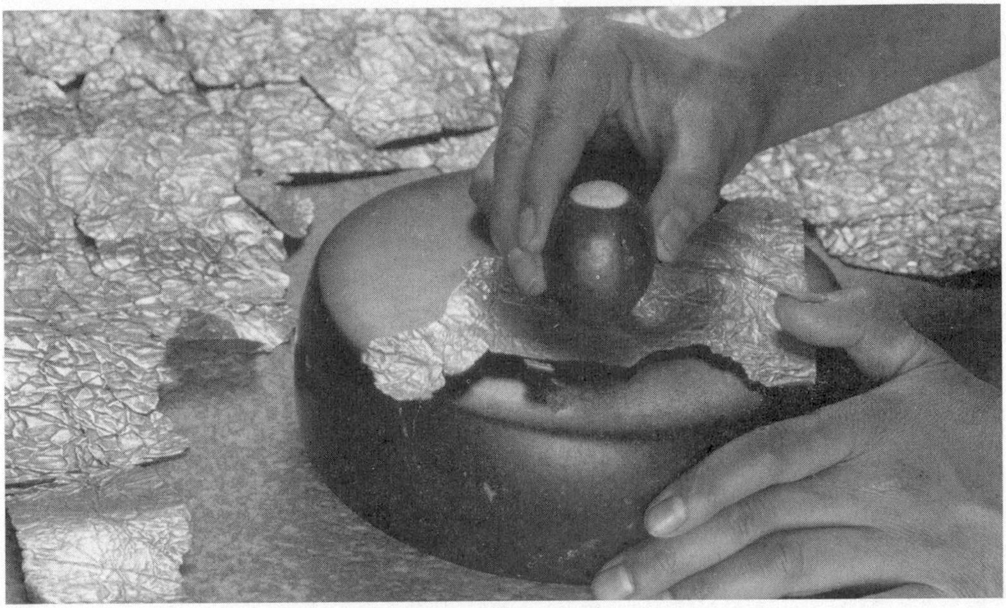

Gold leaf is shown here being worked on a smooth stone.

What is **German silver**?

Nickel silver, sometimes known as German silver or nickel brass, is a silver-white alloy composed of 52 percent to 80 percent copper, 10 percent to 35 percent zinc, and 5 percent to 35 percent nickel. It may also contain a small percent of lead and tin. There are other forms of nickel silver, but the term "German silver" is the name used in the silverware trade.

Which metal is the main component of **pewter**?

Tin—at least 90 percent. Antimony, copper, and zinc may be added in place of lead to harden and strengthen pewter. Pewter may still contain lead, but high lead content will both tarnish the piece and dissolve into food and drink to become toxic. The alloy used today in fine quality pieces contain 91-95 percent minimum tin, 8 percent maximum antimony, 2.5 percent maximum copper, and 0-5 percent maximum bismuth, as determined by the European Standard for pewter.

Where were the first successful **ironworks** in America?

Although iron ore in this country was first discovered in North Carolina in 1585, and the manufacture of iron was first undertaken (but never accomplished) in Virginia in 1619, the first successful ironworks in America was established by Thomas Dexter and Robert Bridges near the Saugus River in Lynn, Massachusetts. As the original promoters of the enterprise, they hired John Winthrop, Jr. from England to begin production. By 1645, a blast furnace had begun operations, and by 1648 a forge was working there.

What is **high speed steel**?

High speed steel is a general name for high alloy steels that retain their hardness at very high temperatures and are used for metal-cutting tools. All high speed steels are based on either tungsten or molybdenum (or both) as the primary heat-resisting alloying element. These steels require a special heat so that their unique properties can be fully realized. The manufacturing process consists of heating the steel to a temperature of 2,150°F to 2,400°F (1,175°C to 1,315°C) to obtain solution of a substantial percentage of the alloy carbides, quenching to room temperature, tempering at 1,000°F to 1,150°F (535°C to 620°C), and again cooling to room temperature.

Who invented **stainless steel**?

Metallurgists in several countries developed stainless steel, a group of iron-based alloys combined with chromium in order to be resistant to rusting and corrosion. Chromium was used in small amounts in 1872 to strengthen the steel of the Eads Bridge over the Mississippi River, but it wasn't until the 1900's that a truly rust-resistant alloy was developed. Metallurgists in several countries developed stainless steel between 1903 and 1912. An American, Elwood Haynes, developed several alloy steels and in 1911 produced stainless steel. Harry Brearly of Great Britain receives most of the credit for its development. Frederick Beckett, a Canadian-American metallurgist, and German scientists P. Monnartz and W. Borchers were among the early developers.

What material is used to make a **tuning fork**?

A tuning fork, an instrument that when struck emits a fixed pitch, is generally made of steel. Some tuning forks are made of aluminum, magnesium-alloy, fused quartz, or other elastic material.

Which countries have **uranium** deposits?

Uranium, a radioactive metallic element, is the only natural material capable of sustaining nuclear fission. But only one isotope, uranium-235, which occurs in one molecule out of 40 of natural uranium, can undergo fission under neutron bombardment. Mined in various parts of the world, it must then be converted during purification to uranium dioxide (UO_2). Uranium deposits occur throughout the world; the largest are in the United States (the Colorado Plateau and low-grade reserves in Florida, Tennessee, North Dakota, and South Dakota), Canada (Ontario, Northwest Territories, and west-central), South Africa (the Witwatersrand), and Gabon (Oklo). Other countries and areas having significant low-grade deposits are Brazil, Russia, North Africa, and Sweden. Previously significant reserves in Zaire are almost exhausted.

What is **technetium**?

Technetium (Tc, element 43) is a radioactive metallic element that does not occur naturally either in its pure form or as compounds; it is produced during nuclear fission. A fission product of molybdenum (Mo, element 42), Tc can also occur as a fission product of uranium (U, element 92). It was the first element to be made artificially in 1937 when it was isolated and extracted by C. Perrier and Emilio Segrè (1905-1989).

Tc has found significant application in diagnostic imaging and nuclear medicine. Ingested soluble technetium compounds tend to concentrate in the liver and are valuable in labeling and in radiological examination of that organ. Also, by technetium labeling of blood serum components, diseases involving the circulatory system can be explored.

NATURAL SUBSTANCES

What is **obsidian**?

Obsidian is a volcanic glass that usually forms in the upper parts of lava flows. Embryonic crystal growths, known as crystallites, make the glass an opaque, jet-black color. Red or brown obsidian could result if iron oxide dust is present. There are some well-known formations in existence, including the Obsidian Cliffs in Yellowstone Park and Mount Hekla in Iceland.

Is **lodestone** a magnet?

Lodestone is a naturally occurring variety of magnetic iron oxide or magnetite. Lodestone is frequently called a natural magnet because it attracts iron objects and possesses polarity. It was used by early mariners to find magnetic north. Other names for lodestone are loadstone, leading stone, and Hercules stone.

What is **red dog**?

Red dog is the residue from burned coal dumps. The dumps are composed of waste products incidental to coal mining. Under pressure in these waste dumps, the waste frequently ignites from spontaneous combustion, producing a red-colored ash, which is used for driveways, parking lots, and roads.

What are some uses for **coal** other than as an energy resource?

In the past, many of the aromatic compounds, such as benzene, toluene, and xylene were made from coal. These compounds are now chiefly byproducts of petroleum. Naphthalene and phenanthrene are still obtained from coal tar. Coal tar, a byproduct of coal, is used in roofing.

What is **diatomite**?

Diatomite (also called diatomaceous earth) is a white- or cream-colored, friable, porous rock composed of the fossil remains of diatoms (small water plants with silica cell walls). These fossils build up on the ocean bottoms to form diatomite, and in some places these areas have become dry land or diatomacceous earth. Chemically inert and having a rough texture and other unusual physical properties, it is suitable for many scientific and industrial purposes, including use as a filtering agent; building material; heat, cold, and sound insulator; catalyst carrier; filler absorbent; abrasive; and ingredient in pharmaceutical preparations. Dynamite is made from it by soaking it in the liquid explosive nitroglycerin.

What is **fly ash**?

Fly ash is the very fine portion or ash residue that results from the combustion of coal. The fly ash portion is usually removed electrostatically from the coal combustion gasses before they are released to the atmosphere. About 31 percent of the 57 million metric tons produced annually in the United States are beneficially used; the remainder must be disposed of in ponds or landfills.

In **coal mining** what is meant by **damp**?

Damp is a poisonous or explosive gas in a mine. The most common type of damp is firedamp, also known as methane. White damp is carbon monoxide. Blackdamp (or chokedamp) is a mixture of nitrogen and carbon dioxide formed by mine fires and explosion of firedamp in mines. Blackdamp extinguishes fire and suffocates its victims.

What is **fuller's earth**?

It is a naturally occurring white or brown clay containing aluminum magnesium silicate. Fuller's earth acts as a catalyst and was named for a process known as fulling—a process used to clean grease from wool and cloth. It is currently used for lightening the color of oils and fats, as a pigment extender, as a filter, as an absorbent (for example, in litter boxes to absorb animal waste), and in floor sweeping compounds.

How is **charcoal** made?

Commercial production of charcoal uses wood processing residues, such as sawdust, shavings, milled wood and bark as a raw material. Depending on the material, the residues are placed in kilns or furnaces and heated at low oxygen concentrations. A Herreshoff furnace can produce at least a ton of charcoal per hour.

What products come from **tropical forests**?

Products from Tropical Forests

Woods	**Houseplants**	**Spices**	**Foods**
Balsa	*Anthurium*	Allspice	Avocado
Mahogany	Croton	Black pepper	Banana
Rosewood	*Dieffenbachia*	Cardamom	Coconut
Sandalwood	*Dracaena*	Cayenne	Grapefruit
Teak	Fiddle-leaf fig	Chili	Lemon
	Mother-in-law's tongue	Cinnamon	Lime
Fibers	Parlor ivy	Cloves	Mango
Bamboo	*Philodendron*	Ginger	Orange
Jute/Kenaf	Rubber tree plant	Mace	Papaya
Kapok	*Schefflera*	Nutmeg	Passion fruit
Raffia	Silver vase bromeliad	Paprika	Pineapple
Ramie	*Spathiphyllum*	Sesame seeds	Plantain
Rattan	Swiss cheese plant	Turmeric	Tangerine
	Zebra plant	Vanilla bean	Brazil nuts
Gums, resins			Cane sugar
Chicle latex	**Oils, etc.**		Cashew nuts
Copaiba	Camphor oil		Chocolate
Copal	Cascarilla oil		Coffee
Gutta percha	Coconut oil		Cucumber
Rubber latex	Eucalyptus oil		Hearts of palm
Tung oil	Oil of star anise		Macadamia nuts
	Palm oil		Manioc/tapioca
	Patchouli oil		Okra
	Rosewood oil		Peanuts
	Tolu balsam oil		Peppers
	Annatto		Cola beans
	Curare		Tea
	Diosgenin		
	Quinine		
	Reserpine		
	Strophanthus		
	Strychnine		
	Yang-Yang		

How much wood is used to make a ton of **paper**?

In the United States, the wood used for the manufacture of paper is mainly from small diameter bolts and pulpwood. It is usually measured by the cord or by weight. Although the fiber used in making paper is overwhelmingly wood fiber, a large percentage of other ingredients is needed. One ton of a typical paper requires two cords of wood, but also requires 55,000 gallons (208,000 liters) of water, 102 pounds (46 kilograms) of sulfur, 350 pounds (159 kilograms) of lime, 289 pounds (131 kilograms) of clay, 1.2 tons of coal, 112 kilowatt hours of power, 20 pounds (9 kilograms) of dye and pigments, and 108 pounds (49 kilograms) of starch, as well as other ingredients.

Pieces of petrified wood litter the landscape at Painted Desert National Monument, Arizona.

What does **one acre of trees** yield when cut and processed?

There are about 660 trees on one acre in a forest. When cut, one acre of trees may yield approximately 105,000 board feet of lumber or more than 30 tons of paper or 16 cords of firewood.

Does any type of **wood sink** in water?

Ironwood is a name applied to many hard, heavy woods. Some ironwoods are so dense that their specific gravity exceeds 1.0 and they are therefore unable to float in water. North American ironwoods include the American hornbeam, the mesquite, the desert ironwood, and leadwood (*Krugiodendron ferreum*), which has a specific gravity of 1.34-1.42, making it the heaviest in the United States.

How is petrified wood formed?

Petrified wood is formed when water containing dissolved minerals such as calcium carbonate ($CaCO_3$) and silicate infiltrates wood or other structures. The process takes thousands of years. The foreign material either replaces or encloses the organic matter and often retains all the structural details of the original plant material. Botanists find these types of fossils to be very important since they allow for the study of the internal structure of extinct plants. After a time, wood seems to have turned to stone because the original form and structure are retained. The wood itself does not turn to stone.

The heaviest wood is black ironwood (*Olea laurifolia*), also called South African ironwood. Found in the West Indies, it has a specific gravity of 1.49 and weighs up to 93 pounds (42.18 kilograms) per foot. The lightest wood is *Aeschynomene hispida*, found in Cuba, with a specific gravity of 0.044 and a weight of 2.5 pounds (1.13 kilograms) per foot. Balsa wood (*Ochroma pyramidale*) varies between 2.5 and 24 pounds (one to 10 kilograms) per foot.

What is **amber**?

Amber is the fossil resin of trees. The two major deposits of amber are in the Dominican Republic and Baltic. Amber came from a coniferous tree that is now extinct. Amber is usually yellow or orange in color, semitransparent or opaque with a glossy surface. It is used by both artisans and scientists.

What is **rosin**?

Rosin is the resin produced after the distillation of turpentine, obtained from several varieties of pine trees, especially the longleaf pine (*Pinus palustris*) and the slash pine (*Pinus caribaea*). Rosin has many industrial uses, including the preparation of inks, adhesives, paints, sealants, and chemicals. Rosin is also used by athletes and musicians to make smooth surfaces less slippery.

What are **naval stores**?

Naval stores are products of such coniferous trees as pine and spruce. These products include pitch, tar, resin, turpentine, pine oil, and terpenes. The term "naval stores" originated in the seventeenth century when these materials were used for building and maintaining wooden sailing ships.

Why are **essential oils** called "essential"?

Called essential oils because of their ease of solubility in alcohol to form essences, essential oils are used in flavorings, perfumes, disinfectants, medicine, and other products. They are naturally occurring volatile aromatic oils found in uncombined forms within various parts of plants (leaves, pods, etc.). These oils contain as one of their main ingredients a substance belonging to the terpene group. Examples of essential oils include bergamot, eucalyptus, ginger, pine, spearmint, and wintergreen oils. Extracted by distillation or enfleurage (extraction using fat) and mechanical pressing, these oils can now be made synthetically.

What is **gutta percha**?

Gutta percha is a rubberlike gum obtained from the milky sap of trees of the *Sapotaceae* family, found in Indonesia and Malaysia. Once of great economic value, gutta percha is now being replaced by plastics in many items, although it is still used in some electrical insulation and dental work. The English natural historian John Tradescant (c. 1570-1638) introduced gutta percha to Europe in the 1620s, and its inherent qualities gave it a slow but growing place in world trade. By the end of World War II, however, many manufacturers switched from gutta percha to plastics, which are more versatile and cheaper to produce.

What is **excelsior**?

Excelsior is a trade name dating from the mid-nineteenth century for the curly, fine wood shavings used as packing material when shipping breakable items. It is also used as a cushioning and stuffing material. Poplar, aspen, basswood or cottonwood are woods that are often made into excelsior.

What is **ambergris**?

Ambergris, a highly odorous, waxy substance found floating in tropical seas, is a secretion from the sperm whale (*Physeter catodon*). The whale secretes ambergris to protect its stomach from the sharp bone of the cuttlefish, a squid-like sea mollusk, which it ingests. Ambergris is used in perfumery as a fixature to extend the life of a perfume and as a flavoring for food and beverages. Today ambergris is synthesized and used by the perfume trade, which has voluntarily refused to purchase natural ambergris to protect sperm whales from exploitation.

From where do **frankincense and myrrh** originate?

Frankincense is an aromatic gum resin obtained by tapping the trunks of trees belonging to the genus *Boswellia*. The milky resin hardens when exposed to the air and forms irregular lumps—the form in which it is usually marketed. Also called olibanum, frankincense is used in pharmaceuticals, as a perfume, as a fixative, and in fumigants and incense. Myrrh comes from a tree of the genus *Commiphora*, a native of Arabia and Northeast Africa. It too is a resin obtained from the tree trunk and is used in pharmaceuticals, perfumes, and toothpaste.

Where does **isinglass** come from?

Isinglass is the purest form of animal gelatin. It is manufactured from the swimming bladder of sturgeon and other fishes. It is used in the clarification of wine and beer as well as in the making of some cements, jams, jellies, and soups.

OBSERVATION AND MEASUREMENT

What is **magnetic declination**?

It is the angle between magnetic north and true north at a given point on the Earth's surface. It varies at different points on the Earth's surface and at different times of the year.

Which direction does a **compass needle point** at the **north pole**?

At the north magnetic pole, the compass needle would be attracted by the ground and point straight down.

What is a **Foucault pendulum**?

An instrument devised by Jean Foucault (1819-1868) in 1851 to prove that the Earth rotates on an axis, the pendulum consisted of a heavy ball suspended by a very long fine wire. Sand beneath the pendulum recorded the plane of rotation of the pendulum over time.

A reconstruction of Foucault's experiment is located in Portland, Oregon, at its Convention Center. It swings from a cable 90 feet (27.4 meters) long, making it the longest pendulum in the world.

What are the major eras, periods, and epochs in **geologic time**?

Modern dating techniques have given a range of dates as to when the various geologic time periods have started, as they are listed below:

Era	Period	Epoch	Beginning date (Est. millions of years)
Cenozoic	Quaternary	Holocene	10,000 years ago
		Pleistocene	1.9
	Tertiary	Pliocene	6
		Miocene	25
		Oligocene	38
		Eocene	55
		Paleocene	65
Mesozoic	Cretaceous		135
	Jurassic		200
	Triassic		250
Paleozoic	Permian		285
	Carboniferous (divided into Mississippian and Pennsylvanian periods by some in the U.S.)		350
	Devonian		410
	Silurian		425
	Ordovician		500
	Cambrian		570
Precambrian	Proterozoic		2500
	Archeozoic		3800
	Azoic		4600

What is the **prime meridian**?

The north-south lines on a map run from the North Pole to the South Pole and are called "meridians." The word "meridian" means "noon": When it is noon on one place on the line, it is noon at any other point as well. The lines are used to measure longitudes, or how far east or west a particular place might be, and they are 69 miles (111 kilometers) apart at the equator. The east-west lines are called parallels, and, unlike meridians, are all parallel to each other. They measure latitude, or how far north or south a particular place might be. There are 180 lines circling the Earth, one for each degree of latitude. The degrees of both latitude and longitude are divided into 60 minutes, which are then further divided into 60 seconds each.

The prime meridian is the meridian of 0 degrees longitude, used as the origin for measurement of longitude. The meridian of Greenwich, England, is used almost universally for this purpose.

What is **Mercator's projection** for maps?

The Mercator projection is a modification of a standard cylindrical projection, a technique used by cartographers to transfer the spherical proportions of the Earth to the flat surface of a map. For correct proportions, the parallels, or lines of latitude, are spaced at increasing distances toward the poles, resulting in severe exaggeration of size in the polar regions. Greenland, for example, appears five times larger than it actually is. Created by Flemish cartographer Gerardus Mercator in 1569, this projection is useful primarily because compass directions appear as straight lines, making it ideal for navigation.

Who is regarded as the **founder** of **American geology**?

Born in Scotland, the American William Maclure (1763-1840) was a member of a commission set up to settle claims between the United States and France from 1803 through 1807. In 1809 he made a geographical chart of the United States in which the land areas were divided by rock types. In 1817 he revised and enlarged this map. Maclure wrote the first English language articles and books on United States geology.

When were **relief maps** first used?

The Chinese were the first to use relief maps, in which the contours of the terrain were represented in models. Relief maps in China go back at least to the third century B.C.E. Some early maps were modeled in rice or carved in wood. It is likely that the idea of making relief maps was transmitted from the Chinese to the Arabs and then to Europe. The earliest known relief map in Europe was a map showing part of Austria, made in 1510 by Paul Dox.

From what distance are **satellite photographs** taken?

U.S. Department of Defense satellites orbit at various distances above the Earth. Some satellites are in low orbit, 100 to 300 miles (160 to 483 kilometers) above the surface, while others are positioned at intermediate altitudes from 500 to 1,000 miles (804 to 1,609 kilometers) high. Some have an altitude of 22,300 miles (35,880 kilometers).

What are **Landsat maps**?

They are images of the Earth taken at an altitude of 567 miles (912 kilometers) by an orbiting Landsat satellite, or ERTS (Earth Resources Technology Satellite). The Landsats were originally launched in the 1970s. Rather than cameras, the Landsats use multispectral scanners, which detect visible green and blue wavelengths, and four infrared and near-infrared wavelengths. These scanners can detect differences between soil, rock, water, and vegetation; types of vegetation; states of vegetation (e.g., healthy/unhealthy or underwatered/well-watered); and mineral content. The differences are especially accurate when multiple wavelengths are compared using multispectral scanners. Even visible light images have proved useful—some of the earliest Landsat images showed that some small Pacific islands were up to 10 miles (16 kilometers) away from their charted positions.

The results are displayed in "false-color" maps, where the scanner data is represented in shades of easily distinguishable colors—usually, infrared is shown as red, red as green, and green as blue. The maps are used by farmers, oil companies, geologists, foresters, foreign governments, and others interested in land management. Each image covers an area approximately 115 square miles (185 square kilometers). Maps are offered for sale by the United States Geological Survey.

Other systems that produce similar images include the French SPOT satellites, Russian Salyut and Mir manned space stations, and NASA's Airborne Imaging Spectrometer, which senses 128 infrared bands. NASA's Jet Propulsion Laboratories are developing instruments that will sense 224 bands in infrared, which will be able to detect specific minerals absorbed by plants.

What is **Global Positioning System (GPS)** and how does it work?

The Global Positioning System (GPS) has three parts: the space part, the user part, and the control part. The space part consists of 24 satellites in orbit 11,000 nautical miles (20,300 kilometers) above the Earth. The user part consists of a GPS receiver, which may be hand-held or mounted in a vehicle. The control part consists of five ground stations worldwide to assure the satellites are working properly. Using a GPS receiver an individual can determine his or her location on or above the Earth to within about 300 feet (90 meters).

CLIMATE AND WEATHER

TEMPERATURE

What is **El Niño**?

El Niño is the unusual warming of the surface waters of large parts of the tropical Pacific Ocean. Occurring around Christmastime, it is named after the Christ child. El Niño occurs erratically every three to seven years. It brings heavy rains and flooding to Peru, Ecuador, and southern California, and a milder winter with less snow to the northeastern United States. Studies reveal that El Niño is not an isolated occurrence, but is instead part of a pattern of change in the global circulation of the oceans and atmosphere. The 1982-83 El Niño was one of the most severe climate events of the twentieth century in both its geographical extent as well as in the degree of warming (14°F or 8°C).

What is **La Niña**?

La Niña is the opposite of El Niño. It refers to a period of cold surface temperatures of the tropical Pacific Ocean. La Niña winters are especially harsh with heavy snowfall in the northeastern United States and rain in the Pacific Northweast.

Is the **world** actually **getting warmer**?

During the past century, global surface temperatures have increased at a rate near 1.1°F/century (0.6°C/century). This trend has dramatically increased to a rate approaching 3.6°F/century (2.0°C/century) during the past 25 years. There have been two sustained periods of warming, one beginning around 1910 and ending around 1945, and the most recent beginning about 1976. The year 1998 was the warmest year on record, with an average land temperature that was 1.35°F (0.75°C) above the 1880-2000 average land temperature of 47.3°F (8.5°C). The second warmest year on record was 2001, when the average annual global temperature was 57.9°F (14.4°C), which is 0.9°F (0.5°C) above the 1880-2000 long-term average. For the contiguous U.S., the preliminary 2001 average annual temperature was 54.3°F (12.4°C), which was 1.5°F (0.8°C) above the 1895-2001 mean, the sixth warmest on record.

What is a **heat wave**?

A heat wave is a period of two days in a row when apparent temperatures on the National Weather Service heat index exceed 105°F to 110°F (40°C to 43°C). The temperature standards vary greatly for different locales. Heat waves can be extremely dangerous. According to the National Weather Service, 175-200 Americans die from heat in a normal summer. Between 1936 and 1975, as many as 15,000 Americans died from problems related to heat. In 1980, 1,250 people died during a brutal heat wave in the Midwest. In 1995, more than 500 people died in the city of Chicago from heat related problems. A majority of these individuals were the elderly living in high-rise apartment buildings without proper air conditioning. Large concentrations of buildings, parking lots, and roads create an "urban heat island" in cities.

What is the **heat index**?

The index is a measure of what hot weather feels like to the average person for various temperatures and relative humidities. Heat exhaustion and sunstroke are inclined to happen when the heat index reaches 105°F (40°C). The chart below provides the heat index for some temperatures and relative humidities.

	Air Temperature (°F)										
	70	75	80	85	90	95	100	105	110	115	120
Relative Humidity	Feels like (°F)										
0%	64	69	73	78	83	87	91	95	99	103	107
10%	65	70	75	80	85	90	95	100	105	111	116
20%	66	72	77	82	87	93	99	105	112	120	130
30%	67	73	78	84	90	96	104	113	123	135	148
40%	68	74	79	86	93	101	110	123	137	151	
50%	69	75	81	88	96	107	120	135	150		
60%	70	76	82	90	100	114	132	149			
70%	70	77	85	93	106	124	144				
80%	71	78	86	97	113	136					
90%	71	79	88	102	122						
100%	72	80	91	108							

How can the temperature be determined from the frequency of cricket chirps?

Listen for the chirping of either katydids or crickets, then count the number of chirps you hear in one minute. For the following equations "C" equals the number of chirps per minute:

For katydids, Fahrenheit temperature = 60 + (C-19)/3

For crickets, Fahrenheit temperature = 50 + (C-50)/4

Which place has the **maximum amount of sunshine** in the United States?

Yuma, Arizona, has an annual average of 90 percent of sunny days, or over 4,000 sunny hours per year. St. Petersburg, Florida, had 768 consecutive sunny days from February 9, 1967, to March 17, 1969. On the other extreme, the South Pole has no sunshine for 182 days annually, and the North Pole has none for 176 days.

Why was 1816 known as the **year without a summer**?

The eruption of Mount Tambora, a volcano in Indonesia, in 1815 threw billions of cubic yards of dust over 15 miles (24 kilometers) into the atmosphere. Because the dust penetrated the stratosphere, wind currents spread it throughout the world. As a consequence of this volcanic activity, in 1816 normal weather patterns were greatly altered. Some parts of Europe and the British Isles experienced average temperatures 2.9 to 5.8°F (1.6 to 3.2°C) below normal. In New England heavy snow fell between June 6 and June 11 and frost occurred every month of 1816. Crop failures were experienced in Western Europe and Canada as well as in New England. By 1817 the excess dust had settled and the climate returned to more normal conditions.

Why are the hot, humid days of summer called **"dog days"**?

This period of extremely hot, humid, sultry weather that traditionally occurs in the northern hemisphere in July and August received its name from the dog star Sirius of the constellation Canis Major. At this time of year, Sirius, the brightest visible star, rises in the east at the same time as the sun. Ancient Egyptians believed that the heat of this brilliant star added to the sun's heat to create this hot weather. Sirius was blamed for the withering droughts, sickness, and discomfort that occurred during this time. Traditional dog days start on July 3 and end on August 11.

What is **Indian summer**?

The term Indian summer dates back to at least 1778. The term may relate to the way the Native Americans availed themselves of the nice weather to increase their winter food supplies. It refers to a period of pleasant, dry, warm days in the middle to late autumn, usually after the first killing frost.

AIR PHENOMENA

What is a **bishop's ring**?

It is a ring around the sun, usually with a reddish outer edge. It is probably due to dust particles in the air, since it is seen after all great volcanic eruptions.

When does the **green flash phenomenon** occur?

On rare occasions, the sun may look bright green for a moment, as the last tip of the sun is setting. This green flash occurs because the red rays of light are hidden below the horizon and the blue are scattered in the atmosphere. The green rays are seldom seen because of dust and pollution in the lower atmosphere. It may best be seen when the air is cloudless and when a distant, well-defined horizon exists, as on an ocean.

How often does an **aurora** appear?

Because it depends on solar winds (electrical particles generated by the sun) and sunspot activity, the frequency of an aurora cannot be determined. Auroras usually appear two days after a solar flare (a violent eruption of particles on the sun's surface) and reach their peak two years into the 11-year sunspot cycle. The auroras, occurring in the polar regions, are broad displays of usually colored light at night. The northern polar aurora is called Aurora Borealis or Northern Lights and the southern polar aurora is called the Aurora Australis.

When and by whom were **clouds** first classified?

The French naturalist Jean Lamarck (1744-1829) proposed the first system for classifying clouds in 1802. His work, however, did not receive wide acclaim. A year later the Englishman Luke Howard (1772-1864) developed a cloud classification system that has been generally accepted and is still used today. Clouds are distinguished by their general appearance ("heap clouds" and "layer clouds") and by their height above the

The Aurora Borealis, or Northern Lights, illuminate the sky over a Canadian boreal forest.

ground. Latin names and prefixes are used to describe these characteristics. The shape names are cirrus (curly or fibrous), stratus (layered), and cumulus (lumpy or piled). The prefixes denoting height are cirro (high clouds with bases above 20,000 feet [6,067 meters]) and alto (mid-level clouds from 6,000 to 20,000 feet [1,820 to 6,067 meters]). There is no prefix for low clouds. Nimbo or nimbus is also added as a name or prefix to indicate that the cloud produces precipitation.

What are the **four major cloud groups** and their types?

1. High Clouds—composed almost entirely of ice crystals. The bases of these clouds start at 16,500 feet (5,000 meters) and reach 45,000 feet (13,650 meters).

   Cirrus (from Latin, "lock of hair")—are thin, feather-like crystal clouds in patches or narrow bands. The large ice crystals that often trail downward in well-defined wisps are called "mares tails."

   Cirrostratus—is a thin, white cloud layer that resembles a veil or sheet. This layer can be striated or fibrous. Because of the ice content, these clouds are associated with the halos that surround the sun or moon.

   Cirrocumulus—are thin clouds that appear as small white flakes or cotton patches and may contain super-cooled water.

2. Middle Clouds—composed primarily of water. The height of the cloud bases range from 6,500 to 23,000 feet (2,000 to 7,000 meters).

   Altostratus—appears as a bluish or grayish veil or layer of clouds that can gradually merge into altocumulus clouds. The sun may be dimly visible through it, but flat, thick sheets of this cloud type can obscure the sun.

   Altocumulus—is a white or gray layer or patches of solid clouds with rounded shapes.

3. Low Clouds—composed almost entirely of water that may at times be super-cooled; at subfreezing temperatures, snow and ice crystals may be present as well. The bases of these clouds start near the Earth's surface and climb to 6,500 feet (2,000 meters) in the middle latitudes.

   Stratus—are gray, uniform, sheet-like clouds with a relatively low base, or they can be patchy, shapeless, low gray clouds. Thin enough for the sun to shine through, these clouds bring drizzle and snow.

   Stratocumulus—are globular rounded masses that form at the top of the layer.

   Nimbostratus—are seen as a gray or dark, relatively shapeless, massive cloud layer containing rain, snow, and ice pellets.

4. Clouds with Vertical Development—contain super-cooled water above the freezing level and grow to great heights. The cloud bases range from 1,000 feet (300 meters) to 10,000 feet (3,000 meters).

   Cumulus—are detached, fair-weather clouds with relatively flat bases and dome-shaped tops. These usually do not have extensive vertical development and do not produce precipitation.

   Cumulonimbus—are unstable, large, vertical clouds with dense boiling tops that bring showers, hail, thunder, and lightning.

How **hot** is **lightning**?

The temperature of the air around a bolt of lightning is about 54,000°F (30,000°C), which is six times hotter than the surface of the sun, yet many times people survive being struck by a bolt of lightning. American park ranger Roy Sullivan, for example, was hit by lightning seven times between 1942 and 1977. In cloud-to-ground lightning, its energy seeks the shortest route to Earth, which could be through a person's shoulder, down the side of the body, through the leg, and to the ground. As long as the lightning does not pass across the heart or spinal column, the victim usually does not die.

Does lightning ever strike twice in the same place?

It is not true that lightning does not strike twice in the same place. In fact, tall buildings, such as the Empire State Building in New York, can be struck several times during the same storm. During one storm, lightning struck the Empire State Building 12 times.

How many **volts** are in **lightning**?

A stroke of lightning discharges from 10 to 100 million volts of electricity. An average lightning stroke has 30,000 amperes.

How is the **distance** of a lightning flash calculated?

Count the number of seconds between seeing a flash of lightning and hearing the sound of the thunder. Divide the number by five to determine the number of miles away that the lightning flashed.

What is **ball lightning**?

Ball lightning is a rare form of lightning in which a persistent and moving luminous white or colored sphere is seen. It can last from a few seconds to several minutes, and it travels at about a walking pace. Spheres have been reported to vanish harmlessly, or to pass into or out of rooms—leaving, in some cases, sign of their passage such as a hole in a window pane. Sphere dimensions vary but are most commonly from four to eight inches (10 to 20 centimeters) in diameter.

Other types of lightning include the common streak lightning (a single or multiple zigzagging line from cloud to ground); forked lightning (lightning that forms two branches simultaneously); sheet lightning (a shapeless flash covering a broad area); ribbon lightning (streak lightning blown sideways by the wind to make it appear like parallel successive strokes); bead or chain lightning (a stroke interrupted or broken into evenly spaced segments or beads); and heat lightning (lightning seen along the horizon during hot weather and believed to be a reflection of lightning occurring beyond the horizon).

What are **fulgurites**?

Fulgurites (from the Latin word *fulgur,* meaning lightning) are petrified lightning, created when lightning strikes an area of dry sand. The intense heat of the lightning melts the sand surrounding the stroke into a rough, glassy tube forming a fused record of its path. These tubes may be one-half to two inches (1.5 to five centimeters) in diameter, and up to 10 feet (three meters) in length. They are extremely brittle and break easily. The inside walls of the tube are glassy and lustrous while the outside is rough, with sand particles adhering to it. Fulgurites are usually tan or black in color, but translucent white ones have been found.

What is **Saint Elmo's fire**?

Saint Elmo's fire has been described as a corona from electric discharge produced on high grounded metal objects, chimney tops, and ship masts. Since it often occurs during thunderstorms, the electrical source may be lightning. Another description refers to this phenomenon as weak static electricity formed when an electrified cloud touches a high exposed point. Molecules of gas in the air around this point become ionized and glow. The name originated with sailors who were among the first to witness the display of spearlike or tufted flames on the tops of their ships' masts. Saint Elmo (which is a corruption of Saint Ermo) is the patron saint of sailors, so they named the fire after him.

What is the order of **colors** in a **rainbow**?

Red, orange, yellow, green, blue, indigo, and violet are the colors of the rainbow, but these are not necessarily the sequence of colors that an observer might see. Rainbows are formed when raindrops reflect sunlight. As sunlight enters the drops, the different wavelengths of the colors that compose sunlight are refracted at different lengths to produce a spectrum of color. Each observer sees a different set of raindrops at a slightly different angle. Drops at different angles from the observer send different wave lengths (i.e., different color) to the observer's eyes. Since the color sequence of the rainbow is the result of refraction, the color order depends on how the viewer sees this refraction from the viewer's angle of perception.

WIND

Where do **haboobs** occur?

Haboobs, derived from the Arabic word "habb" meaning to blow, are violent dust storms with strong winds of sand and dust. They are most common in the Sahara region of Africa and the deserts of southwestern United States, Australia, and Asia.

What is **wind shear**?

Wind shear refers to rapid changes in wind speed and/or direction over short distances and is usually associated with thunderstorms. It is especially dangerous to aircraft.

What is the effect of a **microburst** on aircraft?

Microbursts are downbursts with a diameter of 2.5 miles (4 kilometers) or less. Often associated with thunderstorms, they can generate winds of hurricane force that change direction abruptly. Headwinds can become tailwinds in a matter of seconds, resulting in a loss of airspeed and loss of altitude. After microbursts caused several major air catastrophes in the 1970s and 1980s, the Federal Aviation Administration (FAA) installed warning and radar systems at airports to alert pilots to wind shear and microburst conditions.

What conditions result in **microclimates**?

Microclimates are small-scale regions where the average weather conditions are measurably different from the larger, surrounding region. Differences in temperature, precipitation, wind, or cloud cover can produce microclimates. Frequent causes of microclimates are differences in elevation, mountains that alter wind patterns, shorelines, and man-made structures, such as buildings, that can alter the wind patterns.

What is the **Coriolis effect**?

The 19th-century French engineer Gaspard C. Coriolis (1792-1843) discovered that the rotation of the Earth deflects streams of air. Because the Earth spins to the east, all moving objects in the Northern Hemisphere tend to turn somewhat to the right of a straight path, while those in the Southern Hemisphere turn slightly left. The Coriolis effect explains the lack of northerly and southerly winds in the tropics and polar regions; the northeast and southeast trade winds and the polar easterlies all owe their westward deflection to the Coriolis effect.

When was the **jet stream** discovered?

A jet stream is a flat and narrow tube of air that moves more rapidly than the surrounding air. Discovered by World War II bomber pilots flying over Japan and the Mediterranean Sea, jet streams have become important with the advent of airplanes capable of cruising at over 30,000 feet (9,144 meters). The currents of air flow from west to east and are usually a few miles deep, up to 100 miles (160 kilometers) wide, and well over 1,000 miles (1,600 kilometers) in length. The air current must flow at over 57.5 miles (92 kilometers) per hour.

There are two polar jet streams, one in each hemisphere. They meander between 30 and 70 degrees latitude, occur at altitudes of 25,000 to 35,000 feet (7,620 to 10,668 meters), and achieve maximum speeds of over 230 miles (368 kilometers) per hour. The subtropical jet streams (again one per hemisphere) wander between 20 and 50 degrees latitude. They are found at altitudes of 30,000 to 45,000 feet (9,144 to 13,715 meters) and have speeds of over 345 miles (552 kilometers) per hour.

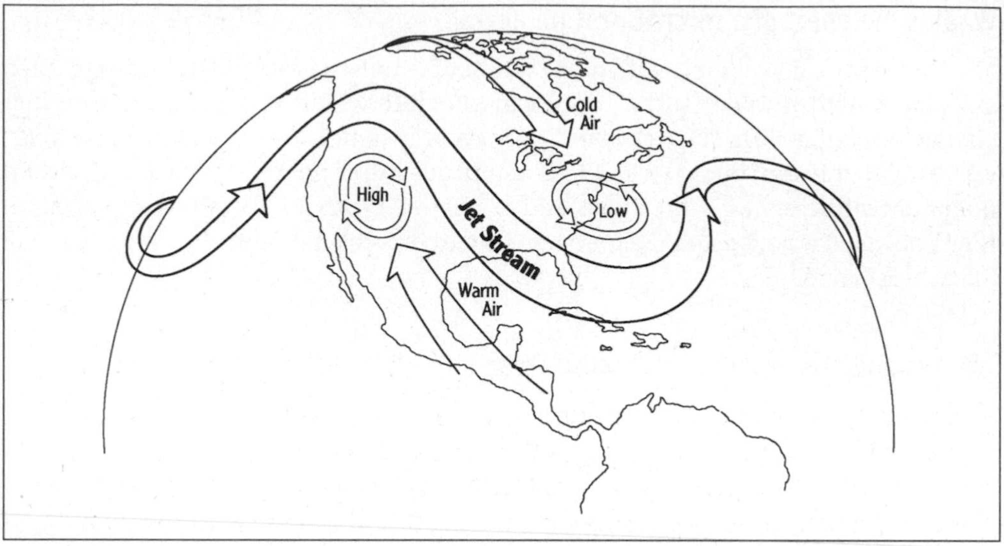

Jet stream

Why are the **horse latitudes** called by that name?

The horse latitudes are two high pressure belts characterized by low winds about 30 degrees north and south of the equator. Dreaded by early sailors, these areas have undependable winds with periods of calm. In the northern hemisphere, particularly near Bermuda, sailing ships carrying horses from Spain to the New World were often becalmed. When water supplies ran low, these animals were the first to be rationed water. Dying from thirst or tossed overboard, the animals were sacrificed to conserve water for the men. Explorers and sailors reported that the seas were "strewn with bodies of horses," which may be why the areas are called the horse latitudes. The term might also be rooted in complaints by sailors who were paid in advance and received no overtime when the ships slowly traversed this area. During this time they were said to be "working off a dead horse."

What is a **Siberian express**?

This term describes storms that are severely cold and cyclonic; they descend from northern Canada and Alaska to other parts of the United States.

What is an **Alberta clipper**?

An Alberta Clipper is a little gyrating storm that develops on the Pacific front, usually over the Rocky Mountains of Alberta, Canada. This quick-moving storm moves southeast into the Great Plains, leaving a trail of cold air.

What is a **Chinook**?

It is a wind that is generally warm and originates from the eastern slope of the Rocky Mountains. It often moves from the southwest in a downslope manner, causing a noticeable rise in temperature that helps to warm the plains just east of the Rocky Mountains.

The Chinook is classified as a katabatic wind. A katabatic wind develops because of cold, heavy air spilling down sloping terrain, moving the lighter, warmer air in front of it. The air is dried and heated as it streams down the slope. At times the falling air becomes warmer than the air it restores. Some katabatic winds have been interestingly named, like Taku, a frigid wind in Alaska, or Santa Ana, a warmer wind from the Sierras.

Who is associated with developing the **concept of wind chill**?

The Antarctic explorer Paul A. Siple (1908-1968) coined the term in his 1939 dissertation, "Adaptation of the Explorer to the Climate of Antarctica." Siple was the youngest member of Admiral Richard Byrd's Antarctica expedition in 1928-30, and later made other trips to the Antarctic as part of Byrd's staff and for the United States Department of the Interior assigned to the United States Antarctic Expedition. He also served in many other endeavors related to the study of cold climates.

What is meant by the **wind chill factor**?

The wind chill factor, or wind chill index, is a number that expresses the cooling effect of moving air at different temperatures. It indicates in a general way how many calories of heat are carried away from the surface of the body. The National Weather Service began reporting the equivalent wind chill temperature along with the actual air temperature in 1973. For years it was believed that the index overestimated the wind's cooling effect on skin. In 2001-02 a new wind chill index was instituted, and additional corrections are expected in the next few years.

Is there a **formula** for **computing the wind chill**?

Here is how you calculate the *Old Wind Chill Index*:

$$T_{wc} = 0.081 \times (3.71 \times \sqrt{V} + 5.81 - 0.25 \times V) \times (T - 91.4) + 91.4$$

Here is how you calculate the *New Wind Chill Index* (2001-2002):

$$T_{wc} = 35.74 + 0.6215T - 35.75(V^{0.16}) + 0.4275T(V^{0.16})$$

where T_{wc} is the wind chill in degrees F, V is the wind speed in miles per hour and T is the temperature in degrees F.

How does a **cyclone** differ from a **hurricane** or a **tornado**?

All three wind phenomena are rotating winds that spiral in toward a low-pressure center as well as upward. Their differences lie in their size, wind velocity, rate of travel, and duration. Generally, the faster the winds spin, the shorter (in time) and smaller (in size) the event becomes.

A cyclone has rotating winds from 10 to 60 miles per hour (16 to 97 kilometers per hour); can be up to 1,000 miles (1,600 kilometers) in diameter, travels about 25 miles per hour (40 kilometers per hour), and lasts from one to several weeks. A hurricane (or typhoon, as it is called in the Pacific Ocean area) has winds that vary from 75 to 200 miles per hour (120 to 320 kilometers per hour), moves between 10 to 20 miles per hour (16 to 32 kilometers per hour), can have a diameter up to 600 miles (960 kilometers), and can exist from several days to more than a week. A tornado can reach a rotating speed of 300 miles per hour (400 kilometers per hour), travels between 25 to 40 miles per hour (40 to 64 kilometers per hour), and generally lasts only minutes, although some have lasted for five to six hours. Its diameter can range from 300 yards (274 meters) to one mile (1.6 kilometers) and its average path length is 16 miles (26 kilometers), with a maximum of 300 miles (483 kilometers).

Typhoons, hurricanes, and cyclones tend to breed in low-altitude belts over the oceans, generally from five degrees to fifteen degrees latitude north or south. A tornado generally forms several thousand feet above the Earth's surface, usually during warm, humid weather; many times it is in conjunction with a thunderstorm. Although a tornado can occur in many places, they mostly appear on the continental plains of North America (i.e., from the Plains States eastward to western New York and the southeastern Atlantic states). Eighty-two percent of tornadoes materialize during the warmest hours of the day (noon to midnight), while 23 percent of all tornado activity occurs between 4 p.m. and 6 p.m.

What is the **Enhanced Fujita Scale**?

Proposed by the National Weather Service in February 2006, and first put into use on February 1, 2007, the Enhanced Fujita Scale (EFS) was created to better reflect actual damages recorded since the original Fujita Scale was developed. The original scale, which was felt to be too general, did not take into careful enough account the different types of construction. The new scale ranks tornadoes from EF0 up to EF5.

Enhanced Fujita Scale

Scale	Wind Speed (mph/kph)	Damages
EF0	65–85/105–137	Tree branches break off, trees with shallow roots fall over; house siding and gutters damaged; some roof shingles peel off or other minor roof damage.

Scale	Wind Speed (mph/kph)	Damages
EF1	86–110/137–177	Mobile homes overturned; doors, windows, and glass broken; severe damage to roofs.
EF2	111–135/178–217	Large tree trunks split and big trees fall over; mobile homes destroyed, and homes on foundations are shifted; cars lifted off the ground; roofs torn off; some lighter objects thrown at the speed of missiles.
EF3	136–165/218–265	Trees broken and debarked; mobile homes completely destroyed and houses on foundations lose stories, and buildings with weaker foundations are lifted and blown distances; commercial buildings such as shopping malls are severely damaged; heavy cars are thrown and trains are tipped over.
EF4	166–200/266–322	Frame houses leveled; cars thrown long distances; larger objects become dangerous projectiles.
EF5	>200/ >323	Homes are completely destroyed and even steel-reinforced buildings are severely damaged; objects the size of cars are thrown distances of 300 feet (90 meters) or more. Total devastation.

What is the **Beaufort scale**?

The Beaufort scale was devised in 1805 by a British Admiral, Sir Francis Beaufort (1774-1857), to help mariners in handling ships. It uses a series of numbers from 0 to 17 to indicate wind speeds and applies to both land and sea.

Beaufort number	Name	Wind speed Miles per hour	Kilometers per hour
0	Calm	less than 1	less than 1.5
1	Light air	1-3	1.5-4.8
2	Light breeze	4-7	6.4-11.3
3	Gentle breeze	8-12	12.9-19.3
4	Moderate breeze	13-18	21-29
5	Fresh breeze	19-24	30.6-38.6
6	Strong breeze	25-31	40.2-50
7	Moderate gale	32-38	51.5-61.1
8	Fresh gale	39-46	62.8-74
9	Strong gale	47-54	75.6-86.9
10	Whole gale	55-63	88.5-101.4
11	Storm	64-73	103-117.5
12-17	Hurricane	74 and above	119.1 and above

Which **month** is the **most dangerous for tornadoes** in the United States?

According to one study, May is the most dangerous month for tornadoes in the United States, with an average of 329, while February's average is the safest with only three. In another study the months December and January were usually the safest, and the months having the greatest number of tornadoes were April, May, and June. In February, tornado frequency begins to increase. February tornadoes tend to occur in the central Gulf states; in March the center of activity moves eastward to the southeastern Atlantic states, where tornado activity peaks in April. In May the center of activity is in the southern Plains states; in June this moves to the northern Plains and Great Lakes area (into western New York). The most costly outbreak of tornadoes occurred in May 1999, when at least 74 tornadoes touched down in less than 48 hours in Oklahoma and Kansas, including an F5 (see scale above) on the outskirts of Oklahoma City causing $$1.1 billion in damage.

How are **hurricanes classified**?

The Saffir/Simpson Hurricane Damage-Potential scale assigns numbers 1 through 5 to measure the disaster potential of a hurricane's winds and its accompanying storm surge. The purpose of the scale, developed in 1971 by Herbert Saffir and Robert Simpson, is to help disaster agencies gauge the potential significance of these storms in terms of assistance.

Saffir/Simpson Hurricane Scale Ranges

Scale number (category)	Barometric pressure (in inches)	Winds (miles per hour)	Surge (in feet)	Damage
1	≥28.94	74-95	4-5	Minimal
2	28.50-28.91	96-110	6-8	Moderate
3	27.91-28.47	111-130	9-12	Extensive
4	27.17-27.88	131-155	13-18	Extreme
5	<27.17	>155	>18	Catastrophic

Damage categories:

Minimal—No real damage to building structures. Some tree, shrubbery, and mobile home damage. Coastal road flooding and minor pier damage.

Moderate—Some roof, window, and door damage. Considerable damage to vegetation, mobile homes, and piers. Coastal and low-lying escape routes flood two to four hours before center of storm arrives. Small craft can break moorings in unprotected areas.

Extensive—Some structural damage to small or residential buildings. Mobile homes destroyed. Flooding near coast destroys structures and floods of homes five feet (1.5 meters) above sea level as far inland as six miles (9.5 kilometers).

Extreme—Extensive roof, window, and door damage. Major damage to lower floors of structures near the shore, and some roof failure on small residences. Complete beach erosion. Flooding of terrain 10 feet (three meters) above sea level as far as six miles (9.5 kilometers) inland requiring massive residential evacuation.

Catastrophic—Complete roof failure to many buildings; some complete building failure, with small utility buildings blown away. Major damage to lower floors of all structures 19 feet (5.75 meters) above sea level located within 500 yards (547 meters) of the shoreline. Massive evacuation of residential areas on low ground five to 10 miles (eight to 16 kilometers) from shoreline may be required.

How do **hurricanes** get their **names**?

Since 1950, hurricane names have been officially selected from library sources and are decided on during the international meetings of the World Meteorological Organization (WMO). The names are chosen to reflect the cultures and languages found in the Atlantic, Caribbean, and Hawaiian regions. When a tropical storm with rotary action and wind speeds above 39 miles (63 kilometers) per hour develops, the National Hurricane Center near Miami, Florida, selects a name from one of the six listings for Region 4 (Atlantic and Caribbean area). Letters Q, U, X, Y, and Z are not included because of the scarcity of names beginning with those letters. Once a storm has done great damage, its name is retired from the six-year list cycle.

Hurricane Names: 2009 through 2013

2009	2010	2011	2012	2013
Ana	Alex	Arlene	Alberto	Andrea
Bill	Bonnie	Bret	Beryl	Barry
Claudette	Colin	Cindy	Chris	Chantal
Danny	Danielle	Don	Debby	Dorian
Erika	Earl	Emily	Ernesto	Erin
Fred	Fiona	Franklin	Florence	Fernand
Grace	Gaston	Gert	Gordon	Gabrielle
Henri	Hermine	Harvey	Helene	Humberto
Ida	Igor	Irene	Isaac	Ingrid
Joaquin	Julia	Jose	Joyce	Jerry
Kate	Karl	Katia	Kirk	Karen
Larry	Lisa	Lee	Leslie	Lorenzo
Mindy	Matthew	Maria	Michael	Melissa
Nicholas	Nicole	Nate	Nadine	Nestor
Odette	Otto	Ophelia	Oscar	Olga
Peter	Paula	Philippe	Patty	Pablo
Rose	Richard	Rina	Rafael	Rebekah

2009	2010	2011	2012	2013
Sam	Shary	Sean	Sandy	Sebastien
Teresa	Thomas	Tammy	Tony	Tanya
Victor	Virginie	Vince	Valerie	Van
Wanda	Walter	Whitney	William	Wendy

Which United States **hurricanes** have been the **most destructive**?

Hurricane	Year	Category	Damage
1. Katrina (Louisiana and nearby states)	2005	3	$100-135,000,000,000
2. Andrew (SE Florida/SE Louisiana)	1992	4	$36,000,000,000
3. Charley (Florida)	2004	4	$14,000,000,000
4. Hugo (S Carolina)	1989	4	$14,000,000,000
5. Ivan (Alabama/Florida)	2004	3	$14,000,000,000
6. Agnes (Florida)	1972	1	$11,000,000,000
7. Betsy (SE Florida/Louisiana)	1965	4	$10,800,000,000
8. Francis (Florida)	2004	2	$8,900,000,000
9. Camille (Alabama, Florida, Mississippi)	1969	5	$7,500,000,000
10. Jeanne (eastern Texas)	2004	3	$6,900,000,000

PRECIPITATION

What is a **"white-out"**?

An official definition for "white-out" does not exist. It is a colloquial term that can describe any condition during snowfall that severely restricts visibility. That may mean a blizzard, or snowsquall, etc. If you get some sunlight in the mix, that makes the situation even worse—it's like driving in fog with your headlights on high-beam. The light gets backscattered right into your eyes and you can't see.

What is the **dew point**?

The dew point is the temperature at which air is full of moisture and cannot store any more. When the relative humidity is 100 percent, the dew point is either the same as or lower than the air temperature. If a fine film of air contacts a surface and is chilled to below the dew point, then actual dew is formed. This is why dew often forms at night or early morning: as the temperature of the air falls, the amount of water vapor the air can hold also decreases. Excess water vapor then condenses as very small drops

> ### How fast does rain fall?
>
> The speed of rainfall varies with drop size and wind speed. A typical raindrop in still air falls about 600 feet (182 meters) per minute or about seven miles (11 kilometers) per hour.

on whatever it touches. Fog and clouds develop when sizable volumes of air are cooled to temperatures below the dew point.

What is the **shape of a raindrop**?

Although a raindrop has been illustrated as being pear-shaped or tear-shaped, high-speed photographs reveal that a large raindrop has a spherical shape with a hole not quite through it (giving it a doughnut-like appearance). Water surface tension pulls the drop into this shape. As a drop larger than 0.08 inch (two millimeters) in diameter falls, it will become distorted. Air pressure flattens its bottom and its sides bulge. If it becomes larger than one-quarter inch (6.4 millimeters) across, it will keep spreading crosswise as it falls and will bulge more at its sides, while at the same time, its middle will thin into a bow-tie shape. Eventually in its path downward, it will divide into two smaller spherical drops.

Where is the **rainiest place on Earth**?

The wettest place in the world is Tutunendo, Colombia, with an average annual rainfall of 463.4 inches (1,177 centimeters) per year. The place that has the most rainy days per year is Mount Wai-'ale'ale on Kauai, Hawaii. It has up to 350 rainy days annually.

In contrast, the longest rainless period in the world was from October 1903 to January 1918 at Arica, Chile—a period of 14 years. In the United States the longest dry spell was 767 days at Bagdad, California, from October 3, 1912, to November 8, 1914.

When do **thunderstorms** occur?

In the United States thunderstorms usually occur in the summertime, especially from May through August. Thunderstorms tend to occur in late spring and summer when large amounts of tropical maritime air move across the United States. Storms usually develop when the surface air is heated the most from the sun (2 to 4 p.m.). Thunderstorms are relatively rare in the New England area, North Dakota, Montana, and other northern states (latitude 60 degrees), where the air is often too cold. These storms are also rare along the Pacific Ocean because the summers there are too dry for these storms to occur. Florida, the Gulf states, and the southeastern states tend to have the most storms, averaging 70 to 90 annually. The mountainous southwest averages 50 to 70 storms annually. In the world, thunderstorms are most plentiful in the areas between latitude 35 degrees north and 35 degrees south; in these areas there can be as many as 3,200 storms within a 12-hour nighttime period. As many as 1,800 storms can occur at once throughout the world.

Lightning performs a vital function; it returns to the Earth much of the negative charge the Earth loses by leakage into the atmosphere. The annual death toll in the United States from lightning is greater than the annual death toll from tornadoes or hurricanes—150 Americans die annually from lightning-related causes, and 250 are injured.

How far away can **thunder** be heard?

Thunder is the crash and rumble associated with lightning. It is caused by the explosive expansion and contraction of air heated by the stroke of lightning. This results in sound waves that can be heard easily six to seven miles (9.7 to 11.3 kilometers) away. Occasionally such rumbles can be heard as far away as 20 miles (32.2 kilometers). The sound of great claps of thunder is produced when intense heat and the ionizing effect of repeated lightning occurs in a previously heated air path. This creates a shockwave that moves at the speed of sound.

How large can **hailstones** become?

The average hailstone is about one-quarter inch (0.64 centimeter) in diameter. However, hailstones weighing up to 7.5 pounds (3.4 kilograms) are reported to have fallen in Hyderabad state in India in 1939, although scientists think these huge hailstones may be several stones that partly melted and stuck together. On April 14, 1986, hailstones weighing 2.5 pounds (one kilogram) were reported to have fallen in the Gopalgang district of Bangladesh.

The largest hailstone recorded in the U.S. weighed nearly two pounds—many times larger than these golf ball size specimens.

The largest hailstone ever recorded in the United States fell in Coffeyville, Kansas, on September 3, 1970. It measured 5.57 inches (14.15 centimeters) in diameter and weighed 1.67 pounds (0.75 kilogram).

Hail is precipitation consisting of balls of ice. Hailstones usually are made of concentric, or onion-like, layers of ice alternating with partially melted and refrozen snow, structured around a tiny central core. It is formed in cumulonimbus or thunderclouds when freezing water and ice cling to small particles in the air, such as dust. The winds in the cloud blow the particles through zones of different temperatures, causing them to accumulate additional layers of ice and melting snow and to increase in size.

Hail Size Estimates

Description	Size	Description	Size
Pea size	0.25 inch	Golfball	1.75 inches
Penny/Dime	0.75 inch	Hen Egg	2.00 inches
Nickel	0.88 inch	Tennis Ball	2.50 inches
Quarter	1.00 inch	Baseball	2.75 inches
Half Dollar or Susan B. Anthony Dollar	1.25 inches	Grapefruit	4.00 inches
Ping Pong Ball	1.50 inches		

What is the difference between **freezing rain** and **sleet**?

Freezing rain is rain that falls as a liquid but turns to ice on contact with a freezing object to form a smooth ice coating called glaze. Usually freezing rain only lasts a short time, because it either turns to rain or to snow. Sleet is frozen or partially frozen rain in the form of ice pellets. Sleet forms when rain falls from a warm layer of air, passes through a freezing air layer near the Earth's surface, and forms hard, clear, tiny ice pellets that can hit the ground so fast that they bounce off with a sharp click.

How does **snow form**?

Snow is not frozen rain. Snow forms by sublimation of water vapor—the turning of water vapor directly into ice, without going through the liquid stage. High above the ground, chilled water vapor turns to ice when its temperature reaches the dew point. The result of this sublimation is a crystal of ice, usually hexagonal. Snow begins in the form of these tiny hexagonal ice crystals in the high clouds; the young crystals are the seeds from which snowflakes will grow. As water vapor is pumped up into the air by updrafts, more water is deposited on the ice crystals, causing them to grow. Soon some of the larger crystals fall to the ground as snowflakes.

Are all **snowflakes** shaped alike?

Some snowflakes may have strikingly similar shapes, but these twins are probably not molecularly identical. In 1986, cloud physicist Nancy Knight believed she found a uniquely cloned pair of crystals on an oil coated slide that had been hanging from an airplane. This pair may have been the result of breaking off from a star crystal, or were attached side by side, thereby

Snowflakes may appear similar in shape but are indeed unique on a molecular level.

experiencing the same weather conditions simultaneously. Unfortunately the smaller aspects of each of the snow crystals could not be studied because the photograph was unable to capture possible molecular differences. So, even if the human eye may see twins flakes, on a minuscule level these flakes are different.

Is it ever **too cold** to snow?

No matter how cold the air gets, it still contains some moisture, and this can fall out of the air in the form of very small snow crystals. Very cold air is associated with no snow because these invasions of air from northerly latitudes are associated with clearing conditions behind cold fronts. Heavy snowfalls are associated with relatively mild air in advance of a warm front. The fact that snow piles up, year after year, in Arctic regions illustrates that it is never too cold to snow.

When does **frost** form?

A frost is a crystalline deposit of small thin ice crystals formed on objects that are at freezing or below freezing temperatures. This phenomenon occurs when atmospheric water vapor condenses directly into ice without first becoming a liquid; this process is called sublimation. Usually frost appears on clear, calm nights, especially during early autumn when the air above the Earth is quite moist. Permafrost is permanently frozen ground that never thaws out completely.

WEATHER PREDICTION

What is the difference between a National Weather Service **statement, advisory, watch**, and **warning**?

The National Weather Service will issue a *statement* as a "first alert" of the possibility of severe weather. An *advisory* is issued when weather conditions are not life threatening, but individuals need to be alert to weather conditions. A weather *watch* is issued when conditions are more favorable than usual for dangerous weather conditions, e.g. tornadoes and violent thunderstorms. A watch is a recommendation for planning,

How much water is in an inch of snow?

An average figure is 10 inches (25 centimeters) of snow is equal to one inch (2.5 centimeters) of water. Heavy, wet snow has a high water content; four to five inches (10 to 12 centimeters) may contain one inch (2.5 centimeters) of water. A dry, powdery snow might require 15 inches (38 centimeters) of snow to equal one inch (2.5 centimeters) of water.

preparation, and increased awareness (i.e., to be alert for changing weather, listen for further information, and think about what to do if the danger materializes). A *warning* is issued when a particular weather hazard is either imminent or has been reported. A warning indicates the need to take action to protect life and property. The type of hazard is reflected in the type of warning (e.g., tornado warning, blizzard warning).

What is **Doppler radar**?

Doppler radar measures frequency differences between signals bouncing off objects moving away from or toward it. By measuring the difference between the transmitted and received frequencies, Doppler radar calculates the speed of the air in which the rain, snow, ice crystals, and even insects are moving. It can then be used to predict speed and direction of wind and amount of precipitation associated with a storm. The National Weather Service has installed a series of NEXRAD (Next Generation Radar) Doppler Radar systems throughout the country. They are especially helpful in measuring the speed of tornadoes and other violent thunderstorms.

When did **modern weather forecasting** begin?

On May 14, 1692, a weekly newspaper, *A Collection for the Improvement of Husbandry and Trade,* gave a seven-day table with pressure and wind readings for the comparable dates of the previous year. Readers were expected to make up their own forecasts from the data. Other journals soon followed with their own weather features. In 1771, a new journal called the *Monthly Weather Paper* was completely devoted to weather prediction. In 1861, the British Meteorological Office began issuing daily weather forecasts. The first broadcast of weather forecasts was done by the University of Wisconsin's station 9XM at Madison, Wisconsin, on January 3, 1921.

What is **barometric pressure** and what does it mean?

Barometric, or atmospheric, pressure is the force exerted on a surface by the weight of the air above that surface, as measured by an instrument called a barometer. Pressure is greater at lower levels because the air's molecules are squeezed under the weight of the air above. So while the average air pressure at sea level is 14.7 pounds per square inch (1,013.53 hecto Pascals), at 1,000 feet (304 meters) above sea level, the pressure drops to 14.1 pounds per square inch (972.1 hecto Pascals), and at 18,000 feet (5,486 meters) the pressure is 7.3 pounds (503.32 hecto Pascals), about half of the figure at sea level. Changes in air pressure bring weather changes. High pressure areas bring clear skies and fair weather; low pressure areas bring wet or stormy weather. Areas of very low pressure have serious storms, such as hurricanes.

Can **groundhogs** accurately predict the weather?

Over a 60-year period, groundhogs have accurately predicted the weather (i.e., when spring will start) only 28 percent of the time on Groundhog Day, February 2. Groundhog Day was first celebrated in Germany, where farmers would watch for a badger to emerge from winter hibernation. If the day was sunny, the sleepy badger would be frightened by his shadow and duck back for another six weeks' nap; if it was cloudy he would stay out, knowing that spring had arrived. German farmers who emigrated to Pennsylvania brought the celebration to America. Finding no badgers in Pennsylvania, they chose the groundhog as a substitute.

Can weather be predicted from the stripes on a **wooly-bear caterpillar**?

It is an old superstition that the severity of the coming winter can be predicted by the width of the brown bands or stripes around the wooly-bear caterpillar in the autumn. If the brown bands are wide, says the superstition, the winter will be mild, but if the brown bands are narrow, a rough winter is foretold. Studies at the American Museum of Natural History in New York failed to show any connection between the weather and the caterpillar's stripes. This belief is only a superstition; it has no basis in scientific fact.

Are there **trees** that **predict the weather** and tell time?

Observing the leaves of a tree may be an old-fashioned method of predicting the weather, but farmers have noted that when maple leaves curl and turn bottom up in a blowing wind, rain is sure to follow. Woodsmen claim they can tell how rough a winter is going to be by the density of lichens on a nut tree. Before the katydid awakes, a black gum tree is able to indicate the oncoming winter. Trees can also be extraordinary timekeepers: Griffonia, in tropical west Africa, has two-inch (five-centimeter) inflated pods that burst with a hearty noise, indicating that it is time for farmers of the Accra Plains to plant crops; Trichilia is a 60-foot (18-meter) tree that flowers in February and again in August, signaling that it is time, just before the second rains arrive, for the second planting of corn. In the Fiji Islands, planting yams is cued by the flowering of the coral tree.

Is a **halo** around the **sun or moon** a sign of rain or snow approaching?

The presence of a ring around the sun or, more commonly, the moon in the night sky, indicates very high ice crystals composing cirrostratus clouds. The brighter the ring, the greater the odds of precipitation and the sooner it may be expected. Rain or snow will not always fall, but two times out of three, precipitation will start to fall within twelve to eighteen hours. These cirroform clouds are a forerunner of an approaching warm front and an associated low pressure system.

What would cause **frogs and toads** to fall from the sky like a **rain shower**?

Documented cases of showers of frogs have been recorded since 1794, usually during heavy summer rainstorms. Whirlwinds, waterspouts, and tornadoes are given as the conventional explanation. Extensive falls of fish, birds, and other animals have also been reported.

THE ENVIRONMENT

ECOLOGY, RESOURCES, ETC.

What is **biodiversity**?

Biodiversity refers to genetic variability within a species, diversity of populations of a species, diversity of species within a natural community, or the wide array of natural communities and ecosystems throughout the world. Some scientists estimate that there may be between 15 and 100 million species throughout the world. Biodiversity is threatened at the present time more than at any other time in history. In the time since the North American continent was settled, as many as 500 plant and animal species have disappeared. Some recent examples of threats to biodiversity in the United States include: 50 percent of the United States no longer supports its original vegetation; in the Great Plains, 99 percent of the original prairies are gone; and across the United States, we destroy 100,000 acres of wetlands each year.

What is a **biome**?

It is a plant and animal community that covers a large geographical area. Complex interactions of climate, geology, soil types, water resources, and latitude all determine the kinds of plants and animals that thrive in different places. Fourteen major ecological zones, called "biomes," exist over five major climatic regions and eight zoogeographical regions. Important land biomes include tundra, coniferous forests, deciduous forests, grasslands, savannas, deserts, chaparral, and tropical rainforests.

How does the process work in a **food chain**?

A food chain is the transfer of food energy from the source in plants through a series of organisms with repeated eating and being eaten. The number of steps or "links" in a sequence is usually four to five. The first trophic level (group of organisms that get their energy the same way) is plants; the animals that eat plants (called herbivores) form the second trophic level. The third level consists of primary carnivores (animal-eating animals like wolves) who eat herbivores, and the fourth level are animals (like killer whales) that eat primary carnivores. Food chains overlap because many organisms eat more than one type of food, so that these chains can look more like food webs. In 1891 German zoologist Karl Semper introduced the food chain concept.

A saguaro cactus forest thrives within this Sonoran Desert biome near Tucson, Arizona.

What is a **food web**?

A food web consists of interconnecting food chains. Many animals feed on different foods rather than exclusively on one single species of prey or one type of plant. Animals that use a variety of food sources have a greater chance of survival than those with a single food source. Complex food webs provide greater stability to a living community.

What is **eutrophication**?

Eutrophication is a process in which the supply of plant nutrients in a lake or pond is increased. In time, the result of natural eutrophication may be dry land where water once flowed, caused by plant overgrowth.

Natural fertilizers, washed from the soil, result in an accelerated growth of plants, producing overcrowding. As the plants die off, the dead and decaying vegetation depletes the lake's oxygen supply, causing fish to die. The accumulated dead plant and animal material eventually changes a deep lake to a shallow one, then to a swamp, and finally it becomes dry land.

While the process of eutrophication is a natural one, it has been accelerated enormously by human activities. Fertilizers from farms, sewage, industrial wastes, and some detergents all contribute to the problem.

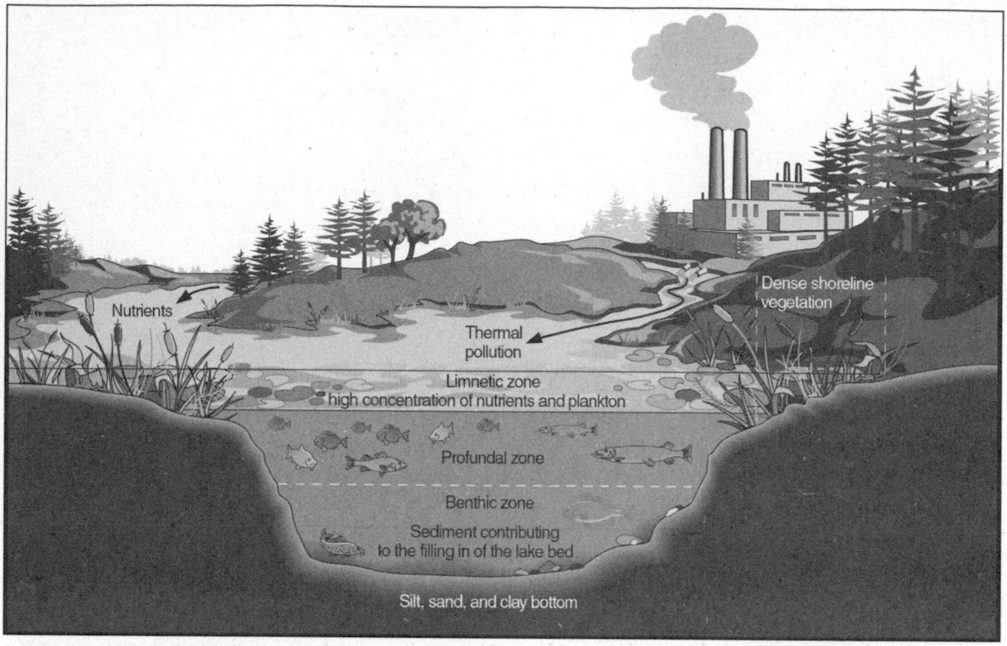

The structure of a eutrophic lake.

How many acres of **wetlands have been lost** in the United States?

Wetlands are the lands between aquatic and terrestrial areas, such as bogs, marshes, swamps, and coastal waters. At one time considered wastelands, scientists now recognize the importance of wetlands to improve water quality, stabilize water levels, prevent flooding, regulate erosion, and sustain a variety of organisms. The United States has lost approximately 100 million acres of wetland areas between colonial times and the 1970s. The 1993 Wetlands Plan established a goal of reversing the trend of 100,000 acres of wetland loss to 100,000 acres of wetland recovery.

How does **ozone** benefit life on Earth?

Ozone, a form of oxygen with three atoms instead of the normal two, is highly toxic; less than one part per million of this blue-tinged gas is poisonous to humans. In the Earth's upper atmosphere (stratosphere), it is a major factor in making life on Earth possible. About 90 percent of the planet's ozone is in the ozone layer. The ozone belt shields and filters the Earth from excessive ultraviolet (UV) radiation generated by the sun. Scientists predict that a diminished or depleted ozone layer could lead to increased health problems for humans, such as skin cancer, cataracts, and weakened immune systems. Increased UV can also lead to reduced crop yields and disruption of aquatic ecosystems, including the marine food chain. While beneficial in the stratosphere, near ground level it is a pollutant that helps form photochemical smog and acid rain.

How large is the Antarctic ozone hole?

The term "hole" is widely used in popular media when reporting on ozone. However, the concept is more correctly described as a low concentration of ozone. In September 2000, scientists at the National Aeronautics and Space Administration announced that the "hole" over Antarctica, first discovered in 1985, was measured to be 9.3 million square miles (24 million square kilometers) in size in 2007. But this was a smaller hole than the record, set in September 2006, when the ozone hole was a gaping 10.6 million square miles in area.

What is the **greenhouse effect**?

The greenhouse effect is a warming near the Earth's surface that results when the Earth's atmosphere traps the sun's heat. The atmosphere acts much like the glass walls and roof of a greenhouse. The effect was described by John Tyndall (1820-1893) in 1861. It was given the greenhouse analogy much later in 1896 by the Swedish chemist Svante Arrhenius (1859-1927). The greenhouse effect is what makes the Earth habitable. Without the presence of water vapor, carbon dioxide, and other gases in the atmosphere, too much heat would escape and the Earth would be too cold to sustain life. Carbon dioxide, methane, nitrous oxide, and other greenhouse gases absorb the infrared radiation rising from the Earth and hold this heat in the atmosphere instead of reflecting it back into space.

In the 20th century, the increased build-up of carbon dioxide, caused by the burning of fossil fuels, has been a matter of concern. There is some controversy concerning whether the increase noted in the Earth's average temperature is due to the increased amount of carbon dioxide and other gases, or is due to other causes. Volcanic activity, destruction of the rainforests, use of aerosols, and increased agricultural activity may also be contributing factors.

What compounds cause **ozone depletion** in the **stratosphere**?

Research in the 1970s linked chlorofluorocarbons (CFCs), such as freon, to the depletion of the ozone layer. In 1978, the use of CFC propellants in spray cans was banned in the United States. In 1987, the Montreal Protocol was signed and the signatory nations committed themselves to a reduction in the use of CFCs and other ozone-depleting substances.

What are the **greenhouse gases**?

Scientists recognize carbon dioxide (CO_2), methane (CH_4), chlorofluorocarbons (CFCs), nitrous oxide (N_20), and water vapor as significant greenhouse gases. Green-

An atmosphere with natural levels of greenhouse gases (left) compared with an atmosphere of increased greenhouse effect (right).

house gases account for less that one percent of the Earth's atmosphere. These gases trap heat in the Earth's atmosphere, preventing the heat from escaping back into space. Human activities, such as using gasoline for automobiles for fuel, account for the release of carbon dioxide and nitrogen oxides.

Emissions of Greenhouse Gases in the United States, 1990-2000 (Million Metric Tons of Gas)

Gas	1990	1995	1996	1997	1998	1999	P2000
Carbon Dioxide	4,969.4	5,273.5	5,454.8	5,533.0	5,540.0	5,630.7	5,805.5
Methane	31.7	31.1	29.9	29.6	28.9	28.7	28.2
Nitrous Oxide	1.2	1.3	1.2	1.2	1.2	1.2	1.2
HFCs, PFCs, and SF_6	*	*	*	*	*	*	*

P = Preliminary data, *Less than 0.05 million metric tons of gas, HFCs = hydrofluorocarbons, PFCs = perfluorocarbons, SF_6 = sulfur hexafluoride

Why is **El Niño** harmful?

Along the west coast of South America, near the end of each calendar year, a warm current of nutrient-poor tropical water moves southward, replacing the cold, nutrient-rich surface water. Because this condition frequently occurs around Christmas, local residents call it El Niño (Spanish for child), referring to the Christ child. In most years the warming lasts for only a few weeks. However, when El Niño conditions last

What is red tide and what causes it?

Red tide is a term used for a brownish or reddish discoloration occurring in ocean, river, or lake water. It is caused by the rapid reproduction of a variety of toxic organisms, especially the toxic red dinoflagellates that are members of the genera *Gymnodidium* and *Gonyaulax*. Some red tides are harmless, but millions of fish may be killed during a "bloom," as the build-up is called. Other red tides can poison shellfish and the birds or humans who eat the contaminated food. Scientists do not fully understand why the "bloom" occurs.

for many months, the economic results can be catastrophic. It is this extended episode of extremely warm water that scientists now refer to as El Niño. During a severe El Niño, large numbers of fish and marine plants may die. Decomposition of the dead material depletes the water's oxygen supply, which leads to the bacterial production of huge amounts of smelly hydrogen sulfide. A greatly reduced fish (especially anchovy) harvest affects the world's fishmeal supply, leading to higher prices for poultry and other animals that normally are fed fishmeal. Anchovies and sardines are also major food sources for marine mammals, such as sea lions and seals. When the food source is in short supply, these animals travel further from their homes in search of food. Not only do many sea lions and seals starve, but also a large proportion of the infant animals die. The major El Niño event of 1997-1998 indirectly caused 2,100 deaths and $33 billion in damage globally.

What **percentage** of the Earth's surface is **tropical rain forest**?

Rain forests account for approximately 7 percent of the Earth's surface, or about three million square miles (7.7 million square kilometers).

What is the rate of **species extinction** in the **tropical rain forests**?

Biologists estimate that tropical rain forests contain approximately one-half of the Earth's animal and plant species. These forests contain 155,000 of the 250,000 known plant species and innumerable insect and animal species. Nearly 100 species become extinct each day. This is equivalent to four species per hour. At the current rates, 5-10 percent of the tropical rain forest will become extinct every decade.

What is the **largest rain forest**?

The Amazon Basin is the world's largest continuous tropical rain forest. It covers about 2.7 million square miles (6.9 million square kilometers).

How **rapidly** is **deforestation** occurring?

Worldwide, we are losing enough forestland annually to cover an area the size of the state of Panama. To put that figure into numbers, that is a net loss of 7.3 million hectares (18 million acres) every year. Actually, about 13 million hectares (32 million acres) are being chopped down yearly, but there are restoration projects going on that help replant forests. This rate of loss (which is an average taken from the years 2000 through 2005) is somewhat better than the 8.9 million hectare (22 million acre) loss that was experienced during the previous decade. Although replanting is great, new forest growth does not make for as healthy a habitat for wildlife as old forest growth.

How rapidly is the **tropical rain forest** being **destroyed**?

Tropical rain forests once covered more than four billion acres (1.6 billion hectares) of the Earth. Today, nearly half of the tropical rain forests are gone. Approximately 33.8 million acres of tropical forest are lost per year. This translates to 2.8 million acres lost per month, which can be broken down to 93,000 acres/day, 3,800 acres/hour, or 64 acres/minute. It equals more than the total area of New Hampshire, Vermont, Massachusetts, Rhode Island, Connecticut, New Jersey, and Delaware combined. At the current rate, scientists predict that no rain forests will remain by the middle of the twenty-first century.

Which countries have the largest amount of **protected areas**?

Protected areas include national parks, nature reserves, national monuments, and other sites. There are at least 44,3000 protected areas around the world, covering more than 10 percent of the total land area.

Country	Protected AreaProtected (miles^2)	(km^2)	Area Total %
Venezuela	217,397	563,056	61.7
Greenland	379,345	1,025,405	45.2
Saudi Arabia	318,811	825,717	34.4
United States	902,091	2,336,406	24.9
Indonesia	138,002	357,425	18.6
Australia	395,911	1,025,405	13.4
Canada	357,231	925,226	9.3
China	263,480	682,410	7.1
Brazil	215,312	557,656	6.6
Russia	204,273	529,067	3.1

What causes the most **forest fires** in the western United States?

Lightning is the single largest cause of forest fires in the western states.

What is the **importance** of the **rain forest**?

Half of all medicines prescribed worldwide are originally derived from wild products, and the United States National Cancer Institute has identified more than two thousand tropical rainforest plants with the potential to fight cancer. Rubber, timber, gums, resins and waxes, pesticides, lubricants, nuts and fruits, flavorings and dyestuffs, steroids, latexes, essential and edible oils, and bamboo are among the forest's products that would be drastically affected by the depletion of the tropical forests.

What was the United States' **first national park**?

On March 1,1872, an Act of Congress signed by Ulysses S. Grant established Yellowstone National Park as the first national park, inspiring a worldwide national park movement.

When was the **U.S. National Park Service** established?

The National Park Service was created by an Act signed by President Woodrow Wilson on August 25, 1916.

What are some of the **largest National Parks**?

The largest National Parks are in Alaska:

Park	Area (acres)
Wrangell-St. Elias	8,323,148
Gates of the Arctic	7,523,898
Denali	4,740,912
Katmai	3,674,530
Glacier Bay	3,224,840
Lake Clark	2,619,733
Kobuk Valley	1,750,737

The five largest parks in the 48 contiguous states are:

Park	Location	Area (acres)
Death Valley	California	3,291,779
Yellowstone	Idaho, Montana, Wyoming	2,219,791
Everglades	Florida	1,398,903
Grand Canyon	Arizona	1,217,403
Glacier	Montana	1,013,572

John Muir (left), founder of the Sierra Club and modern conservation movement, pictured here with fellow advocate John Burroughs.

Who is considered the **founder** of **modern conservation**?

American naturalist John Muir (1838-1914) was the father of conservation and the founder of the Sierra Club. He fought for the preservation of the Sierra Nevada Mountains in California, and the creation of Yosemite National Park. He directed most of the Sierra Club's conservation efforts and was a lobbyist for the Antiquities Act.

Another prominent influence was George Perkins Marsh (1801-1882), a Vermont lawyer and scholar. His outstanding book *Man and Nature* emphasizes the mistakes of past civilizations that resulted in destruction of natural resources. As the conservation movement swept through the country in the last three decades of the 19th century, a number of prominent citizens joined the efforts to conserve natural resources and to preserve wilderness areas. Writer John Burroughs, forester Gifford Pinchot, botanist Charles Sprague Sargent, and editor Robert Underwood Johnson were early advocates of conservation.

Who coined the term **"Spaceship Earth"**?

American inventor and environmentalist Buckminster Fuller (1895-1983) coined the term "Spaceship Earth" as an analogy of the need for technology to be self-contained and to avoid waste.

Who started Earth Day?

The first Earth Day, April 22, 1970, was coordinated by Denis Hayes at the request of Gaylord Nelson, a U.S. senator from Wisconsin. Nelson is sometimes called the father of Earth Day. His main objective was to organize a nationwide public demonstration so large it would get the attention of politicians and force the environmental issue into the political dialogue of the nation. Important official actions that began soon after the celebration of the first Earth Day were: the establishment of the Environmental Protection Agency (EPA); the creation of the President's Council on Environmental Quality; and the passage of the Clean Air Act, establishing national air quality standards. In 1995 Gaylord Nelson received the Presidential Medal of Freedom for his contributions to the environmental protection movement.

When was the **Environmental Protection Agency** created?

In 1970, President Richard M. Nixon created the Environmental Protection Agency (EPA) as an independent agency of the U.S. government by executive order. The creation of a federal agency by executive order rather than by an act of the legislative branch is somewhat of an exception to the rule. The EPA was established in response to public concern about unhealthy air, polluted rivers and groundwater, unsafe drinking water, endangered species, and hazardous waste disposal. Responsibilities of the EPA include environmental research, monitoring, and enforcement of legislation regulating environmental activities.

What is a **"green product"**?

Green products are environmentally safe products that contain no chlorofluorocarbons, are degradable (can decompose), and are made from recycled materials. "Deep-green" products are those from small suppliers who build their identities around their claimed environmental virtues. "Greened-up" products come from the industry giants and are environmentally improved versions of established brands.

EXTINCT AND ENDANGERED PLANTS AND ANIMALS

When was the term **"dinosaur"** first used?

The term *dinosaur* was first used by Richard Owen in 1841 in his report on British fossil reptiles. The term, meaning "fearful lizard" was used to describe the group of large extinct reptiles whose fossil remains had been found by many collectors.

What is the name of the **early Jurassic mammal** that is now extinct?

The fossil site of the mammal *hadrocodium wui* was in Yunnan Province, China. This newly described mammal is at least 195 million years old. The estimated weight of the whole mammal is about 0.07 ounces (2 grams). Its tiny skull was smaller than a human thumbnail.

Did **dinosaurs and humans** ever coexist?

No. Dinosaurs first appeared in the Triassic Period (about 220 million years ago) and disappeared at the end of the Cretaceous Period (about 65 million years ago). Modern humans (*Homo sapiens*) appeared only about 25,000 years ago. Movies that show humans and dinosaurs existing together are only Hollywood fantasies.

How **long** did **dinosaurs live**?

The life span has been estimated at 75 to 300 years. Such estimates are educated guesses. From examination of the microstructure of dinosaur bones, scientists have inferred that they matured slowly and probably had proportionately long life spans.

How does a **mastodon** differ from a **mammoth**?

Although the words are sometimes used interchangeably, the mammoth and the mastodon were two different animals. The mastodon seems to have appeared first, while a side branch may have led to the mammoth.

The *mastodon* lived in Africa, Europe, Asia, and North and South America. It appeared in the Oligocene epoch (25 to 38 million years ago) and survived until less than one million years ago. It stood a maximum of 10 feet (three meters) tall and was covered with dense woolly hair. Its tusks were aligned straight forward and were nearly parallel to each other.

The *mammoth* evolved less than two million years ago and died out about 10 thousand years ago. It lived in North America, Europe, and Asia. Like the mastodon, the mammoth was covered with dense, woolly hair, with a long, coarse layer of outer hair to protect it from the cold. It was somewhat larger than the mastodon, standing 9 to 15 feet (2.7 to 4.5 meters). The mammoth's tusks tended to spiral outward, then up.

The gradual warming of the Earth's climate and the change in environment were probably primary factors in the animals' extinction. Early man killed many of them as well, perhaps hastening the process.

Why did **dinosaurs** become **extinct**?

There are many theories as to why dinosaurs disappeared from the Earth about 65 million years ago. Scientists debate whether dinosaurs became extinct gradually or all at once. The gradualists believe that the dinosaur population steadily declined at the end of Cretaceous Period. Numerous reasons have been proposed for this. Some claim the dinosaurs' extinction was caused by biological changes that made them less competitive with other organisms, especially the mammals that were just beginning to appear. Overpopulation has been argued, as has the theory that mammals ate too many dinosaur eggs for the animals to reproduce themselves. Others believe that disease—everything from rickets to constipation—wiped them out. Changes in climate, continental drift, volcanic eruptions, and shifts in the Earth's axis, orbit, and/or magnetic field have also been held responsible.

The catastrophists argue that a single disastrous event caused the extinction not only of the dinosaurs but also of a large number of other species that coexisted with them. In 1980, American physicist Luis Alvarez (1911-1988) and his geologist son, Walter Alvarez (b. 1940), proposed that a large comet or meteoroid struck the Earth 65 million years ago. They pointed out that there is a high concentration of the element iridium in the sediments at the boundary between the Cretaceous and Tertiary Periods. Iridium is rare on Earth, so the only source of such a large amount of it had to be outer space. This iridium anomaly has since been discovered at over 50 sites around the world. In 1990, tiny glass fragments, which could have been caused by the extreme heat of an impact, were identified in Haiti. A 110-mile (177-kilometer) wide crater in the Yucatan Peninsula, long covered by sediments, has been dated to 64.98 million years ago, making it a leading candidate for the site of this impact.

A hit by a large extraterrestrial object, perhaps as much as six miles (9.3 kilometers) wide, would have had a catastrophic effect upon the world's climate. Huge amounts of dust and debris would have been thrown into the atmosphere, reducing the amount of sunlight reaching the surface. Heat from the blast may also have caused large forest fires, which would have added smoke and ash to the air. Lack of sunlight would kill off plants and have a domino-like effect on other organisms in the food chain, including the dinosaurs.

It is possible that the reason for the dinosaurs' extinction may have been a combination of both theories. The dinosaurs may have been gradually declining, for whatever reason. The impact of a large object from space merely delivered the coup de grâce.

The fact that dinosaurs became extinct has been cited as proof of their inferiority and that they were evolutionary failures. However, these animals flourished for 150 million years. By comparison, the earliest ancestors of humanity appeared only about three million years ago. Humans have a long way to go before they can claim the same sort of success as the dinosaurs.

How did the **dodo** become extinct?

The dodo became extinct around 1800. Thousands were slaughtered for meat, but pigs and monkeys, which destroyed dodo eggs, were probably most responsible for the dodo's extinction. Dodos were native to the Mascarene Islands in the Central Indian Ocean.

When did the last passenger pigeon die?

At one time, 200 years ago, the passenger pigeon (*Ectopistes migratorius*) was the world's most abundant bird. Although the species was found only in eastern North America, it had a population of three to five billion birds (25 percent of the North American land bird population). Overhunting caused a chain of events that reduced their numbers below minimum threshold for viability. In the 1890s several states passed laws to protect the pigeon, but it was too late. The last known wild bird was shot in 1900. The last passenger pigeon, named Martha, died on September 1, 1914, in the Cincinnati Zoo.

They became extinct on Mauritius soon after 1680 and on Réunion about 1750. They remained on Rodriguez until 1800.

What is the difference between an **"endangered" species** and a **"threatened" species**?

An "endangered" species is one that is in danger of extinction throughout all or a significant portion of its range. A "threatened" species is one that is likely to become endangered in the foreseeable future.

Under what **conditions** is a species considered **"endangered"**?

This determination is a complex process that has no set of fixed criteria that can be applied consistently to all species. The known number of living members in a species is not the sole factor. A species with a million members known to be alive but living in only one small area could be considered endangered, whereas another species having a smaller number of members, but spread out in a broad area, would not be considered so threatened. Reproduction data—the frequency of reproduction, the average number of offspring born, the survival rate, etc.—enter into such determinations. In the United States, the director of the U.S. Fish and Wildlife Service (within the Department of the Interior) determines which species are to be considered endangered, based on research and field data from specialists, biologists, botanists, and naturalists.

According to the Endangered Species Act of 1973, a species can be listed if it is threatened by any of the following:

1. The present or threatened destruction, modification, or curtailment of its habitat or range.
2. Utilization for commercial, sporting, scientific, or educational purposes at levels that detrimentally affect it.

3. Disease or predation.
4. Absence of regulatory mechanisms adequate to prevent the decline of a species or degradation of its habitat.
5. Other natural or man-made factors affecting its continued existence.

If the species is so threatened, the director then determines the "critical habitat," that is the species' inhabitation areas that contain the essential physical or biological features necessary for the species' preservation. The critical habitat can include non-habitation areas, which are deemed necessary for the protection of the species.

In a span of just 200 years the passenger pigeon passed from the world's most abundant bird species into extinction.

What is the status of the **elephant** in Africa?

From 1979 to 1989, Africa lost half of its elephants from poaching and illegal ivory trade, with the population decreasing from an estimated 1.3 million to 600,000. This led to the transfer of the African elephant from threatened to endangered status in October 1989 by CITES (the Convention on International Trade in Endangered Species). An ivory ban took effect on January 18, 1990. Botswana, Namibia, and Zimbabwe have agreed to restrict the sale of ivory to a single, government-controlled center in each country. All countries have further pledged to allow independent monitoring of the sale, packing, and shipping processes to ensure compliance with all conditions. Finally, all three countries have promised that all net revenues from the sale of ivory will be directed back into elephant conservation for use in monitoring, research, law enforcement, other management expenses or community-based conservation programs within elephant range.

Are **turtles** endangered?

Worldwide turtle populations have declined due to several reasons, including habitat destruction; exploitation of species by humans for their eggs, leather, and meat; and their becoming accidentally caught in the nets of fishermen. In particular danger are sea turtles, such as Kemp's ridley sea turtle (*Lepidochelys kempii*), which is believed to have a population of only a few hundred. Other species include the Central American river turtle (*Dermatemys mawii*), the green sea turtle (*Chelonia mydas*), and the leatherback sea turtle (*Dermochelys coriacea*). Endangered tortoises include the angulated tortoise (*Geochelone yniphora*), the desert tortoise (*Gopherus agassizii*), and the Galapagos tortoise (*Geochelone elephantopus*).

What is a **dolphin-safe tuna**?

The order *Cetacea*, composed of whales, dolphins, and porpoises, were spared from the extinction of large mammals at the end of the Pleistocene about 10,000 years ago. But from 1000 B.C.E. on they, especially the whale, have been relentlessly hunted by man for their valuable products. The twentieth century, with its many technological improvements, has become the most destructive period for the *Cetacea*. In 1972, the United States Congress passed the Marine Mammal Protection Act; one of its goals was to reduce the number of small cetaceans (notably Stenalla and Delphinus) killed and injured during commercial fishing operations, such as the incidental catch of dolphins in tuna purse-seines (nets that close up to form a huge ball to be hoisted aboard ship). Dolphins are often found swimming with schools of yellowfin tuna and are caught along with the tuna by fisherman who use purse-seine nets. The dolphins are drowned by this fishing method because they must be able to breathe air to survive. The number of incidental deaths and injuries in 1972 was estimated at 368,000 for United States fishing vessels and 55,078 for non-United States vessels. In 1979 the figures were reduced to 17,938 and 6,837 respectively. But in the 1980s, the dolphins killed by foreign vessels rose dramatically to over 100,000 a year. Most of the slaughter occurs in the eastern Pacific Ocean from Chile to Southern California. In 1999, the United States attempted to weaken the definition of dolphin-safe tuna by allowing tuna fleets to chase and net dolphins. The ruling was not upheld by the United States District Court.

To further reduce the numbers of dolphins killed during tuna catches, the three largest sellers of canned tuna in the United States, spearheaded by the Starkist company, decided that they would not sell tuna that has been caught by these methods harmful to dolphins.

POLLUTION

How are **hazardous waste** materials classified?

There are four types of hazardous waste materials—corrosive, ignitable, reactive, and toxic.

Corrosive materials can wear away or destroy a substance. Most acids are corrosive and can destroy metal, burn skin, and give off vapors that burn the eyes.

Ignitable materials can burst into flames easily. These materials pose a fire hazard and can irritate the skin, eyes, and lungs. Gasoline, paint, and furniture polish are ignitable.

Reactive materials can explode or create poisonous gas when combined with other chemicals. Combining chlorine bleach and ammonia, for example, creates a poisonous gas.

Toxic materials or substances can poison humans and other life. They can cause illness or death if swallowed or absorbed through the skin. Pesticides and household cleaning agents are toxic.

What is **bioremediation**?

Bioremediation is the degradation, decomposition, or stabilization of pollutants by microorganisms such as bacteria, fungi, and cyanobacteria. Oxygen and organisms are injected into contaminated soil and/or water (e.g. oil spills). The microorganisms feed on and eliminate the pollutants. When the pollutants are gone, the organisms die.

What is the **Pollutant Standard Index**?

The U.S. Environmental Protection Agency and the South Coast Air Quality Management District of El Monte, California, devised the Pollutant Standard Index to monitor concentrations of pollutants in the air and inform the public concerning related health effects. The scale measures the amount of pollution in parts per million, and has been in use nationwide since 1978.

PSI Index	Health Effects	Cautionary Status
0	Good	
50	Moderate	
100	Unhealthful	
200	Very unhealthful	Alert: elderly or ill should stay indoors and reduce physical activity.
300	Hazardous	Warning: General population should stay indoors and reduce physical activity.
400	Extremely hazardous	Emergency: all people remain indoors windows shut, no physical exertion.
500	Toxic	Significant harm; same as above.

What is the **Toxic Release Inventory** (TRI)?

TRI is a government mandated, publicly available compilation of information on the release of over 650 individual toxic chemicals and toxic chemical categories by manufacturing facilities in the United States. The law requires manufacturers to state the amounts of chemicals they release directly to air, land, or water, or that they transfer to off-site facilities that treat or dispose of wastes. The U.S. Environmental Protection Agency compiles these reports into an annual inventory and makes the information available in a computerized database. In 2000, 23,484 facilities released 7.1 billion pounds (3.2 billion kilograms) of toxic chemicals into the environment. Over 260 million pounds (118 million kilograms) of this total were released into surface water; 1.9 billion pounds (0.86 million kilograms) were emitted into the air; over 4.13 billion pounds (1.87 billion kilograms) were released to land; and over 278 million pounds (126 million kilograms) were injected into underground wells. The total amount of toxic chemicals released in 2000 was 6.7 percent lower than the amount released in 1999.

What **chemicals,** which were once hailed as wonder chemicals that would benefit society, are now **banned or strictly controlled** ?

Dichlorodiphenyl-trichloro-ethene (DDT), polychlorinated biphenyls (PCBs) and chlorofluorocarbons (CFCs) were once widely used. Increased awareness of the detrimental effects on the environment from these chemicals led to all of them being banned or strictly controlled.

Which **industries** release the most **toxic chemicals**?

The metal mining industry released the most toxic chemicals for the year 2000, accounting for 47.3 percent of total chemical releases.

Industry	Total Releases (pounds)	Percent of Total
Metal mining	3,357,765,313	47.3
Manufacturing industries	2,284,399,698	32.2
Electric utilities	1,152,242,786	16.2
Hazardous waste/Solvent recovery	284,950,589	4.0
Coal mining	15,968,001	0.2
Petroleum terminals/bulk storage	3,878,087	0.1
Chemical wholesale distributors	1,611,790	0.02

How did **DDT** affect the environment?

Although DDT was synthesized as early as 1874 by Othmar Zeidler, it was the Swiss chemist Paul Müller (1899-1965) who recognized its insecticidal properties in 1939. He was awarded the 1948 Nobel Prize in medicine for his development of dichlorodiphenyl-trichloro-ethene, or DDT. Unlike the arsenic-based compounds then in use, DDT was effective in killing insects and seemed not to harm plants and animals. In the following 20 years it proved to be effective in controlling disease-carrying insects (mosquitoes that carry malaria and yellow fever, and lice that carry typhus) and in killing many plant crop destroyers. Publication of Rachel Carson's *Silent Spring* in 1962 alerted scientists to the detrimental effects of DDT. Increasingly, DDT-resistant insect species and the accumulative hazardous effects of DDT on plant and animal life cycles led to its disuse in many countries during the 1970s.

What are **PCBs**?

Polychlorinated biphenyls (PCBs) are a group of chemicals that were widely used before 1970 in the electrical industry as coolants for transformers and in capacitors and other electrical devices. They caused environmental problems because they do not break down and can spread through the water, soil, and air. They have been linked by some scientists to cancer and reproductive disorders and have been shown to cause liver function abnormalities. Government action has resulted in the control of the use, disposal, and production of PCBs in nearly all areas of the world, including the United States.

How do **chlorofluorocarbons** affect the Earth's ozone layer?

Chlorofluorocarbons (CFCs) are hydrocarbons, such as freon, in which part or all of the hydrogen atoms have been replaced by fluorine atoms. These can be liquids or gases, are non-flammable and heat-stable, and are used as refrigerants, aerosol propellants, and solvents. When released into the air, they slowly rise into the Earth's upper atmosphere, where they are broken apart by ultraviolet rays from the sun. Some of the resultant molecular fragments react with the ozone in the atmosphere, reducing the amount of ozone. The CFC molecules' chlorine atoms act as catalysts in a complex set of reactions that convert two molecules of ozone into three molecules of ordinary oxygen. This is depleting the beneficial ozone layer faster than it can be recharged by natural processes. The resultant "hole" lets through more ultraviolet light to the Earth's surface and creates health problems for humans, such as cataracts and skin cancer, and disturbs delicate ecosystems (for example, making plants produce fewer seeds). In 1978 the United States government banned the use of fluorocarbon aerosols, and currently aerosol propellants have been changed from fluorocarbons to hydrocarbons, such as butane. The Montreal Protocol of 1987 initiated worldwide cooperation to reduce the use of CFCs.

Since the late 1980s a substantial slowdown has taken place in the atmospheric buildup of two prime ozone-destroying compounds, CFC 11 and CFC 12. Based upon these measurements, experts suggest that concentrations of these CFCs will peak before the turn of the century, allowing the ozone layer to begin the slow process of repairing itself. It is believed that it will take 50 to 100 years for reactions in the atmosphere to reduce the concentrations of ozone-destroying chlorine and bromine back to natural levels. Until then, these chemicals will continue to erode the global ozone layer.

What are the components of **smog**?

Smog, the most widespread pollutant in the United States, is a photochemical reaction resulting in ground-level ozone. Ozone, an odorless, tasteless gas in the presence of light can initiate a chain of chemical reactions. Ozone is a desirable gas in the stratospheric layer of the atmosphere, but it can be hazardous to health when found near the Earth's surface in the troposphere. The hydrocarbons, hydrocarbon derivations, and nitric oxides emitted from such sources as automobiles are the raw materials for photochemical reactions. In the presence of oxygen and sunlight, the nitric oxides combine with organic compounds, such as the hydrocarbons from unburned gasoline, to produce a whitish haze, sometimes tinged with a yellow-brown color. In this process, a large number of new hydrocarbons and oxyhydrocarbons are produced. These secondary hydrocarbon products may comprise as much as 95 percent of the total organics in a severe smog episode.

What is an example of how we can **alleviate air pollution**?

The scrubbing of flue gases refers to the removal of sulfur dioxide (SO_2) and nitric oxide (NO), which are major components of air pollution. Wet scrubbers use a chemical solvent of lime, limestone, sodium alkali, or diluted sulfuric acid to remove the SO_2 formed during combustion. Dry scrubbing uses either a lime/limestone slurry or ammonia sprayed into the flue gases.

What was the distribution of **radioactive fallout** after the 1986 **Chernobyl accident**?

Radioactive fallout, containing the isotope cesium 137, and nuclear contamination covered an enormous area, including Byelorussia, Latvia, Lithuania, the central portion of the then Soviet Union, the Scandinavian countries, the Ukraine, Poland, Austria, Czechoslovakia, Germany, Switzerland, northern Italy, eastern France, Romania, Bulgaria, Greece, Yugoslavia, the Netherlands, and the United Kingdom. The fallout, extremely uneven because of the shifting wind patterns, extended 1,200 to 1,300 miles (1,930 to 2,090 kilometers) from the point of the accident. Roughly 5 percent of the reactor fuel—or seven tons of fuel containing 50 to 100 million curies—was released. Estimates of the effects of this fallout range from 28,000 to 100,000 deaths from cancer and genetic defects within the next 50 years. In particular, livestock in high rainfall areas received unacceptable dosages of radiation.

What is **acid rain**?

The term "acid rain" was coined by British chemist Robert Angus Smith (1817-1884) who, in 1872, published *Air & Rain: The Beginnings of a Chemical Climatology*. Since then, acid rain has unfortunately become an increasingly used term for rain, snow, sleet, or other precipitation that has been polluted by acids such as sulfuric and nitric acids.

When gasoline, coal, or oil are burned, their waste products of sulfur dioxide and nitrogen dioxide combine in complex chemical reactions with water vapor in clouds to form acids. The United States alone discharges 40 million metric tons of sulfur and nitrogen oxides into the atmosphere. This, combined with natural emissions of sulfur and nitrogen compounds, has resulted in severe ecological damage. Hundreds of lakes in North America (especially northeastern Canada and United States) and in Scandinavia are so acidic that they cannot support fish life. Crops, forests, and building materials, such as marble, limestone, sandstone, and bronze, have been affected as well, but the extent is not as well documented. However, in Europe, where so many living trees are stunted or killed, the new word "Waldsterben" (forest death) has been coined to describe this new phenomenon.

In 1990, amendments to the U.S. Clean Air Act contained provisions to control emissions that cause acid rain. It included the reductions of sulfur dioxide emissions from 19 million tons to 9.1 million tons annually and the reduction of industrial nitrogen oxide emissions from six to four million tons annually.

Year	Sulfur Dioxide Emissions (million tons)	Nitrogen Oxide Emissions (million tons)
1990	15.73	6.66
1995	11.87	6.09
1996	12.51	5.91
1997	12.96	6.04
1998	13.13	5.97
1999	12.45	5.49
2000	11.28	5.11

How **acidic** is acid rain?

Acidity or alkalinity is measured by a scale known as the pH (potential for Hydrogen) scale. It runs from zero to 14. Since it is logarithmic, a change in one unit equals a tenfold increase or decrease. So a solution at pH 2 is 10 times more acidic than one at pH 3 and 100 times as acidic as a solution at pH 4. Zero is extremely acid, 7 is neutral, and 14 is very alkaline. Any rain below 5.0 is considered acid rain; some scientists use the value of 5.6 or less. Normal rain and snow containing dissolved carbon dioxide (a weak acid) measure about pH 5.6. Actual values vary according to geographical area. Eastern Europe and parts of Scandinavia have 4.3 to 4.5; the rest of Europe is 4.5 to 5.1; eastern United States and Canada ranges from 4.2 to 4.6, and Mississippi Valley has a range of 4.6 to 4.8. The worst North American area, having 4.2, is centered around Lake Erie and Lake Ontario. For comparison, some common items and their pH values are listed below:

Concentrated sulfuric acid	1.0
Lemon juice	2.3
Vinegar	3.3
Acid rain	4.3
Normal rain	5.0 to 5.6
Normal lakes and rivers	5.6 to 8.0
Distilled water	7.0
Human blood	7.35 to 7.45
Seawater	7.6 to 8.4

What are the **sources of oil pollution** in the oceans?

Most oil pollution results from accidental discharges of oil when oil tankers are loaded and unloaded and minor spillage from tankers. Other sources of oil pollution include improper disposal of used motor oil, oil leaks from motor vehicles, routine ship maintenance, leaks in pipelines that transport oil, and accidents at storage facilities and refineries.

Source	Percent of total oil spillage
Runoff from rivers and surface water	31%
Tanker activity (loading, unloading, etc.)	20%
Sewage plants and refineries	13%
Natural seepage from ocean floor	9%
Smaller craft (fishing vessels, ferries, etc.)	9%
Oil tanker accidents	3-5%

What are the most commonly collected **debris** items found along **ocean coasts**?

Debris Item	Total number reported (2000)	Percentage of total collected (2000)
Cigarette butts	1,027,303	20.25%
Plastic pieces	337,384	6.65%
Food bags/wrappers (plastic)	284,287	5.6%
Foamed plastic pieces	268,945	5.3%
Caps, lids (plastic)	255,253	5.03%
Paper pieces	219,256	4.32%
Beverage cans	184,294	3.63%
Beverage bottles (glass)	177,039	3.49%
Straws	161,639	3.19%

What causes **formaldehyde** contamination in homes?

Formaldehyde contamination is related to the widespread construction use of wood products bonded with urea-formaldehyde resins and products containing formaldehyde. Major formaldehyde sources include subflooring of particle board; wall paneling made from hardwood plywood or particle board; and cabinets and furniture made from particle board, medium density fiberboard, hardwood plywood, or solid wood. Urea-formaldehyde foam insulation (UFFI) has received the most media notoriety and regulatory attention. Formaldehyde is also used in drapes, upholstery, carpeting, wallpaper adhesives, milk cartons, car bodies, household disinfectants, permanent-press clothing, and paper towels. In particular, mobile homes seem to have higher formaldehyde levels than houses do. Six billion pounds (2.7 billion kilograms) of formaldehyde are used in the United States each year.

The release of formaldehyde into the air by these products (called outgassing) can develop poisoning symptoms in humans. The EPA classifies formaldehyde as a potential human carcinogen (cancer-causing agent).

Which pollutants lead to **indoor air pollution**?

Indoor air pollution, also known as "tight building syndrome," results from conditions in modern, high energy efficiency buildings, which have reduced outside air exchange, or have inadequate ventilation, chemical contamination, and microbial contamination. Indoor air pollution can produce various symptoms, such as headache, nausea, and eye, nose, and throat irritation. In addition, houses are affected by indoor air pollution emanating from consumer and building products and from tobacco smoke. Some of the most common indoor pollutants are carbon monoxide, nitrogen dioxide, formaldehyde, asbestos, lead, mercury, radon, pesticides, organic gases (e.g., from paint, paint strippers, aerosol sprays, cleaning and disinfectant supplies), and biological pollutants (mold, mildew, bacteria, viruses).

What is the Resource Conservation and Recovery Act?

In 1976, the United States Congress passed the Resource Conservation and Recovery Act (RCRA), which was amended in 1984 and 1986. This law requires the EPA to identify hazardous wastes and set standards for their management including generation, transportation, treatment, storage, and disposal of hazardous waste. The law requires all firms that store, treat, or dispose of more than 220 pounds (100 kilograms) of hazardous wastes per month to have a permit stating how such wastes are managed.

What is the **Toxic Substances Control Act** (TOSCA)?

In 1976, the United States Congress passed the Toxic Substances Control Act (TOSCA). This act requires the premarket testing of toxic substances. When a chemical substance is planned to be manufactured, the producer must notify the Environmental Protection Agency (EPA), and, if the data presented is determined to be inadequate to approve its use, the EPA will require the manufacturer to conduct further tests. Or, if it is later determined that a chemical is present at a level that presents an unreasonable public or environmental risk, or if there is insufficient data to know the chemical's effects, manufacturers have the burden of evaluating the chemical's characteristics and risks. If testing does not convince the EPA of the chemical's safety, the chemical's manufacturing, sale, or use can be limited or prohibited.

What is the **Superfund Act**?

In 1980, the United States Congress passed the Comprehensive Environmental Response, Compensation, and Liability Act, commonly known as the Superfund program. This law (along with amendments in 1986 and 1990) established a $16.3-billion Superfund financed jointly by federal and state governments and by special taxes on chemical and petrochemical industries (which provide 86 percent of the funding). The purpose of the Superfund is to identify and clean up abandoned hazardous-waste dump sites and leaking underground tanks that threaten human health and the environment. To keep taxpayers from footing most of the bill, cleanups are based on the polluter-pays principle. The EPA is charged with locating dangerous dump sites, finding the potentially liable culprits, ordering them to pay for the entire cleanup and suing them if they don't. When the EPA can find no responsible party, it draws money out of the Superfund for cleanup.

How many **hazardous waste sites** are there?

As of 2009, there were 1,650 sites.

What is the **NIMBY syndrome**?

NIMBY is the acronym for "Not In My Back Yard," referring to major community resistance to new incinerator sitings, landfills, prisons, roads, etc. NIMFY is "Not In My Front Yard."

What are **Brownfields**?

The Environmental Protection Agency defines Brownfields as abandoned, idled, or underused industrial or commercial sites where expansion or redevelopment is complicated by real or perceived environmental contamination. Real estate developers perceive Brownfields as inappropriate sites for redevelopment. There are approximately 450,000 Brownfields in the United States, with the heaviest concentrations being in the Northeast and Midwest.

When was metal recycling started?

The first metal recycling in the United States occurred in 1776 when patriots in New York City toppled a statue of King George III, which was melted down and made into 42,088 bullets.

Which **government agencies** regulate the storage of **nuclear waste**?

The Department of Energy, Environmental Protection Agency, and Nuclear Regulatory Commission are responsible for the disposal of spent nuclear fuel and other radioactive waste. The Department of Energy (DOE) has the responsibility for developing permanent disposal capacity for spent fuel and other high-level radioactive waste. The Environmental Protection Agency (EPA) has responsibility for developing environmental standards to evaluate the safety of a geologic repository. The Nuclear Regulatory Commission (NRC) has responsibility for developing regulations to implement the EPA safety standards and for licensing the repository.

How is **nuclear waste** stored?

Nuclear wastes consist either of fission products formed from the splitting of uranium, cesium, strontium, or krypton, or from transuranic elements formed when uranium atoms absorb free neutrons. Wastes from transuranic elements are less radioactive than fission products; however, these elements remain radioactive far longer— hundreds of thousands of years. The types of waste are irradiated fuel (spent fuel) in the form of 12-foot (4-meter) long rods, high-level radioactive waste in the form of liquid or sludge, and low-level waste (non-transuranic or legally high-level) in the form of reactor hardware, piping, toxic resins, water from fuel pool and other items that have become contaminated with radioactivity.

Currently, most spent nuclear fuel in the United States is safely stored in specially designed pools at individual reactor sites around the country. If pool capacity is reached, licensees may move toward use of above-ground dry storage casks. The three low-level radioactive waste disposal sites are Barnwell located in South Carolina, Hanford located in Washington, and Envirocare located in Utah. Each site accepts low-level radioactive waste from specific regions of the country.

Most high-level nuclear waste has been stored in double-walled, stainless-steel tanks surrounded by three feet (one meter) of concrete. The current best storage method, developed by the French in 1978, is to incorporate the waste into a special molten glass mixture, then enclose it in a steel container and bury it in a special pit. The Nuclear Waste Policy Act of 1982 specified that high-level radioactive waste would be disposed of underground in a deep geologic repository. Yucca Mountain, Nevada,

The United States is currently home to more than 9,000 landfill sites.

was chosen as the single site to be developed for disposal of high-level radioactive waste. However, as of the late 1990s, selection of the Yucca Mountain site was controversial due to dormant volcanoes in the vicinity and known earthquake fault lines.

When was the first **garbage incinerator** built?

The first garbage incinerator in the United States was built in 1885 on Governor's Island in New York Harbor.

Why did the ship ***Mobro*** gain international fame?

The *Mobro* was the Long Island, New York, garbage barge that was loaded with garbage and could not dispose of it. It was rejected by six states and three countries, drawing attention to the landfill capacity shortage in the Northeast. The garbage was finally burned in Brooklyn and the ash brought to a landfill near Islip.

How critical is the problem of **landfilling** in the United States?

Landfilling has been an essential component of waste management for several decades. In 1960, 62 percent of all garbage was sent to landfills, and by 1980 the figure had risen to 81 percent. By 1990, 84 percent of the 269 million tons of municipal solid waste that was generated was sent to landfills. An increased awareness of the benefits

When was paper recycling started?

Paper recycling was actually born in 1690 in the United States when the first paper mill was established by the Rittenhouse family on the banks of Wissahickon Creek, near Philadelphia. The paper at this mill was made from recycled rags.

of recycling has brought a decline in the actual number of landfills from 4,482 in 1995 to 2,142 in 2000 as well as a decrease in the amount of municipal solid waste that is sent to landfills. Figures for 2000 indicate that only 60 percent of the municipal solid waste generated was sent to landfills. The total amount of recycled waste increased from 8 percent to 33 percent between 1990 and 2000.

How much **methane fuel** does a ton of garbage make?

Over a period of 10 to 15 years, a ton of garbage will make 14,126 cubic feet (400 cubic meters) of fuel, although a landfill site will generate smaller amounts for 50 to 100 years. One ton of garbage can produce more than 100 times its volume in methane over a decade. Landfill operators tend not to maximize methane production.

How much space does a **recycled ton of paper** save in a landfill?

Each ton (907 kilograms) saves more than three cubic yards of landfill space.

What **natural resources** are saved by **recycling paper**?

One ton (907 kilograms) of recycled waste paper would save an average of 7,000 gallons (26,460 liters) of water, 3.3 cubic yards (2.5 cubic meters) of landfill space, three barrels of oil, 17 trees, and 4,000 kilowatt-hours of electricity—enough energy to power the average home for six months. It would also reduce air pollution by 74 percent.

How much **newspaper** must be recycled to **save one tree**?

One 35 to 40 foot (10.6 to 12 meter) tree produces a stack of newspapers four feet (1.2 meters) thick; this much newspaper must be recycled to save a tree.

How much **waste paper** does a **newspaper** generate?

An average yearly newspaper subscription (for example, the *San Francisco Chronicle*) received every day produces 550 pounds (250 kilograms) of waste paper per subscription per year. The average *New York Times* Sunday edition produces eight million pounds (3.6 million kilograms) of waste paper.

What problems may be encountered when **polyvinyl chloride (PVC) plastics** are burned?

Chlorinated plastics, such as PVC, contribute to the formation of hydrochloric acid gases. They also may be a part of a mix of substances containing chlorine that form a precursor to dioxin in the burning process. Polystyrene, polyethylene, and polyethylene terephthalate (PET) do not produce these pollutants.

How can **plastics** be made **biodegradable**?

Plastic does not rust or rot. This is an advantage in its usage, but when it comes to disposal of plastic the advantage turns into a liability. Degradable plastic has starch in it so that it can be attacked by starch-eating bacteria to eventually disintegrate the plastic into bits. Chemically degradable plastic can be broken up with a chemical solution that dissolves it. Used in surgery, biodegradable plastic stitches slowly dissolve in the body fluids. Photodegradable plastic contains chemicals that disintegrate over a period of one to three years when exposed to light. One-quarter of the plastic yokes used to package beverages are made from a plastic called Ecolyte, which is photodegradable.

What do the **numbers** inside the **recycling symbol** on plastic containers mean?

The Society of the Plastics Industry developed a voluntary coding system for plastic containers to assist recyclers in sorting plastic containers. The symbol is designed to be imprinted on the bottom of the plastic containers. The numerical code appears inside three arrows that form a triangle. A guide to what the numbers mean is listed below. The most commonly recycled plastics are polyethylene terephthalate (PET) and high-density polyethylene (HDPE).

Code	Material	Examples
1	Polyethylene terephthalate (PET/PETE)	2-liter soft drink bottle
2	High-density polyethylene (HDPE)	Milk and water jugs
3	Vinyl (PVC)	Plastic pipes, shampoo bottles
4	Low-density polyethylene (LDPE)	Produce bags, food storage containers
5	Polypropylene (PP)	Squeeze bottles, drinking straws
6	Polystyrene (PS)	Fast-food packaging, packaging
7	Other	Food containers

How many **curbside recycling programs** are there in the United States?

The first municipal-wide curbside recycling program was started in 1974 in University City, Missouri, where city officials designed and distributed a container for collecting newspapers. Curbside recycling programs continue to increase in the United States. In 1997, there were 7,375 curbside recycling programs. By 1999 the number of curbside recycling programs had increased to 9,349.

What **products** are made from **recycled plastic**?

Resin	Common Uses	Products Made from Recycled Resin
HDPE	Beverage bottles, milk jugs, milk and soft drink crates, pipe, cable, film	Motor oil bottles, detergent bottles, pipes and pails
LDPE	Film bags such as trash bags, coatings, and plastic bottles	New trash bags, pallets, carpets, fiberfill, non-food
PET	Soft drink, detergent, and juice bottles	Bottles/containers
PP	Auto battery cases, screw-on caps and lids; some yogurt and	Auto parts, batteries, carpets margarine tubs, plastic film
PS	Housewares, electronics, fast food carry-out packaging, plastic utensils	Insulation board, office equipment, reusable cafeteria trays
PVC	Sporting goods, luggage, pipes, auto parts. In packaging for shampoo bottles, blister packaging, and films	Drainage pipes, fencing, house siding

A new clothing fiber called Fortrel EcoSpun is made from recycled plastic soda bottles. The fiber is knit or woven into garments such as fleece for outerwear or long underwear. The processor estimates that every pound of Fortrel EcoSpun fiber results in 10 plastic bottles being kept out of landfills.

When offered a choice between **plastic or paper bags** for your groceries, wich should you choose?

The answer is neither. Both are environmentally harmful and the question of which is the more damaging has no clear-cut answer. On one hand, plastic bags degrade slowly in landfills and can harm wildlife if swallowed, and producing them pollutes the environment. On the other hand, producing the brown paper bags used in most supermarket uses trees and pollutes the air and water. Overall, white or clear polyethylene bags require less energy for manufacture and cause less damage to the environment than do paper bags not made from recycled paper. Instead of having to choose between paper and plastic bags, you can bring your own reusable canvas or string containers to the store, and save and reuse any paper or plastic bags you get.

Is **washing dishes by hand** better for the environment than using an **automatic dishwasher**?

Dishwashers often save energy and water compared to hand washing. Depending on the brand, dishwashers typically consume 7.5 to 12 gallons (28 to 45 liters) of water per normal wash. Hand-washing a day's worth of dishes may use up to 15 gallons (57 liters) of water. One university study found that dishwashers consume about 37 percent less water than washing by hand.

Several steps can be taken for additional energy savings when using a dishwasher. The setting on a home's water heater can be turned down to 120°F (49°C) if the dishwasher has a booster heater. While some machines feature a no-heat, air-dry setting, simply opening the door after the final rinse to let the dishes air dry will save energy. Prewashing the dishes before loading generally wastes water since most machines can handle even heavily soiled plates.

What is a **WOBO**?

A WOBO (world bottle) is the first mass-produced container designed for secondary use as a building product. It was conceived by Albert Heineken of the Heineken beer family. The beer bottles were designed in a special shape to be used, when empty, as glass bricks for building houses. The actual building carried out with WOBOs was only a small shed and a double garage built on the Heineken estate at Noordwijk, near Amsterdam. Although not implemented, WOBO was a sophisticated and intelligent design solution to what has emerged as a major environmental issue in recent years.

BIOLOGY

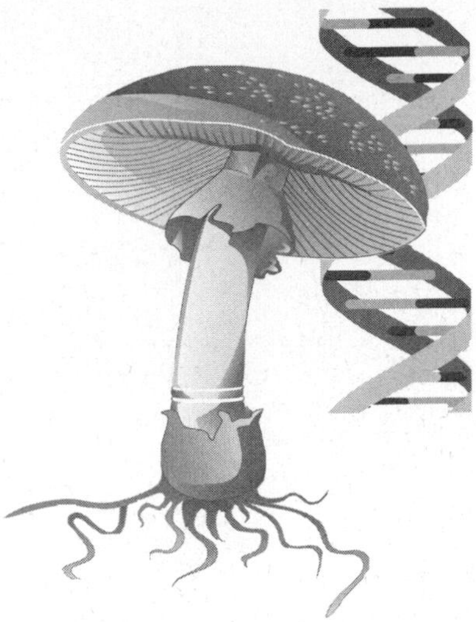

CELLS

What is the **cell theory**?

The cell theory is the concept that all living things are made up of essential units called "cells." The cell is the simplest collection of matter that can live. There are diverse forms of life existing as single-celled organisms. More complex organisms, including plants and animals, are multicellular—cooperatives of many kinds of specialized cells that could not survive for long on their own. All cells are related by division from earlier cells and have been modified in various ways during the long evolutionary history of life on Earth. Everything an organism does occurs fundamentally at the cellular level.

What **scientists** made **important discoveries** associated with the cell?

In the late 1600s, Robert Hooke (1635-1703) was the first to see a cell, initially in a section of cork, and then in bones and plants. In 1824, Henri Dutrochet (1776-1847) proposed that animals and plants had similar cell structures. Robert Brown (1773-1858) discovered the cell nucleus in 1831, and Matthias Schleiden (1804-1881) named the nucleolus (the structure within the nucleus now known to be involved in the production of ribosomes) around that time. Schleiden and Theodor Schwann (1810-1882) described a general cell theory in 1839, the former stating that cells were the basic unit of plants and Schwann extending the idea to animals. Robert Remak (1815-1865) was the first to describe cell division in 1855. Chromosomes were named and observed in the nucleus of a cell in 1888 by Wilhelm von Waldeyen-Hartz (1836-1921). Walther Flemming (1843-1905) was the first individual to follow chromosomes through the entire process of cell division.

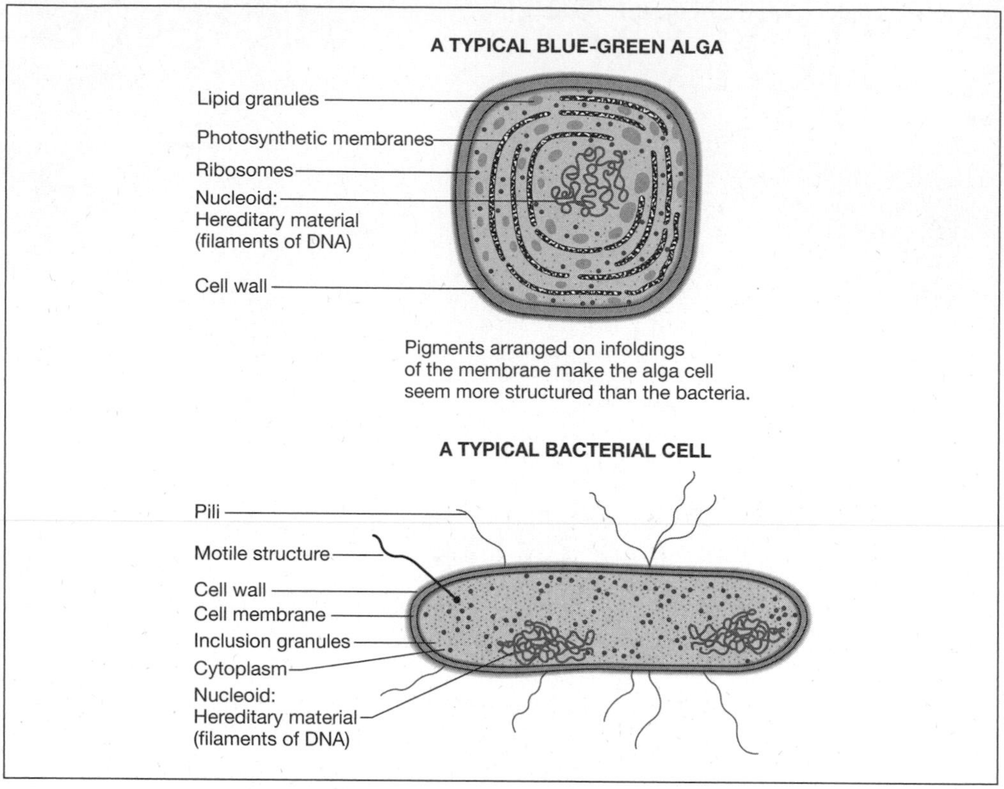

Two typical prokaryotic cells: A blue-green algae and a bacteria.

What is the difference between **prokaryotic** and **eukaryotic cells**?

Every organism is composed of one of two structurally different types of cells: prokaryotic cells or eukaryotic cells. Only monera have prokaryotic cells. Protists, plants, fungi, and animals all have eukaryotic cells.

Prokaryotic	Eukaryotic
No nucleus	Nucleus
No membrane-bound organelles	Many organelles
1-10μm in size	2-1,000μm in size
Evolved 3.5 billion years ago	Evolved 1.5 billion years ago

How many **mitochondria** are there in a cell?

The number of mitochondria varies according to the type of cell, but each cell in the human liver has over 1,000 mitochondria. A mitochondrion (singular form) is a self-replicating, double-membraned body found in the cytoplasm of all eukaryotic (having a nucleus) cells. The number of mitochondria per cell varies between one and 10,000, and averages about 200. The mitochondria are the sites for much of the metabolism necessary for the production of ATP, lipids, and protein synthesis.

What are the **functions** of **organelles** of **prokaryotic** and **eukaryotic** cells in plants and animals?

Structure	Function	Prokaryotes	Eukaryotes (Animals)	Eukaryotes (Plants)
Cell wall	Protects, supports cell	Yes	No	Yes
Cytoskeleton	Structural support; cell movement	No	Yes	Yes
Flagella and cilia	Motility or moving fluids over surfaces	Yes	Often present	Mostly absent except for sperm, respiratory and digestive epithelia
Plasma membrane	Regulates what passes into and out of cell; cell-to-cell recognition	Yes	Yes	Yes
Nucleus	Control center of cell; directs protein synthesis and cell reproduction	No	Yes	Yes
Chromosomes	Contain hereditary information	No	Yes	Yes
Nucleolus	Assembles ribosomes	No	Yes	Yes
Ribosomes	Sites of protein synthesis	Yes	Yes	Yes
Mitochondria	Power plant of the cell; site of oxidative metabolism	No	Yes	Yes
Chloroplast	Site of photosynthesis	No	No	Yes
Lysosomes	Digest worn-out mitochondria and cell debris; play role in cell death	No	Yes	Yes
Endoplasmic reticulum	Forms compartments and vesicles	No	Yes	Yes
Golgi complex	Modifies and packages proteins for export from cell; forms secretory vesicles	No	Yes	Yes

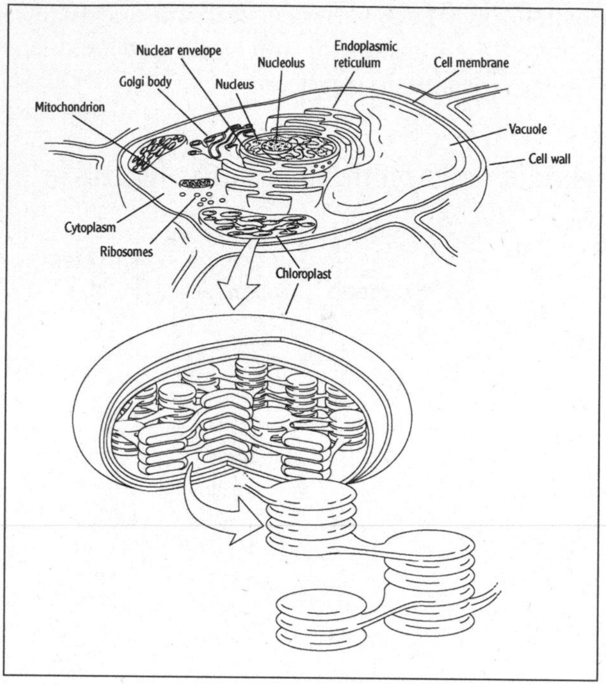

Plant cell with chloroplast.

How many **chloroplasts** are in plant cells?

Chloroplasts are the functional units where photosynthesis takes place—the process whereby green plants use light energy for the synthesis of sugar from carbon dioxide and water, with oxygen released as a by-product. They contain the green pigments chlorophyll a and b, which trap light energy for photosynthesis. A unicellular plant may have only a single large chloroplast, whereas a plant leaf cell may have as many as 20 to 100.

Do all cells have a **nucleus**?

Red blood cells are the only cells in the human body that do not have a nucleus. As a result, they cannot divide. They are produced in bone marrow at the rate of 140,000 per minute. They exist in the body's circulatory system for about 120 days before being destroyed in the liver.

What are the stages in the type of cell division called **mitosis**?

Cell division in eukaryotes (higher organisms) consists of two stages: mitosis, the division of the nucleus, and cytokinesis, the division of the whole cell. The first process in the actual division of the cell is mitosis. In mitosis, the replicated chromosomes are maneuvered so that each new cell gets a full complement of chromosomes—one of each. The process is divided into four phases: prophase, metaphase, anaphase, and telophase. Nuclear division of sex cells is called meiosis. Sexual reproduction generally requires two parents and it always involves two events (meiosis and fertilization).

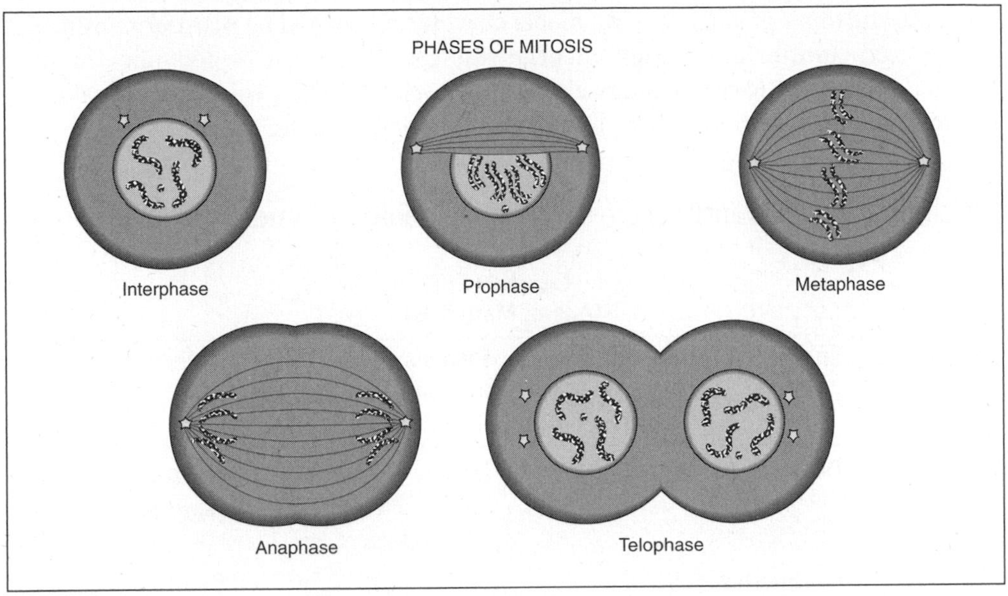

The phases of mitosis.

EVOLUTION AND GENETICS

What is the significance of **Darwin's finches**?

In his studies on the Galapagos Islands, Charles Darwin observed patterns in animals and plants that suggested to him that species changed over time to produce new species. Darwin collected several species of finches. The species were all similar, but each had developed beaks and bills specialized to catch food in a different way. Some species had heavy bills for cracking open tough seeds. Others had slender bills for catching insects. One species used twigs to probe for insects in tree cavities. All the species resembled one species of South American finch. In fact, all the plants and animals of the Galapagos Islands were similar to those of the nearby (600 miles/1,000 km away) coast of South America. Darwin felt that the simplest explanation for this similarity was that a few species of plants and animals from South America must have migrated to the Galapagos Islands. These few plants and animals then changed during the years they lived in their new home, giving rise to many new species. Evolutionary theory proposes that species change over time in response to environmental challenges.

What is **punctuated equilibrium**?

Punctuated equilibrium is a model of macroevolution first detailed in 1972 by Niles Eldredge and Stephen J. Gould. It can be considered either a rival or supplementary model to the more gradual-moving model of evolution posited by neo-Darwinism. The punctuated equilibrium model essentially asserts that most of geological history shows periods of little evolutionary change, followed by short (geologically-speaking, a few million years) periods of time of rapid evolutionary change.

Which **biological events** occurred during the **geologic time divisions**?

Cenozoic Era
(Age of Mammals)

Period	Epoch	Beginning date in est. millions of years	Plants and microorganisms	Animals
Quaternary	Holocene (Recent)	10,000 years ago	Decline of woody plants and rise of herbaceous plants	Age of *Homo sapiens*; humans dominate
	Pleistocene	1.9	Extinction of many species (from 4 ice ages)	Extinction of many large mammals (from 4 ice ages)
Tertiary	Pliocene	6.0	Development of grass-lands; decline of forests; flowering plants	Large carnivores; many grazing mammals; first known human-like primates
	Miocene	25.0		Many modern mammals evolve
	Oligocene	38.0	Spread of forests; flowering plants, rise of monocotyledons	Apes evolve; all present mammal families evolve; saber-toothed cats
	Eocene	55.0	Gymnosperms and angiosperms dominant	Beginning of age of mammals; modern birds
	Paleocene	65.0		Evolution of pri-mate mammals

Mesozoic Era
(Age of Reptiles)

Cretaceous		135.0	Rise of angiosperms; gymnosperms decline	Dinosaurs reach peak and then become extinct; toothed birds

Period	Epoch	Beginning date in est. millions of years	Plants and microorganisms	Animals
				become extinct; first modern birds; primitive mammals
Jurassic		200.0	Ferns and gymnosperms common	Large, specialized dinosaurs; insectivorous marsupials
Triassic		250.0	Gymnosperms and ferns dominate	First dinosaurs; egg-laying mammals.
		Paleozic Era (Age of Ancient Life)		
Permian		285.0	Conifers evolve.	Modern insects like reptiles; extinction of many Paleozic invertebrates
Carboniferous (divided into Mississippian and Pennsylvanian periods by some in the U.S.)		350.0	Forests of ferns and gymnosperms; swamps; club mosses and horsetails	Ancient sharks abundant; many echinoderms, mollusks and insect forms; first reptiles; spread of ancient amphibians
Devonian		410.0	Terrestrial plants established; first forests; gymnosperms appear	Age of fish; amphibians; wingless insects and millipedes appear
Silurian		425.0	Vascular plants appear; algae dominant	Fish evolve; marine arachnids dominant; first insects; crustaceans
Ordovician		500.0	Marine algae dominant; terrestrial plants first appear	Invertebrates dominant; first fish appear
Cambrian		570.0	Algae dominant	Age of marine invertebrates

Precambrian Era

Period	Epoch	Beginning date in est. millions of years	Plants and microorganisms	Animals
Archeozoic and Proterozoic Eras		3800.0	Bacterial cells; then primitive algae and fungi; marine protozoans	Marine invertebrates at end of period
Azoic		4600.0	Origin of the Earth.	

Austrian monk and scientist Gregor Mendel experimented with garden peas to establish the principle of heredity.

How did **humans evolve**?

It has been proposed that the Homo lineage of modern humans (*Homo sapiens*) originated from a hunter of nearly five feet tall, *Homo habilis,* who is widely presumed to have evolved from an australopithecine ancestor. Near the beginning of the Pleistocene epoch (two million years ago), *Homo habilis* is thought to have transformed into *Homo erectus* (Java Man), who used fire and possessed culture. Middle Pleistocene populations of *Homo erectus* are said to show steady evolution toward the anatomy of *Homo sapiens* (Neanderthals, Cro-Magnons, and modern humans), 120,000 to 40,000 years ago. Pre-modern *Homo sapiens* built huts and made clothing.

Who is generally known as the **founder of genetics**?

Gregor Mendel (1822-1884), an Austrian monk and biologist, is considered the founder of genetics. Using his knowledge of statistics to analyze biological phenomena, Mendel discovered specific and regular ratios that he used to formulate the laws of heredity. It was the English biologist William Bateson (1861-1926), however, who brought Mendel's work to the attention of the scientific world and who coined the term "genetics."

What is meant by **Mendelian inheritance**?

Mendelian inheritance refers to genetic traits carried through heredity; the process was studied and described by Austrian monk Gregor Mendel (1822-1884). Mendel was the first to deduce correctly the basic principles of heredity. Mendelian traits are also called single gene or monogenic traits, because they are controlled by the action of a single gene or gene pair. More than 4,300 human disorders are known or suspected to be inherited as Mendelian traits, encompassing autosomal dominant (e.g., neurofibromatosis), autosomal recessive (e.g., cystic fibrosis), sex-linked dominant and recessive conditions (e.g., color-blindness and hemophilia).

Overall, incidence of Mendelian disorders in the human population is about one percent. Many non-anomalous characteristics that make up human variation are also inherited in Mendelian fashion.

What is the significance of ***On the Origin of Species***?

Charles Darwin (1809-1882) first proposed a theory of evolution based on natural selection in his treatise *On the Origin of Species.* The publication of *On the Origin of Species* ushered in a new era in our thinking about the nature of man. The intellectual revolution it caused and the impact it had on man's concept of himself and the world were greater than those caused by the works of Newton and others. The effect was immediate, the first edition being sold out on the day of publication (November 24, 1859). *Origin* has been referred to as "the book that shook the world." Every modern discussion of man's future, the population explosion, the struggle for existence, the purpose of man and the universe, and man's place in nature rests on Darwin.

The work was a product of his analyses and interpretations of his findings from his voyages on the H.M.S. *Beagle* as a naturalist. In Darwin's day, the prevailing explanation for organic diversity was the story of creation in the book of Genesis in the Bible. *Origin* was the first publication to present scientifically sound, well-organized evidence for evolution. Darwin's theory of evolution was based on natural selection in which the best—the fittest—survive, and if there is a difference in genetic endowment among individuals, the race will, by necessity, steadily improve. It is a two-step process: the first consists of the production of variation, and the second of the sorting of this variability by natural selection in which the favorable variations tend to be preserved.

The viceroy butterfly (left) has naturally evolved to resemble the monarch butterfly—a species more unpalatable to predators.

Who coined the phrase **"survival of the fittest"**?

Although frequently associated with Darwinism, this phrase was coined by Herbert Spencer (1820-1903), an English sociologist. It is the process by which organisms that are less well-adapted to their environment tend to perish and better-adapted organisms tend to survive.

What is **Batesian mimicry**?

In 1861, Henry Walter Bates (1825-1892), a British naturalist, proposed that a nontoxic species can evolve (especially in color and color pattern) to look like a toxic or unpalatable species, or to act like a toxic species, to avoid being eaten by a predator. The classic example is the viceroy butterfly, which resembles the unpalatable monarch butterfly. This is called Batesian mimicry. In another example, the larva of the hawk moth puffs up its head and thorax when disturbed, looking like the head of a small poisonous snake, complete with eyes. The mimicry even involves behavior; the larva weaves its head back and forth and hisses like a snake. Subsequently, Fritz Müller (1821-1897), a German-born zoologist, discovered that all the species of similar appearance become distasteful to predators. This phenomenon is called Müllerian mimicry.

When was the **Scopes (monkey) trial**?

John T. Scopes (1900-1970), a high-school biology teacher, was brought to trial by the State of Tennessee in 1925 for teaching the theory of evolution. He challenged a recent law passed by the Tennessee legislature that made it unlawful to teach in any public school any theory that denied the divine creation of man. He was convicted and sentenced, but the decision was reversed later and the law repealed in 1967.

At the present time, pressure against school boards still affects the teaching of evolution. Recent drives by anti-evolutionists either have tried to ban the teaching of evolution or have demanded "equal time" for "special creation" as described in the biblical book of Genesis. This has raised many questions about the separation of church and state, the teaching of controversial subjects in public schools, and the ability of scientists to communicate with the public. The gradual improvement of the fossil record, the result of comparative anatomy, and many other developments in biological science have contributed toward making evolutionary thinking more generally accepted.

What is the **Red Queen hypothesis**?

This hypothesis, also called the law of constant extinction, is named after the Red Queen in Lewis Carroll's *Through the Looking Glass,* who said, "Now here, you see, it takes all the running you can do to keep in the same place." The idea is that an evolutionary advance by one species represents a deterioration of the environment for all remaining species. This places pressure on those species to advance just to keep up.

What is the difference between a **plasmid** and a **prion**?

A plasmid is a small, circular, self-replicating DNA molecule separate from the bacterial chromosome. Plasmids do not normally exist outside the cell and are generally beneficial to the bacterial cell. Plasmids are often used to pick up foreign DNA for use in genetic engineering. A prion is an infectious form of a protein or malformed protein that may increase in number by converting related proteins to more prions. Prions may cause a number of degenerative brain diseases such as "mad cow disease" or Creutzfeldt-Jakob disease in humans.

What is **polymerase chain reaction**?

Polymerase chain reaction, or PCR, is a laboratory technique that amplifies or copies any piece of DNA very quickly without using cells. The DNA is incubated in a test tube with a special kind of DNA polymerase, a supply of nucleotides, and short pieces of syntethic single-stranded DNA that serve a primers for DNA synthesis. With automation, PCR can make billions of copies of a particular segment of DNA in a few hours. Each cycle of the PCR procedure takes only about five minutes. At the end of the cycle, the DNA segment—even one with hundreds of base pairs—has been doubled. A PCR machine repeats the cycle over and over. PCR is much faster than the days it takes to clone a piece of DNA by making a recombinant plasmid and letting it replicate within bacteria.

PCR was developed by the biochemist Kary Mullis (1994-) in 1983 while working for Cetus Corporation, a California biotechnology firm. In 1993, Mullis won the Nobel Prize in Chemistry for developing PCR.

What is **genetic engineering**?

Genetic engineering, also known popularly as molecular cloning or gene cloning, is the artificial recombination of nucleic acid molecules in the test tube, their insertion into a virus, bacterial plasmid, or other vector system, and the subsequent incorporation of the chimeric molecules into a host organism in which they are capable of continued propagation. The construction of such molecules has also been termed gene manipulation because it usually involved the production of novel genetic combinations by biochemical means.

Genetic engineering techniques include cell fusion and the use of recombinant DNA (RNA) or gene-splicing. In cell fusion, the tough outer membranes of sperm and egg cells are stripped off by enzymes, and then the fragile cells are mixed and combined with the aid of chemicals or viruses. The result may be the creation of a new life form from two species. Recombinant DNA techniques transfer a specific genetic activity from one organism to the next through the use of bacterial plasmids (small circular pieces of DNA lying outside the main bacterial chromosome) and enzymes, such as restriction endonucleases (which cut the DNA strands); reverse transcriptase (which makes a DNA strand from an RNA strand); DNA ligase (which joins DNA strands together); and tag polymerase (which can make a double-stranded DNA molecule from a single stranded "primer" molecule). The process begins with the isolation of suitable DNA strands and fragmenting them. After these fragments are combined with vectors, they are carried into bacterial cells where the DNA fragments are "spliced" on to plasmid DNA that has been opened up. These hybrid plasmids are now mixed with host cells to form transformed cells. Since only some of the transformed cells will exhibit the desired characteristic or gene activity, the transformed cells are separated and grown individually in cultures. This methodology has been successful in producing large quantities of hormones (such as insulin) for the biotechnology industry. However, it is more difficult to transform animal and plant cells. Yet the technique exists to make plants resistant to diseases and to make animals grow larger. Because genetic engineering interferes with the processes of heredity and can alter the genetic structure of our own species, there is much concern over the ethical ramifications of such power, as well as the possible health and ecological consequences of the creation of these bacterial forms. Some applications of genetic engineering in the various fields are listed below:

Agriculture: Crops having larger yields, disease- and drought-resistancy; bacterial sprays to prevent crop damage from freezing temperatures; and livestock improvement through changes in animal traits.

Industry: Use of bacteria to convert old newspaper and wood chips into sugar; oil- and toxin-absorbing bacteria for oil spill or toxic waste clean-ups; and yeasts to accelerate wine fermentation.

Medicine: Alteration of human genes to eliminate disease (experimental stage); faster and more economical production of vital human substances to alleviate deficiency and disease symptoms (but not to cure them) such as insulin, interferon (cancer therapy), vitamins, human growth hormone ADA, antibodies, vaccines, and antibiotics.

Research: Modification of gene structure in medical research, especially cancer research. Food processing: Rennin (enzyme) in cheese aging.

What was the **first commercial use** of **genetic engineering**?

Recombinant DNA technology was first used commercially to produce human insulin from bacteria. In 1982, genetically engineered insulin was approved for use by diabetics. Insulin is normally produced by the pancreas, and the pancreas of slaughtered animals such as swine or sheep was used as a source of insulin. To provide a reliable source of human insulin, researchers obtained DNA from human cells carrying the gene with the information for making human insulin. Researchers made a copy of DNA carrying this insulin gene and moved it into a bacterium. When the bacterium was grown in the lab, the microbe split from one cell into two cells, and both cells got a copy of the insulin gene. Those two microbes grew, then divided into four, those four into eight, the eight into sixteen, and so forth. With each cell division, the two new cells each had a copy of the gene for human insulin. And because the cells had a copy of the genetic “recipe card” for insulin, they could make the insulin protein.

What is the **largest protein** produced by genetic engineering?

Blood-clotting factor VIII, produced by Bayer, is the largest protein so far prepared by genetic engineering and is the first genetically engineered drug. Assembled from 2,332 amino acids, it has a molecular weight of 300,000. (By comparison, human insulin consists of only 51 amino acids.) As a coagulating agent, factor VIII plays a critical life-sustaining role. In hemophiliacs, this protein is missing or does not function properly. As a result, even a minor incident of untreated bleeding can lead to death.

What is the **Human Genome Project**?

Begun in 1990, the U.S. Human Genome Project is an effort coordinated by the Department of Energy and the National Institutes of Health. The project originally was planned to last 15 years, but effective resource and technological advances have accelerated the expected completion date to 2003. Project goals are to identify all the approximately 30,000 genes in human DNA, determine the sequences of the three billion chemical base pairs that make up human DNA, store this information in databases, improve tools for data analysis, transfer related technologies to the private sector, and address the ethical, legal, and social issues (ELSI) that may arise from the project. The goal is not only to pinpoint these genes, but also to decode the biochemical information down to the so called "letters" of inheritance, the four basic constituents of all genes called nucleotides: A (adenine), C (cytosine), G (guanine), and T (thymine). Since these letters are linked in pairs of sequences in the double helix of DNA, this means that three billion pairs are involved in this process. The sequencing of the human genome has been hailed as the most ground-breaking scientific event of our time. It will, in equal measure, offer insight into our collective history and our individual identities and open up untold possibilities for the diagnosis, treatment, and prevention of disease. Not since Watson and Crick's discovery of the structure of DNA has a scientific investigation been greeted with such fanfare.

What is **cloning**?

A clone is a group of cells derived from the original cell by fission (one cell dividing into two cells) or by mitosis (cell nucleus division with each chromosome splitting into two). It perpetuates an existing organism's genetic make-up. Gardeners have been making clones (copies) of plants for centuries by taking cuttings of plants to make genetically identical copies. For plants that refuse to grow from cuttings, or for the animal world, modern scientific techniques have greatly extended the range of cloning. The technique for plants starts with taking a cutting of a plant, usually the "best" one in terms of reproductivity or decorativeness or other standard. Since all the plant's cells contain the genetic information from which the entire plant can be reconstructed, the cutting can be taken from any part of the plant. Placed in a culture medium having nutritious chemicals and a growth hormone, the cells in the cutting divide, doubling in size every six weeks until the mass of cells produces small, white, globular points called embryoids. These embryoids develop roots, or shoots, and begin to look like tiny plants. Transplanted into compost, these plants grow into exact copies of the parent plant. The whole process takes 18 months. This process, called tissue culture, has been used to make clones of oil palm, asparagus, pineapples, strawberries, brussels sprouts, cauliflower, bananas, carnations, ferns, etc. Besides making high productive copies of the best plant available, this method controls viral diseases that are passed through seed generations.

Can **human beings** be **cloned**?

In theory, yes. There are, however, many technical obstacles to human cloning, as well as moral, ethical, philosophical, religious, and economic issues to be resolved before a human being could be cloned. Most scientists would agree that cloning a human is unsafe under current conditions.

Nuclear transplantation or somatic cell nuclear transfer is the concept of moving the cell nucleus and its genetic material from one cell to another. Somatic cell nuclear transfer may be used to make tissue that is genetically compatible with that of the recipient, and it can be used in the treatment of specific disease.

	Nuclear Transplantation	Human Reproductive Cloning
End product	Cells growing in a petri dish	Human being
Purpose	To treat a specific disease of tissue generation	Replace or duplicate a human
Time frame	A few weeks (growth in culture)	9 months
Surrogate mother needed	No	Yes
Human created	No	Yes
Ethical implications	Similar to all embryonic cell research	Highly complex issues
Medical implications	Similar to any cell-based therapy	Safety and long-term efficacy concerns

What was the **first animal** to be successfully **cloned**?

In 1970, British molecular biologist John B. Gurdon (1933-) cloned a frog. He transplanted the nucleus of an intestinal cell from a tadpole into a frog's egg that had had its nucleus removed. The egg developed into an adult frog that had the tadpole's genome in all of its cells and was therefore a clone of the tadpole.

What was the **first mammal** to be successfully **cloned**?

The first mammal cloned from adult cells was Dolly, a ewe, born in July 1996. Dolly was born in a research facility in Scotland. Ian Wilmut led the team of biologists that removed a nucleus from a mammary cell of an adult ewe and transplanted it into an enucleated egg extracted from a second ewe. Electrical pulses were administered to fuse the nucleus with its new host. When the egg began to divide and develop into an embryo, it was transplanted into a surrogate mother ewe. Dolly was the genetic twin of the ewe that donated the mammary cell nucleus. On April 13, 1998, Dolly gave birth to Bonnie.

What are **stem cells**?

Stem cells are derived from totipotent cells of the early embryo. As totipotent cells they have the ability to differentiate into all of the cell types ultimately present in the adult, including muscle, blood, nerves or any other tissue.

Dolly the sheep, the world's first adult animal to be successfully cloned.

Who originated the idea called **panspermia**?

Panspermia is the idea that microorganisms, spores, or bacteria attached to tiny particles of matter have traveled through space, eventually landing on a suitable planet and initiating the rise of life there. The word itself means "all-seeding." The British scientist Lord Kelvin (1824-1907) suggested in the 19th century that life may have arrived here from outer space, perhaps carried by meteorites. In 1903, the Swedish chemist Svante Arrhenius (1859-1927) put forward the more complex panspermia idea that life on Earth was "seeded" by means of extraterrestrial spores, bacteria, and microorganisms coming here on tiny bits of cosmic matter.

What is the **difference** between **DNA** and **RNA**?

DNA (deoxyribonucleic acid) is a nucleic acid formed from a repetition of simple building blocks called nucleotides. The nucleotides consist of phosphate (PO_4), sugar (deoxyribose), and a base that is either adenine (A), thymine (T), guanine (G), or cytosine (C). In a DNA molecule, this basic unit is repeated in a double helix structure made from two chains of nucleotides linked between the bases. The links are either between A and T or between G and C. The structure of the bases does not allow other kinds of links. The famous double helix structure resembles a twisted ladder. The 1962 Nobel Prize in physiology or medicine was awarded to James Watson (b. 1928), Francis Crick (b. 1916), and Maurice Wilkins (b. 1916) for determining the molecular structure of DNA.

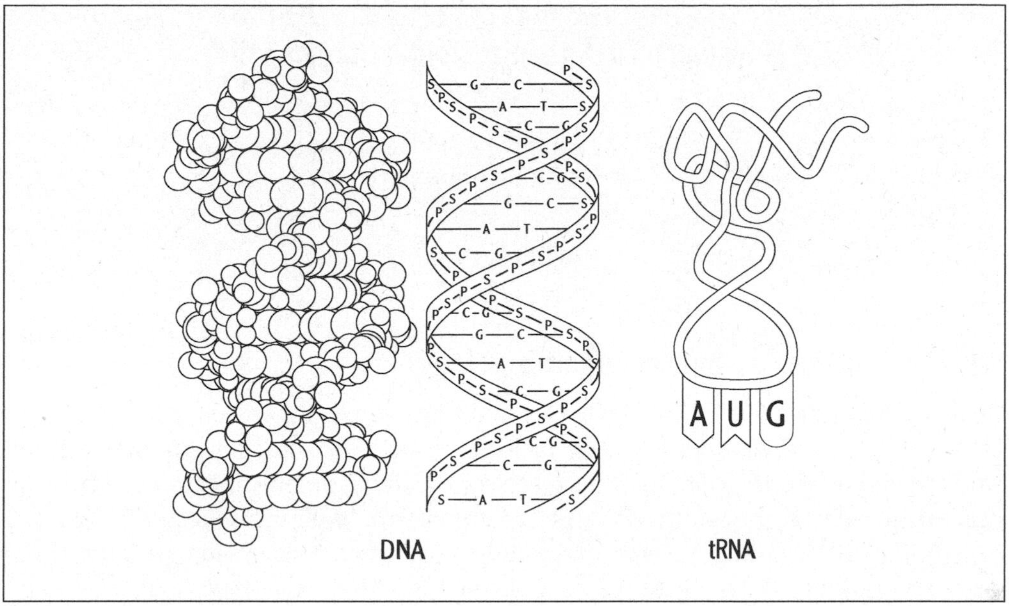

Double helix of DNA and RNA.

RNA (ribonucleic acid) is also a nucleic acid, but it consists of a single chain and the sugar is ribose rather than deoxyribose. The bases are the same except that the thymine (T), which appears in DNA is replaced by another base called uracil (U), which links only to adenine (A).

What is **p53**?

Discovered in 1979, p53—sometimes referred to as "The Guardian Angel of the Genome"—is a gene that, when a cell's DNA is damaged, acts as an "emergency brake" to halt the resulting cycle of cell division that can lead to tumor growth and cancer. It also acts as an executioner, programming damaged cells to self-destruct before their altered DNA can be replicated. However, when it mutates, p53 can lose its suppressive powers or have the devastating effect of actually promoting abnormal cell growth. Indeed, p53 is the most commonly mutated gene found in human tumors. Scientists have discovered a compound that could restore function to a mutant p53. Such a discovery may lead to the development of anti-cancer drugs targeting the mutant p53 gene.

Which **organism** has the **largest number** of **chromosomes**?

Ophioglossum reticulatum, a species of fern, has the largest number of chromosomes with more than 1,260 (630 pairs).

How much DNA is in a typical human cell?

If the DNA in a single human cell were stretched out and laid end-to-end, it would measure approximately 6.5 feet (two meters). The average human body contains 10 to 20 billion miles (16 to 32 billion kilometers) of DNA distributed among trillions of cells.

Who is considered the **founder of embryology**?

Kaspar Friedrich Wolff (1733-1794), a German surgeon, is regarded as the founder of embryology. Wolff produced his revolutionary work *Theoria generationis* in 1759. Until that time it was generally believed that each living organism developed from an exact miniature of the adult within the seed or sperm. Wolff introduced the idea that cells in a plant or animal embryo are initially unspecified (undefined) but later differentiate to produce the separate organs and systems with distinct types of tissues.

What does **"ontogeny recapitulates phylogeny"** mean?

Ontogeny is the course of development of an organism from fertilized egg to adult; phylogeny is the evolutionary history of a group of organisms. So the phrase, originating in 19th-century biology, means that as an embryo of an advanced organism grows, it will pass through stages that look very much like the adult phase of less advanced organisms. For example, at one point the human embryo has gills and resembles a tadpole.

LIFE PROCESSES, STRUCTURES, ETC.

What is a **biological clock**?

First recognized by the Chinese in the third century B.C.E., the biological clock is an intrinsic mechanism that controls the rhythm of various metabolic activities of plants and animals. Some, such as mating, hibernation, and migration, have a yearly cycle; others, such as ovulation and menstrual cycles of women, follow a lunar month. The majority, however, have a 24-hour, day-night cycle called the circadian rhythm. This day-night cycle, first recognized in plants over 250 years ago and existing in virtually all species of plants and animals, regulates these organisms' metabolic functions: plants opening and closing their petals or leaves, germination and flowering functions, changes in human body temperature, hormone secretion, blood sugar and blood pressure levels, and sleep cycles.

Research in chronobiology, the study of these daily rhythms, reveals that many accidents occur between 1 and 6 a.m., that most babies are born in the morning hours, that heart attacks tend to occur between 6 and 9 a.m., and that most Olympic records are broken in the late afternoon. The clock regulator may be the pineal gland located in the heads of animals (including humans).

Is there any scientific basis for **biorhythms**?

There is little, if any, scientific support for this theory, which claims there are three precise cycles that control human behavior. These are: a physical cycle of 23 days; an emotional cycle of 28 days; and an intellectual cycle of 33 days. Hazardous critical days are proposed to occur when two or more cycles intersect.

In contrast, biological rhythms such as activity cycles, feeding cycles, and sleeping cycles are well known. They vary from individual to individual and most are tied to the 24-hour rotation period of the Earth. Biological rhythms are real; biorhythms are a hoax.

What is the **"Spiegelman monster"**?

Sol Spiegelman, an American microbiologist, conducted an experiment to identify the smallest molecule capable of replicating itself. He began with a virus called QB, which consisted of a single molecule of ribonucleic acid (RNA) composed of 4,500 nucleotides (units of nucleic acid).

Usually this virus is able to make copies of itself only by invading a living cell because it requires a cellular enzyme called replicase. When Spiegelman added the replicase along with a supply of free nucleotides in a test tube to the virus, the virus replicated itself for several generations when a mutant appeared having fewer than 4,500 nucleotides. Being smaller, this mutant replicated faster than the original virus. Then another mutant appeared and displaced the first, and so it went. Finally, the virus degenerated into a little piece of ribonucleic acid with only 220 nucleotides, the smallest bit necessary for recognizing the replicase. This little test tube monster could continue to replicate at high speed, provided it had a source of building blocks.

Who was regarded as the **founder** of **biochemistry**?

Jan Baptista van Helmont (1577-1644) is called the father of biochemistry because he studied and expressed vital phenomena in chemical terms. The term "biochemistry," coined by F. Hoppe-Seyler in 1877, is the science dealing with the dynamics of living chemical processes or metabolism. It was formed from both the chemists' animal and vegetable chemistry, and the biologists' and doctors' physiological, zoological, or biological chemistry.

Helmont devoted his life to the study of chemistry as the true key to medicine and is considered to be one of the founders of modern pathology because he studied the external agents of diseases as well as the anatomical changes caused by diseases.

What was the first **amino acid** to be discovered?

Asparagine, isolated from the asparagus plant, was discovered in 1806 by the French chemist Nicolas-Louis Vauquelin.

CLASSIFICATION, MEASUREMENTS, AND TERMS

What is **bioinformatics**?

Bioinformatics is the field of science in which biology, computer science, and information technology merge into a single discipline. The ultimate goal of the field is to enable the discovery of new biological insights as well as to create a global perspective from which unifying principles in biology can be discerned. There are three important sub-disciplines within bioinformatics: 1) the development of new algorithms and statistics with which to assess relationships among members of the large data sets; 2) the analysis and interpretation of various types of data including nucleotide and amino acid sequences, protein domains, and protein structures; and 3) the development and implementation of tools that enable efficient access and management of different types of information.

What is **radiocarbon dating**?

Radiocarbon dating is a process for determining the age of a prehistoric object by measuring its radiocarbon content. The technique was developed by an American chemist, Dr. Willard F. Libby (1908-1980), in the late 1940s. All living things contain radiocarbon (carbon 14), an isotope that occurs in a small percentage of atmospheric carbon dioxide as a result of cosmic ray bombardment. After an animal or plant dies, it no longer absorbs radiocarbon and the radiocarbon present begins to decay (break down by releasing particles) at an exact and uniform rate. Its half-life of 5,730 years made it useful for measuring prehistory and events occurring within the past 35,000 to 50,000 years. A recent development, called the Accelerated Mass Spectrometer, which separates and detects atomic particles of different mass, can establish more accurate dates with a smaller sample. The remaining radiocarbon can be measured and compared to that of a living sample. In this way, the age of the 50,000-year-old or less animal or plant (or more precisely the elapsed time since its death) can be determined.

Since Libby's work, other isotopes having longer half-lives have been used as "geologic clocks" to date very old rocks. The isotope uranium-238 (decaying to lead-206) has a half-life of 4.5 billion years, uranium-235 (decaying to lead-207) has a value of 704 million years, thorium-232 (decaying to lead-278) has a half-life of 14 billion years, rubidium-87 (decaying to strontium-87) has a half-life value of 48.8 billion years, potassium-40 (decaying to argon-40) has a value of 1.25 billion years, and samarium-147 (decaying to neodymium-143) has a value of 106 billion years. These isotopes are used in dating techniques of gas formation light emission (called thermoluminescence). Other ways to date the past include dating by tree rings (counting its annual growth rings), and dating by thermoremanent magnetism (the magnetic field of the rock is compared to a date chart of changes in the Earth's magnetic field).

Who coined the term **biology**?

Biology was first used by Karl Burdach (1776-1847) to denote the study of man. Jean Baptiste Pierre Antoine de Monet Lamarck (1744-1829) gave the term a broader meaning in 1812. He believed in the integral character of science. For the special sciences, chemistry, meteorology, geology, and botany-zoology, he coined the term "biology." Lamarckism epitomizes the belief that changes acquired during an individual's lifetime as the result of active, quasi-purposive, functional adaptations can somehow be imprinted upon the genes, thereby becoming part of the heritage of succeeding generations. Today, very few professional biologists believe that anything of the kind occurs—or can occur.

Biology is the science that deals with living things (Greek *bios,* "life"). Once broadly divided into two areas—zoology (Greek *zoon,* "animal"), the study of animals, and botany (Greek *botanes,* "plant"), the study of plants—biology is now divided and sub-divided into hundreds of special fields involving the structure, function, and classification of forms of life. These include anatomy, ecology, embryology, evolution, genetics, paleontology, and physiology.

Jean Baptiste Lamarck's theories on evolution preceded and influenced those of Charles Darwin.

Where did the term **molecular biology** originate?

Warren Weaver (1898-1978), the director of the Rockefeller Foundation's Division of Natural Sciences, originated the term molecular biology. Weaver used X-ray diffraction to investigate the molecular basis of inheritance and the structure of biological macromolecules. He called this relatively new field molecular biology in a 1938 report.

What is **gnotobiotics**?

Gnotobiotics is the scientific study of animals or other organisms that are raised in germ-free environments or ones that contain only specifically known germs. These animals are first removed from the womb and then are placed in sterilized cages called isolators. Scientists are able to use these animals to determine how specific agents, such as viruses, bacteria, and fungi, affect the body.

What are the **five kingdoms** presently used to categorize living things?

Carolus Linnaeus (1707-1778) in 1735 divided all living things into two kingdoms in his classification system that was based on similarities and differences of organisms. However, since then, fungi seemed not to fit nicely into either kingdom. Although fungi were generally considered plants, they had no chlorophyll, roots, stems, or leaves, and hardly resemble any true plant. They also have several features found in the animal kingdom, as well as unique features characteristic of themselves alone. So fungi were placed into a third kingdom. In 1959, R. H. Whittaker proposed the current five kingdom system, based on new evidence from biochemical techniques and electron microscope observations that revealed fundamental differences among organisms. Each kingdom is listed below.

Monera—One-celled organisms lacking a membrane around the cell's genetic matter. Prokaryote (or procaryote) is the term used for this condition where the genetic material lies free in the cytoplasm of the cell without a membrane to form the nucleus of the cell. The kingdom consists of bacteria and blue-green algae (also called blue-green bacteria or cyanobacteria). Bacteria do not produce their own food but blue-green algae do. Blue-green algae, the primary form of life 3.5 to 1.5 billion years ago, produce most of the world's oxygen through photosynthesis.

Protista—Mostly single-celled organisms with a membrane around the cell's genetic material called eukaryotes (or eucaryotes) because of the nuclear membrane and other organelles found in the cytoplasm of the cell. Protista consists of true algae, diatoms, slime molds, protozoa, and euglena. Protistans are diverse in their modes of nutrition, etc. They may be living examples of the kinds of ancient single cells that gave rise to the kingdoms of multicelled eukaryotes (fungi, plants, and animals).

Fungi—One-celled or multicelled eukaryotes (having a nuclear membrane or a membrane around the genetic material). The nuclei stream between cells, giving the appearance that cells have multiple nuclei. This unique cellular structure, along with the unique sexual reproduction pattern, distinguishes the fungi from all other organisms. Consisting of mushrooms, yeasts, molds, etc., the fungi do not produce their own food.

Plantae—Multicellular organisms having cell nuclei and cell walls, which directly or indirectly nourish all other forms of life. Most use photosynthesis (a process by which green plants containing chlorophyll utilize sunlight as an energy source to synthesize complex organic material, especially carbohydrates from carbon dioxide, water, and inorganic salts) and most are autotrophs (produce their own food from inorganic matter).

Animalia—Multicellular organisms whose eukaryotic cells (without cell walls) form tissues (and from tissues form organs). Most get their food by ingestion of other organisms; they are heterotrophs (cannot produce their food from inorganic elements). Most are able to move from place to place (mobile) at least during part of the life cycle.

Who devised the current animal and plant **classification system**?

The naming and organizing of the millions of species of plants and animals is frequently called taxonomy; such classifications provide a basis for comparisons and generalizations. A common classification format is a hierarchical arrangement in which a group is classified within a group, and the level of the group is denoted in a ranking.

Carolus Linnaeus (1707-1778) composed a hierarchical classification system for plants (1753) and animals (1758) using a system of nomenclature (naming) that continues to be used today. Every plant and animal was given two scientific names (binomial method) in Latin, one for the species and the other for the group or genus within the species. He categorized the organisms by perceived physical differences and similarities. Although Linnaeus

Taxonomist Carolus Linnaeus devised a classification system for animal and plant species still used to this day.

How many different organisms have been identified by biologists?

Approximately 1.5 million different species of plants, animals and microorganisms have been described and formally named. Some biologists believe another 10 million species are still to be discovered, classified, and named.

started with only two kingdoms, contemporary classifiers have expanded them into five kingdoms. Each kingdom is divided into two or more phyla (major groupings; phylum is the singular form). Members within one phylum are more closely related to one another than they are to members of another phylum. These phyla are subdivided into parts again and again; members of each descending level have a closer relationship to each other than those of the level above. Generally, the ranking of the system, going from general to specific, are Kingdom, Phylum (plant world uses the term division), Class, Order, Family, Genus, and Species. In addition, intermediate taxonomic levels can be created by adding the prefixes "sub" or "super" to the name of the level, for example, "subphylum" or "superfamily." Zoologists working on parts of the animal classification many times are not uniform in their groupings. The system is still evolving and changing as new information emerges and new interpretations develop. Below is listed a comparison of hierarchy for four of the five kingdoms.

Taxonomic level	Human	Grasshopper	White Pine	Typhoid Bacterium
Kingdom	Animalia	Animalia	Plantae	Protista
Phylum	Chordata	Anthropoda	Tracheophyta	Schizomycophyta
Class	Mammalia	Insecta	Gymnospermae	Schizomycetes
Order	Primates	Orthoptera	Coniferales	Eubacteriales
Family	Hominidae	Arcridiidae	Pinaceae	Bacteriaceae
Genus	*Homo*	*Schistocerca*	*Pinus*	*Eberthella*
Species	*sapiens*	*americana*	*strobus*	*typhosa*

FUNGI, BACTERIA, ALGAE, ETC.

Are any **bacteria visible** to the **naked eye**?

Epulopiscium fishelsoni, which lives in the gut of surgeonfish, was first identified in 1985 and mistakenly classified as a protozoan. Later studies analyzed the organism's genetic material and proved it to be a bacterium of unprecedented size—0.015 inches (0.38 millimeters) in diameter, or about the size of a period in a small-print book.

How **fast** do **bacteria reproduce**?

Bacteria can reproduce very rapidly in a favorable environment, whether in a laboratory culture or a natural habitat. For example, *Escherichia coli* growing under optimal conditions can divide every 20 minutes. A laboratory culture started with a single cell can produce a colony of 10^7 to 10^8 bacteria in about 12 hours.

What is **anthrax**?

Bacillus anthracis, the etiologic agent of anthrax, is a large, gram-positive, nonmotile, spore-forming bacterial rod. The three virulence factor of *B. anthracis* are edema toxin, lethal toxin, and a capsular antigen. Human anthrax has three major clinical forms: cutaneous, inhalation and gastrointestinal. If left untreated, anthrax in all forms can lead to septicemia (blood poisoning) and death.

What are **diatoms**?

Diatoms are microscopic algae in the phylum bacillarrophyte of the protista kingdom. Yellow or brown in color, almost all diatoms are single-celled algae, dwelling in fresh and salt water, especially in the cold waters of the North Pacific Ocean and the Antarctic. Diatoms are an important food source for marine plankton (floating animal and plant life) and many small animals.

Diatoms have hard cell walls; these "shells" are made from silica that they extract from the water. It is unclear how they accomplish this. When they die, their glassy shells, called frustules, sink to the bottom of the sea, which hardens into rock called diatomite. One of the most famous and accessible diatomites is the Monterrey Formation along the coast of central and southern California.

How is a **fairy ring** formed?

A fairy ring, or fungus ring, is found frequently in a grassy area. There are three types: those that do not affect the surrounding vegetation, those that cause increased growth, and those that damage the surrounding environment. The ring is started from a mycelium (the underground, food-absorbing part of a fungus). The fungus growth is on the outer edge of the grassy area because the inner band of decaying mycelium "use-up" the resources in the soil at the center. This creates a ring effect. Each succeeding generation is farther out from the center.

What is the scientific study of **fungi** called?

Mycology is the science concerning fungi. In the past, fungi have been classified in other kingdoms, but currently they are recognized as a separate kingdom based on their unique cellular structure and their unique pattern of sexual reproduction.

Fungi are heterotrophs (cannot produce their own food from inorganic matter). They secrete enzymes that digest food outside their bodies and their fungal cells absorb the products. Their activities are essential in the decomposition of organic material and cycling of nutrients in nature.

Some fungi, called saprobes, obtain nutrients from non-living organic matter. Other fungi are parasites; they obtain nutrients from the tissues of living host organisms. The great majority of fungi are multicelled and filamentous. A mushroom is a modified reproductive structure in or upon which spores develop. Each spore dispersed from it may grow into a new mushroom.

What is a **lichen**?

Lichens are organisms that grow on rocks, tree branches, or bare ground. They are composed of a green algae and a colorless fungus living together symbiotically. They do not have roots, stems, flowers, or leaves. The fungus, having no chlorophyll, cannot manufacture its own food, but can absorb food from the algae that it enwraps completely, providing protection from the sun and moisture.

This relationship between the fungus and algae is called symbiosis (a close association of two organisms not necessarily to both their benefits). Lichens were the first recognized and are still the best examples of this phenomenon. A unique feature of lichen symbiosis is that it is so perfectly developed and balanced as to behave as a single organism.

Who was first to coin the word **virus**?

The English physician Edward Jenner (1749-1823), founder of virology and a pioneer in vaccination, first coined the word "virus." Using one virus to immunize against another one was precisely the strategy Jenner used when he inoculated someone with cowpox (a disease that attacks cows) to make them immune to smallpox. This procedure is called vaccination, from the word vaccine (the Latin name for cowpox). Vaccines are usually a very mild dose of the disease-causing bacteria or virus (weakened or dead). These vaccines stimulate the creation of antibodies in the body that recognize and attack a particular infection. A virus is a minute parasitic organism that reproduces only inside the cell of its host. Viruses replicate by invading host cells and taking over the cell's "machinery" for DNA replication. Viral particles then can break out of the cells, causing disease.

Who were the founders of **modern bacteriology**?

French chemist Louis Pasteur is considered one of the founders of modern bacteriology.

The German bacteriologist Robert Koch (1843-1910) and the French chemist Louis Pasteur (1822-1895) are considered the founders. Pasteur devised a way to heat food or beverages at a temperature low enough not to ruin them, but high enough to kill most of the microorganisms that would cause spoilage and disease. This process is called pasteurization in his honor. By demonstrating that tuberculosis was an infectious disease caused by a specific bacillus and not by bad heredity, Koch laid the groundwork for public health measures that would significantly reduce such diseases. His working methodologies for isolating microorganisms, his laboratory procedures, and his four postulates for determination of disease agents gave medical investigators valuable insights into the control of bacterial infections.

Why are **Koch's postulates** significant?

The German bacteriologist Robert Koch (1843-1910) developed four rules in his study of disease-producing organisms, which later investigators found useful. The following conditions must be met to prove that a bacterium causes a particular disease:

1. The microorganism must be found in large numbers in all diseased animals but not in healthy ones.
2. The organism must be isolated from a diseased animal and grown outside the body in a pure culture.
3. When the isolated microorganism is injected into other healthy animals, it must produce the same disease.
4. The suspected microorganism must be recovered from the experimental hosts, isolated, compared to the first microorganism, and found to be identical.

PLANT WORLD

PHYSICAL CHARACTERISTICS, FUNCTIONS, ETC.

If you were to compress the history of the earth into a single year, what would be some major "dates" in **plant evolution**?

Time (million years)	Event	Date
3600	first algae	Mar. 21
433	land plants appear	Nov. 27
400	ferns and gymnosperms	Nov. 30
300	major coal deposits formed	Dec. 8
65	flowering plants appear	Dec. 26

What is the **best type** of **pollination**?

Effective pollination occurs when viable pollen is transferred to plant's stigmas, ovule-bearing organs, or ovules (seed precursors). Without pollination, there would be no fertilization. Since plants are immobile organisms, they usually need external agents to transport their pollen from where it is produced in the plant to where fertilization can occur. This situation produces cross-pollination, wherein one plant's pollen is moved by an agent to another plant's stigma. Some plants are able to self-pollinate—transfer their own pollen to their own stigmas. But of the two methods, cross-pollination seems the better, for it allows new genetic material to be introduced.

Cross-pollination agents include insects, wind, birds, mammals, and water. Many times flowers offer one or more "rewards" to attract these agents—sugary nectar, oil, solid food bodies, perfume, a place to sleep, or sometimes the pollen itself. Other times the plant can "trap" the agent into transporting the pollen. Generally, plants use color and fragrances as attractants to lure these agents. For example, a few orchids use a combination of smell and color to mimic the female of certain species of bees and wasps so successfully that the corresponding males will attempt to mate with them. Through this process (pseudocopulation) the orchids achieve pollination. While some plants cater to a variety of agents, other plants are very selective and are pollinated by a single species of insect only. This extreme pollinator specificity tends to maintain the purity of a plant species.

Plant structure can accommodate the type of agent used. For example, plants such as grasses and conifers, whose pollen is carried by the wind, tend to have a simple structure lacking petals, with freely exposed and branched stigmas to catch airborne pollen and dangling anthers (pollen-producing parts) on long filaments. This type of anther allows the light, round pollen to be easily caught by the wind. These plants are found in areas such as prairies and mountains, where insect agents are rare. In contrast, semi-enclosed, nonsymmetrical, long-lived flowers such as iris, rose, and snapdragon have a "landing platform" and nectar in the flower base to accommodate insect agents such as the bee. The sticky, abundant pollen can easily become attached to the insect to be borne away to another flower.

What is **tropism**?

Tropism is the movement of a plant in response to a stimulus. The categories include:

Chemotropism—a response to chemicals by plants in which incurling of leaves may occur.

Geotropism or gravitropism—a response to gravity in which the plant moves in relation to gravity. Shoots of a plant are negatively geotropic (growing upward), while roots are positively geotropic (growing downward).

Hydrotropism—a response to water or moisture in which roots grow toward the water source.

Paraheliotropism—a response by the plant leaves to avoid exposure to the sun.

Phototropism—a response to light in which the plant may be positively phototropic (moving toward the light source) or negatively phototropic (moving away from the light source). Main axes of shoots are usually positively phototropic, whereas roots are generally insensitive to light.

Thermotropism—a response to temperature by plants.

Thigmotropism or haptotropism—a response to touch by the climbing organs of a plant. For example, the plant's tendrils may curl around a support in a spring-like manner.

TREES AND SHRUBS

What are the **longest-lived tree species** in the **United States**?

Of the 850 different species of tree in the United States, the oldest species is the bristlecone pine (*Pinus longaeva*), which grows in the deserts of Nevada and southern California (especially in the White Mountains). Some of these trees are believed to be over 4,600 years old. The potential life span of these pines is estimated to be 5,500 years. But these ages are very young when compared to the oldest surviving species in the world, which is the maiden-hair tree (*Ginkgo biloba*) of Zhexiang, China. This tree first appeared during the Jurassic era some 160 million years ago. Also called icho, or the ginkyo ("silver apricot"), this species has been cultivated in Japan since 1100 B.C.E.

Longest-Lived Tree Species in the United States

Name of tree	Number of years
Bristlecone pine (*Pinus longaeva*)	3,000-4,700
Giant sequoia (*Sequoiadendron giganteum*)	2,500
Redwood (*Sequoia sempervirens*)	1,000-3,500
Douglas fir (*Pseudotsuga menziesii*)	750
Bald cypress (*Taxodium distichum*)	600

How are **tree rings** used to date historical events?

Tree fragments of unknown age and the rings of living trees can be compared in order to establish the date when the fragment was part of a living tree. Thus, tree rings can be used to establish the year in which an event took place as long as the event involved the maiming or killing of a tree. Precise dates can be established for the building of a medieval cathedral or an American Indian pueblo; the occurrence of an earthquake, landslide, volcanic eruption, or a fire; and even the date when a panel of wood was cut for a Dutch painting. Every year, the tree produces an annular ring composed of one wide, light ring and one narrow, dark ring. During spring and early summer, tree stem cells grow rapidly and are larger; this produces the wide, light ring. In winter, growth is

Tree rings reflect the age of a tree and shed light on climatic conditions such as seasonal rainfall.

greatly reduced and cells are much smaller; this produces the narrow, dark ring. In the coldest part of winter or the dry heat of summer, no cells are produced.

Who first recorded that the **number of rings** in the cross-section of a tree trunk tell its **age**?

The painter and engineer Leonardo da Vinci (1452- 1519) noticed this phenomenon. He also saw that the year's dampness can be determined by the space between the tree's rings. The farther apart the rings, the more moisture there was in the ground around the tree.

Why are fall leaves **bright red in some years** and **dull in others**?

Two factors are necessary in the production of red autumn leaves. There must be warm, bright, sunny days during which the leaves manufacture sugar. Warm days must be followed by cool nights with temperatures below 45°F (7.2°C). This weather combination traps the sugar and other materials in the leaves. This results in the manufacture of red anthocyanin. A warm cloudy day restricts the formation of bright colors. With decreased sunlight, sugar production is decreased and this small amount of sugar is transported back to the trunk and roots, where it has no color effect.

Prior to the **chestnut blight** devastation of the American chestnut, what was the proportion of chestnut trees in the eastern forest?

In 1900 the American chestnut (*Castenea dentata Marsh*) was an important forest tree widespread across eastern North America until the chestnut blight fungus (*Cryphonectria parasitica*) devastated it, reducing it to small trees and stumps. In central and southern Pennsylvania, New Jersey, and southern New England, the chestnut formed almost half of the hardwood forest. In its entire range, the species dominated the deciduous forests making up almost one-quarter of the trees.

What part of a **chestnut tree** is not killed by chestnut blight?

The roots survive the blight and sprout again to attempt a new tree.

Why do tree **leaves turn color** in the fall?

The carotenoids (pigments in the photosynthesizing cells), which are responsible for the fall colors, are present in the leaves during the growing season. However, the colors are eclipsed by the green chlorophyll. Toward the end of summer, when the chlorophyll production ceases, the other colors of the carotenoids (such as yellow, orange, red, or purple) become visible. Listed below are the autumn leaf colors of some common trees.

Tree	Color
Sugar maple and sumac	Flame red and orange
Red maple, dogwood, sassafras, and scarlet oak	Dark red
Poplar, birch, tulip tree, willow	Yellow
Ash	Plum purple
Oak, beech, larch, elm, hickory, and sycamore	Tan or brown
Locust	Stays green until leaves drop
Black walnut and butternut	Drops leaves before they turn color

What is the **tallest tree**?

The tallest tree ever measured was the Australian eucalyptus (*Eucalyptus regnans*) at Watts River, Victoria, Australia. In 1872 it was reported to measure 435 feet (132 meters) tall and it was most likely over 500 feet (152 meters) originally. According to the National Register of Big Trees 2002-03, the tallest living tree is a Coastal redwood (*Sequoia sempervirens*) in Redwood National Park, California at 321 feet (98 meters).

Which tree has the **largest measured trunk** circumference?

The tree in the United States with the largest circumference of 85.3 feet (26 meters) is a Giant sequoia *(Sequoiadendron giganteum)* in Sequoia National Park, California.

What is a **banyan tree**?

The banyan tree (*Ficus benghalensis*), a native of tropical Asia, is a member of the Ficus or fig genus. It is a magnificent evergreen, sometimes 100 feet (30.48 meters) in height. As the massive limbs spread horizontally, the tree sends down roots that develop into secondary, pillar-like supporting trunks. Over a period of years a single tree may spread to occupy a tremendous area, as much as 2,000 feet (610 meters) around the periphery.

Which **conifers** in North America **lose their leaves** in winter?

Dawn redwood trees (*Metasequoia*) are deciduous. Their leaves are bright green in summer and turn coppery red in the fall before they drop. Previously known only as a fossil, the tree was found in China in 1941 and has been growing in the United States since the 1940s. The U.S. Department of Agriculture distributed seeds to experimental growers in the United States, and the dawn redwood tree now grows all over the country.

The only native conifers that shed all of their leaves in the fall are the bald cypress (*Taxodium distichum*) and the Larch (*Larix larcina*).

What are the distinguishing characteristics of **pine**, **spruce,** and **fir** trees?

The best way to tell the difference between the three trees is by their cones and leaves:

Pines

White Pine	Five needles in each bundle; needles soft and 3-5 inches long. Cones can be 4-8 inches long
Scotch Pine	Two needles in each bundle. Needles are stiff, yellow green, 1.5-3 inches long. Cones are 2-5 inches long.

Spruce

White Spruce	Dark green needles are rigid, but not prickly, grow from all sides of the twig and are less than an inch long. Cones are 1-2.5 inches long and hang downward.
Blue Spruce	Needles are about an inch long, silvery blue, very stiff and prickly; needles grow from all sides of the branch. Cones are 3.5 inches long.

Fir

Balsam Fir	Needles are flat, 1-1.5 inches long and arranged in pairs opposite each other. Cones are upright, cylindrical and 2-4 inches long.
Fraser Fir	Looks like a balsam but needles are smaller and more rounded.
Douglas Fir	Single needles, 1-1.5 inches long and very soft. Cone scales have bristles that stick out.

Does the **rose family** produce any trees?

The apple, pear, peach, cherry, plum, mountain ash, and hawthorn trees are members of the rose family (*Rosaceae*).

Why do the **leaves of mimosa** ("sensitive plant") close in **response to touch**?

When the plant perceives touch, the stimulus is relayed to rest of the plant. Electrical signals then turn on motor cells that in turn control the leaf movement.

What is the **fastest growing** land plant?

Bamboo is the quickest to gain height. Bamboo can grow one meter, or almost three feet, in twenty-four hours. This growth is produced partly by cell division and partly by cell enlargement.

FLOWERS AND OTHER PLANTS

Who is known as the **founder** of **botany**?

The ancient Greek, Theophrastus (ca. 372-ca. 287 B.C.E.), is known as the father of botany. His two large botanical works, *On the History of Plants* and *On the Causes of Plants,* were so comprehensive that 1,800 years went by before any new discovery in botany was made. He integrated the practice of agriculture into botany and established a theory of plant growth and the analysis of plant structure. He related plants to their natural environment and identified, classified, and described 550 different plants.

What are the **parts of a flower**?

Sepal—found on the outside of the bud or on the underside of the open flower. It serves to protect the flower bud from drying out. Some sepals ward off predators by their spines or chemicals.

Petals—serve to attract pollinators and are usually dropped shortly after pollination occurs.

Nectar—contains varying amounts of sugar and proteins that can be secreted by any of the floral organs. It usually collects inside the flower cup near the base of the cup formed by the flower parts.

Stamen—is the male part of a flower and consists of a filament and anther where pollen is produced.

Pistil—is the female part, which consists of the stigma, style, and ovary containing ovules. After fertilization the ovules mature into seeds.

What is meant by an **"imperfect" flower**?

An imperfect flower is one that is unisexual, having either stamens (male parts) or pistils (female parts) but not both.

How does a **bulb** differ from a **corm**, a **tuber**, and a **rhizome**?

Many times the term "bulb" is applied to any underground storage organ in which a plant stores energy for its dormant period. Dormancy is one of nature's devices a plant utilizes to get through difficult weather conditions (winter cold or summer drought).

A true bulb—consists of fleshy scales containing a small basal plate (a modified stem from which the roots emerge) and a shoot. The scales that surround the embryo are modified leaves that contain the nutrients for the bulb during dormancy and early growth. Some bulbs have a tunic (a paper-thin covering) around the scales. The basal plate can also hold the scales together. New bulbs

Are poinsettias poisonous to children and pets?

It is *not true* that poinsettias are poisonous to children and pets. Even if a child ate an entire plant, an upset stomach is probably all he or she would experience.

form from the lateral buds on the basal plate. Tulips, daffodils, lilies, and hyacinths are examples of bulb flowers.

A corm—is actually a stem that has been modified into a mass of storage tissue. The eye(s) at the top of the corm is a growing point. The corm is covered by dry leaf bases similar to the tunic-covering of the bulb. Roots grow from the basal plate on the underside of the corm. New corms form on top of or beside the old one. Corm-type flowers include gladiolus, freesia, and crocus.

A tuber—is a solid underground mass of stem like a corm but it lacks both a basal plate and a tunic. Roots and shoots grow from "eyes" (growth buds) out of its sides, bottom, and sometimes its top. Some tubers are roundish. Others are flattened and lumpy. Some examples of tubers are gloxinia, caladium, ranunculuses, and anemone.

A tuberous root—is a swollen root that has taken in moisture and nutrients. It resembles a tuber. New growth occurs on the base of the old stem, where it joins the root. A tuberous root can be divided by cutting off a section with an eye-bearing portion from where the old stem was attached. Dahlias have tuberous roots.

A rhizome or a rootstock—is a thickened, branching storage stem that usually grows laterally along or slightly below the soil surface. Roots develop downward on the bottom surface, while buds and leaves sprout upwards from the top of the rhizome. It is propagated by cutting the parent plant into sections. Japanese, Siberian, and bearded irises; cannas; calla lilies; and trillium are rhizomes.

What plants are considered to be **child safe**?

These are some plants that are considered to be child safe even if they are swallowed by a child:

African violet
Aster
Begonia
Boston fern
California poppy
Coleus
Dandelion
Easter lily
Gardenia
Impatiens
Jade plant
Marigold
Norfolk Island pine
Petunia
Purple passion
Rose
Spider Plant
Swedish ivy
Tiger lily
Violet
Wandering Jew
Zebra plant

The slender-leaved sundew, a carnivorous plant that attracts and feeds on insects.

How are **carnivorous plants** categorized?

Carnivorous plants are plants that attract and catch animal prey digesting and absorbing the body juices for the nutrients. There are between 450 and 500 species and 12 genera of carnivorous plants classified according to the nature of their trapping mechanisms. Active traps display rapid motion in their capture of prey. The Venus fly trap (*Dionaea muscipula*) and the bladderwort (*Utricularia vulgaris*) are active traps. Semi-active traps employ a two-stage trap in which the prey is caught in the trap's adhesive fluid. As the prey struggles, the plant is triggered to slowly tighten its grip. The sundew (species *Drosera*) and butterwort (*Pinguicula vulgaris*) are semi-active traps. Passive traps entice insects by nectar. The insects fall into a reservoir of water and drown. An example of the passive trap is the pitcher plant (five genera). The Green Swamp Nature Preserve in southeastern North Carolina has the most numerous types of carnivorous plants.

What special significance does the **passionflower** have?

Spanish friars of the sixteenth century first gave the name to this flower. They saw in the form of the passionflower (*Passiflora*) a representation of the passion of Christ: the flowers have five petals and five sepals, which was thought to symbolize the 10 faithful apostles present at the crucifixion; the corona of five filaments was believed to resemble Christ's crown of thorns; the five stamens represented the five wounds in Christ's body, and the three stigmas stood for the nails driven into his hands and feet. Most species of passionflower are native to the tropical areas of the Western Hemisphere.

What flowers are designated as **symbolic of each month** of the year?

Month	Flower
January	Carnation
February	Violet
March	Jonquil
April	Sweet Pea
May	Lily of the Valley
June	Rose
July	Larkspur
August	Gladiola
September	Aster
October	Calendula
November	Chrysanthemum
December	Narcissus

What do the **different colors** and varieties of **roses symbolize**?

Rose	Meaning
Yellow rose	Jealousy; unfaithfulness
Red rosebud	Youth; beauty
White rose	Silence
Lancaster rose	Union
Burgundy rose	Unconscious beauty
Musk rose	Capricious beauty
Dog rose	Pleasure and pain
Cabbage rose	Ambassador of love
Bridal rose	Happy love
Carolina rose	Dangerous love
May rose	Precocity
Moss rose	Voluptuousness
Christmas rose	Tranquility
Pompon rose	Gentility

Is there a **national flower** for the United States?

The United States adopted the rose as the national flower on October 7, 1986, after many years of deliberation. Other flowers suggested were the dogwood, the mountain laurel, and the columbine.

How was **anise** used in ancient times?

The Romans brought the licorice-flavored herb from Egypt to Europe, where they used it for payment of taxes. It became popular flavoring for cakes, cookies, bread, and candy.

What is the **first wildflower to bloom** in the spring in the northern United States?

The first flower of the northern spring is unusual and interesting, but rarely seen, because it blooms in the swamp. Commonly called skunk cabbage (*Spathyema foetidus*), it appears in February. The first spring flower that is generally known in New England and the Middle West is the *Hepatica,* or liverleaf, which blooms in March or early April.

What is **wormwood**?

Artemisia absinthium, known as wormwood, is a hardy, spreading, fragrant perennial, two to four feet (61 to 122 centimeters) tall. It is native to Europe but widely naturalized in North America. The liqueur absinthe is flavored from this plant.

What is a **weed**?

The dictionary definition is any plant considered undesirable, unattractive, or troublesome, especially a plant growing where it is not wanted in cultivated ground. Some celebrated authors have had their own definition of a weed. Ralph Waldo Emerson wrote, "What is a weed? A plant whose virtues have not yet been discovered." James Russell Lowell wrote in 1848, "A weed is no more than a flower in disguise." Ella Wheeler Wilcox, a Wisconsin poet (more famous for her expression "Laugh, and the world laughs with you; Weep, and you weep alone") wrote in her poem "The Weed" that "a weed is but an unloved flower." Finally, Shakespeare wrote in *Richard III,* "great weeds do grow apace."

What is the origin of the name **Jimson weed**?

Jimson weed (*Datura stramonium*) is a corruption of the name Jamestown weed, given to a highly poisonous plant. The Jamestown, Virginia, colonists were familiar with this weed. It is also known as thorn apple, mad apple, stinkwort, angel's trumpet, devil's trumpet, stinkweed, dewtry, and white man's weed. Every part of this plant is potentially deadly if consumed in even moderate amounts. Even so, some of the alkaloids found in this plant are used by doctors as a preanesthetic.

What are **luffa sponges**?

Luffas are nonwoody vines of the cucumber family. The interior fibrous skeletons of the fruit are used as sponges. The common name is sometimes spelled loofah. Dishcloth gourd, rag gourd, and vegetable sponge are other popular names for this sponge.

Does **ivy cause damage** growing on a brick wall?

Experts at the New York Botanical Garden say it is possible for ivy to damage walls that are already in bad condition. Mortar that is in good shape is not normally subject to any damage.

A thick growth of ivy traps moisture against the walls. The adhesive disks that attach the ivy to the wall are subject to decay. This and other organic matter forms humic acid, which is capable of dissolving carbonate rock, like marble and lime mortar.

Why do cats like **catnip**?

Catnip (*Nepeta cataria*) is a hardy perennial herb attractive to cats. Also known as catmint or catnep, it belongs to the mint family. The whole cat family (*Felidae*) reacts to catnip. Mountain lions, lynx, tigers, and lions roll over, rub their face, extend their claws, and do a body twist when they smell catnip's pungent odor. The oil from the leaves of catnip probably excites cats because it contains a chemical called trans-neptalactone, which closely resembles an excretion in a female cat's urine.

Why are some mushrooms called **toadstools**?

The term toadstool goes back to the Middle Ages when it was popularly associated with the toad that was thought to be poisonous. Toadstools, with their stool-like shape, are mushrooms that are inedible or poisonous. It is said that when a toad is alarmed, the warts on its back secrete a poisonous substance called bufonenin.

What is unique about the **water-lily** *Victoria amazonica?*

It is very big! Found only on the Amazon River, this water-lily has leaves that are up to six feet (1.8 meters) in diameter. The 12-inch (30-centimeter) flowers open at dusk on two successive nights.

GARDENING, FARMING, ETC.

What is considered the **most fertile, productive** type of **soil**?

There are three broad categories of garden soils: clay, sandy, and loam. Clay soils are heavy with the particles sticking close together. Working clay soil with your fingers you should get a shiny ball in your hand. Most plants have a hard time getting at the nutrients in clay soil, and the soil tends to get waterlogged. Clay soils can be good for a few deep rooted plants, such as mint, peas, and broad beans.

Sandy soils are light and have particles that do not stick together. Rolling sandy soil in your hand produces crumbs that split apart. A sandy soil is good for many alpine and arid plants, some herbs such as tarragon and thyme, and vegetables such as onions, carrots and tomatoes.

Loam soils are considered the best garden soils, because they are a well balanced mix of smaller and larger materials. They give up nutrients to plant roots easily and they drain well, but loam also retains water very well. Loam soil forms a ball in your fingers, but it feels gritty and shouldn't shine like clay soil.

What do the numbers on a bag of **fertilizer** indicate?

The three numbers, such as 15-20-15, refer to the percentages by weight of macronutrients found in the fertilizer. The first number stands for nitrogen, the second for phosphorus, and the third for potassium. In order to determine the actual amount of each element in the fertilizer, multiply the percentage by the fertilizer's total weight in pounds. For example, in a 50-pound bag of 15-20-15, there are 7.5 pounds of nitrogen, 10 pounds of phosphorus, and 7.5 pounds of potassium. The remaining pounds are filler.

What does **"pH"** mean when applied to **garden soil**?

Literally, pH stands for "potential of hydrogen" and is the term used by soil scientists to represent the hydrogen ion concentration in a soil sample. The relative alkalinity and acidity is commonly expressed in terms of the symbol pH. The neutral point in the scale is seven. Soil testing below seven is said to be acid; soil testing above pH seven is alkaline. The pH values are based on logarithms with a base of ten. Thus, a soil testing pH 5 is ten times as acidic as soil testing pH 6, while a soil testing pH 4 is one hundred times as acidic as soil testing pH 6.

What is the **best soil pH** for growing plants?

Nutrients such as phosphorous, calcium, potassium, and magnesium are most available to plants when the soil pH is between 6.0 and 7.5. Under highly acid (low pH) conditions, these nutrients become insoluble and relatively unavailable for uptake by plants. High soil pH can also decrease the availability of nutrients. If the soil is more alkaline than pH 8, phosphorous, iron, and many trace elements become insoluble and unavailable for plant uptake.

Is there a quick and easy way to test for **soil acidity** or **alkalinity**?

Some gardeners make a simple taste and smell test to check the soil. Acid soil smells and tastes sour. Some put a soil sample in a jar of vinegar. If the vinegar starts to bubble, your soil has plenty of lime. If there are no bubbles, lime the soil with four ounces (113 grams) of lime for every square yard (0.84 square meter).

When is the **best time to work the soil**?

Although it is possible to prepare the soil at any time of year, fall digging is the best time. Dig in the fall and leave the ground rough. Freezing and thawing during winter breaks up clods and aerates the soil. Insects that otherwise survive the winter are mostly turned out. The soil settling during winter will lessen the likelihood of air pockets in the soil when planting the following spring. Fall preparation provides time for soil additives such as manure and compost to break down before planting time.

How can **garden soil** be used as **potting soil**?

The garden soil must be pasteurized and then mixed with coarse sand and peat moss. Soil may be pasteurized by putting the soil in a covered baking dish in the oven. When a meat thermometer stuck in the soil has registered 180°F (82°C) for 30 minutes, the soil is done.

What is the composition of **synthetic soil**?

Synthetic soil is composed of a variety of organic and inorganic materials. Inorganic substances used include pumice, calcinated clay, cinders, vermiculite, perlite, and sand. Vermiculite and perlite are used for water retention and drainage. Organic materials used include wood residues, manure, sphagnum moss, plant residues, and peat. Sphagnum peat moss is also helpful for moisture retention and lowers the pH of the mixture. Lime may be added to offset the acidity of peat. Synthetic soil may also be referred to as growing medium, soil mixes, potting mixture, plant substrate, greenhouse soil, potting soil, and amended soil. Most synthetic soils are deficient in important mineral nutrients, which can be added during the mixing process or with water.

What is meant by the term **double-digging**?

Double-digging produces an excellent deep planting bed for perennials, especially if the area is composed of heavy clay. It involves removing the top 10 inches (25 centimeters) of soil and moving it to a holding area, then spading the next 10 inches (25 centimeters) and amending this layer with organic matter and/or fertilizer. Then the soil from the "first" digging is amended as well, then replaced.

What is meant by **xeriscaping**?

A xeriscape, a landscape of low water-use plants, is the modern approach to gardening in areas that experience water shortages. Taken from the Greek word xeros, meaning dry, this type of gardening uses drought-resistant plants and low maintenance grasses, which require water only every two to three weeks. Drip irrigation, heavy mulching of plant beds, and organic soil improvements are other xeriscape techniques that allow better water absorption and retention, which in turn decrease garden watering time.

When a plant is said to be **"double dormant,"** what does that mean?

Plants that are double dormant require a unique sort of layering or stratification in order for the seeds to germinate. The seeds of these plants must have a period of warmth and moisture followed by a cold spell. Both the seed coat and the seed embryo require this double dormancy if they are to germinate. In nature this process usually takes two years. Some well-known plants that live the life of double dormancy include some lilies, dogwood, junipers, lilac, tree peony, and viburnum.

What is meant by the phrase **rain shadow** in gardening?

The ground in the lee of a wall or solid fence receives less rainfall than the ground on the windward side. The wall or fence creates an area of rain shadow.

What does the term **hydroponics** mean?

This term refers to growing plants in some medium other than soil; the inorganic plant nutrients (such as potassium, sulphur, magnesium, and nitrogen) are continuously supplied to the plants in solution. Hydroponics is mostly used in areas where there is little soil or unsuitable soil. Since it allows precise control of nutrient levels and oxygenation of the roots, it is often used to grow plants used for research purposes. Julius von Sachs (1832-1897), a researcher in plant nutrition, pioneered modern hydroponics. Research plants have been grown in solution culture since the mid-1800s. William Gericke, a scientist at the University of California, defined the word hydroponics in 1937. In the 50 years that hydroponics has been used on a commercial basis, it has been adapted to many situations. NASA will be using hydroponics in the space station for crop production and to recycle carbon dioxide into oxygen. Although successful for research, hydroponics has many limitations and may prove frustrating for the amateur gardener.

How are **seedlings hardened off** before planting?

Hardening off is a gardening term for gradually acclimatizing seedlings raised indoors to the outdoor environment. Place the tray of seedlings outdoors for a few hours each day in a semi-protected spot. Lengthen the amount of time they stay out by an hour or so each day; at the end of the week, they will be ready for planting outdoors.

What is the difference between **container-grown**, **balled-and-burlapped**, and **bare-rooted** plants?

Container-grown plants have been grown in some kind of pot—usually peat, plastic, or clay—for most or all of their lives. Balled-and-burlapped plants have been dug up with the soil carefully maintained around their roots in burlap. Bare-rooted plants have also been dug from their growing place but without retaining the root ball. Typically, plants from a mail-order nursery come bare-rooted with their roots protected with damp sphagnum moss. Bare-rooted plants are the most susceptible to damage.

What is meant by **companion planting**?

There is not a lot of scientific documentation on this subject, but gardeners and farmers have noticed for years certain affinities that some plants have when planted near other plants. Nasturtiums, for example, lure aphids away from apple trees and attract blackfly away from vegetables. Onions and garlic act as both a fungicide and an insecticide, possibly because they accumulate sulfur very efficiently, and many pests avoid the odor. Some plants do not make good neighbors. Below is a sample list of good and bad companion plants:

	Close Neighbors	Distant Neighbors
Bush Beans	Potatoes, lettuce, tomatoes	Onions
Carrots	Leaf lettuce, onions, tomatoes	—
Corn	Potatoes, beans, cucumbers	—
Cucumbers	Beans, corn	Potatoes
Lettuce	Carrots, cucumbers	—
Onions	Tomatoes, lettuce	Beans
Potatoes	Beans, corn	Cucumbers
Tomatoes	Onions, carrots	Potatoes

Which plants are best for **container** gardening?

Most vegetables can be grown in a container—even large ones like pumpkins. Miniature varieties of vegetables are better because they require less space and develop earlier. Fluorescent lights help leaf crops to grow indoors even in winter. Most root crops are best grown outdoors. Fruit crops such as tomatoes can be grown indoors, but need warm temperatures and at least six hours of summer sunshine. Some of the plants that may be grown are: bush beans, pole beans, beets, broccoli, cabbage, carrots, cucumbers, kale, lettuce, onions, peppers, summer squash, and tomatoes.

What is the difference between an **arboretum** and a **botanical garden**?

An arboretum is technically a garden or collection of trees, often rare ones grown for study, research, or ornamentation. In practice, most arboretums also display shrubs and other plants. A botanical garden is primarily an institution for research in the field of botany and horticulture. The modern botanic garden has large collections of growing plants in a greenhouse and outdoors usually in elaborate gardens, in addition to research laboratories, a library and herbarium.

Who established the first **botanical garden** in the United States?

John Bartram planned and laid out a botanic garden of five to six acres (two to 2.5 hectare) in 1728. It is located in Philadelphia, Pennsylvania.

What is **Ikebana**?

Ikebana is the Japanese expression for "the arrangement of living material in water." It is the ancient Japanese art of flower arrangement. Ikebana follows certain ancient rules that aim at achieving perfect harmony, beauty, and balance. Some describe Ikebana as sculpture with flowers. In Japan it has been practiced for fourteen hundred years. Buddhist monks in the sixth century practiced the art using pebbles, rock, and wood with plants and flowers. In Japan Ikebana was evolved and practiced exclusively by men—priests first, then warriors and noblemen. Today, of course, Ikebana is practiced by millions of women as well as men, although the great flower schools in Japan are mostly headed by men.

What was a **victory garden**?

During World War I, patriots grew "liberty gardens." In World War II, U.S. Secretary of Agriculture Claude R. Wickard encouraged householders to plant vegetable gardens wherever they could find space. By 1945 there were said to be 20 million victory gardens producing about 40 percent of all American vegetables in many unused scraps of land. Such sites as the strip between a sidewalk and the street, town squares, and the land around Chicago's Cook County jail were used. The term "victory garden" derives from an English book by that title written by Richard Gardner in 1603.

Should **tomato plants** be staked?

There are only a few advocates who continue to recommend non-staking. They argue for the natural sprawling growing method because it tends to give a greater yield. Staking keeps the plants off the ground, where they are susceptible to disease and attacks by snails. Staked tomatoes are much easier to harvest and make better use of garden space. They ripen faster and more evenly when staked. The method of staking has different advocates as well. Some say a sturdy five-foot stick is best, while others argue for a wire cage, and still others claim a wooden teepee arrangement is best.

Is there a **"best" time to weed** in the vegetable garden?

Weeding is usually the most unpopular and the most time-consuming garden chore. Some studies (using weeding with peas and beans as examples) have shown that weeding done during the first three to four weeks of vegetable growth produced the best crops and that unabated weed growth after that time did not significantly reduce the vegetable yields.

What are the best annual and perennial plants to grow to attract **butterflies**?

Ageratum, cosmos, globe candytuft, heliotrope, lantana, marigold, mexican sunflower, torch flower, nasturtium, sweet alyssum, buddleias (known as butterfly bush), dianthus, violas, and zinnia attract butterflies.

Which flowers should be planted in the garden to attract **hummingbirds**?

Scarlet trumpet honeysuckle, weigela, butterfly bush, beardtongue, coralbells, red-hot-poker, foxglove, beebalm, nicotiana, petunia, summer phlox, and scarlet sage provide brightly colored (in shades of reds and orange), nectar-bearing attractants for hummingbirds.

Why should **lawn clippings** be left on the grass after mowing?

The clippings are a valuable source of nutrients for the lawn. They provide nitrogen, potassium, and phosphorous to feed the new grass and reduce the need for fertilizer. Young, tender, short clippings decompose fast. Furthermore, when clippings are left on the lawn instead of being added to the trash collection, the amount of waste added to landfills is decreased.

What is **snowmold** and how do you treat it?

Snowmold is a lawn disease common in the northern United States, characterized by a white, cottony growth. The fungus *Fusarium nivale* often grows beneath the snow as it melts in early spring. Avoiding late fall fertilizing in wet areas can prevent the spread of this disease. The lawn may be treated at the first sign of the disease with a fungicide and again in 10 to 14 days.

How can **daffodils** be encouraged to bloom the year after they are planted?

Try fertilizing daffodils (*Narcissus pseudonarcissus*) as soon as the new shoots appear. This helps the roots renew themselves and will also aid in leaf and flower development. If they don't bloom, the problem could be overcrowding, which hinders flower production. Try digging the bulbs up every third or fifth year, separating them, and re-spacing them.

How can **geraniums** be kept alive during the winter?

While they must be kept from freezing, geraniums can survive the winter happily in a cool sunny spot, such as a cool greenhouse, a bay window, or a sunny unheated basement. They need only occasional watering while in this semi-dormant state. Cuttings from these plants can be rooted in late winter or early spring for a new crop of geraniums (some sources suggest rooting in the fall). In homes without a suitable cool and sunny spot, the plants can be forced into dormancy by allowing the soil to dry completely, then gently knocking the soil off of the roots. While the plants can simply be hung from the rafters in a cool (45° to 50°F, or 7° to 10°C), slightly humid room, they will do better if put into individual paper bags, with the openings tied shut. The plants should be checked regularly. The leaves will dry and shrivel, but if the stems shrivel, the plants should be lightly misted with water. If any show mold or rot, cut off the affected sections, move the plants to a drier area, and leave the bags open for a day or two. In the early spring, prune the stems back to healthy green tissue and pot in fresh soil.

What is meant by the **chilling requirement** for fruit trees?

When a fruit tree's fruiting period has ended, a dormant period must follow, during which the plant rests and regains strength for another fruit set the following year. The length of this set is measured in hours and occurs at temperatures between 32° and 45°F (0° to 7.2°C). A cherry tree requires about 700 hours of chilling time.

What is a **five-in-one tree**?

These very curious trees consist of a rootstock with five different varieties of the same fruit—usually apples—grafted to it. The blooming period is usually magnificent with various colors of blooms appearing on the same tree.

What is meant by **espaliering** a fruit tree and why is it done?

To espalier a fruit tree means to train it to grow flat against a surface. It can be grown in small places such as against a wall, and it will thrive even if its roots are underneath sidewalks or driveways. Since many fruit trees must be planted in pairs, espaliered fruit trees can be planted close together, providing pollen for each other, yet taking up little space.

How are **seedless grapes** grown?

Since seedless grapes cannot reproduce in the conventional way that grapes usually do (i.e., dropping seeds), growers have to take cuttings from other seedless grape plants and root them. Although the exact origin of seedless grapes is unknown, they might have been first cultivated in present-day Iran or Afghanistan thousands of years ago. Initially, the first seedless grape was a genetic mutation in which the hard seed casing failed to develop—the mutation is called stenospermoscarpy. One modern seedless grape commonly bought today is the green Thompson seedless grape, from which 90 percent of all raisins are made.

What is **pleaching**?

Pleaching is a method of shearing closely planted trees or shrubs into a high wall of foliage. Many kinds of trees have been used, including maples, sycamores, and lindens. Because of the time needed in caring for pleached allees, as the walls of foliage are called, they are infrequently seen in American gardens, but they are frequently observed in European ones.

What is a **dwarf conifer**?

Conifers are evergreen shrubs and trees with needle-shaped leaves, cones, and resinous wood, such as the pines, spruces, firs, and junipers. After 20 years, dwarf or slow-growing forms of these otherwise tall trees are typically about three feet (91 centimeters) tall.

What is the secret of **bonsai**, the Japanese art of growing dwarf trees?

These miniature trees with tiny leaves and twisted trunks can be centuries old. To inhibit growth of the plants, they have been carefully deprived of nutrients, pruned of their fastest-growing shoots and buds, and kept in small pots to reduce the root systems. Selective pruning, pinching out terminal buds, and wiring techniques are devices used to control the shape of the trees. Bonsai possibly started during the Chou dynasty (900-250 B.C.E.) in China, when emperors made miniature gardens that were dwarf representations of the provincial lands that they ruled.

What is the difference between **poison ivy**, **oak**, and **sumac**?

These North American woody plants grow in almost any habitat and are quite similar in appearance. Each has alternating compound leaves of three leaflets each, berrylike fruits, and rusty brown stems. But poison ivy (*Rhus radicans*) acts more like a vine than a shrub at times and can grow high into trees. Its grey fruit is not hairy, and its leaves are slightly lobed. On the other hand, poison oak (*Rhus toxicodendron*) is often shrubby, but it can climb. Its leaflets are lobed and resemble oak leaves; its fruit is hairy. Poison sumac (*Rhus vernix*) grows only in North American wet acid swamps. This shrub can grow as high as 12 feet (3.6 meters). The fruit it produces hangs in a cluster and is grayish-brown in color. Poison sumac has sharply pointed, dark green, compound, alternating leaves; and greenish-yellow inconspicuous flowers. All parts of poison ivy, poison oak, and poison sumac can cause serious dermatitis.

What is a natural way to get rid of **poison ivy**?

Poison ivy can be killed by spraying or treating the plants with a saltwater solution. Large plants can be killed by cutting the vines at or below ground level and soaking the base with brine. A second application after two weeks may be needed. Do not burn the plants; smoke and ash may cause the rash on exposed parts of the body, eyes, nasal passages, and lungs.

What is the **railroad worm**?

The apple maggot (*Rhagoletis pomonella*), which becomes the apple fruit fly, is frequently called the railroad worm. Inhabiting orchards in the eastern United States and Canada, the larvae feed on the fruit pulp of apples, plums, cherries, etc., and cause damage to fruit crops.

How can **fruit trees** be protected from being eaten by **field mice**?

Valuable trees, especially newly planted fruit trees, can be protected by wrappings or guards of wire, wood veneer, or plastic. Other controls, such as pieces of lava rocks soaked in garlic, are effective as repellents, and garlic sprays will repel most rodents.

Which type of **fence** protects a garden from **deer**?

A post and wire-mesh fence with a sharp-angled, narrow gate, which people and small animals can navigate, but deer cannot, plus the installation of a motion-sensing security light with a beeper helps keep deer away. Electric fences are also a good deterrent, but for smaller gardens snow fencing works well.

How can **squirrels** be kept away from vegetable and flower gardens?

Squirrels like to take a bite out of tomatoes, cucumbers, and melons, dig up bulbs, and ruin anything colorful in the flower garden. The traditional recommendation of spread-

Agricultural chemist George Washington Carver developed important methods of crop management and hundreds of new uses for crops.

ing mothballs around is apparently not too successful. A better method is laying down one to two inch (2.5 to five centimeter) mesh sheets of chicken wire. Squirrels will avoid the mesh, apparently because they fear getting their toes stuck in it. Another method to try is sprinkling hot pepper around the plants, renewing it after it rains.

Before chemical sprays came along to control plant disease and pests, what were some of the **traditional spray formulas** used on plants?

Gardeners have used kitchen cupboard and organic plant materials for a very long time. Baking soda spray is a good fungicide. Mix two tablespoons of baking soda in four pints of water. Garlic spray is made by crushing a large garlic bulb into two pints of water. Boil for five minutes and allow to cool. Garlic spray is a good insecticide and fungicide. The weed horsetail, the leaves of elder, and the leaves of the fern bracken have been made into sprays and used to fight mildew, black spot, many fungi and bacteria attacking garden plants.

What were some of the accomplishments of **Dr. George Washington Carver**?

Because of the work of Dr. George Washington Carver (1864-1943) in plant diseases, soil analysis, and crop management, many southern farmers who adopted his methods increased their crop yields and profits. Carver developed recipes using cowpeas, sweet potatoes, and peanuts. He eventually made 118 products from sweet potatoes, 325 from peanuts, and 75 from pecans. He promoted soil diversification and the adoption of peanuts, soybeans, and other soil-enriching crops. His other work included developing plastic material from soy beans, which Henry Ford later used in part of his automobile. He extracted dyes and paints from the Alabama red clay and worked with hybrid cotton. Carver was a widely talented man who became an almost mythical American folk hero.

ANIMAL WORLD

PHYSICAL CHARACTERISTICS, ETC.

Which animal has the **longest gestation** period?

The animal with the longest gestation period is not a mammal; it is the viviparous amphibian the Alpine black salamander, which can have a gestation period of up to 38 months at altitudes above 4,600 feet (1,402 meters) in the Swiss alps. It bears two fully metamorphosed young.

What are the **largest** and **smallest** living animals?

Largest animals	**Name**	**Length and weight**
Sea mammal	Blue or sulphur-bottom whale (*Balaenoptera musculus*)	100-110 feet (30.5-33.5 meters) long; weighs 135-209 tons (122.4-189.6 tonnes)
Land mammal	African bush elephant (*Loxodonta africana*)	Bull is 10.5 feet (3.2 meters) tall at shoulder; weighs 5.25-6.2 tons (4.8-5.6 tonnes)
Living bird	North African ostrich (*Struthio c. camelus*)	8 to 9 feet (2.4-2.7 meters) tall; weighs 345 pounds (156.5 kilograms)
Fish	Whale shark (*Rhincodon typus*)	41 feet (12.5 meters) long; weighs 16.5 tons (15 tonnes)
Reptile	Saltwater crocodile (*Crocodylus porosus*)	14-16 feet (4.3-4.9 meters) long; weighs 900-1,500 pounds (408-680 kilograms)
Rodent	Capybara (*Hydrochoerus hydrochaeris*)	3.25-4.5 feet (1-1.4 meters) long; weighs 250 pounds (113.4 kilograms)

Smallest animals	Name	Length and weight
Sea mammal	Commerson's dolphin (*Cephalorhynchus* commersonii)	4-5.6 feet (1.25-1.7 meters); weighs 50-70 pounds (22.7-31.8 kilograms)
Land mammal	Bumblebee or Kitti's hog-nosed bat (*Craseonycteris thong longyai*) or the pygmy shrew (*Suncus erruscus*)	1 inch (2.54 centimeters) long; weighs .062 to .07 ounces (1.6-2 grams) 1.5-2 inches (3.8-5 centimeters) long; weighs 0.052-.09 ounces (1.5-2.6 grams)
Bird	Bee hummingbird (*Mellisuga helenea*)	2.25 inches (5.7 centimeters) long; weighs 0.056 ounces (1.6 grams)
Fish	Dwarf goby (*Trimmatam nanus*)	0.35 inches (8.9 millimeters) long
Reptile	Gecko (*Spaerodactylus ariasae*)	0.63 inches (1.6 centimeters) long
Rodent	Pygmy mouse (*Baiomys taylori*)	4.3 inches (10.9 centimeters) long; weighs 0.24-0.28 ounces (6.8-7.9 grams)

Do bears in zoos **hibernate**?

Bears do not hibernate in zoos because temperatures in cages and enclosures remain warm throughout the year and the bears are constantly fed by keepers. Hibernation occurs only with lack of food and temperatures below the freezing point.

How do animals and people **identify smells**?

The sense of smell allows animals and humans as well as other organisms to identify food, mates, and predators, and provides sensory pleasure (e.g. flowers) and warnings of danger (e.g. chemical dangers). There are specialized receptor cells in the nose that have proteins that bind chemical odorants and cause the receptor cells to send electrical signals to the olfactory bulb of the brain. Cells in the olfactory bulb relay this information to olfactory areas of the forebrain to generate the perception of smells.

Besides humans, which animals are the **most intelligent**?

According to Edward O. Wilson, a behavioral biologist, the ten most intelligent animals are the following:

1. Chimpanzee (two species)
2. Gorilla
3. Orangutan

Prior to hibernation, bears in the wild gorge on food—sometimes from human sources.

4. Baboon (seven species, including drill and mandrill)
5. Gibbon (seven species)
6. Monkey (many species, especially macaques, the patas, and the Celebes black ape)
7. Smaller toothed whale (several species, especially killer whale)
8. Dolphin (many of the approximately 80 species)
9. Elephant (two species)
10. Pig

Do animals other than humans have **fingerprints**?

It is known that gorillas and other primates have fingerprints. Of special interest, however, is that our closest relative, the chimpanzee, does not. Koala bears also have fingerprints. Researchers in Australia have determined that the fingerprints of koala bears closely resemble those of human fingerprints in size, shape, and pattern.

Do animals have **color vision**?

Most reptiles and birds appear to have a well-developed color sense. Most mammals, however, are color-blind. Apes and monkeys have the ability to tell colors apart; dogs and cats seem to be color-blind and see only shades of black, white, and gray.

Can animals **regenerate** parts of their bodies?

Regeneration does occur in some animals; however, it progressively declines the more complex the animal species becomes. Among primitive invertebrates (lacking a backbone), regeneration frequently occurs. For example, a planarium (flatworm) can split symmetrically, each part becoming a clone of the other. In higher invertebrates regeneration occurs in echinoderms (such as starfish) and arthropods (such as insects and crustaceans). Regeneration of appendages (limbs, wings, and antennae) occurs in insects (such as cockroaches, fruit flies, and locusts) and in crustaceans (such as lobsters, crabs, and crayfish). For example, regeneration of the crayfish's missing claw occurs at its next molt (shedding of its hard cuticle exterior shell/skin for the growing and the subsequent hardening of a new cuticle exterior). However, sometimes the regenerated claw does not achieve the same size of the missing claw. But after every molt (occurring two to three times a year) it grows and will eventually become nearly as large as the original claw. On a very limited basis, some amphibians and reptiles can replace a lost leg or tail.

What is the frequency that separates animal **hearing** from human?

The frequency of a sound is the pitch. Frequency is expressed in Hertz or Hz. Sounds are classified as infrasounds (below the human range of hearing), sonic range (within the range of human hearing) and ultrasound (above the range of human hearing).

Animal	Frequency range heard (Hz)
Dog	15 to 50,000
Human	20 to 20,000
Cat	60 to 65,000
Dolphin	150 to 150,000
Bat	1,000 to 120,000

Do all animals have **red blood**?

The color of blood is related to the compounds that transport oxygen. Hemoglobin, containing iron, is red and is found in all vertebrates (animals having a backbone) and a few invertebrates (animals lacking a backbone). Annelids (segmented worms) have either a green pigment, chlorocruorin, or a red pigment, hemerythrin. Some crustaceans (arthropods having divided bodies and generally having gills) have a blue pigment, hemocyanin, in their blood.

Which land animal **runs the fastest**?

The cheetah can accelerate from zero to 45 miles (64 kilometers) per hour in two seconds; it has been timed at speeds of 70 miles (112 kilometers) per hour over short distances. In most chases, cheetahs average around 40 miles (63 kilometers) per hour. Humans, by comparison, can run very short distances at almost 28 miles (45 kilometers) per hour maximum.

INSECTS, SPIDERS, ETC.

How many **species of insects** are there?

Estimates of the number of recognized insect species range from about 750,000 to upward of one million—but some experts think that this represents less than half of the number that exists in the world. About 7,000 new insect species are described each year, but unknown numbers are lost annually from the destruction of their habitats, mainly tropical forests.

What is the **most destructive insect** in the world?

The most destructive insect is the desert locust (*Schistocera gregaria*), the locust of the Bible, whose habitat ranges from the dry and semi-arid regions of Africa and the Middle East, through Pakistan and northern India. This short-horn grasshopper can

The desert locust—the world's most destructive insect.

eat its own weight in food a day, and during long migratory flights a large swarm can consume 20,000 tons (18,144,000 kilograms) of grain and vegetation a day.

Who introduced the **gypsy moth** into the United States?

In 1869, Professor Leopold Trouvelot brought gypsy moth egg masses from France to Medford, Massachusetts. His intention was to breed the gypsy moth with the silkworm to overcome a wilt disease of the silkworm. He placed the egg masses on a window ledge, and evidently the wind blew them away. About 10 years later these caterpillars were numerous on trees in that vicinity, and in 20 years, trees in eastern Massachusetts were being defoliated. In 1911, a contaminated plant shipment from Holland also introduced the gypsy moth to that area. These pests have now spread to 25 states, especially in the northeastern United States. Scattered locations in Michigan and Oregon have also reported occurrences of gypsy moth infestations.

What are some **beneficial insects**?

Beneficial insects include bees, wasps, flies, butterflies, moths, and others that pollinate plants. Many fruits and vegetables depend on insect pollinators for the production of seeds. Insects are an important source of food for birds, fish, and many animals. In some countries such insects as termites, caterpillars, ants, and bees are eaten as food by people. Products derived from insects include honey and beeswax, shellac, and silk. Some predators such as mantises, ladybugs or lady beetles, and lacewings feed on other harmful insects. Other helpful insects are parasites that live on or in the body of harmful insects. For example, some wasps lay their eggs in caterpillars that damage tomato plants.

What are the stages of **insect metamorphosis**?

There are two types of metamorphoses (marked structural changes in the growth processes): complete and incomplete. In complete metamorphosis, the insect (such as the ant, moth, butterfly, termite, wasp, or beetle) goes through all the distinct stages of growth to reach adulthood. In incomplete metamorphosis, the insect (such as the grasshopper, cricket, or louse) does not go through all the stages of complete metamorphoses.

Complete metamorphosis

Egg—One egg is laid at a time or many (as much as 10,000).

Larva—What hatches from the eggs is called "larva." A larva can look like a worm.

Pupa—After reaching its full growth, the larva hibernates, developing a shell or "pupal case" for protection. A few insects (e.g., the moth) spin a hard covering called a "cocoon." The resting insect is called a pupa (except the butterfly, which is called a chrysalis), and remains in the hibernation state for several weeks or months.

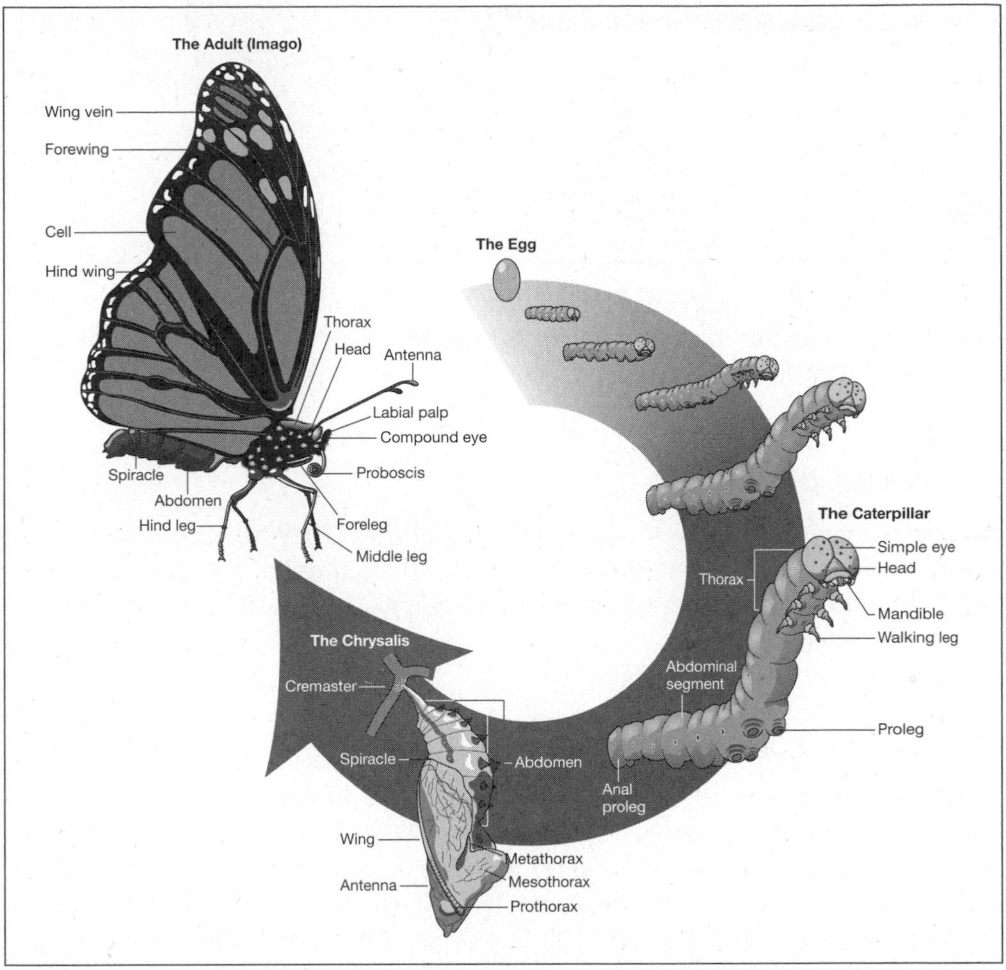

The life cycle of a butterfly represents complete metamorphoses.

Adult—During hibernation, the insect develops its adult body parts. When it has matured physically, the fully grown insect emerges from its case or cocoon.

Incomplete metamorphosis

Egg—One egg or many eggs are laid.

Early-stage nymph—Hatched insect resembles an adult, but smaller in size. However, those insects that would normally have wings have not yet developed them.

Late-stage nymph—At this time, the skin begins to molt (shed), and the wings begin to bud.

Adult—The insect is now fully grown.

How does a **butterfly** differ from a **moth**?

Characteristic	Butterflies	Moths
Antennae	Knobbed	Unknobbed
Active-time of day	Day	Night
Coloration	Bright	Dull
Resting wing position	Vertically above body	Horizontally beside body

Note: While these guidelines generally hold true, there are exceptions. Moths have hairy bodies, and most have tiny hooks or bristles linking the fore-wing to the hind-wing; butterflies do not have either characteristic.

Do butterflies see **color**?

Butterflies have highly developed sensory capabilities. They have the widest visual spectrum of any animal and are able to see from the red end of the spectrum all the way to the near ultraviolet. They are therefore able to distinguish colors that humans are unable to see.

What are **"killer bees"**?

Africanized honeybees—the term entomologists prefer rather than killer bees—are a hybrid originating in Brazil, where African honeybees were imported in 1956. The breeders, hoping to produce a bee better suited to producing more honey in the tropics, instead found that African bees soon hybridized with and mostly displaced the familiar European honeybees. Although they produce more honey, Africanized honeybees are more dangerous than European bees because they attack intruders in greater numbers. Since their introduction, they have been responsible for approximately 1,000 human deaths. In addition to such safety issues, concern is growing regarding the effect of possible hybridization on the U.S. beekeeping industry.

In October 1990, the bees crossed the Mexican border into the United States; they reached Arizona in 1993. In 1996, six years after their arrival in the United States, Africanized honey bees could be found in parts of Texas, Arizona, New Mexico, and California. They are also found in Nevada. Their migration northward has slowed partially because they are a tropical insect and can't live in colder climates. Experts have suggested two possible ways of limiting the spread of the Africanized honeybees. The first is drone-flooding, a process by which large numbers of European drones are kept in areas where commercially reared European queen bees mate, thereby ensuring that only limited mating occurs between Africanized drones and European queens. The second method is frequent re-queening, in which a beekeeper replaces a colony's queen with one of his or her own choosing. The beekeeper

Who discovered the "dance of the bees"?

In 1943, Karl von Frisch (1886-1982) published his study on the dance of the bees. It is a precise pattern of movements performed by returning forager (worker) honeybees in order to communicate the direction and distance of a food source to the other workers in the hive. The dance is performed on the vertical surface of the hive and two kinds of dances have been recognized: the round dance (performed when food is nearby) and the waggle dance (done when food is farther away).

can then be assured that the queens are European and that they have already mated with European drones.

What are **migratory beekeepers**?

A migratory beekeeper is a person who transports his or her bee colonies to different areas to produce better honey or to collect fees for pollinating such crops as fruit trees, almonds, and alfalfa. They frequently travel north in the spring and summer to pollinate crops and then back south in the fall and winter to maintain the colonies in the warmer southern weather. Approximately 1,000 migratory beekeepers operate in the United States, transporting approximately two million bee colonies a year.

How many bees are in a **bee colony**?

On the average, a bee colony contains from 50,000 to 70,000 bees, which produce a harvest of from 60 to 100 pounds of honey per year (five to eight gallons). A little more than a third of the honey produced by the bees is retained in the hive to sustain the population.

How many **flowers** need to be tapped for bees to gather enough nectar to produce **one pound of honey**?

Bees must gather four pounds of nectar, which requires the bees to tap about two million flowers, to produce one pound of honey. The honey is gathered by worker bees, whose life span is three to six weeks, long enough to collect about a teaspoon of nectar.

How much weight can an ant carry?

Ants are the "superweight lifters" of the animal kingdom. They are strong in relation to their size and can carry objects ten to twenty times their own weight—some species

A formicine ant overpowers a termite soldier.

can carry objects up to fifty times their own weight. Ants are able to carry these objects great distances and even climb trees while carrying them. This is comparable to a 100-pound person picking up a small car, carrying it seven to eight miles on his back and then climbing the tallest mountain while still carrying the car!

How are **ants** distinguished from **termites**?

Both insect orders—ants (order *Hymenoptera*) and termites (order *Isoptera*)—have segmented bodies with multi-jointed legs. Listed below are some differences.

Characteristic	Ant	Termite
Wings	Two pairs with the front pair being much longer than the back pair	Two pairs of equal length
Antenna	Bends at right angle	Straight
Abdomen	Wasp-waist (pinched in)	No wasp-waist

Which insect has the **best sense of smell**?

Giant male silk moths may have the best sense of smell in the world. They can smell a female's perfume nearly seven miles (11 kilometers) away.

Do male **mosquitoes** bite humans?

No. Male mosquitoes live on plant juices, sugary saps, and liquids arising from decomposition. They do not have a biting mouth that can penetrate human skin as female mosquitoes do. In some species, the females, who lay as many as 200 eggs, need blood to lay their eggs.

What is a **"daddy longlegs"**?

The name applies to two different kinds of invertebrates. The first is a harmless, nonbiting long-legged arachnid. Also called a harvestman, it is often mistaken for a spider, but it lacks the segmented body shape that a spider has. Although it has the same number of legs (eight) as a spider, the harvestman's legs are far longer and thinner. These very long legs enable it to raise its body high enough to avoid ants or other small enemies. Harvestmen are largely carnivorous, feeding on a variety of small invertebrates, such as insects, spiders, and mites. They never spin webs as spiders do. They also eat some juicy plants and in captivity can be fed almost anything edible, from bread and milk to meat. Harvestmen also need to drink frequently. The term "daddy longlegs" also is used for a cranefly—a thin-bodied insect with long, thin legs that has a snoutlike proboscis with which it sucks water and nectar.

Which is stronger—steel or the silk from a **spider's web**?

Spider silk. Well known for its strength and elasticity, the strongest spider silk has tensile strength second only to fuse quartz fibers and five times greater than that of steel of equivalent weight. It is also five times as impact-resistant as bulletproof Kevlar. Tensile strength is the longitudinal stress that a substance can bear without tearing apart. The tension necessary to bring a compound thread 0.004 inches (0.01 centimeters) in diameter to the breaking point was found to be 2.8 ounces (80 grams).

In terms of tensile strength, spider web silk is many times stronger than steel.

How long have **cockroaches** been on the earth?

The earliest cockroach fossils are about 280 million years old. Some cockroaches

How is the light in fireflies produced?

The light produced by fireflies (*Photinus pyroles*), or lightning bugs, is a kind of heatless light called bioluminescence caused by a chemical reaction in which the substance luciferin undergoes oxidation when the enzyme luciferase is present. The flash is a photon of visible light that radiates when the oxidating chemicals produce a high-energy state and revert back to their normal state. The flashing is controlled by the nervous system and takes place in special cells called photocytes. The nervous system, photocytes, and the tracheal end organs control the flashing rate. The air temperature also seems to be correlated with the flashing rate. The higher the temperature, the shorter the interval between flashes—eight seconds at 65°F (18.3°C) and four seconds at 82°F (27.7°C). Scientists are uncertain as to why this flashing occurs. The rhythmic flashes could be a means of attracting prey or enabling mating fireflies to signal in heliographic codes (that differ from one species to another), or they could serve as a warning signal.

measured three to four inches (7.5 to 10 centimeters) long. Cockroaches (order Dictyoptera) are nocturnal scavenging insects that eat not only human food but book-bindings, ink, and whitewash as well.

How does an **earthworm** "recycle" the earth?

It is estimated that there are more than 4,000 earthworm species. These animals have long been known to provide many useful ecological services, including making the ground suitable for plants by aerating and draining the soil with their burrows. In addition, worms can consume 30 percent of their body weight each day in plant, animal, and other matter. Much of this is in turn excreted on the earth's surface in the form of "casts." The worms then re-bury these casts with their borrowing process, thereby essentially recycling the earth.

How many pairs of legs does a **centipede** have?

Centipedes, or members of the class Chilopoda, always have an uneven number of pairs of walking legs, varying from 15 to more than 171. The true centipedes (order Scolopendromorpha) have 21 or 23 pairs of legs. Common house centipedes (*Scutigera coleoptrato*) have 15 pairs of legs.

How do **fleas** jump so far?

The jumping power of fleas comes both from strong leg muscles and from pads of a rubber-like protein called resilin. The resilin is located above the flea's hind legs. To jump, the flea crouches, squeezing the resilin, and then it relaxes certain muscles. Stored energy from the resilin works like a spring, launching the flea. A flea can jump well both vertically and horizontally. Some species can jump 150 times their own length. To match that record, a human would have to spring over the length of two and a quarter football fields—or the height of a 100-story building—in a single bound. The common flea (*Pulex irritans*) has been known to jump 13 inches (33 centimeters) in length and 7.25 inches (18.4 centimeters) in height.

What is the life span of a **fruit fly**?

The length of adult life can vary considerably. Under ideal conditions, an adult *Drosophila melanogaster* can live as long as 40 days. In crowded conditions, its life span may drop to 12 days. Under normal laboratory conditions, however, adults generally die after only six or seven days.

What causes the **Mexican jumping bean** to move?

The bean moth (*Carpocapa saltitans*) lays its eggs in the flower or in the seed pod of the spurge, a bush known as *Euphorbia sebastiana*. The egg hatches inside the seed pod, producing a larva or caterpillar. The jumping of the bean is caused by the active shifting of weight inside the shell as the caterpillar moves. The jumps of the bean are stimulated by sunshine or by heat from the palm of the hand.

AQUATIC LIFE

How is the **age of fish** determined?

One way to determine the age of a fish is by its scales, which have growth rings just as trees do. Scales have concentric bony ridges or "circuli," which reflect the growth patterns of the individual fish. The portion of the scale that is embedded in the skin contains clusters of these ridges (called "annuli"); each cluster marks one year's growth cycle.

How do fish swimming in a school **change their direction** simultaneously?

The movement, which confuses predators, happens because fish detect pressure changes in the water. The detection system, called the lateral line, is found along each side of the fish's body. Along the line are clusters of tiny hairs inside cups filled with a jellylike substance. If a fish becomes alarmed and turns sharply, it causes a pressure wave in the water around it. This wave pressure deforms the "jelly" in the lateral line of nearby fish. This moves the hairs which trigger nerves, and a signal is sent to the brain telling the fish to turn.

At what **speeds** do fish **swim**?

The maximum swimming speed of a fish is somewhat determined by the shape of its body and tail and by its internal temperature. The cosmopolitan sailfish (*Istiophorus platypterus*) is considered to be the fastest fish species, at least for short distances, swimming at greater than 60 miles (95 kilometers) per hour. Some American fishermen believe, however, that the bluefin tuna (*Thunnus thynnus*) is the fastest, but the fastest speed recorded for them so far is 43.4 miles (69.8 kilometers) per hour. Data is extremely difficult to secure because of the practical difficulties in measuring the speeds. The yellowfin tuna (*Thunnus albacares*) and the wahoe (*Acanthocybium solandri*) are also fast, timed at 46.35 miles (74.5 kilometers) per hour and 47.88 miles (77 kilometers) per hour during 10- to 20-second sprints. Flying fish swim at 40+ miles (64+ kilometers) per hour, dolphins at 37 miles (60 kilometers) per hour, trout at 15 miles (24 kilometers) per hour, and blenny at five miles (eight kilometers) per hour. Humans can swim 5.19 miles (8.3 kilometers) per hour.

How are **pearls** created?

Pearls are formed in saltwater oysters and freshwater clams. There is a curtain-like tissue called the mantle within the body of these mollusks. Certain cells on the side of the mantle toward the shell secrete nacre, also known as mother-of-pearl, during a specific stage of the shell-building process. A pearl is the result of an oyster's reaction to a foreign body, such as a piece of sand or a parasite, within the oyster's shell. The oyster neutralizes the invader by secreting thin layers of nacre around the foreign body, eventually building it into a pearl. The thin layers are alternately composed of calcium carbonate, argonite, and conchiolin. Irritants intentionally placed within an oyster result in the production of what are called cultured pearls.

How are **coral reefs** formed?

Coral reefs grow only in warm, shallow water. The calcium carbonate skeletons of dead corals serve as a framework upon which layers of successively younger animals attach themselves. Such accumulations, combined with rising water levels, slowly lead to the formation of reefs that can be hundreds of meters deep and long. The coral animal, or polyp, has a columnar form; its lower end is attached to the hard floor of the reef; the upper end is free to extend into the water. A whole colony consists of thousands of individuals. There are two kinds of corals, hard and soft, depending on the type of skeleton secreted. The polyps of hard corals deposit around themselves a solid skeleton of calcium carbonate (chalk), so most swimmers see only the skeleton of the coral; the animal is in a cuplike formation into which it withdraws during the daytime.

What gives **coral** their **colors**?

Coral have a symbiotic relationship with zooxanthellae. Zooxanthellae are photosynthetic dinoflagellates (one-celled animals) that give coral their characteristic colors of pink, purple and green. Coral that have expelled the zooxanthellae appear white.

What are **giant tube worms**?

These worms were found in 1977 when the submersible *Alvin* was exploring the ocean floor of the Galapagos Ridge (located 1.5 miles [2.4 kilometers] below the Pacific Ocean surface and 200 miles [322 kilometers] from the Galapagos Islands). *Riftia pachyptila Jones*, named after worm expert Meredith Jones of the Smithsonian Museum of Natural History, were discovered near the hydrothermal (hot water) ocean vents. Growing to lengths of five feet (1.5 meters), the worms lack both mouth and gut, and are topped with feathery plumes composed of over 200,000 tiny tentacles. The phenomenal growth of these worms is due to their internal food source—symbiotic bacteria, over 100 billion per ounce of tissue—that live within the worms' troposome tissues. To these troposome tissues, the tube worms transport absorbed oxygen from the water, together with carbon dioxide and hydrogen sulfide. Utilizing this supply, the bacteria living there in turn produce carbohydrates and proteins that the worms need to thrive.

This was only one of *Alvin*'s discoveries during its historic voyage. Scientists expected to find a "desert" at these ocean depths where no light penetrated. Most of the world's organisms rely on photosynthesis (the use of light to make organic compounds) at the base of their food chains. But in these depths, giant tube worms, vent crabs, and mollusks thrive because these vent communities depend on chemoautotropic (chemically self-feeding) bacteria, which derive their life-sustaining energy from the oxidation of substances spewing from the vents, or in symbiotic relationships, such as that with the giant tube worms.

How much electricity does an **electric eel** generate?

An electric eel (*Electrophorus electricus*) has current-producing organs made up of electric plates on both sides of its vertebral column running almost its entire body length. The charge—on the average of 350 volts, but as great as 550 volts—is released by the central nervous system. The shock consists of four to eight separate charges, which last only two- to three-thousandths of a second each. These shocks, used as a defense mechanism, can be repeated up to 150 times per hour without any visible fatigue to the eel. The most powerful electric eel, found in the rivers of Brazil, Colombia, Venezuela, and Peru, produces a shock of 400 to 650 volts.

How do dolphins sleep?

Dolphins apparently sleep by shutting down half of their brain and resting quietly in the water.

How do **salmon** find the way to their **spawning grounds**?

Scientists do not know exactly how a salmon "remembers" the way back to its native stream after an ocean journey possibly lasting several years and covering several thousand miles. They agree, however, that salmon, like homing pigeons, appear to have an innate compass or "search recognition" mechanism that operates independently of astronomical or physical signs. Some scientists theorize that this internal compass uses the infinitely small electrical voltages generated by the ocean currents as they travel through the earth's magnetic field. Others believe that the salmon's homing mechanism may take its cues from the varying salinities of the water or specific smells encountered along the journey.

What are the main classes of **mollusk shells**?

Scientists recognize five main classes of mollusks: gastropods, bivalves, tooth shells, chitons, and cephalopods. A sixth class, monoplacophora, was once thought to be extinct, but scientists have discovered them in very deep ocean waters. They are now considered very rare.

Most shells belong in one of two main classes: gastropods or bivalves. Three-quarters of the world's mollusks, or about 60,000 species, are classified as gastropods, which possess one-piece shells that are usually coiled. Limpets, cones, olives, murex, cowries, and whelks belong to this class. The 11,000 species of bivalves have two-piece shells, normally hinged along one side. Clams, oysters, cockles, and mussels are some familiar bivalves.

The three minor classes have far fewer species. Scientists recognize about 500 kinds of tooth shells. These shells are tapered, hollow tubes that curve slightly so as to resemble long needles or elephant tusks, prompting some collectors to refer to them as tusk shells. The shells of chitons, of which there are about 600 species, are made up of eight separate movable plates that are kept in place by a leathery oval band called a girdle or belt. They are also called "coat of mail" shells because of their resemblance to armor. The 650 species of cephalopods are quite different from other mollusks. Some have shells that surround their soft bodies. For example, the well-known chambered nautilus inhabits a shell consisting of a series of gradually larger chambers separated by paper-thin walls. Others, such as cuttlefish and squid, have shells inside their bodies to help support them. Octopuses, another kind of cephalopod, have no shells.

How many kinds of **sharks** are there and how many are dangerous?

The United Nations' Food and Agricultural Organization lists 354 species of sharks, ranging in length from six inches (15 centimeters) to 49 feet (15 meters). While 35 species are known to have attacked humans at least once, only a dozen do so on a regular basis. The relatively rare Great White shark (*Carcharodan carcharias*) is the largest predatory fish. The largest specimen accurately measured was 20 feet, 4 inches (6.2 meters) long and weighed 5,000 pounds (2,270 kilograms).

REPTILES AND AMPHIBIANS

What is the difference between a **reptile** and an **amphibian**?

Reptiles are clad in scales, shields, or plates, and their toes have claws; amphibians have moist, glandular skins, and their toes lack claws. Reptile eggs have a thick, hard or parchment-like shell that protects the developing embryo from moisture loss, even on dry land; the eggs of amphibians lack this protective outer covering and are always laid in water or in damp places. Young reptiles are miniature replicas of their parents in general appearance if not always in coloration and pattern; juvenile amphibians pass through a larval, usually aquatic, stage before they metamorphose (change in form and structure) into the adult form. Reptiles include alligators, crocodiles, turtles, and snakes; amphibians include salamanders, toads, and frogs.

Which **poisonous snakes** are native to the United States?

Snake	Average Length
Rattlesnakes	
Eastern diamondback (*Crotalus adamateus*)	33-65 in (84-165 cm)
Western diamondback (*Crotalus atrox*)	30-65 in (76-419 cm)
Timber rattlesnake (*Crotalus horridus horridus*)	32-54 in (81-137 cm)
Prairie rattlesnake (*Crotalus viridis viridis*)	32-46 in (81-117 cm)
Great Basin rattlesnake (*Crotalus viridis lutosus*)	32-46 in (81-117 cm)
Southern Pacific rattlesnake (*Crotalus viridis helleri*)	30-48 in (76-122 cm)
Red diamond rattlesnake (*Crotalus ruber ruber*)	30-52 in (76-132 cm)
Mojave rattlesnake (*Crotalus scutulatus*)	22-40 in (56-102 cm)
Sidewinder (*Crotalus cerastes*)	18-30 in (46-76 cm)

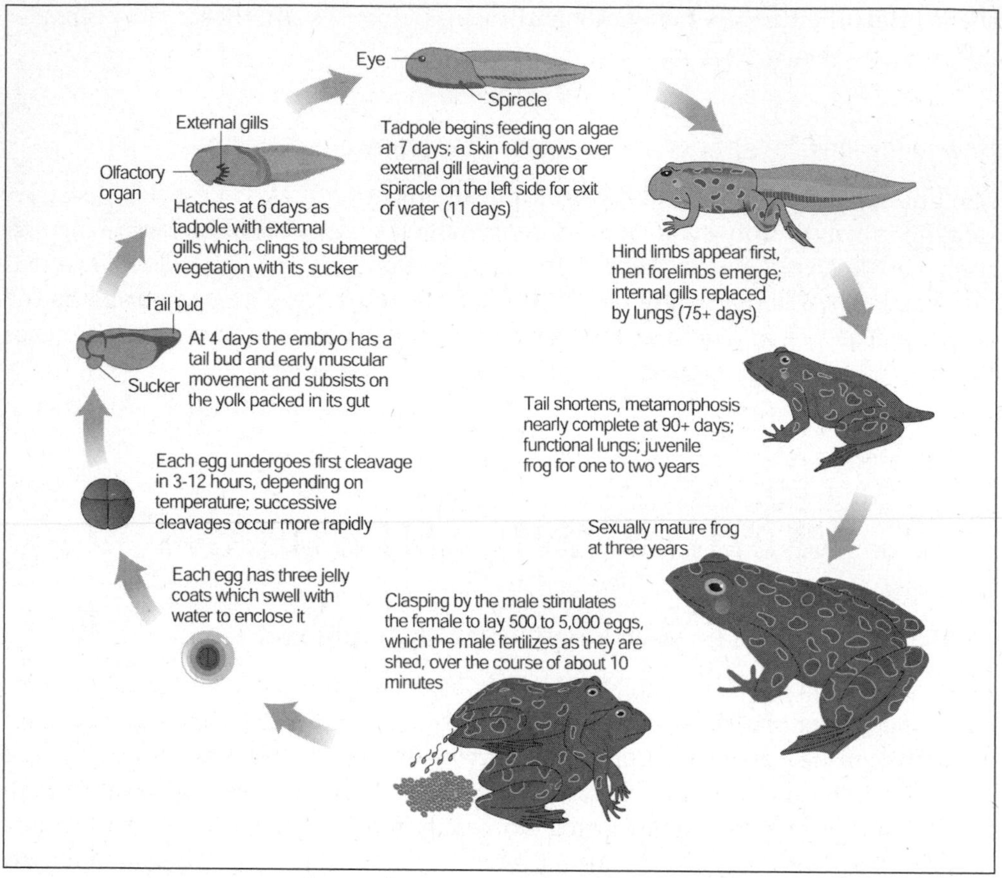

The life cycle of a frog.

Moccasins	
Cottonmouth (*Agkistrodon piscivorus*)	30-50 in (76-127 cm)
Copperhead (*Agkistrodon contortrix*)	24-36 in (61-91 cm)
Cantil (*Agkistrodon bilineatus*)	30-42 in (76-107 cm)
Coral snakes	
Eastern coral snake (*Micrurus fulvius*)	16-28 in (41-71 cm)

What is the **fastest snake** on land?

The black mamba *(Dendroaspis polylepis),* a deadly poisonous African snake that can grow up to 13 feet (four meters) in length, has been recorded reaching a speed of seven miles (11 kilometers) per hour. A particularly aggressive snake, it chases animals at high speeds holding the front of its body above the ground.

How fast can a **crocodile** run on land?

In smaller crocodiles, the running gait can change into a bounding gallop that can achieve speeds of two to 10 miles (three to 17 kilometers) per hour.

How is the gender of baby **alligators** determined?

The gender of an alligator is determined by the temperature at which the eggs are incubated. High temperatures of 90°-93°F (32°-34°C) result in males; low temperatures of 82°-86°F (28°-30°C) yield females. This determination takes place during the second and third week of the two-month incubation. Further temperature fluctuations before or after this time do not alter the gender of the young. The heat from the decaying matter on top of the nest incubates the eggs.

How does the **Surinam toad** nurture its young?

Unlike most toads and frogs, the female Surinam toad carries her eggs in special pockets in the skin on her back. Each egg develops in its own pocket in the female's skin. The tadpoles' tails are "plugged in" to the mother's system, similar to the placenta of mammals, exchanging nutrients and gases. The tadpoles develop quickly, undergoing metamorphosis while still in the pockets. Upon transformation into miniature frogs they break free of their pocket walls to begin independent lives.

What are a **turtle's** upper and lower **shell** called?

The turtle (order Testudines) uses its shell as a protective device. The upper shell is called the dorsal carapace and the lower shell is called the ventral plastron. The shell's sections are referred to as the scutes. The carapace and the plastron are joined at the sides.

BIRDS

How do birds learn to sing the **distinctive melody** of their respective species?

The ability to learn the proper song appears to be influenced by both heredity and experience. Scientists have speculated that a bird is genetically programmed with the ability to recognize the song of its own species and with the tendency to learn its own song. As a bird begins to sing, it goes through a stage of practice (which closely resembles the babbling of human infants) through which it perfects the notes and structure of its distinctive song. In order to produce a perfect imitation, the bird must apparently hear the song from an adult during its first months of life.

Which birds lay the **largest** and **smallest eggs**?

The elephant bird (*Aepyornis maximus*), an extinct flightless bird of Madagascar, also known as the giant bird or roc, laid the largest known bird eggs. Some of these eggs measured as much as 13.5 inches (34 centimeters) in length and 9.5 inches (24 centimeters) in diameter. The largest egg produced by any living bird is that of the North African ostrich (*Struthio camelus*). The average size is six to eight inches (15 to 20.5 centimeters) in length and four to six inches (five to 15 centimeters) in diameter.

The smallest mature egg, measuring less than 0.39 inch (one centimeter) in length, is that of the vervain hummingbird (*Mellisuga minima*) of Jamaica.

Generally speaking, the larger the bird, the larger the egg. However, when compared with the bird's body size, the ostrich egg is one of the smallest eggs, while the hummingbird's egg is one of the largest. The Kiwi bird of New Zealand lays the largest egg, relative to body size, of any living bird. Its egg weighs up to one pound (0.5 kilogram).

Which bird migrates the **greatest distance**?

The arctic tern (*Sterna paradisaea*) migrates the longest distance of any bird. They breed from subarctic regions to the very limits of land in the arctic of North America and Eurasia. At the end of the northern summer, the arctic tern leaves the north on a migration of more than 11,000 miles (17,699 kilometers) to its southern home in Antarctica. A tern tagged in July on the arctic coast of Russia was recovered the next May near Fremantle, Australia, a record 14,000 miles (22,526 kilometers) distant.

Why do birds **migrate** annually?

Migratory behavior in birds is inherited; however, birds will not migrate without certain physiological and environmental stimuli. In the late summer, the decrease in sunlight stimulates the pituitary gland and the adrenal gland of migrating birds, causing them to produce the hormones prolactin and corticosterone respectively. These hormones in turn cause the birds to accumulate large amounts of fat just under the skin, providing them with enough energy for the long migratory flights. The hormones also cause the birds to become restless just prior to migration. The exact time of departure, however, is dictated by not only by the decreasing sunlight and hormonal changes, but also by such conditions as the availability of food and the onset of cold weather.

The major wintering areas for North American migrating birds are the southern United States and Central America. Migrating ducks follow four major flyways south: the Atlantic flyway, the Mississippi flyway, the central flyway, and the Pacific flyway. Some bird experts propose that the birds return north to breed for several reasons: (1) Birds return to nest because there is a huge insect supply for their young; (2) The higher the Earth's latitude in the summer in the Northern Hemisphere, the longer the daylight available to the parents to find food for their young; (3) Less competition exists for food and nesting sites in the north; (4) In the north, there are fewer mammal predators for nesting birds (which are particularly vulnerable during the nesting stage); (5) Birds migrate south to escape the cold weather, so they return north when the weather improves.

Do all **birds fly**?

No. Among the flightless birds, the penguins and the ratites are the best known. Ratites include emus, kiwis, ostriches, rheas, and cassowaries. They are called ratite because they lack a keel on the breastbone. All of these birds have wings but lost their power to fly millions of years ago. Many birds that live isolated on oceanic islands (for example, the great auk) apparently became flightless in the absence of predators and the consequent gradual disuse of their wings for escape.

What bird has the **biggest wing span**?

Three members of the albatross family, the Wandering Albatross (*Diomedea exulans*), the Royal Albatross (*Diomedea epomophora*), and the Amsterdam Island Albatross (*Diomeda amsterdiamensis*) have the greatest wingspan of any bird species with a spread of 8-11 feet (2.5-3.3 meter).

Why do **geese** fly in formation?

Aerodynamicists have suspected that long-distance migratory birds, such as geese and swans, adapt the "V" formation in order to reduce the amount of energy needed for such long flights. According to theoretical calculations, birds flying in a "V" formation can fly some 10 percent farther than a lone bird can. Formation flying lessens the drag (the air pressure that pushes against the wings). The effect is similar to flying in a thermal upcurrent, where less total lift power is needed. In addition, when flying, each bird creates behind it a small area of disturbed air. Any bird flying directly behind it would be caught in this turbulence. In the "V" formation of

The common flying "V" formation observed in these migratory snow geese is thought to improve aerodynamics and thus efficiency.

Canada geese, each bird flies not directly behind the other, but to one side or above the bird in front.

How fast does a **hummingbird** fly and how far does the hummingbird migrate?

Hummingbirds fly at speeds up to 71 miles (80 kilometers) per hour. Small species beat their wings 50 to 80 times per second, and even faster during courtship displays. For comparison, the following table lists the flight speeds of some other birds:

Bird	Speed (mph)	Speed (kph)
Peregrine falcon	168-217	270.3-349.1
Swift	105.6	169.9
Merganser	65	104.6
Golden plover	50-70	80.5-112.6
Mallard	40.6	65.3
Wandering albatross	33.6	54.1
Carrion crow	31.3	50.4
Herring gull	22.3-24.6	35.9-39.6
House sparrow	17.9-31.3	28.8-50.4
Woodcock	5	8

The longest migratory flight of a hummingbird documented to date is the flight of a rufous hummingbird from Ramsey Canyon, Arizona, to near Mt. Saint Helens, Washington, a distance of 1,414 miles (2,277 kilometers). Bird-banding studies are now in progress to verify that a few rufous hummingbirds do make a 11,000-11,500 mile (17,699-18,503 kilometer) journey along a super Great Basin High route, a circuit that could take a year to complete. Hummingbird studies, however, are difficult to complete because so few banded birds are recovered.

How **fast** does a **hummingbird's wing** move?

Hummingbirds are the only family of birds that can truly hover in still air for any length of time. They need to do so in order to hang in front of a flower while they perform the delicate task of inserting their slim, sharp bills into its depths to drink nectar. Their thin wings are not contoured into the shape of aerofoils and do not generate lift in this way. Their paddle-shaped wings are, in effect, hands that swivel at the shoulder. They beat them in such a way that the tip of each wing follows the line of a figure eight lying on its side. The wing moves forward and downwards into the front loop of the eight, creating lift. As it begins to come up and go back, the wing twists through 180 degrees so that once again it creates a downward thrust. The hummingbird's method of flying does have one major limitation: the smaller a wing, the faster it has to beat in order to produce sufficient downward thrust. An average-sized hummingbird beats its wings 25 times per second. The bee hummingbird, native to Cuba, is only two inches (five centimeters) long and beats its wings at an astonishing 200 times per second.

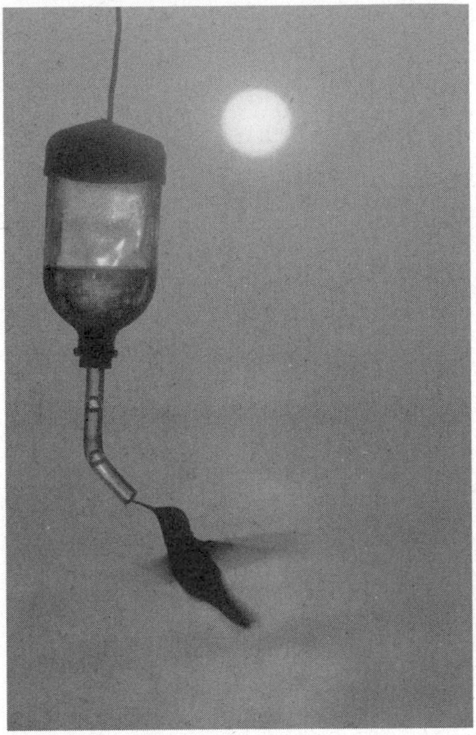

This ruby-throated hummingbird represents the only species native to eastern North America.

What is unusual about the way the **emperor penguin's eggs** are incubated?

Each female emperor penguin (*Aptenodytes forsteri*) lays one large egg. Initially, both sexes share in incubating the egg by carrying it on his or her feet and covering it with a fold of skin. After a few days of passing the egg back and forth, the female leaves to feed in the open water of the Arctic Ocean. Balancing their eggs on their feet, the male penguins shuffle about the rookery, periodically huddling together for warmth during blizzards and frigid weather. If an egg is inadvertently orphaned, a male with no egg will quickly adopt it. Two months after the female's departure, the chick hatches. The male feeds it with a milky substance he regurgitates until the female returns. Now padded with blubber, the females take over feeding the chicks with fish they have stored in their crops. The females do not return to their mate, however, but wander from male to male until one allows her to take his chick. It is then the males' turn to feed in open water and restore the fat layer they lost while incubating.

What are the natural **predators** of the **penguin**?

The leopard seal (*Hydrurga leptonyx*) is the principal predator of both the adult and juvenile penguin. The penguin may also be caught by a killer whale while swimming in open water. Eggs and chicks that are not properly guarded by adults are often devoured by skuas and sheathbills.

When was the **bald eagle** adopted as the national bird of the United States?

On June 20, 1782, the citizens of the newly independent United States of America adopted the bald or "American" eagle as their national emblem. At first the heraldic artists depicted

The bald eagle was heralded as a national emblem of the United States of America in 1782.

a bird that could have been a member of any of the larger species, but by 1902, the bird portrayed on the seal of the United States of America had assumed its proper white plumage on head and tail. The choice of the bald eagle was not unanimous; Benjamin Franklin (1706-1790) preferred the wild turkey. Oftentimes a tongue-in-cheek humorist, Franklin thought the turkey a wily but brave, intelligent, and prudent bird. He viewed the eagle on the other hand as having "a bad moral character" and "not getting his living honestly," preferring instead to steal fish from hardworking fish-hawks. He also found the eagle a coward that readily flees from the irritating attacks of the much smaller kingbird.

Which state was the first to "officially" name a **state bird**?

In 1926, Kentucky officially named the cardinal as its state bird.

How does a **homing pigeon** find its way home?

Scientists currently have two hypotheses to explain the homing flight of pigeons. Neither has been proved to the satisfaction of all the experts. The first hypothesis involves an "odor map." This theory proposes that young pigeons learn how to return to their original point of departure by smelling different odors that reach their home in the winds from varying directions. They would, for example, learn that a certain odor is carried on winds blowing from the east. If a pigeon were transported eastward, the odor would tell it to fly westward to return home. The second hypothesis proposes that a bird may be able to extract its home's latitude and longitude from the Earth's magnetic field. It may be proven in the future that neither theory explains the pigeon's navigational abilities or that some synthesis of the two theories is plausible.

What year was the **European starling** (*Sturnus vulgaris*) imported into the United States?

Eugene Schieffelin imported the European starling into the United States in 1890. Schieffelin wanted to establish every bird found in Shakespeare's works. He also imported English sparrows to New York City in 1860.

Why don't woodpeckers get headaches?

Woodpeckers' skulls are particularly sturdy to withstand the force of the blows as they hammer with their beaks. They are further aided by strong neck muscles to support their heads.

Will wild birds reject baby birds that have been **touched by humans**?

No. Contrary to popular belief, birds generally will not reject hatchlings touched by human hands. The best thing to do for newborn birds that have fallen or have been pushed out of the nest is to locate the nest as quickly as possible and gently put them back.

What can an **orphaned wild bird** eat?

An orphaned songbird needs to be fed every 20 minutes during daylight hours for several weeks. The food should be placed deep in its throat. A soft-billed bird (such as a warbler or catbird) may be given grated carrots, chopped hard-boiled eggs, cottage cheese, fresh fruit, or custard. A young hard-billed bird (such as a sparrow or finch) may be given the same food, but rape, millet, and sunflower seeds should be added to this diet when the bird becomes well-developed. A mixture of dry baby cereal and the yolk of a hard-boiled egg moistened with milk can also be given.

What species of birds will nest in **bird houses**?

In general, the only birds that will occupy birdhouses are species that normally chisel nesting holes or use such ready-made cavities as hollow trunks or holes already excavated by other species. Different species of birds require birdhouses of different dimensions, especially concerning the diameter of the entrance hole. Some birds that will nest in birdhouses are: bluebirds, chickadees, finches, flycatchers, purple martins, nuthatches, sparrows, starlings, titmice, woodpeckers, and wrens. In addition, larger birds such as some ducks and owls may be attracted.

MAMMALS

Which mammal has the shortest **gestation period**?Which one has the longest?

Gestation is the period of time between fertilization and birth in oviparous animals. The shortest gestation period known is 12 to 13 days, shared by three marsupials: the

Is there any truth to the saying "blind as a bat"?

The saying "blind as a bat" is not true. Although bats rely on sound to navigate and find food, they have all the elements found in a normal mammalian eye and they do see.

American or Virginian opossum (*Didelphis marsupialis*); the rare water opossum, or yapok (*Chironectes minimus*) of central and northern South America; and the eastern native cat (*Dasyurus viverrinus*) of Australia. The young of each of these marsupials are born while still immature and complete their development in the ventral pouch of their mother. While 12 to 13 days is the average, the gestation period is sometimes as short as eight days. The longest gestation period for a mammal is that of the African elephant (*Loxodonta africana*) with an average of 660 days, and a maximum of 760 days.

Do any **mammals fly**?

Bats (order Chiroptera with 986 species) are the only truly flying mammals, although several gliding mammals are referred to as "flying" (such as flying squirrel and flying lemur). The "wings" of bats are double membranes of skin stretching from the sides of the body to the hind legs and tail, and are actually skin extensions of the back and belly. The wing membranes are supported by the elongated fingers of the forelimbs (or arms). Nocturnal (active at night), ranging in length from 1.5 inches (25 millimeters) to 1.3 feet (40.6 centimeters), and living in caves or crevices, bats inhabit most of the temperate and tropical regions of both hemispheres. The majority of species feed on insects and fruit, while some tropical species eat pollen and nectar of flowers, and insects found inside them. Moderate-sized species usually prey on small mammals, birds, lizards, and frogs, and some eat fish. But true vampire bats (three species) eat the blood of animals by making an incision in the animal's skin—from these bats, animals can contract rabies. Most bats do not find their way around by sight but have evolved a sonar system, called "echolocation," for locating solid objects. Bats emit vocal sounds through the nose or mouth while flying. These sounds, usually above the human hearing range, are reflected back as echoes. This method enables bats, when flying in darkness, to avoid solid objects and to locate the position of flying insects. Bats have the most acute sense of hearing of any land animal, hearing frequencies as high as 120 to 210 kilohertz. The highest frequency humans can hear is 20 kilohertz.

What are the only mammals on Earth that cannot **jump**?

It might not be surprising to learn that neither the rhinoceros nor the elephant can jump, since their enormous weight makes the feat difficult. However, the third mammal that cannot jump is the pronghorn sheep, which was called an "antelope" in the famous song "Home on the Range." The pronghorn sheep's inability to jump has been a particular disadvantage in its North American home, where fences have prevented populations from migrating and hindered the pronghorn's ability to find mates and breed.

How does the **breath-holding capability** of a human compare with other mammals?

Mammal	Average time in minutes
Human	1
Polar bear	1.5
Pearl diver (human)	2.5
Sea otter	5
Platypus	10
Muskrat	12
Hippopotamus	15
Sea cow	16
Beaver	20
Porpoise	6
Seal	15 to 28
Greenland whale	60
Sperm whale	90
Bottle-nosed whale	120

How does a **bat** catch flying insects in **total darkness**?

Bats use sound waves for communication and navigation. They emit supersonic radiation ranging from as low as 200 Hz to as high as 30,000 Hz. The sounds are emitted through the bat's nostrils and are aided by a complex flap structure to provide precise directivity to the radiation. Echo returns from the emissions allow a bat to pick out a tiny flying insect some distance ahead. Highly sensitive ears and an ability to maneuver with great agility enables many bats to fly around in a darkened cave, catching insects without fear of collision.

What are some animals that have **pouches**?

Marsupials (meaning "pouched" animals) differ from all other living mammals in their anatomical and physiological features of reproduction. Most female marsupials—kangaroos, bandicoots, wombats, banded anteaters, koalas, opossums, wallabies, tasmanian devils, etc.—possess an abdominal pouch (called a marsupium), in which their young are carried. In some small terrestrial marsupials, however, the marsupium is not a true pouch but merely a fold of skin around the mammae (milk nipples).

The short gestation period in marsupials (in comparison to other similarly sized mammals) allows their young to be born in an "undeveloped" state. Consequently, these animals have been viewed as "primitive" or second-class mammals. However, some now see that the reproductive process of marsupials has an advantage over that of placental mammals. A female marsupial invests relatively few resources during the brief gestation period, more so during the lactation (nursing period) when the young are in the marsupium. If the female marsupial loses its young, it can conceive again sooner than a placental mammal in a comparable situation.

What freshwater mammal is **venomous**?

The male duck-billed platypus (*Ornithorhynchus anatinus*) has venomous spurs located on its hind legs. When threatened, the animal will drive them into the skin of a potential enemy, inflicting a painful sting. The venom this action releases is relatively mild and generally not harmful to humans.

How deep do **marine mammals dive**?

Below are listed the maximum depths and the longest durations of time underwater by various aquatic mammals:

Mammal	Maximum depth		Maximum time underwater
	Feet	Meters	
Weddell seal	1,968	600	70 minutes
Porpoise	984	300	15 minutes
Bottle-nosed whale	1,476	450	120 minutes
Fin whale	1,148	350	20 minutes
Sperm whale	> 6,562	> 2,000	90 minutes

Which **mammals lay eggs** and **suckle** their young?

The duck-billed platypus (*Ornithorhynchus anatinus*), the short-nosed echidna or spiny anteater (*Tachyglossus aculeatus*), and the long-nosed echidna (*Zaglossus bruijni*), indigenous to Australia, Tasmania, and New Guinea, are the only three species of mammals that lay eggs (a non-mammalian feature) but suckle their young (a mammalian feature). These mammals (order Monotremata) resemble reptiles in that they lay rubbery shell-covered eggs that are incubated and hatched outside the mother's body. In addition, they resemble reptiles in their digestive, reproductive, and excretory systems, and in a number of anatomical details (eye structure, presence of certain skull bones,

What is the difference between porpoises and dolphins?

Marine dolphins (family Delphinidae) and porpoises (family Phocoenidae) consist of about 40 species. The chief differences between dolphins and porpoises occur in the snout and teeth. True dolphins have a beak-like snout and cone-shaped teeth. True porpoises have a rounded snout and flat or spade-shaped teeth.

pectoral [shoulder] girdle and rib and vertebral structures). They are, however, classed as mammals because they have fur and a four-chambered heart, nurse their young from gland milk, are warm-blooded, and have some mammalian skeletal features.

What is the name of the **seal-like animal** in Florida?

The West Indian manatee (*Trichechus manatus*), in the winter, moves to more temperate parts of Florida, such as the warm headwaters of the Crystal and Homosassa rivers in central Florida or the tropical waters of southern Florida. When the air temperature rises to 50°F (10°C), it will wander back along the Gulf coast and up the Atlantic coast as far as Virginia. Long-range offshore migrations to the coast of Guyana and South America have been documented. This large, plant-eating, water mammal may have been the inspiration for the mermaid legend. In 1893, when the population of manatees in Florida was reduced to several thousand, the state gave it legal protection from being hunted or commercially exploited. However, many animals continue to be killed or injured by the encroachment of humans. Entrapment in locks and dams, collisions with barges and power boat propellers, etc., cause at least 30 percent of the manatee deaths, which total 125 to 130 annually.

What is the only **four-horned animal** in the world?

The four-horned antelope (*Tetracerus quadricornis*) is a native of central India. The males have two short horns, usually four inches (10 centimeters) in length, between their ears, and an even shorter pair, one to two inches (2.5 to five centimeters) long, between the brow ridges over their eyes. Not all males have four horns, and in some the second pair eventually falls off. The females have no horns at all.

What is **Przewalski's horse**?

This native of Mongolia and northeastern China is the last truly wild horse species. Named for Nikolai Przewalski (1839-1888), the Russian colonel who reported its existence in 1870, Przewalski's horse (*Equus przewalskii*) is a stocky, short-legged animal

Przewalski's horse—ancestor of all domestic horse breeds—is thought to be extinct in the wild.

with a dun-colored coat, a pale muzzle and belly, and dark legs, mane, and tail. Its short mane is bristly and erect. This horse has the unusual feature of possessing 66 chromosomes rather than the customary 64 found in a domestic horse. Przewalski's horse was believed to have become extinct in the wild in 1968. However, 1,000 or so survived in zoos and wildlife parks.

In June 1994, a small herd bred in captivity was returned to the wild in Mongolia. They were kept in large enclosures for two years while they adjusted to the harsh climate. The herd is now flourishing and is expected to survive in the wild.

Why were **Clydesdale horses** used as war horses?

The Clydesdales were among a group of European horses referred to as the "Great Horses," which were specifically bred to carry the massively armored knights of the Middle Ages. These animals had to be strong enough to carry a man wearing as much as 100 pounds (45 kilograms) of armor as well as up to 80 pounds (36 kilograms) of armor on their own bodies. However, the invention of the musket quickly ended the use of Clydesdales and other Great Horses on the battlefield as speed and maneuverability became more important than strength.

What is the difference between an **African elephant** and an **Indian elephant**?

The African elephant (*Loxodonta africana*) is the largest living land animal, weighing up to 8.25 tons (7,500 kilograms) and standing 10 to 13 feet (three to four meters) at

How many vertebrae are in the neck of a giraffe?

A giraffe neck has seven vertebrae, the same as other mammals, but the vertebrae are greatly elongated.

the shoulder. The Indian elephant (*Elephas maximus*) weighs about six tons (5,500 kilograms) with a shoulder height of 10 feet (three meters). Other differences are:

African elephant	Indian elephant
Larger ears	Smaller ears
Gestation period of about 670 days	Gestation period of about 610 days
Ear tops turn backwards	Ear tops turn forwards
Concave back	Convex back
Three toenails on hind feet	Four toenails on hind feet
Larger tusks	Smaller tusks
Two finger-like lips at tips of trunk	One lip at tip of trunk

Why do **cows** have four stomachs?

The stomachs of cows, as well as all ruminants, are divided into four sections—the rumen, reticulum, omasum and abomasums. Ruminants eat rapidly and do not chew much of their food completely before they swallow it. The liquid part of their food enters the reticulum first, while the solid part of their food enters the rumen where it softens. Bacteria in the rumen initially break it down as a first step in digestion. Ruminants later regurgitate it into the mouth where they chew their cud. Cows chew their cud about six to eight times per day, spending a total of five to seven hours in rumination. The chewed cud goes directly into the other chambers of the stomach, where various microorganisms assist in further digestion.

What is the difference between a **pig** and a **hog**?

In the United States, the term "pig" refers to younger domesticated swine weighing less than 120 pounds (50 kilograms), while the term "hog" refers to older swine weighing more than this. In Great Britain all domesticated swine are referred to as pigs.

What is the difference between a **rabbit** and a **hare**?

Rabbits are generally smaller than hares and have shorter hind legs and shorter ears. Hares are born with a full coat of fur and their eyes open. Mothers drop their young either

Why are Dalmatians "firehouse dogs"?

Before automobiles, coaches and carriages were often accompanied by dogs that kept horses company and guarded them from theft. Dalmatians were particularly well known for the strong bond they formed with horses, and firemen, who often owned the strongest and speediest horses in the area, kept the dogs at the station to deter horse thieves. Although fire engines have replaced horses, Dalmatians have remained a part of firehouse life, both for the appeal of these beautiful dogs and for their nostalgic tie to the past.

on the bare ground or in a slight depression in the ground. Rabbits are born hairless and blind; their nests are lined with grass, bark, and soft stems and covered with a layer of rabbit fur. Rabbits often live in a group while hares live most of the time by themselves.

What other names are used for a **cougar**?

A cougar is also known as a puma, painter, screamer, mountain lion, silver ghost, and catamount.

What is the only **American canine** that can **climb trees**?

The gray fox (*Urocyon cinereoargenteus*) is the only American canine that can climb trees.

How long does a **gray wolf** live?

The gray wolf (*Canis lupus*), also known as the timber wolf, is the largest and most widespread species of the family Canidae. It can live in the wild for less than 10 years, but under human care, up to 20 years. In many areas, however, it has been hunted and killed because it is believed to pose a threat to humans and domesticated animals (cattle, sheep, and reindeer). It may soon suffer the fate of the red wolf (*Canis rufus*), which once flourished in the southeast and south central United States. The red wolf has been declared biologically extinct in the wild, now existing in captivity and in a small reintroduced population of captive-bred animals in North Carolina. The endangered gray wolf is declining faster in the New World than in the Old. In the United States, it is limited to Alaska (10,000), Northern Minnesota (1,200), and Isle Royale, Michigan (20), with perhaps a few packs in Wisconsin, northern Michigan, and the Rocky Mountain area; in Canada, they number 15,000. Strongly social, living in packs, and weighing between 75 and 175 pounds (43 to 80 kilograms), in physical appearance the gray wolf resembles a large domestic dog, such as the Alaskan malamute.

Which **bear** lives in a **tropical rain forest**?

The Malayan sun bear (*Ursus malayanus*) is one of the rarest animals in the tropical forests of Sumatra, Malay Peninsula, Borneo, Burma, Thailand, and southern China. The smallest bear, with a length of 3.3 to 4.6 feet (one to 1.4 meters) and weighing 60 to 143 pounds (27 to 65 kilograms), it has a strong, stocky body and black coloring. With powerful paws having long, curved claws to help it climb trees in the dense forests, it is an expert tree climber. The sun bear tears at tree bark to expose insects, larvae, and the nests of bees and termites. Fruit, coconut palm, and small rodents, too, are part of its diet. Sleeping and sunbathing during the day, it is active at night. Unusually shy and retiring, cautious and intelligent, the sun bear is declining in population as the forests are being destroyed.

What is the **largest terrestrial mammal** in North America?

The bison (*Bison bison*), which weighs 3,100 pounds (1,400 kilograms) and is six feet (two meters) high.

Do **camels** store water in their humps?

The hump or humps do not store water, since they are fat reservoirs. The ability to go long periods without drinking water—up to ten months if there is plenty of green vegetation and dew to feed on—results from a number of physiological adaptations. One major factor is that camels can lose up to 40 percent of their body weight with no ill effects. A camel can also withstand a variation of its body temperature by as much as 14°F (-10°C). A camel can drink 30 gallons of water in ten minutes and up to 50 gallons over several hours. A one-humped camel is called a dromedary or Arabian camel; a Bactrian camel has two humps and lives in the wilds of the Gobi desert. Today, the Bactrian is confined to Asia, while most of the Arabian camels are on African soil.

How many quills does a **porcupine** have?

For its defensive weapon, the average porcupine has about 30,000 quills or specialized hairs, comparable in hardness and flexibility to slivers of celluloid and so sharply pointed they can penetrate any hide. The quills that do the most damage are the short ones that stud the porcupine's muscular tail. With a few lashes, the porcupine can send a rain of quills that have tiny scale-like barbs into the skin of its adversary. The quills work their way inward because of their barbs and the involuntary muscular action of the victim. Sometimes the quills can work themselves out, but other times the quills pierce vital organs, and the victim dies.

Slow-footed and stocky, porcupines spend much of their time in the trees, using their formidable incisors to strip off bark and foliage for their food, and supplement their diets with fruits and grasses. Porcupines have a ravenous appetite for salt; as her-

The nine-banded armadillo generally gives birth to four same-sexed young.

bivores (plant-eating animals) their diets have insufficient salt. So natural salt licks, animal bones left by carnivores (meat-eating animals), yellow pond lilies, and other items having a high salt content (including paints, plywood adhesives, and the sweat-ed-on clothing of humans) have a strong appeal to porcupines.

Why do **nine-banded armadillos** always have four offspring of the same sex?

The one feature that distinguishes the nine-banded armadillo (*Dasypus novemcinctus*) is that the female almost always gives birth to four young of the same sex. This consistency results from the division of the one fertilized egg into four parts to produce quadruplets.

What is a **capybara**?

The capybara (*Hydrochoerus hydrochoeris*) is the largest of all living rodents. Also called the water hog, water pig, water cary, or carpincho, it looks like a huge guinea pig. Its body length can be 3.25 to 4.5 feet (one to 1.3 meters), and it usually weighs between 120 and 130 pounds (54 to 59 kilograms) or more. A native of northern South America, this rodent leads a semi-aquatic life, feeding on aquatic plants and grasses. A subspecies, native to Panama, is smaller and weighs between 60 and 75 pounds (27 to 34 kilograms).

What is the chemical composition of a **skunk's spray**?

The chief odorous components of the spray have been identified as crotyl mercaptan, isopentyl mercaptan, and methyl crotyl disulfide in the ratio of 4:4:3. The liquid is an oily, pale-yellow, foul-smelling spray that can cause severe eye inflammation. This defensive weapon is discharged from two tiny nipples located just inside the skunk's anus—either as a fine spray or a short stream of rain-sized drops. Although the liquid's range is 6.5 to 10 feet (two to three meters), its smell can be detected 1.5 miles (2.5 kilometers) downwind.

PETS

What are the different **classifications of dogs**?

Dogs are divided into groups according to the purpose for which they have been bred.

Group	Purpose	Representative breeds
Sporting dogs	Retrieving game birds and water fowl	Cocker spaniel, English setter, English springer spaniel, golden retriever, Irish setter, Labrador retriever, pointer.
Hounds	Hunting	Basenji, beagle, dachshund, foxhound, greyhound, saluki, Rhodesian ridgeback.
Terriers	Hunting small animals such as rats and foxes	Airedale terrier, Bedlington terrier, bull terrier, fox terrier, miniature schnauzer, Scottish terrier, Skye terrier, West Highland white terrier.
Toy dogs	Small companions or lap dogs	Chihuahua, Maltese, Pekingese, Pomeranian, pug, Shih Tzu, Yorkshire terrier.
Herding dogs	Protect sheep and other livestock	Australian cattle dog, bouviers des Flandres, collie, German shepherd, Hungarian puli, Old English sheepdog, Welsh corgi.
Working dogs	Herding, rescue, and sled dogs	Alaskan malamute, boxer, Doberman pinscher, great Dane, mastiff, St. Bernard, Siberian husky.
Non-sporting dogs	No specific purpose, not toys	Boston terrier, bulldog, Dalmatian, Japanese akita, keeshond, Lhasa apso, poodle.

What is the **oldest breed** of dog?

Dogs are the oldest domestic animal, originating 12,000 to 14,000 years ago. They are believed to be descendants of wild canines, most likely wolves, which began to frequent human settlements where food was more readily available. The more aggressive canines were probably driven off or killed, while the less dangerous ones were kept to guard, hunt, and later herd other domesticated animals, such as sheep. Attempts at selectively breeding desirable traits likely began soon after.

The oldest purebred dog is believed to be the Saluki. Sumerian rock carvings in Mesopotamia that date to about 7000 B.C.E. depict dogs bearing a striking resemblance to the Saluki. The dogs are 23 to 28 inches (58 to 71 centimeters) tall with a long, narrow head. The coat is smooth and silky and can be white, cream, fawn, gold, red, grizzle (bluish-gray) and tan, black and tan, or tricolor (white, black, and tan). The tail is long and feathered. The Saluki has remarkable sight and tremendous speed, which makes it an excellent hunter.

The oldest American purebred dog is the American Foxhound. It descends from a pack of foxhounds belonging to an Englishman named Robert Brooke who settled in Maryland in 1650. These dogs were crossed with other strains imported from England, Ireland, and France to develop the American Foxhound. This dog stands 22 to 25 inches (56 to 63.5 centimeters) tall. It has a long, slightly domed head, with a straight, squared-out muzzle. The coat is of medium length and can be any color. They are used primarily for hunting.

Which breeds of dogs are **best for families with young children**?

Research has shown that golden retriever, Labrador retriever, beagle, collie, bichon frise, cairn terrier, pug, coonhound, boxer, basset hound or mixes of these breeds are best for families with young children.

Which dogs are the **easiest to train**?

In a study of 56 popular dog breeds the top breeds to train were Shetland sheepdogs, Shih Tzus, miniature toy and standard poodles, Bichons Frises, English Springer Spaniels and Welsh Corgis.

Why do **dogs hear** more than humans?

A dog's ears are highly mobile, allowing it to scan its environment for sounds. The ears capture the sounds and funnel them down to the eardrum. Dogs can hear sounds from four times farther away than humans.

Why do dogs **howl** at **sirens**?

The high pitch of a siren is very similar to the pitch of a dog's howl. A dog's howl is a way of communicating with other dogs—either to indicate location or to define terri-

Wolves, like this red wolf, are believed to be the ancestors of all domestic dog breeds.

tory. When a dog responds to an ambulance or fire engine siren, he is "returning the call of the wild."

What breeds of dogs **do not shed**?

Poodles, Kerry blue terriers, and schnauzers do not shed.

Which breed is known as the **wrinkled dog**?

The shar-pei, or Chinese fighting dog, is covered with folds of loose skin. It stands 18 to 20 inches (46 to 51 centimeters) tall and weighs up to 50 pounds (22.5 kilograms). Its solid-colored coat can be black, red, fawn, or cream. The dog originated in Tibet or the northern provinces of China some 2,000 years ago. The People's Republic of China put such a high tax on shar-peis, however, that few people could afford to keep them, and the dog was in danger of extinction. But a few specimens were smuggled out of China, and the breed has made a comeback in the United States, Canada, and the United Kingdom. Although bred as a fighting dog, the shar-pei is generally an amiable companion.

Which breed is known as the **voiceless dog**?

The basenji dog does not bark. When happy, it will make an appealing sound described as something between a chortle and a yodel. It also snarls and growls on occasion. One

How is the age of a dog or cat computed in human years?

When a cat is one year old, it is about 20 years old in human years. Each additional year is multiplied by four. Another source counts the age of a cat slightly differently. At age one, a cat's age equals 16 human years. At age two, a cat's age is 24 human years. Each additional year is multiplied by four.

When a dog is one year old, it is about 15 years old in human years. At age two it is about 24; after age two, each additional year is multiplied by four.

of the oldest breeds of dogs, and originating in central Africa, the basenji was often given as a present to the pharaohs of ancient Egypt. Following the decline of the Egyptian civilization, the basenji was still valued in central Africa for its hunting prowess and its silence. The dog was rediscovered by English explorers in the 19th century, although it was not widely bred until the 1940s.

The basenji is a small, lightly built dog with a flat skull and a long, rounded muzzle. It measures 16 to 17 inches (40 to 43 centimeters) in height at the shoulder and weighs 22 to 24 pounds (10 to 11 kilograms). The coat is short and silky in texture. The feet, chest, and tail tip are white; the rest of the coat is chestnut red, black, or black and tan.

What **food odors** do dogs like best?

In a study of different foods, researchers found that liver and chicken ranked higher than everything else, including hamburgers, fish, vegetables, and fresh fruit.

What is the **rarest breed** of dog?

The Tahltan bear dog, of which only a few remain, is thought to be the rarest dog. In danger of extinction, this breed was once used by the Tahltan Indians of western Canada to hunt bear, lynx, and porcupine.

What was the **contribution to medical science** of a dog named **Marjorie**?

Marjorie was a diabetic black-and-white mongrel that was the first creature to be kept alive by insulin, a substance that controls the level of sugar in the blood.

Do **dogs and cats** have **good memories**?

Dogs do have long-term memories, especially for those whom they love. Cats have a memory for things that are important to their lives. Some cats seem to have extraordi-

How can pets be treated to remove skunk odor?

From a pet store, purchase one of the products specifically designed to counteract skunk odor. Most of these are of the enzyme or bacterial enzyme variety and can be used without washing the pet first. A dog may also be given a bath with tomato juice, diluted vinegar, or neuthroleum-alpha, or you could try mint mouthwash, aftershave, or soap and water.

nary "memories" for finding places. Taken away from their homes, they seem able to remember where they live. The key to this "homing" ability could be a built-in celestial navigation, similar to that used by birds, or the cats' navigational ability could be attributed to the cats' sensitivity to Earth's magnetic fields. When magnets are attached to cats, their normal navigational skills are disrupted.

What is the **original breed of domestic cat** in the United States?

The American shorthair is believed by some naturalists to be the original domestic cat in America. It is descended from cats brought to the New World from Europe by the early settlers. The cats readily adapted to their new environment. Selective breeding to enhance the best traits began early in the 20th century.

The American shorthair is a very athletic cat with a lithe, powerful body, excellent for stalking and killing prey. Its legs are long, heavy, and muscular, ideal for leaping and for coping with all kinds of terrain. The fur, in a wide variety of color and coat patterns, is thick enough to protect the animal from moisture and cold, but short enough to resist matting and snagging.

Although this cat makes an excellent house pet and companion, it remains very self-sufficient. Its hunting instinct is so strong that it exercises the skill even when well-provided with food. The American shorthair is the only true "working cat" in the United States.

What controls the formation of the color **points** in a **Siamese cat**?

The color points are due to the presence of a recessive gene, which operates at cooler temperatures, limiting the color to well-defined areas—the mask, ears, tail, lower legs, and paws—the places at the far reaches of the cardiovascular system of the cat.

There are four classic varieties of Siamese cats. Seal-points have a pale fawn to cream colored coat with seal-brown markings. Blue-points are bluish-white with slate blue markings. Chocolate-points are ivory colored with milk-chocolate brown colored markings. Lilac-points have a white coat and pinkish-gray markings. There are also some newer varieties with red, cream, and tabby points.

The Siamese originated in Thailand (once called Siam) and arrived in England in the 1880s. They are medium-sized and have long, slender, lithe bodies, with long heads and long, tapering tails. Extroverted and affectionate, Siamese are known for their loud, distinctive voices, which are impossible to ignore.

Why do **cats' eyes shine** in the dark?

A cat's eyes contain a special light-conserving mechanism called the *tapetum lucidum*, which reflects any light not absorbed as it passes through the retina of each eye. The retina gets a second chance (so to speak) to receive the light, aiding the cat's vision even more. In dim light, when the pupils of the cat's eyes are opened the widest, this glowing or shining effect occurs when light hits them at certain angles. The *tapetum lucidum*, located behind the retina, is a membrane composed of 15 layers of special, glittering cells that all together act as a mirror. The color of the glow is usually greenish or golden, but the eyes of the Siamese cat reflect a luminous ruby red.

Which plants are **poisonous to cats**?

Certain common houseplants are poisonous to cats, which should not be allowed to eat the following:

Caladium (Elephant's ears)
Dieffenbachia (Dumb cane)
Euphorbia pulcherrima (Poinsettia)
Hedera (True ivy)
Mistletoe
Oleander
Philodendron
Prunus laurocerasus (Common or cherry laurel)
Rhododendron (Azalea)
Solanum capiscastrum (Winter or False Jerusalem cherry)

Why and how do cats **purr**?

Experts cannot agree on how or why cats purr, or on where the sound originates. Some think that the purr is produced by the vibration of blood in a large vein in the chest cavity. Where the vein passes through the diaphragm, the muscles around the vein contract, nipping the blood flow and setting up oscillations. These sounds are magnified by the air in the bronchial tubes and the windpipe. Others think that purring is the vibrations of membranes, called false vocal cords, located near the vocal cords. No one knows for sure why a cat purrs, but many people interpret the sound as one of contentment.

Why do cats have **whiskers**?

The function of a cat's whiskers is not fully understood. They are thought to have something to do with the sense of touch. Removing them can disturb a cat for some time. Some people believe that the whiskers act as antennae in the dark, enabling the cat to identify things it cannot see. The whiskers may help the cat to pinpoint the direction from which an odor is coming. In addition, the cat is thought to point some of its whiskers downwards to guide it when jumping or running over uneven terrain at night.

Which types of **birds** make the best pets?

There are several birds that make good house pets and have a reasonable life expectancy:

Bird	Life expectancy in years	Considerations
Finch	2-3	Easy care
Canary	8-10	Easy care; males sing
Budgerigar (parakeet)	8-15	Easy care
Cockatiel	15-20	Easy care; easy to train
Lovebird	15-20	Cute, but not easy to care for or train
Amazon parrot	50-60	Good talkers, but can be screamers
African grey parrot	50-60	Talkers; never scream

THE HUMAN BODY

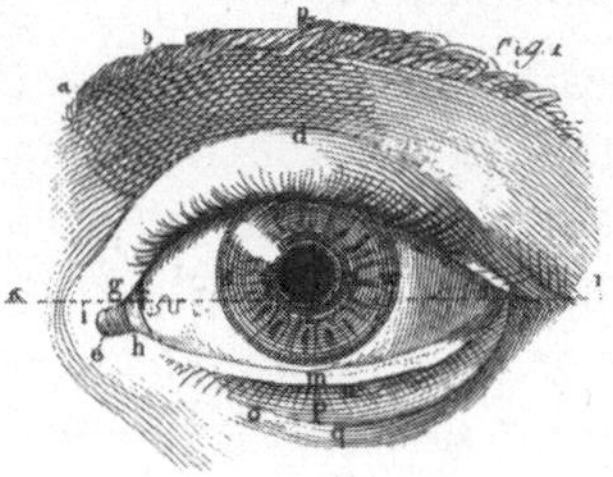

FUNCTIONS, PROCESSES, AND CHARACTERISTICS

Which **chemicals** constitute the human body?

About 24 elements are used by the body in its functions and processes.

Major elements

Element	Percentage	Function
Oxygen	65.0	Part of all major nutrients of tissues; vital to energy production
Carbon	18.5	Essential life element of proteins, carbohydrates, and fats; building blocks of cells
Hydrogen	9.5	Part of major nutrients; building blocks of cells
Nitrogen	3.3	Essential part of proteins, DNA, RNA; essential to most body functions
Calcium	1.5	Forms nonliving bone parts; a messenger between cells
Phosphorous	1.0	Important to bone building; essential to cell energy

Potassium, sulfur, sodium, chlorine, and magnesium each occur at 0.35 percent or less. There are also traces of iron, cobalt, copper, manganese, iodine, zinc, fluorine, boron, aluminum, molybdenum, silicon, chromium, and selenium.

How many **chromosomes** are in a human body cell?

A human being normally has 46 chromosomes (23 pairs) in all but the sex cells. Half of each pair is inherited from the mother's egg; the other, from the father's sperm.

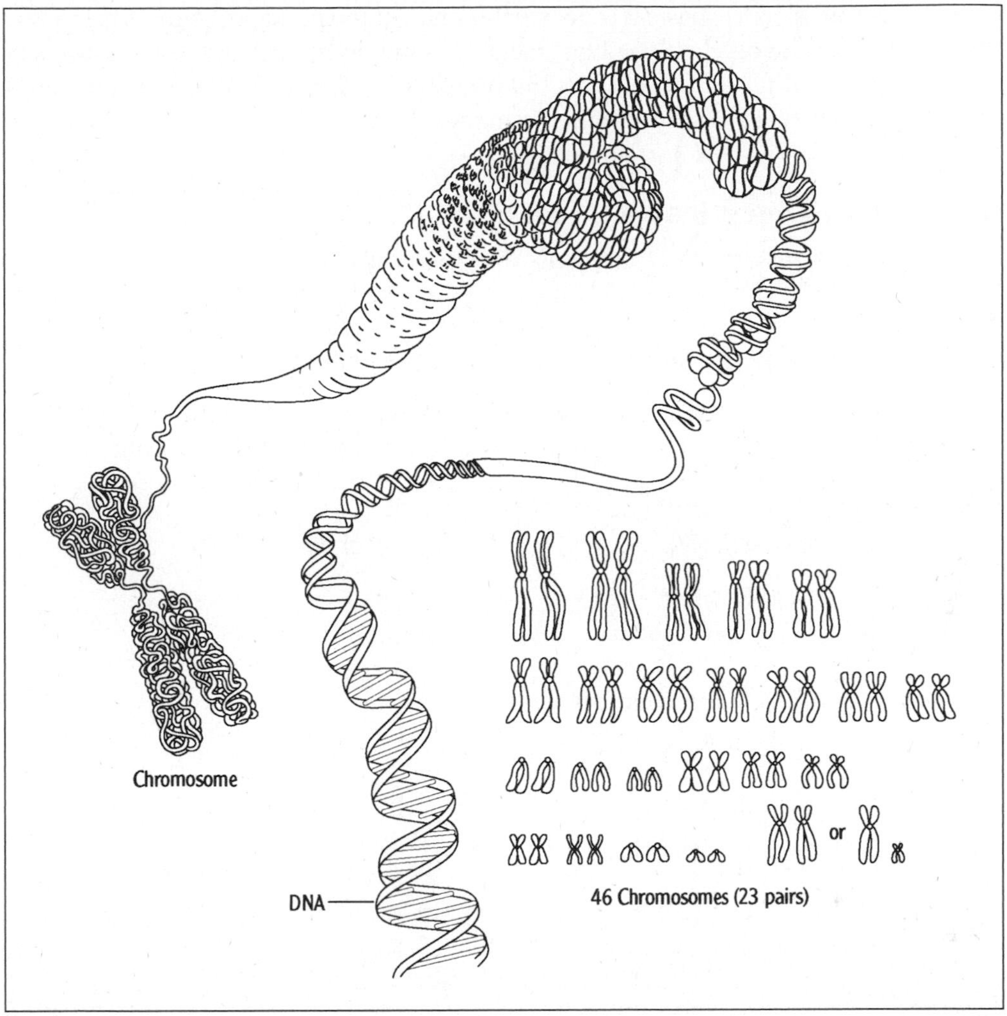

Chromosomes, magnified.

When the sperm and egg unite in fertilization, they create a single cell, or zygote, with 46 chromosomes. When cell division occurs, the 46 chromosomes are duplicated; this process is repeated billions of times over, with each of the cells containing the identical set of chromosomes. Only the gametes, or sex cells, are different. In their cell division, the members of each pair of chromosomes are separated and distributed to different cells. Each gamete has only 23 chromosomes.

Chromosomes contain thousands of genes, each of which has information for a specific trait. That information is in the form of a chemical code, and the chemical compound that codes this genetic information is deoxyribonucleic acid, or DNA. A gene can be seen as a sequence of DNA that is coded for a specific protein. These proteins determine specific physical traits (such as height, body shape, color of hair, eyes, skin, etc.), body chemistry (blood type, metabolic functions, etc.), and some aspects of behavior and intelligence. More than 150 human disorders are inherited, and genes are thought to determine susceptibility to many diseases.

How many cells are in the human body?

Sources give figures that vary from 50 to 75 trillion cells.

What is the **average life span of cells** in the human body?

The human body is self-repairing and self-replenishing. According to one estimate, almost 200 billion cells die each hour. In a healthy body, dying cells are simultaneously replaced by new cells.

Cell type	Length of time
Blood cells	
red blood cells	120 days
lymphocytes	Over 1 year
other white cells	10 hours
platelets	10 days
Bone cells	25-30 years
Brain cells*	Lifetime
Colon cells	3-4 days
Liver cells	500 days
Skin cells	19-34 days
Spermatozoa	2-3 days
Stomach cells	2 days

*Brain cells are the only cells that do not divide further during a person's lifetime. They either last the entire lifetime or, if a cell in the nervous system dies, it is not replaced.

How does the **immune system** work?

The immune system has two main components: white blood cells and antibodies circulating in the blood. The antigen-antibody reaction forms the basis for this immunity. When an antigen (*anti*body *gen*erator)—such as a harmful bacterium, virus, fungus, parasite, or other foreign substance—invades the body, a specific antibody is generated to attack the antigen. The antibody is produced by B lymphocytes (B cells) in the spleen or lymph nodes. An antibody may either destroy the antigen directly or it may "label" it so that a white blood cell (called a

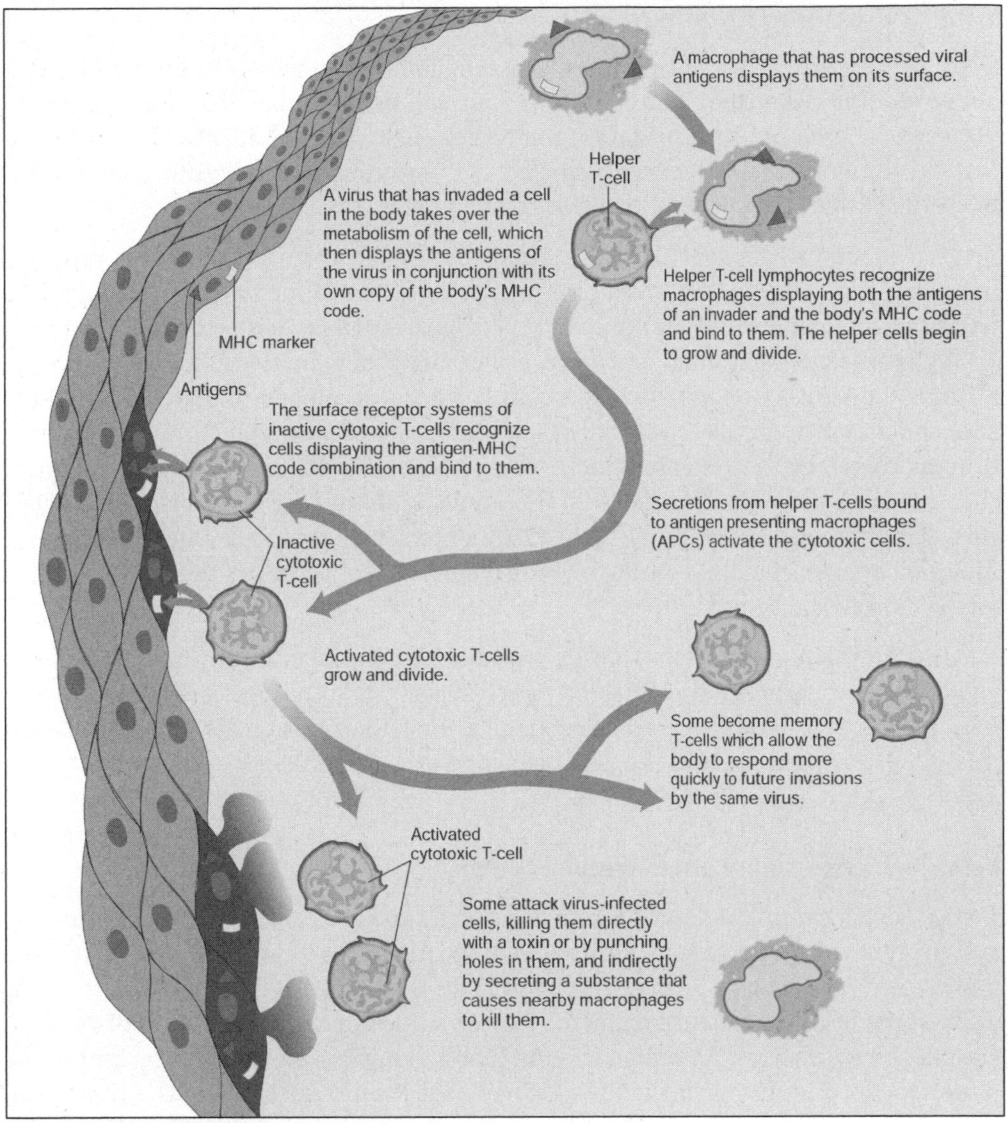

How the immune system works.

macrophage, or scavenger cell) can engulf the foreign intruder. After a human has been exposed to an antigen, a later exposure to the same antigen will produce a faster immune system reaction. The necessary antibodies will be produced more rapidly and in larger amounts. Artificial immunization uses this antigen-antibody reaction to protect the human body from certain diseases by exposing the body to a safe dose of antigen to produce effective antibodies as well as a "readiness" for any future attacks of the harmful antigen.

What is **DNA fingerprinting**?

DNA, or genetic, fingerprinting is a method of determining identity, family relationships, etc. Formulated by Alec Jeffreys (1950-), a British geneticist, the genetic fingerprint is based on the assumption that every person (except identical twins) has a unique sequence of DNA (deoxyribonucleic acid)—a substance present in the nucleus of every cell that determines individual characteristics.

Within the DNA molecule, the sequence of the genetic information is repeated many times along the DNA structure, which resembles a long twisting ladder. The length of the sequence, the number of repetitions, and its precise location within the DNA chain seems to be unique in all cases but identical twins, with the odds being 30 billion to one of a duplication. A process has been developed that translates these sequences into a visual record that resembles a series of bars on X-ray film. In this process the technician isolates the DNA from blood, saliva, hair follicles, or semen; then the DNA strand is separated into thousands of shorter pieces by placing the DNA into an enzyme solution. Finally, the fragments, which are placed in a gelatin-like material, are subjected to a strong electrical current that separates them according to size and electrical behavior.

In criminal investigations, hair, blood, and skin samples left by the criminal can yield a DNA fingerprint, which can be matched against any suspect's DNA fingerprint. DNA fingerprinting is also used to determine the father in paternity cases, since the infant's DNA strand contains the genetic coding of the parents.

How do **T cells** differ from **B lymphocytes**?

Lymphocytes are one variety of white blood cells and are part of the body's immune system. The immune system fights invading organisms that have penetrated the body's general defenses. T cells, responsible for dealing with most viruses, for handling some bacteria and fungi, and for cancer surveillance, are one of the two main classes of lymphocytes. T lymphocytes, or T cells, compose about 60-80 percent of the lymphocytes circulating in the blood. They have been "educated" in the thymus to perform particular functions. Killer T cells are sensitized to multiply when they come into contact with antigens (foreign proteins) on abnormal body cells (cells that have been invaded by viruses, cells in transplanted tissue, or tumor cells). These killer T cells attach themselves to the abnormal cells and release chemicals (lymphokines) to destroy them. Helper T cells assist killer cells in their activities and control other aspects of the immune response. When B lymphocytes, which compose approximately 10-15 percent of total lymphocytes, contact the antigens on abnormal cells, the lymphocytes enlarge and divide to become plasma cells. Then the plasma cells secrete vast numbers of immunoglobulins or antibodies into the blood, which attach themselves to the surfaces of the abnormal cells, to begin a process that will lead to the destruction of the invaders.

What are **endorphins**?

Endorphins and closely related chemicals called enkephalins are part of a larger group called opiods, which have properties very much like drugs such as heroin or morphine. They can act not only as pain killers but also can induce a sense of well-being or euphoria. Clinical applications of endorphin research include possible treatments for some forms of mental illness; treatment or control of pain for chronic pain sufferers; development of new anesthetics; and the development of non-addictive, safe, and effective pain relievers.

What is **REM** sleep?

REM sleep is rapid eye movement sleep. It is characterized by faster breathing and heart rates than NREM (non-rapid eye movement) sleep. The eyes move rapidly, and dreaming, often with elaborate story lines, occurs. The only people who do not have REM sleep are those who have been blind from birth. REM sleep usually occurs in four to five periods, varying from five minutes to about an hour, growing progressively longer as sleep continues.

Scientists do not understand why dreaming is important, but they think the brain is either cataloging the information it picked up during the day and throwing out the data it does not want, or is creating scenarios to work through situations causing emotional distress. Regardless of its function, most people who are deprived of sleep or dreams become disoriented, unable to concentrate, and may even have hallucinations.

Why is it difficult to remember **dreams**?

Almost all dreams occur during rapid eye movement (REM) sleep. It appears that the content of dreams is stored in short-term memory and cannot be transferred into long-term memory unless they are somehow articulated. Sleep studies show that when individuals who believe they never dream are awakened at various intervals during the night they are in the middle of a dream.

Why do people **snore** and how loud can snoring be?

Snoring is produced by vibrations of the soft palate, usually caused by any condition that hinders breathing through the nose. It is more common while sleeping on the back. Research has indicated that a snore can reach 69 decibels, as compared to 70-90 decibels for a pneumatic drill.

How many **calories** does a person burn while **sleeping**?

A 150-pound (68-kilogram) person burns one calorie per minute during bed rest. The approximate caloric expenditure of other activities for a person weighing 150 pounds are given below. Actual numbers may vary, depending on the vigor of the exercise, air temperature, clothing, etc.

Activity	Calories used per hour
Aerobic dance	684
Basketball	500
Bicycling (5.5 mph)	210
Bicycling (13 mph)	660
Bowling	220-270
Calisthenics	300
Circuit weight training	756
Digging	360-420
Gardening	200
Golfing (using power cart)	150-220
Golfing (pulling cart)	240-300
Golfing (carrying clubs)	300-360
Football	500
Handball(social)	600-660
Handball (competitive)	>660
Hoeing	300-360
Housework	180
In-line skating	600
Jogging (5-10 mph)	500-800
Lawn mowing (power)	250
Lawn mowing (hand)	420-480
Racquetball	456
Raking leaves	300-360
Rowing machine	415
Sitting	100
Skiing (cross-country)	600-660
Skiing (downhill)	570
Snow shoveling	420-480
Square dancing	350
Standing	140
Swimming moderately	500-700
Tennis (doubles)	300-360
Tennis (singles)	420-480
Vacuuming	240-300
Volleyball	350
Walking (2 mph)	150-240
Walking (3.5 mph)	240-300
Walking (4 mph)	300-400
Walking (5 mph)	420-480

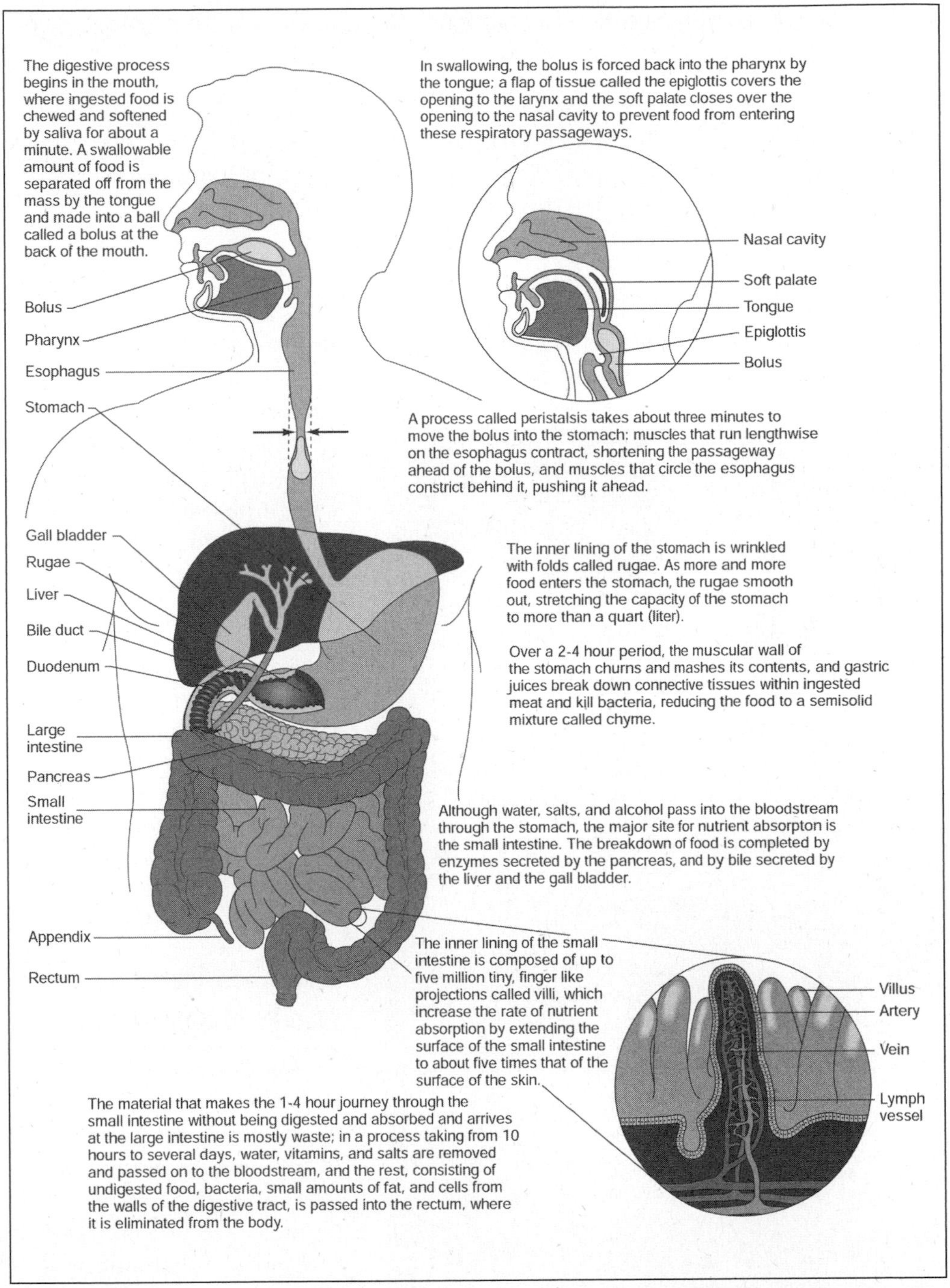

The digestive process.

When a person **swallows** solid or liquid food, what prevents it from going down the windpipe?

Once food is chewed, voluntary muscles move it to the throat. In the pharynx (throat), automatic involuntary reflexes take over. The epiglottis closes over the larynx (voice box), which leads to the windpipe. A sphincter at the top of the esophagus relaxes, allowing the food to enter the digestive tract.

How long does it take food to **digest**?

The stomach holds a little under two quarts (1.9 liters) of semi-digested food that stays in the stomach three to five hours. The stomach slowly releases food to the rest of the digestive tract. Fifteen hours or more after the first bite started down the alimentary canal, the final residue of the food is passed along to the rectum and is excreted through the anus as feces.

Claude Bernard, pioneer in the field of physiology.

What is the length of the human **intestine**?

The small intestine is about 22 feet (seven meters) long. The large intestine is about five feet (1.5 meters) long.

Who is considered the founder of **physiology**?

As an experimenter, Claude Bernard (1813-1878) enriched physiology by his introduction of numerous new concepts into the field. The most famous of these concepts is that of the milieu intérieur or internal environment. The complex functions of the various organs are closely interrelated and are all directed to maintaining the constancy of internal conditions despite external changes. All cells exist in this aqueous (blood and lymph) internal environment, which bathes the cells and provides a medium for the elementary exchange of nutrients and waste material.

Who coined the term **homeostasis**?

Walter Bradford Cannon (1871-1945), who elaborated on Claude Bernard's (1813-1878) concept of the milieu intérieur (interior environment), used the term homeostasis to describe the body's ability to maintain a relative constancy in its internal environment.

In the United States, what is the **average height and weight** for a man and a woman?

The average female is five feet, 3.75 inches (1.62 meters) tall and weighs 152 pounds (69.09 kilograms). The average male is five feet, nine inches (1.75 meters) tall and weighs 180 pounds (81.82 kilograms). Between 1960 and 2000 the average American male became two inches (five centimeters) taller and 45 pounds (20.45 kilograms) heavier, while the average American woman also grew two inches (five centimeters) taller and gained 18 pounds (8.18 kilogram).

What are **desirable weights** for men and women?

The National Heart, Lung, and Blood Institute (NHLBI), in cooperation with the National Institute of Diabetes and Digestive and Kidney Diseases, released guidelines for weight for adults in 1998. These guidelines define degrees of overweight and obesity in terms of body mass index (BMI). Body mass index is based on weight and height and is strongly correlated with total body fat content. The Body Mass Index (BMI) incorporates both your height and weight to assess your weight-related level of risk for heart disease, diabetes, and high blood pressure. To find your BMI, multiply your weight in pounds by 700, divide by your height in inches, then divide by your height again. For example, if you are 5 feet, 10 inches and weigh 185 pounds, the calculation would be as follows:

185 pounds × 700 = 129,500

129,500/70 inches = 1,850

1,850/70 inches = 26.4

A BMI of 25 or less indicates low risk; 25-29 indicates overweight; and a BMI of over 30 indicates obesity. BMI numbers apply to both men and women. Very muscular individuals, such as athletes, may have a high BMI without health risks.

BMI	19	20	21	22	23	24	25	26	27	28	29	30
Height (inches)						Body Weight (pounds)						
58	91	96	100	105	110	115	119	124	129	134	138	143
59	94	99	104	109	114	119	124	128	133	138	143	148
60	97	102	107	112	118	123	128	133	138	143	148	153
61	100	106	111	116	122	127	132	137	143	148	153	158
62	104	109	115	120	126	131	136	142	147	153	158	164
63	107	113	118	124	130	135	141	146	152	158	163	169
64	110	116	122	128	134	140	145	151	157	163	169	174
65	114	120	126	132	138	144	150	156	162	168	174	180
66	118	124	130	136	142	148	155	161	167	173	179	186
67	121	127	134	140	146	153	159	166	172	178	186	191
68	125	131	138	144	151	158	164	171	177	184	190	197
69	128	135	142	149	155	162	169	176	182	189	196	203
70	132	139	146	153	160	167	174	181	188	195	202	209
71	136	143	150	157	165	172	179	186	193	200	208	215
72	140	147	154	162	169	177	184	191	199	206	213	221
73	144	151	159	166	174	182	189	197	204	212	219	227
74	148	155	163	171	179	186	194	202	210	218	225	233
75	152	160	168	176	184	192	200	208	216	224	232	240
76	156	164	172	180	189	197	205	213	221	230	238	246

BMI	31	32	33	34	35	36	37	38	39	40	41	42
Height (inches)						Body Weight (pounds)						
58	148	153	158	162	167	172	177	181	186	191	196	201
59	153	158	163	168	173	178	183	188	193	198	203	208
60	158	163	168	174	179	184	189	194	199	204	209	215
61	164	169	174	180	185	190	195	201	206	211	217	222
62	169	175	180	186	191	196	202	207	213	218	224	229
63	175	180	186	191	197	203	208	214	220	225	231	237
64	180	186	192	197	204	209	215	221	227	232	238	244
65	186	192	198	204	210	216	222	228	234	240	246	252
66	192	198	204	210	216	223	229	235	241	247	253	260
67	198	204	211	217	223	230	236	242	249	255	261	268
68	203	210	216	223	230	236	243	249	256	262	269	276
69	209	216	223	230	236	243	250	257	263	270	277	284
70	216	222	229	236	243	250	257	264	271	278	285	292
71	222	229	236	243	250	257	265	272	279	286	293	301
72	228	235	242	250	258	265	272	279	287	294	302	309
73	235	242	250	257	265	272	280	288	295	302	310	318
74	241	249	256	264	272	280	287	295	303	311	319	326
75	248	256	264	272	279	287	295	303	311	319	327	335
76	254	263	271	279	287	295	304	312	320	328	336	344

BMI	43	44	45	46	47	48	49	50	51	52	53	54
Height (inches)						Body Weight (pounds)						
58	205	210	215	220	224	229	234	239	244	248	253	258
59	212	217	222	227	232	237	242	247	252	257	262	267
60	220	225	230	235	240	245	250	255	261	266	271	276
61	227	232	238	243	248	254	259	264	269	275	280	285
62	235	240	246	251	256	262	267	273	278	284	289	295
63	242	248	254	259	265	270	278	282	287	293	299	304
64	250	256	262	267	273	279	285	291	296	302	308	314
65	258	264	270	276	282	288	294	300	306	312	318	324
66	266	272	278	284	291	297	303	309	315	322	328	334
67	274	280	287	293	299	306	312	319	325	331	338	344
68	282	289	295	302	308	315	322	328	335	341	348	354
69	291	297	304	311	318	324	331	338	345	351	358	365
70	299	306	313	320	327	334	341	348	355	362	369	376
71	308	315	322	329	338	343	351	358	365	372	379	386
72	316	324	331	338	346	353	361	368	375	383	390	397
73	325	333	340	348	355	363	371	378	386	393	401	408
74	334	342	350	358	365	373	381	389	396	404	412	420
75	343	351	359	367	375	383	391	399	407	415	423	431
76	353	361	369	377	385	394	402	410	418	426	435	443

What are the types of human **body shapes**?

The best known example of body typing (classifying body shape in terms of physiological functioning, behavior, and disease resistance) was devised by American psychologist

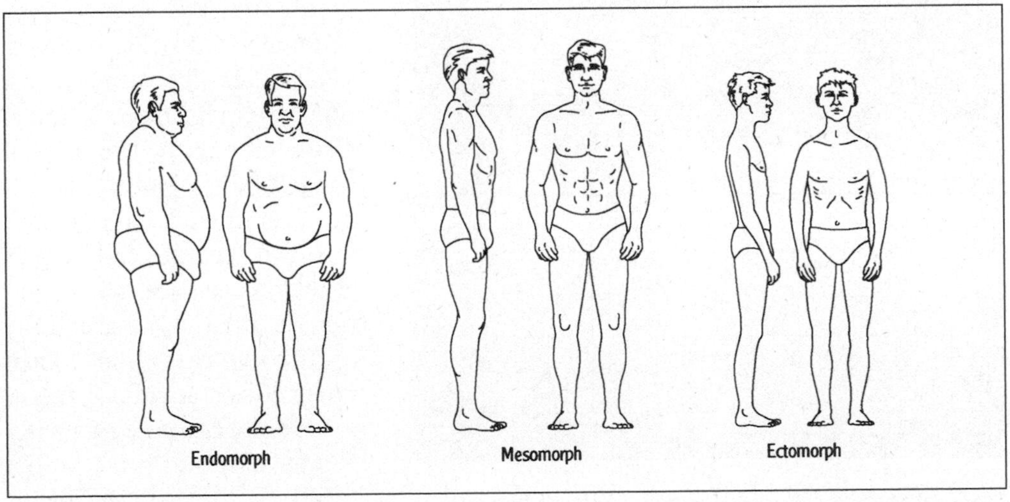

Classification of body types.

William Herbert Sheldon (1898-1977). Sheldon's system, known as somatotyping, distinguishes three types of body shapes, ignoring overall size: endomorph, mesomorph, and ectomorph. The extreme endomorph tends to be spherical: a round head, a large, fat abdomen, weak penguin-like arms and legs, with heavy upper arms and thighs but slender wrists and ankles. The extreme mesomorph is characterized by a massive cubical head, broad shoulders and chest, and heavy muscular arms and legs. The extreme ectomorph has a thin face, receding chin, high forehead, a thin, narrow chest and abdomen, and spindly arms and legs. In Sheldon's system there are mixed body types, determined by component ratings. Sheldon assumed a close relationship between body build and behavior and temperament. This system of body typing has many critics.

Chang and Eng Bunker, the original "Siamese twins" made famous by P.T. Barnum.

Who were the congenitally joined twins who gave rise to the term **Siamese twins**?

The term "Siamese twins" originated with the appearance of Chang and Eng Bunker (1811-1874), conjoined Chinese twins born in Siam (now Thailand), who were used as a circus attraction by P. T. Barnum.

Siamese twins are identical twins joined at some point of their bodies, most commonly at the hip, chest, abdomen, buttocks, or head. Like other identical twins, they originate from a single fertilized egg; in the case of congenitally joined twins, however, the egg fails to split into two separate cell masses at the proper time. The condition is relatively rare; only about 500 cases have been reported worldwide. Surgery to separate Siamese twins is a complex task, and often results in the death of one or both of the twins.

In addition to left- or right-handedness, what other left-right preferences do people have?

Most people have a preferred eye, ear, and foot. In one study, for example, 46 percent were strongly right-footed, while 3.9 percent were strongly left-footed; furthermore, 72 percent were strongly right-handed and 5.3 percent strongly left-handed. Estimates vary about the proportion of left-handers to right-handers, but it may be as high as one in ten. Some 90 percent of healthy adults use the right hand for writing; two-thirds favor the right hand for most activities requiring coordination and skill. There is no male-female difference in these proportions.

What causes **protruding ears**?

If a fold paralleling a part of the outer roll of the ear is sparse, but not absent, the ear will protrude. This trait usually runs in certain families.

Who was the world's **oldest person**?

French actress Jeanne Louise Calment (1875-1997) was the oldest person to ever live with concrete proof of her age. She died at the age of 122 years and 164 days. At the age of 114, she played herself in the film *Vincent and Me* (1990).

How many people living in the United States are **centenarians**?

The number of centenarians in the United States has increased steadily over the decades. In the most recent census (2000), there were 68,000 centenarians, up from 48,000 in 1995. Although the Census Bureau asks for age information in more than one way, the U.S. Census Bureau cautions that the figures may be somewhat skewed since birth certificates were not common until the 1930s.

BONES, MUSCLES, AND NERVES

How many bones are in the human body?

Babies are born with about 300 to 350 bones, but many of these fuse together between birth and maturity to produce an average adult total of 206. Bone counts vary according to the method used to count them, because some systems treat as multiple bones a structure that other systems treat as a single bone with multiple parts.

Location	Number
Skull	22
Ears (pair)	6
Vertebrae	26
Sternum	3
Throat	1
Pectoral girdle	4
Arms (pair)	60
Hip bones	2
Legs (pair)	58
TOTAL	*206*

What is the only **bone** in the human body that **does not touch another bone**?

The hyoid bone is the only bone that does not touch another bone. Found above the larynx, it anchors the tongue muscles. It is also usually broken when a person is hanged or strangled, and therefore will often figure in trials concerning such crimes.

What makes **knuckles crack**?

When a person pulls quickly on his or her finger, a vacuum is created in the joint space between the bones, displacing the fluid liquid normally found in the space. The popping sound occurs when the fluids rush back into the empty gap.

What is the **funny bone**?

The funny bone is not a bone but part of the ulnar nerve located at the the back of the elbow. A bump in this area can cause a tingling sensation or it can make the forearm feel temporarily numb.

What is the **hardest substance** in the body?

Tooth enamel is the hardest substance in the body. It is composed of 96 percent mineral salts and 4 percent organic matter and water.

What is the purpose of **primary teeth**?

Primary teeth (also known as baby, deciduous, temporary, or milk teeth, for their milk-white color) serve many of the same purposes as permanent teeth. They are needed for chewing, they make the face more attractive, and they are necessary for speech development. They also prepare the mouth for the permanent teeth by maintaining space for the permanent teeth to emerge in proper alignment. Each individual has 20 primary teeth followed by 32 permanent teeth.

How many **muscles** are in the human body?

There are about 656 muscles in the body, although some authorities make this figure even as high as 850 muscles. No exact figure is available because authorities disagree about which are separate muscles and which ones slip off larger ones. Also, there is a wide variability from one person to another, though the general plan remains the same.

Muscles are used in three body systems. The skeletal muscles move various parts of the body, are striped or striated fibers, and are called voluntary muscles because the person controls their use. The second system includes smooth muscles found in the stomach and intestinal walls, vein and artery walls, and in various internal organs. Called involuntary muscles, they are not generally controlled by the person. The last are the cardiac muscles, or the heart muscles, containing striped and involuntary muscles.

Which **muscle** is the **most variable** among humans?

The platysma muscle in the side of the neck is probably the most variable. It can cover the whole region in some people while in others it is straplike or in a few situations it is missing completely.

What is the **longest muscle** in the human body?

The longest muscle is the sartorius, which runs from the waist to the knee. Its purpose is to flex the hip and knee. The largest muscle is the gluteus maximus (buttock muscle), which moves the thighbone away from the body and straightens out the hip joint.

What are the **hamstring muscles**?

There are three hamstring muscles, located at the back of the thigh. They flex the leg on the thigh, as in the process of kneeling.

Why does excessive exercise cause **muscles** to become **stiff** and **sore**?

During vigorous exercise, the circulatory system cannot supply oxygen to muscle fibers quickly enough. In the absence of oxygen, the muscle cells begin to produce lactic acid, which accumulates in the muscle. It is this build-up of lactic acid that causes soreness and stiffness.

How many **muscles** does it take to produce a **smile** and a **frown**?

Seventeen muscles are used in smiling. The average frown uses 43.

What is the name of the small fleshy mass hanging from the **back of the mouth**?

The uvula is a small, soft structure, hanging from the free edge of the soft palate. It is composed of muscle, connective tissue, and mucous membrane.

How much **force** does a **human bite** generate?

All the jaw muscles working together can close the teeth with a force as great as 55 pounds (25 kilograms) on the incisors or 200 pounds (90.7 kilograms) on the molars. A force as great as 268 pounds (122 kilograms) for molars has been reported.

What is the **largest nerve** in the body?

The sciatic nerve is the largest in the human body—about as thick as a lead pencil—0.78 inch (1.98 centimeters). It is a broad, flat nerve composed of fibers that run from the spinal cord to the back of each leg.

ORGANS AND GLANDS

What is the **largest organ** in the human body?

The largest and heaviest human organ is the skin, with a total surface area of about 20 square feet (1.9 square meters) for an average person or 25 square feet (2.3 square meters) for a large person; it weighs 5.6 pounds (2.7 kilograms) on average. Although generally it is not thought of as an organ, medically it is. An organ is a collection of various tissues integrated into a distinct structural unit and performing specific functions.

What is the basic unit of the **brain**?

Neurons are the nerve cells that are the major constituent of the brain. At birth the brain has the maximum number of neurons—20 billion to 200 billion neurons. Thousands are lost daily, never to be replaced and apparently not missed, until the cumulative loss builds up in very old age.

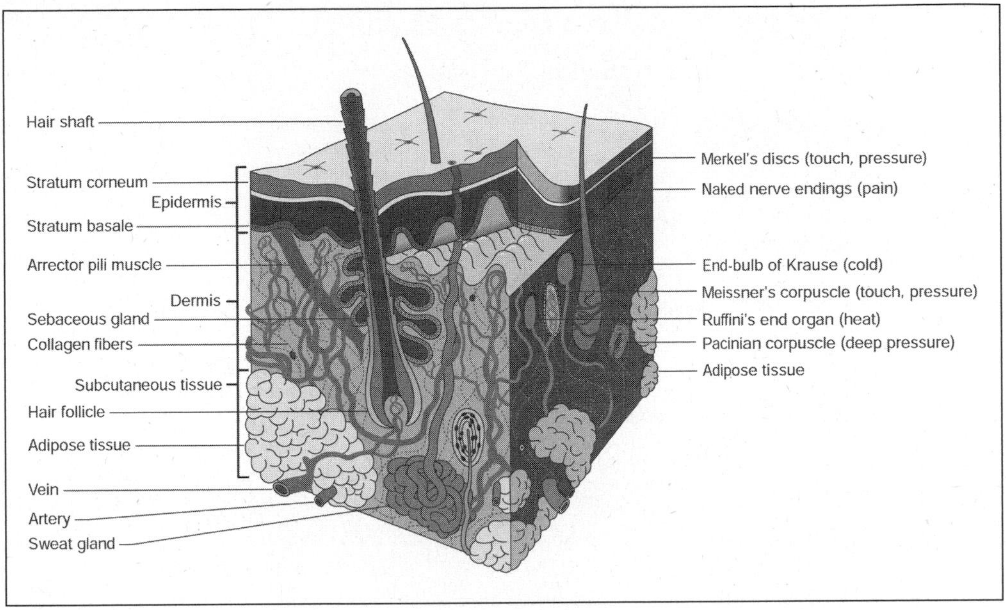

A cross section of the skin. Sensory structures are labeled on the right.

What is the average **weight** of the human **brain**?

The average human brain weighs three pounds (1.36 kilograms). The average female brain capacity is 79.3 cubic inches, slightly smaller than the male brain of 88.5 cubic inches. The largest human brains may be twice those of average size, but size has no relevance to brain performance.

How hard does the **heart** work?

The heart squeezes out about two ounces (71 grams) of blood at every beat and daily pumps at least 2,500 gallons (9,450 liters) of blood. On the average, the adult heart beats 70 to 75 times a minute. The rate of the heartbeat is determined in part by the size of the organism. Generally, the smaller the size, the faster the heartbeat. Thus women's hearts beat six to eight beats per minute faster than men's hearts do. At birth the heart of a baby can beat as fast as 130 times per minute.

How much air does a person breathe **in a lifetime**?

During his or her life, the average person will breathe about 75 million gallons (284 million liters) of air. Per minute, the human body needs two gallons (7.5 liters) of air when lying down, four gallons (15 liters) when sitting, six gallons (23 liters) when walking, and 12 gallons (45 liters) or more when running.

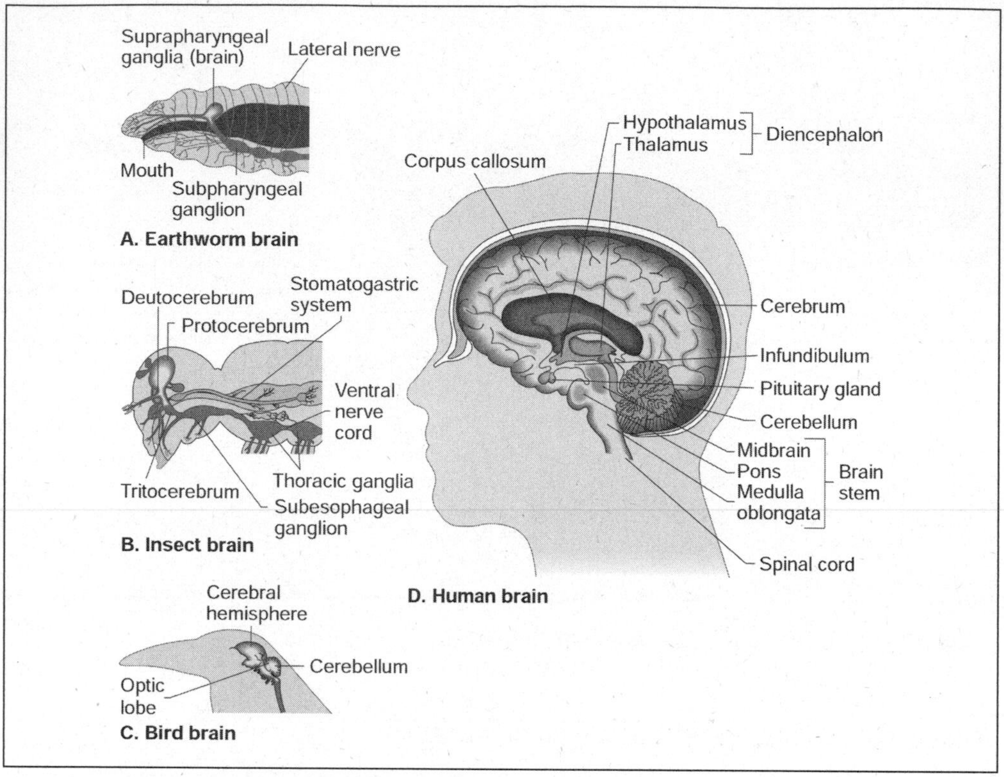

A comparison of the brains of an earthworm, an insect, a bird, and a human.

Are the **lungs** identical?

No, the right lung is shorter than the left by one inch (2.5 centimeters); however, its total capacity is greater. The right lung has three lobes, the left lung has two.

How is there enough room in the **chest cavity** to accommodate a pair of lungs filled with air?

A pair of lungs filled with air contains the same volume of air as in eight large soda bottles—more than 1.5 gallons (6 liters). In order to accommodate this volume, muscles raise and expand the rib cage while the diaphragm, a domed muscular sheet under the lungs, flattens with each breath inhaled.

What causes **hiccups** and how can they be cured?

Hiccupping is the involuntary contraction of the diaphragm. When the diaphragm contracts, the vocal cords close quickly, causing the familiar noise associated with hiccups.

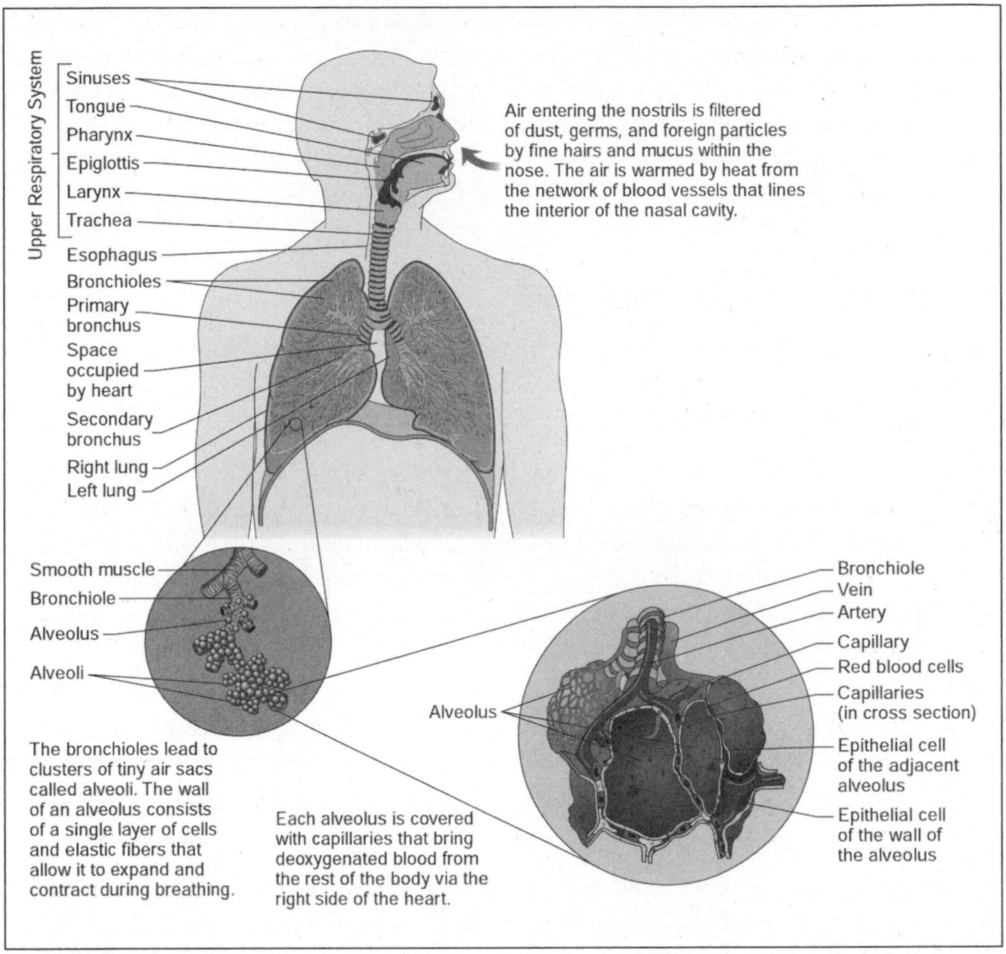

The human respiratory system.

Hiccups help the stomach get rid of a bit of gas, relieve the esophagus of an irritation, or resolves a temporary loss of coordination between the nerves controlling the movement of the diaphragm. A bout of hiccups can be brought on by eating or drinking too fast or fatigue or nervousness. Although hiccups generally go away on their own after a few minutes, several remedies have been recommended to cure one of hiccups: a loud distraction to scare the sufferer of hiccups, swallowing a spoonful of sugar, blowing into a paper bag, or drinking from the opposite side of the glass all have their followers.

What was the likely **purpose** of the human **appendix**?

Experts can only theorize on its use. It may have had the same purpose it does in present-day herbivores, where it harbors colonies of bacteria that help in the digestion of cellulose in plant material. Another theory suggests that tonsils and the appendix might manufacture the antibody-producing white blood cells called B lymphocytes; however, B lymphocytes could also be produced by the bone marrow. The third theory is that the appendix may "attract" body infections to localize the infection in one spot that is not critical to body functioning. The earliest surgical removal of the appendix was by Claudries Amyand (1680-1740) in England in 1736.

What are the seven **endocrine glands**?

The major endocrine glands include the pituitary, thyroid, parathyroids, adrenals, pancreas, testes, and ovaries. These glands secrete hormones into the blood system, which generally stimulate some change in metabolic activity:

Pituitary—secretes ACTH to stimulate the adrenal cortex, which produces aldosterone to control sodium and potassium reabsorption by the kidneys; FSH to stimulate gonad function and prolactin to stimulate milk secretion of breasts; TSH to stimulate thyroid gland to produce thyroxin; LH to stimulate ovulation in females and testerone production in males; GH to stimulate general growth. Stores oxytocin for uterine contraction.

Thyroid gland—secretes triiodothyronine (T3) and thyroxine (T4) to stimulate metabolic rate, especially in growth and development, and secretes calcitonin to lower blood-calcium levels.

Parathyroids—secrete hormone PTH to increase blood-calcium levels; stimulates calcium reabsorption in kidneys.

Adrenals—secrete epinephrine and norepinephrine to help the body cope with stress, and raise blood pressure, heart rate, metabolic rate, blood sugar levels, etc. Aldosterone secreted by the adrenal cortex maintains sodium-potassium balance in kidneys and cortisol helps the body adapt to stress, mobilizes fat, and raises blood sugar level.

Pancreas—secretes insulin to control blood sugar levels, stimulates glycogen production, fat storage, and protein synthesis. Glucagon secretion raises blood sugar level and mobilizes fat.

Ovaries and testes—secrete estrogens, progesterone, or testosterone to stimulate growth and reproductive processes.

Which **gland** is the **largest**?

The liver is the largest gland and the second largest organ after the skin. At 2.5 to 3.3 pounds (1.1 to 1.5 kilograms) the liver is seven times larger than it needs to be to perform its estimated 500 functions. It is the main chemical factory of the body. A ducted gland that produces bile to break down fats and reduce acidity in the digestive process, the liver is also a part of the circulatory system. It cleans poisons from the blood and regulates blood composition.

What regulates **body temperature** in humans?

The hypothalamus controls internal body temperature by responding to sensory impulses from temperature receptors in the skin and in the deep body regions. The hypothalamus establishes a "set point" for the internal body temperature, then constantly compares this with its own actual temperature. If the two do not match, the hypothalamus activates either temperature-decreasing or temperature-increasing procedures to bring them into alignment.

BODY FLUIDS

What is the **normal pH** of blood, urine, and saliva?

Normal pH of arterial blood is 7.4; pH of venous blood is about 7.35. Normal urine pH averages about 6.0. Saliva has a pH between 6.0 and 7.4.

How similar are **seawater** and **blood**?

Component	Seawater (grams/liter)	Blood (grams/liter)
Na (sodium)	10.7	3.2-3.4
K (potassium)	0.39	0.15-0.21
Ca (calcium)	0.42	0.09-0.11
Mg (magnesium)	1.34	0.012-0.036
Cl (chloride)	19.3	3.5-3.8
SO_4 (sulfate)	2.69	0.16-0.34
CO_3 (carbonate)	0.073	1.5-1.9
Protein		70.0

How does the body introduce **oxygen** to the **blood** and where does this happen?

Blood entering the right side of the heart (right auricle or atrium) contains carbon dioxide, a waste product of the body. The blood travels to the right ventricle, which pushes it through the pulmonary artery to the lungs. In the lungs, the carbon dioxide is removed and oxygen is added to the blood. Then the blood travels through the pulmonary vein carrying the fresh oxygen to the left side of the heart, first to the left auricle, where it goes through a one-way valve into the left ventricle, which must push the oxygenated blood to all portions of the body (except the lungs) through a network of arteries and capillaries. The left ventricle must contract with six times the force of the right ventricle, so its muscle wall is twice as thick as the right.

How much **blood** is in the average human body?

A man weighing 154 pounds (70 kilograms) would have about 5.5 quarts (5.2 liters) of blood. A woman weighing 110 pounds (50 kilograms) would have about 3.5 quarts (3.3 liters).

How many miles of **blood vessels** are contained in the body?

If they could be laid end to end, the blood vessels would span about 60,000 miles (96,500 kilometers).

What is the **largest artery** in the human body?

The aorta is the largest artery in the human body.

Why do various parts of the body **fall asleep**?

The sensation of "pins and needles" when an arm or leg "falls asleep" is caused by impaired blood circulation to that limb.

Which of the **major blood types** are the most common in the United States?

Blood type	Frequency in U.S.
O+	37.4%
O-	6.6%
A+	35.7%
A-	6.3%
B+	8.5%
B-	1.5%
AB+	3.4%
AB-	0.6%

In the world, the preponderance of one blood group varies greatly by locality. Group O is generally the most common (46 percent), but in some areas Group A predominates.

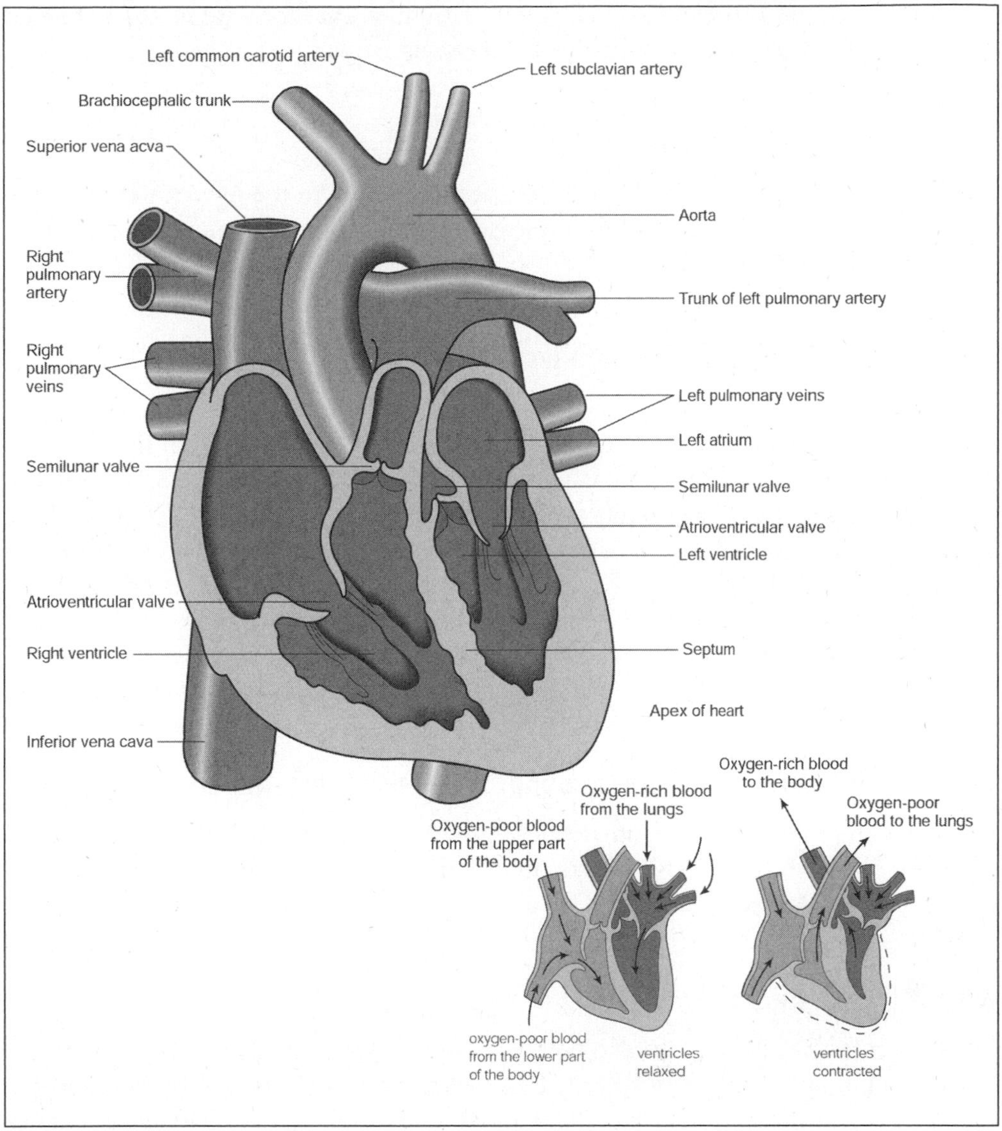

A cutaway of the human heart (top) and a diagram showing blood flow in the heart during diastole (relaxation) and systole (contraction).

Who discovered the **ABO system** of typing blood?

The Austrian physician Karl Landsteiner (1868-1943) discovered the ABO system of blood types in 1909. Landsteiner had investigated why blood transfused from one individual was sometimes successful and other times resulted in the death of the patient. He theorized that there must be several different blood types. A person with one type of blood will have antibodies to the antigens in the blood type they do not have. If a transfusion occurs between two individuals with different blood types, the red blood cells will clump together, blocking the blood vessels.

How often can a person **donate blood**?

Blood is one of the most easily donated tissues. According to the American Red Cross, a person in good health who weights at least 110 pounds (50 kilograms) can donate a unit of blood every eight weeks.

What are **apheresis** and **plateletpheresis**?

Although most blood is donated as whole blood, it is also possible to donate only a portion of blood using a technique called apheresis. Blood is drawn from the vein of a donor into an apheresis instrument, which separates the blood into different portions by centrifugation. By appropriately adjusting the instrument, a selected portion of the blood, such as the platelets, can be recovered, while the rest of the blood is returned to the donor either into the same vein or into a vein in the other arm. This process takes more time than whole blood donation, but the yield of platelets is much greater. Platelets collected by apheresis are particularly useful for patients who require numerous platelet transfusions, for example cancer patients who have received chemotherapy.

Which blood type is the **universal donor** and which is the **universal recipient**?

Persons with blood type O are universal donors. They are able to donate blood to anyone. Persons with blood type AB are universal recipients. They are able to receive blood from any donor.

What is the **Rh factor**?

In addition to the ABO system of blood types, blood types can also be grouped by the Rhesus factor, or Rh factor, an inherited blood characteristic. Discovered independently in 1939 by Philip Levine (1900-1987) and R. E. Stetson and in 1940 by Karl Landsteiner (1868-1943) and A. S. Weiner, the Rh system classifies blood as either having the Rh factor or lacking it. Pregnant women are carefully screened for the Rh factor. If a mother is found to be Rh-negative, the father is also screened. Parents with incompatible Rh factors can lead to potentially fatal blood problems in newborn infants. The condition can be treated with a series of blood transfusions.

What is the amount of **carbon dioxide** found in normal blood?

Carbon dioxide normally ranges from 19 to 50 millimeters per liter in arterial blood and 22 to 30 millimeters per liter in venous blood.

Which **blood type** is the rarest?

The rarest blood type is Bombay blood (subtype h-h), found only in a Czechoslovakian nurse in 1961 and in a brother and sister named Jalbert living in Massachusetts in 1968.

What are the **blood group combinations** that can normally be used to prove that a man is not the father of a particular child?

If the mother is	and the child is	the father can be	but not
O	O	O, A, or B	AB
O	A	A or AB	O or B
O	B	B or AB	O or A
A	O	O, A, or B	AB
A	A	any group	
A	B	B or AB	O or A
A	AB	B or AB	O or A
B	O	O, A, or B	AB
B	B	any group	
B	A	A or AB	O or B
B	AB	A or AB	O or B
AB	AB	A, B, or AB	O

No child can acquire a gene, and consequently a blood grouping, if it is not possessed by either parent.

How do **wounds heal**?

Damage to tissue, such as a cut in the skin, begins to heal with the formation of a sticky lump known as a blood clot. Blood clots prevent blood and other fluids from leaking out. Microscopic sticky threads of the clotting protein fibrin make a tangled mesh that traps blood cells. Within a short time the clot begins to take shape, harden, and become more solid. The clot turns into a scab as it dries and hardens. Skin cells beneath the scab multiply to repair the damage. When the scab falls off the wound will be healed.

What percent of human body weight is **water**?

The human body is 61.8 percent water by weight. Protein accounts for 16.6 percent, fat 14.9 percent, and nitrogen 3.3 percent. Other elements are present in lesser amounts.

Why do **eyes tear** when we work with **onions**?

When an onion is cut, the pierced cells release a sulfur compound, thio-propanal-s-oxide, through a series of rapid chemical reactions. This substance is irritating to the eyes.

What causes people to **sweat** when they eat **spicy foods**?

The chemical capsaicin, a component of spicy foods, causes sweating by stimulating nerve endings in the mouth and tongue that, normally, only respond to a rise in body temperature. As a result, the brain receives a false signal that body temperature has risen, and in turn launches the chain of physiological events that leads to facial sweating.

Why do some people experience a **runny nose** while **eating**?

Called prandial rhinorrhea, this condition occurs when eating stimulates the autonomic nervous system to release the compound acetylcholine. This in turn prompts the increased production of saliva, stomach acid, and nasal mucus. Usually, the spicier the meal, the greater the reaction.

Does your **heart stop beating** when you **sneeze**?

The heart does not stop when you sneeze. Sneezing, however, does affect the cardiovascular system. It causes a change in pressure inside the chest. This change in pressure affects the blood flow to the heart, which in turn affects the heart's rhythm. Therefore, a sneeze does produce a harmless delay between one heartbeat and the next, often misinterpreted as a "skipped beat."

SKIN, HAIR, AND NAILS

How much skin does an average person have?

The average human body is covered with about 20 square feet (two square meters) of skin. Weighing six pounds (2.7 kilograms), the skin is composed of two main layers: the epidermis (outer layer) and the dermis (inner layer). The epidermis layer is replaced continually as new cells, produced in the stratum basale, mature, and are pushed to the surface by the newer cells beneath; the entire epidermis is replaced in about 27 days. The dermis, the lower layer, contains nerve endings, sweat glands, hair follicles, and blood vessels. The upper portion of the dermis has small, fingerlike projections called "papillae," which extend into the upper layer. The patterns of ridges and grooves visible on the skin of the soles, palms, and fingertips are formed from the tops of the dermal papillae. The capillaries in these papillae deliver oxygen and nutrients to the epidermis cells and also function in temperature regulation.

Who first used **fingerprints** as a means of identification?

It is generally acknowledged that Francis Galton (1822-1911) was the first to classify fingerprints. However, his basic ideas were further developed by Sir Edward Henry

How many hairs does the average person have on his or her head?

The amount of hair covering varies from one individual to another. An average person has about 100,000 hairs on their scalp (blondes 140,000, brunettes 155,000, and redheads only 85,000). Most people shed between 50 to 100 hairs daily.

(1850-1931), who devised a system based on the pattern of the thumb print. In 1901 in England, Henry established the first fingerprint bureau with Scotland Yard called the Fingerprint Branch.

Do identical **twins** have the **same fingerprints**?

No. Even identical twins have differences in their fingerprints, which, though subtle, can be discerned by experts.

Are **freckles** dangerous?

Freckles, tan or brown spots on the skin, are small areas of increased skin pigment or melanin. Freckles are signs of sun damage to the skin. There is a genetic tendency to freckle, and often many members of the same family will have freckles. They are usually on the face, arms and other parts of the body that are exposed to the sun. Freckles appear in childhood, fade during the winter months, and reappear in the summer. Freckles themselves pose no health risks, but they are a marker of increased risk for all types of skin cancer.

What is the purpose of **goose-bumps**?

The puckering of the skin that takes place when goose-flesh is formed is the result of contraction of the muscle fibers in the skin. This muscular activity will produce more heat, and raise the temperature of the body.

How much does human **hair grow** in a year?

Each hair grows about nine inches (23 centimeters) every year.

Why does **hair turn gray** as part of the aging process?

The pigment in hair, as well as in the skin, is called melanin. There are two types of melanin: eumelanin, which is dark brown or black, and pheomelanin, which is reddish yellow. Both are made by a type of cell called a melanocyte that resides in the hair bulb and along the bottom of the outer layer of skin, or epidermis. The melanocytes pass this pigment to adjoining epidermal cells called keratinocytes, which produce the protein keratin—hair's chief component. When the keratinocytes undergo their scheduled death, they retain the melanin. Thus, the pigment that is visible in the hair and in the skin lies in these dead keratinocyte bodies. Gray hair is simply hair with less melanin, and white hair has no melanin at all. It remains unclear as to how hair loses its pigment. In the early stages of graying, the melanocytes are still present but inactive. Later they seem to decrease in number. Genes control this lack of deposition of melanin. In some families, many members' hair turns white they are still in their twenties. Generally speaking, among Caucasians 50 percent are gray by age 50. There is, however, wide variation.

Why is some hair **curly** while some hair is **straight**?

The shape of the hair follicle determines how wavy a hair will be. Round follicles produce straight hair. Oval follicles produce wavy hair. Flat follies produce curly hair.

What information can a **forensic scientist** determine from a **human hair**?

A single strand of human hair can identify the age and sex of the owner, drugs and narcotics the individual has taken, and, through DNA evaluation and sample comparisons, from whose head the hair came.

Do the **nails and hair** of a dead person **continue to grow**?

No. Between 12 and 18 hours after death, the body begins to dry out. That causes the tips of the fingers and the skin of the face to shrink, creating the illusion that the nails and hair have grown.

How fast do **fingernails** grow?

Healthy nails grow about 0.12 inch (3mm) each month or 1.4 inches (3.5 cm) each year. The middle fingernail grows the fastest, because the longer the finger the faster its nail growth.

SENSES AND SENSE ORGANS

What are the **floaters** that move around on the eye?

Floaters are semi-transparent specks perceived to be floating in the field of vision. Some originate with red blood cells that have leaked out of the retina. The blood cells swell into spheres, some forming strings, and float around the areas of the retina. Others are shadows cast by the microscopic structures in the vitreous humor, a jellylike substructure located behind the retina. A sudden appearance of a cloud of dark floaters, if accompanied by bright light flashes, could indicate retinal detachment.

What is the difference in the functions of the **rods and cones** found in the eyes?

Rods and cones contain photoreceptors that convert light first to chemical energy and then into electrical energy for transmission to the vision centers of the brain via the optic nerve. Rods are specialized for vision in dim light; they cannot detect color, but they are the first receptors to detect movement and register shapes. There are about 126 million rods in each eye. Cones provide acute vision, functioning best in bright daylight. They allow us to see colors and fine detail. Cones are divided into three different types, which absorb wavelengths in the short (blue), middle (green), and long (red) ranges. There are about six million cones in each eye.

What are **phosphenes**?

If the eyes are shut tightly, the lights seen are phosphenes. Technically, the luminous impressions are due to the excitation of the retina caused by pressure on the eyeball.

What does it mean to have **20/20 vision**?

Many people think that with 20/20 vision the eyesight is perfect, but it actually means that the eye can see clearly at 20 feet (six meters) what a normal eye can see clearly at that distance. Some people can see even better—20/15, for example. With their eyes, they can view objects from 20 feet (six meters) away with the same sharpness that a normal-sighted person would have to move in to 15 feet (4.5 meters) to achieve.

Are more people **nearsighted** or **farsighted**?

About 30 percent of Americans are nearsighted to some degree. About 60 percent are farsighted. If the light rays entering the pupils of the eye converge exactly on the retina, then a sharply focused picture is relayed to the brain. But if the eyeball is shaped differently, the focal point of the light rays is too short or too long, and vision is

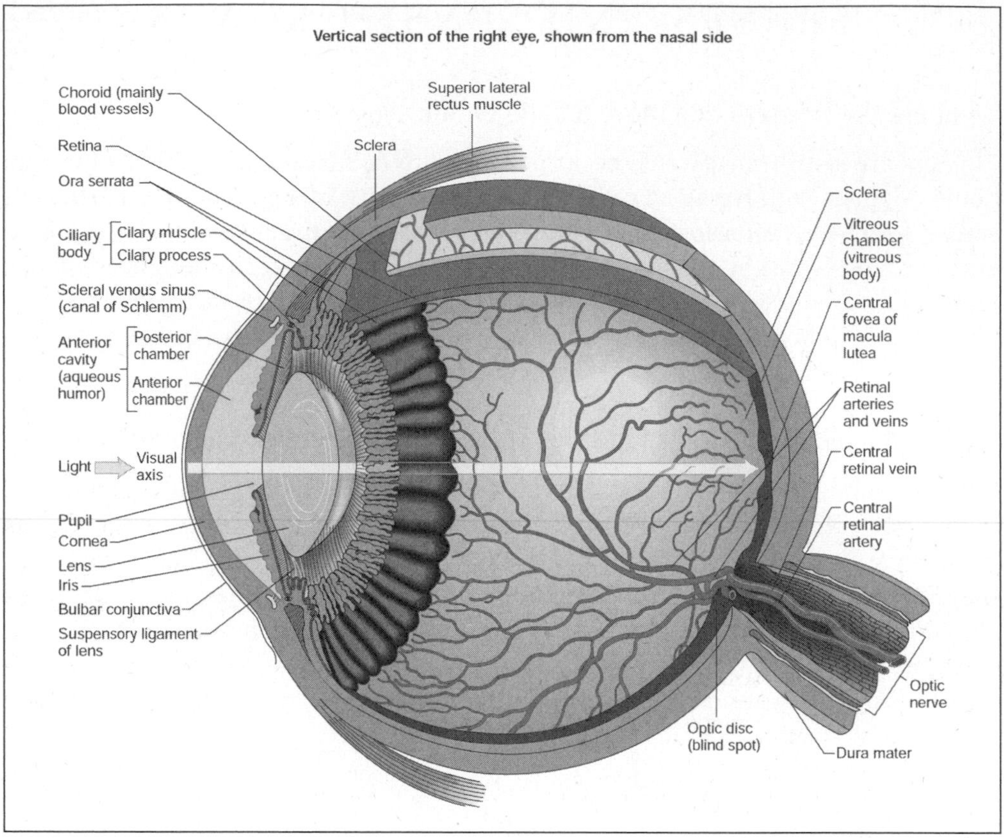

The human eye.

blurred. Convex lenses for farsightedness correct a too-long focal point. Concave lenses correct nearsightedness when the focal point of light rays, being too short, converge in front of the retina.

Who invented **bifocal lenses**?

The original bifocal lens was invented in 1784 by Benjamin Franklin (1706-1790). At that time, the two lenses were joined in a metallic frame. In 1899, J. L. Borsch welded the two lenses together. One-part bifocal lenses were developed by Bentron and Emerson in 1910 for the Carl Zeiss Company.

Why do all **newborn babies** have **blue eyes**?

The color of the iris gives the human eye its color. The amount of dark pigment, melanin, in the iris is what determines its color. In newborns the pigment is concentrated in the folds of the iris. When a baby is a few months old, the melanin moves to the surface of the iris and gives the baby his or her permanent eye color.

What is the **"sand"** that gathers in the **corners of our eyes** when we sleep?

The "sand" is dried mucus. Glands near the eye secrete the mucus to help the eye retain moisture and protect it against foreign particles. During sleep, the closed eyelids retain the moisture of the eyes, and the mucus may gather in the corners and dry out. When a person wakes, the dried mucus may feel like sand in the eyes.

How do **colors** affect one's **moods**?

According to the American Institute for Biosocial Research, "colors are electromagnetic wave bands of energy." Each color has its own wavelength. The wave bands stimulate chemicals in your eye, sending messages to the pituitary and pineal glands. These master endocrine glands regulate hormones and other physiological systems in the body. Stimulated by response to colors, glandular activities can alter moods, speed up heart rates, and increase brain activity.

How does an individual maintain their **balance**?

The ability to maintain one's balance depends on information the brain receives from three different sources—the inner ears, the special sensory receptors in muscles, and joints of the body and the eyes. The inner ears contain two sets of special vestibular sensory organs that are important for balance. Semicircular canals sense rotations of the head in space, and otolith organs sense both gravity and linear movements of the head in space. Sensory information from the muscles and joints gives information about the position of joints and forces acting on the body. The visual system gives important information about which direction is "up" and about movements of the head; this is why an OmniMax theater can give the illusion that you are moving. These signals are processed by the brain to control balance, posture, and a sense of stability.

What are the **three bones** in the **ear** called?

The three bones are the malleus, which means hammer; incus, which means anvil; and stapes, which means stirrup. The bones look somewhat like the objects for which they are named. The stapes is the smallest bone in the body, measuring 1.02 to 1.34 inches (2.6 to 3.4 centimeters) and weighing 0.00071 to 0.0015 ounce (0.002 to 0.004 gram). These three tiny bones in the middle ear conduct sound vibrations from the outer to inner ear.

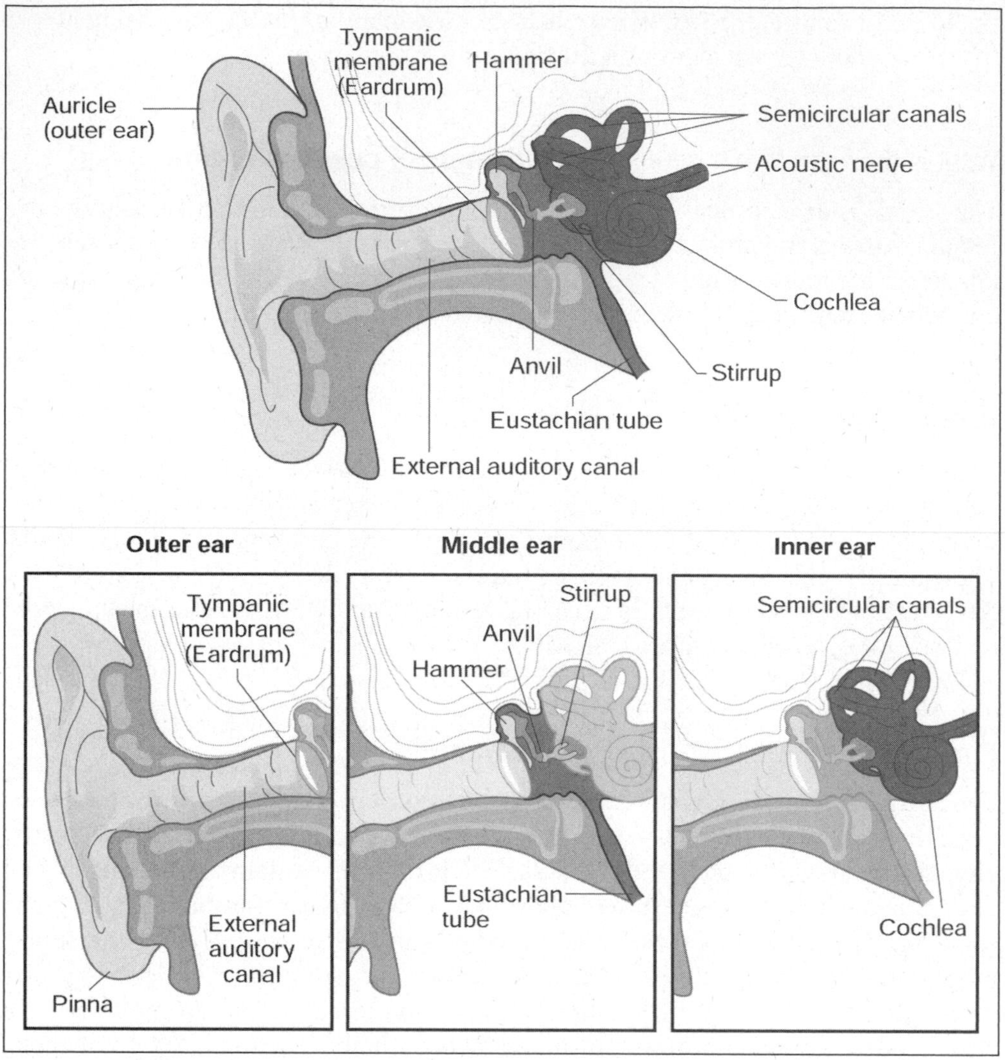

The anatomy of the human ear.

How broad is the **range of sound frequency** that most people can hear?

Most people can hear sounds with frequencies from about 20 to 20,000 hertz. A hertz is a measure of sound frequencies. Environmental sound is measured in decibels to calculate its loudness. Hearing starts with zero decibels; every increase of 10 units is equivalent to a tenfold increase. In comparison, leaves rustling = 10 decibels, a typical office is 50 decibels, pneumatic drills = 80 decibels, riveting machines = 110 decibels, and a jet takeoff at 200 feet (61 meters) measures 120 decibels. Noise above 70 decibels is harmful to hearing; noise at 140 decibels is physically painful.

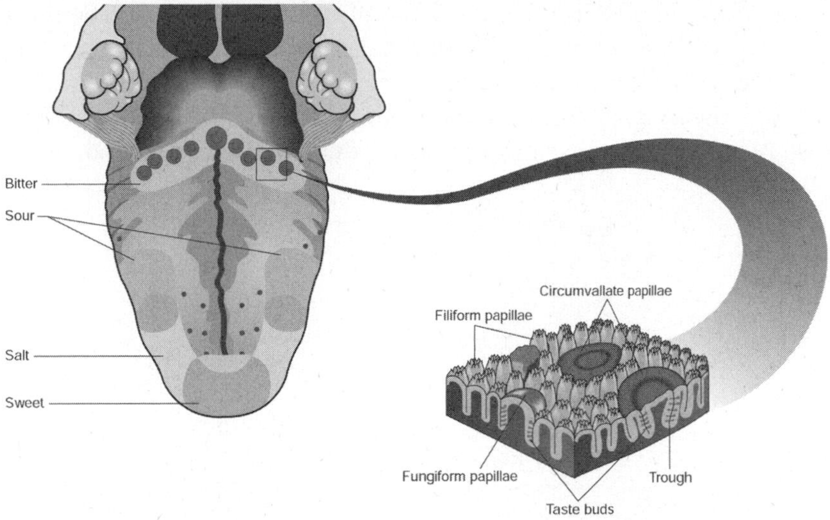

Taste regions of the tongue (left) and taste bud anatomy (right).

Why do humans **get old**?

Solving this question—along with finding ways to stay forever young—has vexed mankind since time immemorial. Scientists have tried to explain why people age with two broad theoretical directions: programmed theories and error theories. Programmed theories state that aging is "programmed" into humankind: we have a biological clock that simply runs down according to a set timeline. Examples of programmed theories include the Programmed Senescence theory, which holds that aging happens because of the switching off and on of genes, and the Immunological Theory, which holds that the human immune system declines at a set pace, leading to defenselessness from illnesses. Error theories define aging according to unavoidable failures and accumulating damages: we simply wear out. Examples of error theories include Somatic Mutation, which holds that genetic mutations cause cells to fail, and the Free Radical Theory, which holds that a buildup of damage by oxygen radicals created during normal metabolism causes cells to stop working.

Advances in society and knowledge have ameliorated aging's effects by allowing people to live longer. Average life expectancy in the United States has grown from about 47 years in 1900 to about 79 years at the beginning of 2000. But nothing, unfortunately, has enabled people to stop growing old.

What are the primary **sensations** of **taste**?

The four primary categories are sweet, sour, salty, and bitter. The sensitivity and location of these areas on the tongue varies from person to person. Some of the nine thousand taste buds are located in the other areas of the mouth as well. The lips (usually very salt-sensitive), the inner cheeks, the underside of the tongue, the back of the throat, and the roof of the mouth are some examples. The sense of taste is intimately associated with the sense of smell, so that foods taste bland to someone suffering from a cold. Also related are the appearance, texture, and temperature of food.

HEALTH AND MEDICINE

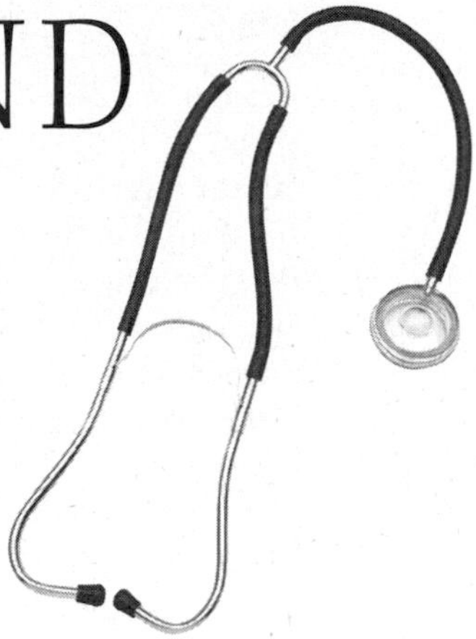

HEALTH HAZARDS, RISKS, ETC.

Which **risk factors** affect one's health?

Such characteristics as age, gender, work, family history, behavior, and body chemistry are some of the factors to consider when deciding whether one is at risk for various conditions. Some risk factors are statistical, describing trends among large groups of people but not giving information about what will happen to individuals. Other risk factors might be described as causative—exposure to them has a direct effect on whether or not the person will become sick.

What are the leading **causes of stress**?

In 1967, when they conducted a study of the correlation between significant life events and the onset of illness, Dr. Thomas H. Holmes and Dr. Richard H. Rahe from the University of Washington compiled a chart of the major causes of stress with assigned point values. They published their findings on stress effects as "The Social Readjustment Scale," printed in *The Journal of Psychosomatic Research*. The researchers calculated that a score of 150 points indicated a 50/50 chance of the respondent developing an illness or a "health change." A score of 300 would increase the risk to 90 percent. This type of rating scale continues to be used to help individuals determine their composite stress level within the last year. Since 1967 other researchers have adapted and modified the checklist, but the basic checklist has remained constant. Of course, many factors enter into an individual's response to a particular event, so this scale, partially represented below, can only be used as a guide.

Event	Point value
Death of spouse	100
Divorce	73
Marital separation	65
Jail term or death of close family member	63
Personal injury or illness	53
Marriage	50
Fired at work	47
Marital reconciliation or retirement	45
Pregnancy	40
Change in financial state	38
Death of close friend	37
Change in employment	36
Foreclosure of mortgage or loan	30
Outstanding personal achievement	28
Trouble with boss	23
Change in work hours or conditions or change in residence or schools	20
Vacation	13
Christmas	12
Minor violations of the law	11

What are the **odds against** being **struck by lightning**?

The National Oceanic and Atmospheric Administration estimates the odds of being struck by lightning at one in 700,000. However, the odds drop to one in 240,000 based on the number of unreported lightning strikes. The odds of being struck by lightning in one's lifetime are 1 in 3,000.

What are the **odds against** being **killed on a motorcycle**?

1,250 to one against.

Can **owning a pet** be beneficial to your health?

As a result of several studies, researchers now believe that regular contact with pets can reduce heart rate, blood pressure, and levels of stress. In a study of 93 heart attack patients, only one of 18 pet owners died compared to one of three patients who did not have pets. Pets offer constancy, stability, comfort, security, affection, and intimacy.

What are the **leading causes of death** in the United States?

In 2005, The U.S. Centers for Disease Control reported that heart disease continues to be the leading cause of death in America. Below are the ten major causes of death in the United States as of 2005.

How many children sustain head injuries while riding bicycles?

Approximately 140,000 children are treated in emergency rooms for head injuries sustained while riding bikes each year. Many bike-related injuries and deaths could be avoided if riders wore helmets properly. Wearing a bike helmet reduces the risk of brain injury by as much as 88 percent and reduces the risk of injury to the face by 65 percent.

Rank	Cause of Death	Number
1	Heart disease	652,091
2	Cancer	559,312
3	Stroke	143,579
4	Chronic lower respiratory disease	130,933
5	Accidents	117,809
6	Diabetes	75,119
7	Alzheimerís disease	71,599
8	Influenza/Pneumonia	63,001
9	Kidney disease	43,901
10	Septicemia	34,136

Did raising the **speed limit** on rural interstate highways from 55 to 65 miles per hour have an effect on the **accident and death rate**?

There was an estimated 20 percent to 30 percent increase in deaths on those roads and a 40 percent increase in serious injuries when the speed limit was raised from 55 miles per hour (88.5 kilometers per hour) to 65 miles per hour (104.5 kilometers per hour) on rural interstate highways.

Which **sport** has the highest rate of **injuries** and what kind of injury is most common?

Football players suffer more injuries than other athletes, collectively. They have 12 times as many injuries as do basketball players, who have the next highest rate of injury. Knee problems are the most common type of injury, with two-thirds of basketball players' injuries and one-third of football players' injuries being knee-related.

Which direction of impact results in the greatest number of fatalities in **automobile crashes**?

Frontal crashes are responsible for the largest percentage of fatalities in passenger cars.

What are the most frequent **sports-related injuries** requiring visits to the emergency room for **children** and **young adults**?

Injuries associated with basketball and cycling are the most frequent sports-related injuries requiring visits to emergency rooms among children and young adults.

Approximate Number of Children's Sports Injuries per Year Requiring Visits to Emergency Rooms

Sport	Number of Emergency Room Visits
Basketball and cycling*	900,000*
Football	250,000
Baseball	250,000
Soccer	100,000
Ice or roller skating and skateboarding	150,000
Gymnastics and cheerleading	146,000
Playground injuries	137,000
Water and snow sports	100,000

*These sports are not necessarily more dangerous; there are probably more children and young adults engaging in these activities than in other sports.

Sports-related injuries are more likely to be to the brain or skull and upper and lower extremities, more likely to be a fracture, strain or sprain, and more likely to have diagnostic and therapeutic services provided, especially orthopedic care.

Why is exposure to **asbestos** a health hazard?

Exposure to asbestos has long been known to cause asbestosis. This is a chronic, restrictive lung disease caused by the inhalation of tiny mineral asbestos fibers that scar lung tissues. Asbestos has also been linked with cancers of the larynx, pharynx, oral cavity, pancreas, kidneys, ovaries, and gastrointestinal tract. The American Lung Association reports that prolonged exposure doubles the likelihood that a smoker will develop lung cancer. It takes cancer 15 to 30 years to develop from asbestos. Mesothelioma is a rare cancer affecting the surface lining of the pleura (lung) or peritoneum (abdomen) that generally spreads rapidly over large surfaces of either the thoracic or abdominal cavities. No effective treatment exists for mesothelioma.

Asbestos fibers were used in building materials between 1900 and the early 1970s as insulation for walls and pipes, as fireproofing for walls and fireplaces, in soundproofing and acoustic ceiling tiles, as a strengthener for vinyl flooring and joint compounds, and as a paint texturizer. Asbestos poses a health hazard only if the tiny fibers are released into the air, but this can happen with any normal fraying or cracking. Asbestos removal aggravates this normal process and multiplies the danger level—it should only be handled by a contractor trained in handling asbestos. Once released, the particles can hang suspended in the air for more than 20 hours.

Can **ozone** be harmful to humans?

Ozone (O_3) in the lower atmosphere contributes to air pollution. It is formed by chemical reactions between sunlight and oxygen in the air in the presence of impurities, such as those found in automobile exhaust. Ozone can damage rubber, plastic, and plant and animal tissue. Exposure to certain concentrations can cause headaches, burning eyes, and irritation of the respiratory tract in many individuals. Asthmatics and others with impaired respiratory systems are particularly susceptible. Exposure to low concentrations for only a few hours can significantly affect normal persons while exercising. Symptoms include chest pain, coughing, sneezing, and pulmonary congestion.

Why is **radon** a health hazard?

Radon is a colorless, odorless, tasteless, radioactive gaseous element produced by the decay of radium. It has three naturally occurring isotopes found in many natural materials, such as soil, rocks, well water, and building materials. Because the gas is continually released into the air, it makes up the largest source of radiation that humans receive. A 1999 National Academy of Sciences (NAS) report noted that radon was the second leading cause of lung cancer. It has been estimated that it may cause as much as 12 percent, or about 15,000 to 22,000 cases, of lung cancer deaths annually. Smokers seem to be at a higher risk than non-smokers. The U.S. Environmental Protection Agency (EPA) recommends that in radon testing the level should not be more than four picocuries per liter. The estimated national average is 1.5 picocuries per liter. Because EPA's "safe level" is equivalent to 200 chest X-rays per year, some experts believe that lower levels are appropriate. The American Society of Heating, Refrigeration, and Air-Conditioning Engineers (ASHRAE) recommends two picocuries/liter. The EPA estimates that nationally 8 percent to 12 percent of all houses are above the four picocuries/liter limit; whereas in another survey in 1987 it was estimated that 21 percent of homes were above this level.

How is human exposure to **radiation** measured?

The radiation absorbed dose (rad) and the roentgen equivalent man (rem) were used for many years to measure the amount and effect of ionizing radiation absorbed by humans. While officially replaced by the gray and the sievert, both are still used in many reference sources. The rad equals the energy absorption of 100 ergs per gram of irradiated material (an erg is a unit of work or energy). The rem is the absorbed dose of ionizing radiation that produces the same biological effect as one rad of X-rays or gamma rays (which are equal). The rem of X-rays and gamma rays is therefore equal to the rad; for each type of radiation, the number of rads is multiplied by a specific factor to find the number of rems. The millirem, 0.001 rems, is also frequently used; the average radiation dose received by a person in the United States is about 360 millirems per year. Natural radiation accounts for about 82 percent of a person's yearly exposure, and manufactured sources for 18 percent. Indoor radon has only recently been recognized as a significant source of natural radiation, with 55 percent of the natural radiation coming from this source.

In the SI system (*Système International d'Unités,* or International System of Units), the gray and the sievert are used to measure radiation absorbed; these units have largely superseded the older rad and rem. The gray (Gy), equal to 100 rads, is now the base unit. It is also expressed as the energy absorption of one joule per kilogram of irradiated material. The sievert (Sv) is the absorbed dose of radiation that produces the same biological effect as one gray of X-rays or gamma rays. The sievert is equal to 100 rems, and has superseded the rem. The becquerel (Bq) measures the radioactive strength of a source, but does not consider effects on tissue. One becquerel is defined as one disintegration (or other nuclear transformation) per second.

What is the **effect** of **radiation** on humans?

When ionizing radiation penetrates living tissue, random collisions with atoms and molecules in its path cause the formation of ions and reactive radicals. These ions and reactive radicals break chemical bonds and cause other molecular changes that produce biological injury. At the cellular level, radiation exposure inhibits cell division, and produces chromosomal damage and gene mutations as well as various other changes. Large enough doses of ionizing radiation will kill any kind of living cell.

How much radiation does the average **dental X-ray** emit?

Dental examinations are estimated to contribute 0.15 millirems per year to the average genetically significant dose, a small amount when compared to other medical X-rays.

How does the United States Environmental Protection Agency (EPA) classify **carcinogens**?

A carcinogen is an agent that can produce cancer (a malignant growth or tumor that spreads throughout the body, destroying tissue). The EPA classifies chemical and physical substances according to their toxicity to humans.

EPA classification system for carcinogens

Group A. Human carcinogen

This classification indicates that there is sufficient evidence from epidemiological studies to support a cause-effect relationship between the substance and cancer.

Group B. Probable human carcinogen

B_1: Substances are classified as B_1 carcinogens on the basis of sufficient evidence from animal studies, and limited evidence from epidemiological studies.

B_2: Substances are classified as B_2 carcinogens on the basis of sufficient evidence from animal studies, with inadequate or nonexistent epidemiological data.

Group C. Possible human carcinogen

For this classification, there is limited evidence of carcinogenicity from animal studies and no epidemiological data.

Group D. Not classifiable as to human carcinogenicity

The data from human epidemiological and animal studies are inadequate or completely lacking, so no assessment as to the substance's cancer-causing hazard is possible.

Group E. Evidence of noncarcinogenicity for humans

Substances in this category have tested negative in at least two adequate (as defined by the EPA) animal cancer tests in different species and in adequate epidemiological and animal studies. Classification in group E is based on available evidence; substances may prove to be carcinogenic under certain conditions.

What is "good" and "bad" **cholesterol**?

Chemically a lipid, cholesterol is an important constituent of body cells. This fatty substance, produced mostly in the liver, is involved in bile salt and hormone formation, and in the transport of fats in the bloodstream to the tissues throughout the body. Both cholesterol and fats are transported as lipoproteins (units having a core of cholesterol and fats in varying proportions with an outer wrapping of carrier protein [phospholoids and apoproteins]). An overabundance of cholesterol in the bloodstream can be an inherited trait, can be triggered by dietary intake, or can be the result of a metabolic disease, such as diabetes mellitus. Fats (from meat, oil, and dairy products) strongly affect the cholesterol level. High cholesterol levels in the blood may lead to a narrowing of the inner lining of the coronary arteries from the build-up of a fatty tissue called atheroma. This increases the risk of coronary heart disease or stroke. How-

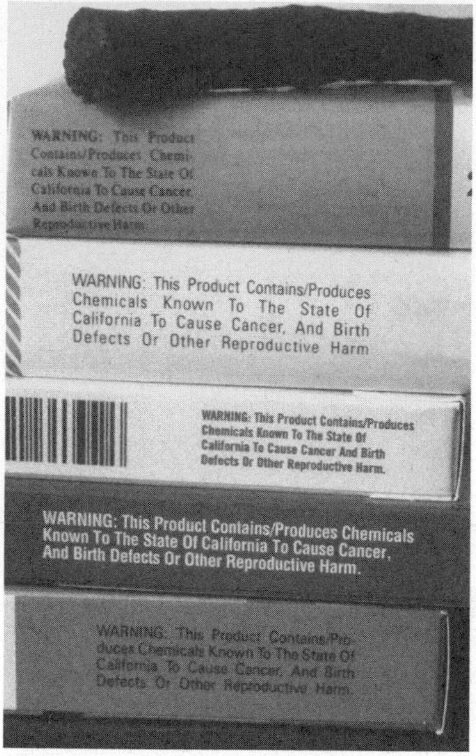

Cigarette smoke contains traces of nearly 4,000 different chemicals.

ever, if most cholesterol in the blood is in the form of high density lipoproteins (HDL), then it seems to protect against arterial disease. HDL picks up cholesterol in the arteries and brings it back to the liver for excretion or reprocessing. HDL is referred to as "good cholesterol." Conversely, if most cholesterol is in the form of low-density lipoproteins (LDL), or very-low-density lipoproteins (VLDL), then arteries can become clogged. "Bad cholesterol" is the term used to refer to LDL and VLDL.

How does **blood alcohol level** affect the body and behavior?

The effects of drinking alcoholic beverages depend on body weight and the amount of actual ethyl alcohol consumed. The level of alcohol in the blood is calculated in milligrams (one milligram equals 0.035 ounce) of pure (ethyl) alcohol per deciliter (3.5 fluid ounces), commonly expressed in percentages.

Number of drinks	Blood alcohol level	Effect of drinks
1	0.02-.03%	Changes in behavior, coordination, and ability to think clearly
2	0.05%	Sedation or tranquilized feeling
3	0.08-0.10%	Legal intoxication in many states
5	0.15-0.20%	Person is obviously intoxicated and may show signs of delirium
12	0.30-0.40%	Loss of consciousness
24	0.50%	Heart and respiration become so depressed that they cease to function and death follows

What is the composition of **cigarette smoke**?

Cigarette smoke contains about 4,000 chemicals. Carbon dioxide, carbon monoxide, methane, and nicotine are some of the major components, with lesser amounts of acetone, acetylene, formaldehyde, propane, hydrogen cyanide, toluene, and many others.

FIRST AID, POISONS, ETC.

Who discovered **cardiopulmonary resuscitation** (CPR) as a method to resuscitate an individual whose heart had stopped?

Cardiopulmonary resuscitation (CPR) is a first-aid technique that combines mouth-to-mouth resuscitation and rhythmic compression of the chest to a person whose heart has stopped. The Scottish surgeon William Tossach first performed mouth-to-mouth resuscitation in 1732. The technique was not further developed (or widely used) for many centuries until Dr. Edward Schafer developed a method of chest pressure to stimulate respiration. In 1910 the American Red Cross adopted and began to teach Schafer's method. A team of specialists at Johns Hopkins Medical School, O. R. Langworthy, R. D. Hooker, and William B. Kouwenhoven, attempted to improve on the technique. Kouwenhoven realized that chest compression could maintain blood flow in a person whose heart had stopped. In 1958 Kouwenhoven's method of chest compression was used on a two-year-old child whose heart had stopped. The American Red Cross endorsed the technique in 1963.

What is the **"ABCD" survey** first responders use to evaluate an emergency?

"A" stands for airway. It is important to be certain the airway from the mouth or nose to the lungs is clear. The airway can be opened by tilting the head back and lifting the chin.

"B" stands for breathing. Be certain the person is breathing or perform rescue breathing (CPR) to ensure a supply of oxygen.

"C" stands for circulation. If a pulse cannot be found, then there is no blood circulating. Emergency personnel can attempt to get the heart to resume breathing by performing rhythmic chest thrusts (CPR). Adults require 15 chest compressions for every two rescue breaths. It also means to check for profuse bleeding which must be controlled.

"D" stands for disability. It involves checking for consciousness and the likelihood of spinal cord or neck injury.

What is the **Heimlich maneuver**?

This effective first-aid technique to resuscitate choking and drowning victims was introduced by Dr. Henry J. Heimlich (b. 1920) of Xavier University in Cincinnati, Ohio. It is a technique for removing a foreign body from the trachea or pharynx where it is preventing flow of air to the lungs. When the victim is in the vertical position, the maneuver consists of applying subdiaphragmatic pressure by wrapping one's arms around the victim's waist from behind, making a fist with one hand and placing it against the victim's abdomen between the navel and the rib cage, clasping one's fist with the other hand, and pressing in with a quick, forceful thrust. Repeat several times if necessary. When the victim is in the horizontal position (which some experts recommend), the rescuer straddles the victim's thighs.

What safety rules should be observed during a **thunderstorm**?

These safety rules should be observed when lightning threatens:

1. Stay indoors. Seek shelter in buildings. If no buildings are available, the best protection is a cave, ditch, canyon, or under head-high clumps of trees in open forest glades. If there is no shelter, avoid the highest object in the area. Keep away from isolated trees.
2. Get out of the water and off small boats.
3. Do not use the telephone.
4. Do not use metal objects like fishing rods and golf clubs.
5. Stay in your automobile if you are traveling.
6. Do not use plug-in electrical equipment like hair dryers, electric razors, or electric toothbrushes during the storm.

What items should be included in a household **first-aid kit**?

According to the American Medical Association and National Safety Council, a first-aid kit should contain:

Allergy and medication information for each family member
Antiseptic cream
Antiseptic wipes
Aspirin or an aspirin substitute such as acetaminophen or ibuprofen
Adhesive bandages
Elastic bandages
Emergency telephone numbers
First-aid manual
Gauze bandages
Triangular bandage
Calamine lotion
Flashlight
Foil blanket
Hydrogen peroxide or rubbing alcohol
Medical exam gloves
Roll of sterile cotton
Round-ended tweezers

Safety pins
Snub-nosed scissors
Syrup of ipecac

What are some common causes of **poisoning**?

Poisoning is defined as the exposure to any substance in sufficient quantity to cause adverse health effects. Poisonings can be grouped into several different categories, including intentional, accidental, occupational and environmental, social and iatrogenic. Accidental poisonings are the most common, with more than 90 percent occurring in children at home. Intentional poisonings are usually suicide-related, with carbon monoxide being one of the most frequently used agents. Toxic chemical releases in industrial accidents are an occupational and environmental hazard.

How deadly is **strychnine**?

The fatal dose of strychnine or deadly nightshade (the plant from which it is obtained) is 0.0005 to 0.001 ounces (15 to 30 milligrams). It causes severe convulsions and respiratory failure. If the patient lives for 24 hours, recovery is probable.

Which part of **mistletoe** is poisonous?

The white berries contain toxic amines, which cause acute stomach and intestinal irritation with diarrhea and a slow pulse. Mistletoe should be considered a potentially dangerous Christmas decoration, especially if children are around.

What first-aid remedies may be used for **bee stings**?

If a person is allergic to bee stings, he or she should seek professional medical care immediately. For persons not allergic to bee stings, the following steps may be taken: The stinger should be removed by scraping with a knife, a long fingernail, or a credit card, rather than by trying to pull it out. A wet aspirin may be rubbed on the area of the sting to help neutralize some of the inflammatory agents in the venom (unless the person is allergic or sensitive to aspirin taken by mouth).

A paste made of meat tenderizer (or other product that contains papain) mixed with water will relieve the pain. Adults may take an antihistamine along with a mild pain reliever such as aspirin, ibuprofen, or acetaminophen.

Which first-aid measures can be used for a bite by a **black widow spider**?

The black widow spider (*Latrodectus mactans*) is common throughout the United States. Its bite is severely poisonous, but no first-aid measures are of value. Age, body size, and degree of sensitivity determine the severity of symptoms, which include an initial pinprick with a dull numbing pain, followed by swelling. An ice cube may be placed over the bite to relieve pain. Between 10 and 40 minutes after the bite, severe abdominal pain and rigidity of stomach muscles develop. Muscle spasms in the extremities, ascending paralysis, and difficulty in swallowing and breathing follow. The mortality rate is less than one percent, but anyone who has been bitten should see a doctor; the elderly, infants, and those with allergies are most at risk, and should be hospitalized.

How can the amount of **lead in tap water** be reduced in an older house having lead-containing pipes?

The easiest way is to let the tap run until the water becomes very cold before using it for human consumption. By letting the tap run, water that has been in the lead-containing pipes for awhile is flushed out. Also, cold water, being less corrosive than warm, contains less lead from the pipes. Lead (Pb) accumulates in the blood, bones, and soft tissues of the body as well as the kidneys, nervous system, and blood-forming organs. Excessive exposure to lead can cause seizures, mental retardation, and behavior disorders. Infants and children are particularly susceptible to low doses of lead and suffer from nervous system damage.

Another source of lead poisoning is old, flaking lead paint. Lead oxide and other lead compounds were added to paints before 1950 to make the paint shinier and more durable. Fourteen percent of the lead ingested by humans comes from the seam soldering of food cans, according to the United States Food and Drug Administration (FDA). The FDA has proposed a reduction in this lead to 50 percent over the next five years. Improperly glazed pottery can be a source of poisoning, too. Acidic liquids such as tea, coffee, wine, and juice can break down the glazes so that the lead can leak out of the pottery. The lead is ingested little by little over a period of time. People can also be exposed to lead in the air. Lead gasoline additives, nonferrous smelters, and battery plants are the most significant contributors of atmospheric lead emissions.

DISEASES, DISORDERS, AND OTHER HEALTH PROBLEMS

What is the difference between a **virus** and a **retrovirus**?

A virus is a rudimentary biosystem that has some of the aspects of a living system such as having a genome (genetic code) and the ability to adapt to its environment. A virus, however, cannot acquire and store energy and is therefore not functional outside of its hosts. Viruses and retroviruses infect cells by attaching themselves to the host cell and either entering themselves or injecting their genetic material into the cell and then reproducing its genetic material within the host cell. The reproduced virus then is released to find and attack more host cells. The difference between a virus and retrovirus is a function of how each replicates its genetic material. A virus has a single strand of genetic material—either DNA or RNA. A retrovirus consists of a single strand of RNA. Once a retrovirus enters a cell, it collects nucleotides and assembles itself as a double strand of DNA that splices itself into the host's genetic material. Retroviruses were first identified by David Baltimore (b. 1938) and Howard Temin (b. 1934). They were awarded the Nobel Prize in Medicine for their discovery.

What was the **first retrovirus** discovered?

Dr. Robert Gallo (b. 1937) discovered the first retrovirus, human T cell lymphoma virus (HTLV), in 1979. The second human retrovirus to be discovered was human immunodeficiency virus, HIV.

Which **disease** is the **most common**?

The most common noncontagious disease is periodontal disease, such as gingivitis or inflammation of the gums. Few people in their lifetime can avoid the effects of tooth decay. The most common contagious disease in the world is coryza or the common cold. There are nearly 62 million cases of the common cold in the United States annually.

Which **disease** is the **deadliest**?

The most deadly infectious disease was the pneumonic form of the plague, the so-called Black Death of 1347-1351, with a mortality rate of 100 percent. Today, the disease with the highest mortality (almost 100 percent) is rabies in humans when it prevents the victim from swallowing water. This disease is not to be confused with being bitten by a rabid animal. With immediate attention, the rabies virus can be prevented from invading the nervous system and the survival rate in this circumstance is 95 percent. AIDS (acquired immunodeficiency syndrome), first reported in 1981, is caused by HIV (the human immunodeficiency virus). In 1993, HIV infection was the most common cause of death among persons aged 25 to 44 years. In 1999 alone, 14,802 U.S. residents died from the AIDS/HIV infection, according to the National Center for Health Statistics. Although still a significant cause of death among persons aged 25 to 44, it is no longer the most common cause of death.

What is the difference between human immunodeficiency virus **(HIV)** and **AIDS**?

The term AIDS applies to the most advanced stages of HIV infection. The Center for Disease Control (CDC) definition of AIDS includes all HIV-infected people who have fewer than 200 CD4+ T cells per cubic millimeter of blood. (Healthy adults usually have CD4+ T cell counts of 1,000 or more.) The definition also includes 26 clinical conditions (mostly opportunistic infections) that affect people with advanced HIV disease.

How many individuals are infected with **HIV/AIDS**?

As of 2007, the estimate for the number of people worldwide who are either HIV positive or have AIDS is 32.9 million. This is down from 39.5 million in 2006, mostly because of more accurate reporting methods used in such places as India and sub-Saharan Africa.

What are the symptoms and signs of **AIDS**?

The early symptoms (AIDS-related complex, or ARC, symptoms) include night sweats, prolonged fevers, severe weight loss, persistent diarrhea, skin rash, persistent cough, and shortness of breath. The diagnosis changes to AIDS (acquired immunodeficiency syndrome) when the immune system is affected and the patient becomes susceptible to opportunistic infections and unusual cancers, such as herpes viruses (herpes simplex, herpes zoster, cytomegalovirus infection), *Candida albicans* (fungus) infection, *Cryptosporidium enterocolitis* (protozoan intestinal infection), *Pneumocystis carinii* pneumonia (PCP, a common AIDS lung infection), toxoplasmosis (protozoan brain infection), progressive multifocal leukoencephalopathy (PML, a central nervous system disease causing gradual brain degeneration), *Mycobacterium avium intracellulare* infection (MAI, a common generalized bacterial infection), and Kaposi's sarcoma (a malignant skin cancer characterized by blue-red nodules on limbs and body, and internally in the gastrointestinal and respiratory tracts, where the tumors cause severe internal bleeding).

The signs of AIDS are generalized swollen glands, emaciation, blue or purple-brown spots on the body, especially on the legs and arms, prolonged pneumonia, and oral thrush.

How is the term **zoonosis** defined?

A zoonosis is any infectious disease or parasitic disease of animals that can be transmitted to humans. Lyme disease and Rocky Mountain spotted fever, for example, are indirectly spread to humans from an animal through the bite of a tick. Common household pets also can directly transmit diseases to humans unless preventive measures are taken. Cat-scratch fever and toxoplasmosis may be contracted from cats. Wild animals and dogs can transmit rabies. However, most zoonosis diseases are relatively rare and can be treated once detected. Such sensible actions as regularly vaccinating pets and wearing long-sleeved shirts and pants when hiking can prevent the spread of most zoonoses.

What is meant by **vectors** in medicine?

A vector is an animal that transmits a particular infectious disease. A vector picks up disease organisms from a source of infection, carries them within or on its body, and later deposits them where they infect a new host. Mosquitoes, fleas, lice, ticks, and flies are the most important vectors of disease to humans.

Which species of mosquito causes **malaria** and **yellow fever** in humans?

The bite of the female mosquito of the genus *Anopheles* can contain the parasite of the genus *Plasmodium*, which causes malaria, a serious tropical infectious disease affecting 200 to 300 million people worldwide. More than one million African babies and children die from the disease annually. The *Aedes aegypti* mosquito transmits yellow fever, a serious infectious disease characterized by jaundice, giving the patient yellowish skin; 10 percent of the patients die.

What is **"mad cow disease"** and how does it affect humans?

Mad cow disease, bovine spongiform encephalopathy (BSE), is a cattle disease of the central nervous system. First identified in Britain in 1986, BSE is a transmissible spongiform encephalopathy (TSE), a disease characterized by the damage caused to the brain tissue. The tissue is pierced with small holes like a sponge. The disease is incurable, untreatable, and fatal. Researchers believe BSE is linked to Creutzfeldt-Jakob disease (CJD) in humans through the consumption of contaminated bovine products. CJD is a fatal illness marked by brain tissue deterioration and progressive degeneration of the central nervous system.

How is **Lyme disease** carried?

The cause of Lyme disease is the spirochete *Borrelia burgdorferi* that is transmitted to humans by the small tick *Ixodes dammini* or other ticks in the Ixodidae family. The tick injects spirochete-laden saliva into the bloodstream or deposits fecal matter on the skin. This multisystemic disease usually begins in the summer with a skin lesion called erythema chronicum migrans (ECM), followed by more lesions, a malar rash, conjunctivitis, and urticaria. The lesions are eventually replaced by small red blotches. Other common symptoms in the first stage include fatigue, intermittent headache, fever, chills, and muscle aches.

In stage two, which can be weeks or months later, cardiac or neurologic abnormalities sometimes develop. In the last stage (weeks or years later) arthritis develops with marked swelling, especially in the large joints. If tetracycline, penicillin, or erythromycin is given in the early stages, the later complications can be minimized. High dosage of intravenously given penicillin can also be effective on the late stages.

When were the first cases of **West Nile virus** reported in the United States?

The first cases of West Nile virus were identified in 1999 in the New York City area. West Nile virus is primarily a disease of birds found in Africa, West Asia, and the Middle East. It is transmitted to humans mainly via mosquito bites (mainly from the species *Culex pipiens*). The female mosquito catches the virus when it bites an infected bird and then passes it on when it later bites a human. In humans it causes encephalitis, an infection of the brain that can be lethal.

Why is **Legionnaire's disease** known by that name?

Legionnaire's disease was first identified in 1976 when a sudden, virulent outbreak of pneumonia took place at a hotel in Philadelphia, Pennsylvania, where delegates to an American Legion convention were staying. The cause was eventually identified as a previously unknown bacterium that was given the name *Legionnella pneumophilia*. The bacterium probably was transmitted by an airborne route. It can spread through cooling tower or evaporation condensers in air-conditioning systems, and has been known to flourish in soil and excavation sites. Usually, the disease occurs in late summer or early fall, and its severity ranges from mild to life-threatening, with a mortality rate as high as 15 percent. Symptoms include diarrhea, anorexia, malaise, headache, generalized weakness, recurrent chills, and fever accompanied by cough, nausea, and chest pain. Antibiotics such as Erythroycin(tm) are administered along with other therapies (fluid replacement, oxygen, etc.) that treat the symptoms.

Which name is now used as a synonym for **leprosy**?

Hansen's disease is the name of this chronic, systemic infection characterized by progressive lesions. Caused by a bacterium, *Mycobacterium leprae*, that is transmitted through airborne respiratory droplets, the disease is not highly contagious. Continuous close contact is needed for transmittal. Antimicrobial agents, such as sulfones (dapsone in particular), are used to treat the disease.

How many types of **herpes virus** are there?

There are five human herpes viruses:

Herpes simplex type 1—causes recurrent cold sores and infections of the lips, mouth, and face. The virus is contagious and spreads by direct contact with the lesions or fluid from the lesions. Cold sores are usually recurrent at the same sites and reoccur where there is an elevated temperature at the affected site, such as with a fever or prolonged sun exposure. Occasionally this virus may occur on the fingers with a rash of blisters. If the virus gets into the eye, it could cause conjunctivitis, or even a corneal ulcer. On rare occasions, it can spread to the brain to cause encephalitis.

Herpes simplex type 2—causes genital herpes and infections acquired by babies at birth. The virus is contagious and can be transmitted by sexual intercourse. The virus produces small blisters in the genital area that burst to leave small painful ulcers, which heal within 10 days to three weeks. Headache, fever, enlarged lymph nodes, and painful urination are the other symptoms.

Varicella-zoster (Herpes zoster)—causes chicken pox and shingles. Shingles can be caused by the dormant virus in certain sensory nerves that reemerge with the decline of the immune system (because of age, certain diseases, and the use of immunosuppressants), excessive stress, or use of corticosteroid drugs. The painful rash of small blisters dry and crust over, eventually leaving small pitted scars. The rash tends to occur over the rib area or a strip on one side of the neck or lower body. Sometimes it involves the lower half of the face and can affect the eyes. Pain that can be severe and long-lasting affects about half of the sufferers and is caused by nerve damage.

Epstein-Barr—causes infectious mononucleosis (acute infection having high fever, sore throat and swollen lymph glands, especially in the neck, which occurs mainly during adolescence) and is associated with Burkitt's lymphoma (malignant tumors of the jaw or abdomen that occur mainly in African children and in tropical areas).

Cytomegalovirus—usually results in no symptoms but enlarges the cells it infects; it can cause birth defects when a pregnant mother infects her unborn child.

Three other human herpes viruses are also known: Human herpes virus 6 (HHV-6), commonly associated with roseola, and human herpes viruses 7 and 8 (HHV 7/8), whose disease association is not yet understood. Herpes gestationis is a rare skin-blister disorder occurring only in pregnancy and is not related to the herpes simplex virus.

What is **necrotizing fasciitis**?

This very rare infection is caused by strains of Group A streptococcus, close relatives of the bacteria that cause strep throat and scarlet fever. When this chain-linked bacteria enters the body through a small cut, bite, or scratch, the infected skin becomes discolored, then blisters and cracks, exposing the destroyed tissue below. Within hours, an infected person can lose inches of flesh, or, in extreme cases, his or her life. If the infection is diagnosed early, antibiotics are generally enough to stop the infection. However, amputation of an affected limb may be the only means of curing an advanced case. The bacteria are often called "flesh-eating bacteria" in sensational media accounts.

How are **warts** caused?

A wart is a lump on the skin produced when one of the 30 types of papillomavirus invades skin cells and causes them to multiply rapidly. There are several different types of warts: common warts, usually on injury sites; flat warts on hands, accompanied by itching; digitate warts having fingerlike projections; filiform warts on eyelids, armpits, and necks; plantar warts on the soles of the feet; and genital warts, pink cauliflower-like areas that, if occurring in a woman's cervix, could predispose her to cervical cancer. Each is produced by a specific virus, and most are usually symptomless. Wart viruses are spread by touch or by contact with the skin shed from a wart.

What is **lactose intolerance**?

Lactose, the principal sugar in cow's milk and found only in dairy products, requires the enzyme lactase for human digestion. Lactose intolerance occurs when the lining of the walls of a person's small intestine does not produce normal amounts of this enzyme. Lactose intolerance causes abdominal cramps, bloating, diarrhea, and excessive gas when more than a certain amount of milk is ingested. Most people are less able to tolerate lactose as they grow older.

A person having lactose intolerance need not eliminate dairy products totally from the diet. Decreasing the consumption of milk products, drinking milk only during meals, and getting calcium from cheese, yogurt, and other dairy products having lower lactose values are options. Another alternative is to buy a commercial lactose preparation that can be mixed into milk. These preparations convert lactose into simple sugars that can be easily digested.

What is the difference between **Type I** and **Type II diabetes**?

Type I is insulin-dependent diabetes mellitus (IDDM) and Type II is non-insulin-dependent diabetes mellitus (NIDDM). In Type I diabetes there is an absolute deficiency of insulin. It accounts for approximately 10 percent of all cases of diabetes and has a greater prevalence is children. In Type II diabetes, insulin secretion may be normal, but the target cells for insulin are less responsive than normal. The incidence of Type II diabetes increases greatly after age 40 and is normally associated with obesity and lack of exercise as well as genetic predisposition. The symptoms of Type II diabetes are usually less severe than Type I, but long-term complications are similar in both types.

What causes a **stomach ulcer**?

For decades, doctors thought that genetics or anxiety or even spicy foods caused stomach ulcers. Scientists now believe that stress and spicy foods only worsen the pain of an ulcer. The gastric ulcer itself is caused by a bacterium called *Helicobacter pylori*. Researcher Barry Marshall (1951-) of Australia observed that many ulcer patients had these bacteria present in their systems. So in 1984, to decide whether there was a link, he consumed a large amount of the bacteria. He developed ulcers 10 days later. Ulcers are now treated with antibiotics. In 1994, the *Helicobacter pylori* bacteria was classified as a carcinogen by the National Institutes of Health; ulcer sufferers would therefore do well to consult a doctor instead of ignoring or masking the pain with antacids.

What is **carpal tunnel syndrome**?

Carpal tunnel syndrome occurs when a branch of the median nerve in the forearm is compressed at the wrist as it passes through the tunnel formed by the wrist bones (or carpals), and a ligament that lies just under the skin. The syndrome occurs most often in middle age and more so in women than men. The symptoms are intermittent at first, then become constant. Numbness and tingling begin in the thumb and first two fingers; then the hand and sometimes the whole arm becomes painful. Treatment involves wrist splinting, weight loss, control of edema; treatments for arthritis may help also. If not, a surgical procedure in which the ligament at the wrist is cut can relieve pressure on the nerve. Those who work continuously with computer keyboards are particularly vulnerable to carpal tunnel syndrome. To minimize the risk of developing this problem, operators should keep their wrists straight as they type, rather than tilting the hands up. It is also best to place the keyboard at a lower position than a standard desktop.

What is the medical term for **tennis elbow**?

The technical term for tennis elbow is epicondylitis. A result of repeated strain on the forearm, it is a painful inflammation of the muscle and surrounding tissues of the elbow. A number of behaviors can cause its onset, ranging from playing tennis or golf to carrying a heavy load with the arm extended.

What is **Lou Gehrig's disease**?

Sometimes called Lou Gehrig's disease, amyotrophic lateral sclerosis (ALS) is a motor neuron disease of middle or late life. It results from a progressive degeneration of nerve cells controlling voluntary motor functions that ends in death three to 10 years after onset. There is no cure for it. At the beginning of the disease, the patient notices weakness in the hands and arms, with involuntary muscle quivering and possible muscle cramping or stiffness. Eventually all four extremities become involved. As nerve degeneration progresses, disability occurs and physical independence declines until the patient, while mentally and intellectually aware, can no longer swallow or move.

What is **narcolepsy**?

Although most people think of a narcoleptic as a person who falls asleep at inappropriate times, victims of narcolepsy also share other symptoms, including excessive day-

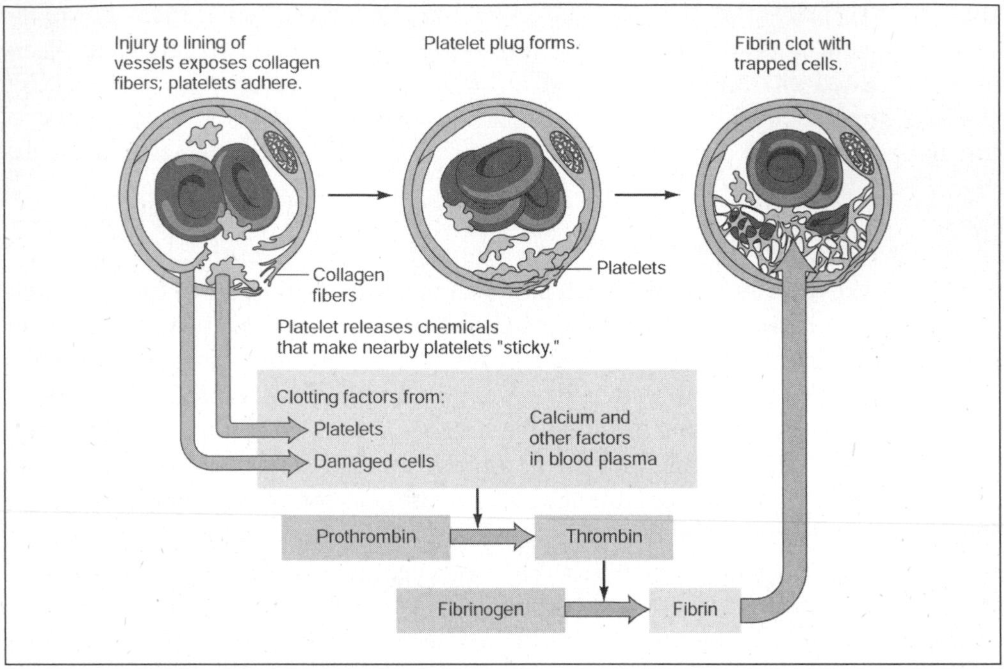

The blood clotting process. Persons with Christmas disease lack a crucial clotting factor that keeps this process from proceeding properly.

time sleepiness, hallucinations, and cataplexy (a sudden loss of muscle strength following an emotional event). Persons with narcolepsy experience an uncontrollable desire to sleep, sometimes many times in one day. Episodes may last from a few minutes to several hours.

How does **jet lag** affect one's body?

The physiological and mental stress encountered by airplane travelers when crossing four or more time zones is commonly called jet lag. Patterns of hunger, sleep, and elimination, along with alertness, memory, and normal judgment, may all be affected. More than 100 biological functions that fluctuate during the 24-hour cycle (circadian rhythm) can become desynchronized. Most people's bodies adjust at a rate of about one hour per day. Thus after four time zone changes, the body will require about four days to return to its usual rhythms. Flying eastward is often more difficult than flying westward, which adds hours to the day.

What is **factor VIII**?

Factor VIII is one of the enzymes involved in the clotting of blood. Hemophiliacs lack this enzyme and are at high risk of bleeding to death unless they receive supplemental doses of factor VIII. The lack of factor VIII is due to a defective gene, which shows a sex-linked inherited pattern (it affects about one in 10 thousand males). Females can carry the gene. Hemorrhage into joints and muscles usually makes up the majority of bleeding episodes.

What is the "**Christmas factor**"?

In the clotting of blood, factor IX, or the Christmas factor, is a coagulation factor present in normal plasma, but deficient in the blood of persons with hemophilia B or Christmas disease. It was named after a man named Christmas who, in 1952, was the first patient in whom this genetic disease was shown to be distinct from hemophilia (another genetic blood-clotting disease in which the blood does not have factor VIII).

What is the difference between **heatstroke** and **heat exhaustion**?

Heatstroke	**Heat Exhaustion**
Caused by: Body cannot regulate its own temperature due to intensive sweating under conditions of high heat and humidity. Advanced age can be a factor.	**Caused by:** Person doesn't get enough liquid and salt in very hot, humid weather.
Symptoms: Weakness, vertigo, nausea, headache, heat cramps, mild heat exhaustion, excessive sweating. Sweating stops just before heatstroke. Temperature rises rapidly, as high as 106°F (41°C); blood pressure is elevated. Skin is flushed at first, then turns ashen or purplish. Delirium or coma is common.	**Symptoms:** Excessive sweating, weakness, vertigo, and sometimes heat cramps. Skin is cold and pale, clammy with sweat; pulse is thready and blood pressure is low. Body temperature is normal or sub-normal. Vomiting may occur. Unconsciousness is rare.
First Aid: Heatstroke is a medical emergency. Call for medical assistance. Move person to a cool, indoor place. Loosen or remove clothing. Primary objective is to reduce body temperature, preferably by iced bath or sponging down with cool water until pulse lowers to below 110 per minute and body temperature is below 103°F (39.4°C). Caution is necessary.	**First Aid:** Lay person in cool place. Loosen clothing. Give water to drink with 1 tsp. salt to each quart of water. Fluid intake usually brings about full recovery. Seek medical assistance if severe.

What is the medical term for a **heart attack**?

Myocardial infarction is the term used for a heart attack in which part of the heart muscle's cells die as a result of reduced blood flow through one of the main arteries (many times due to arteriosclerosis). The outlook for the patient is dependant on the size and location of the blockage and extent of damage, but 33 percent of patients die within 20

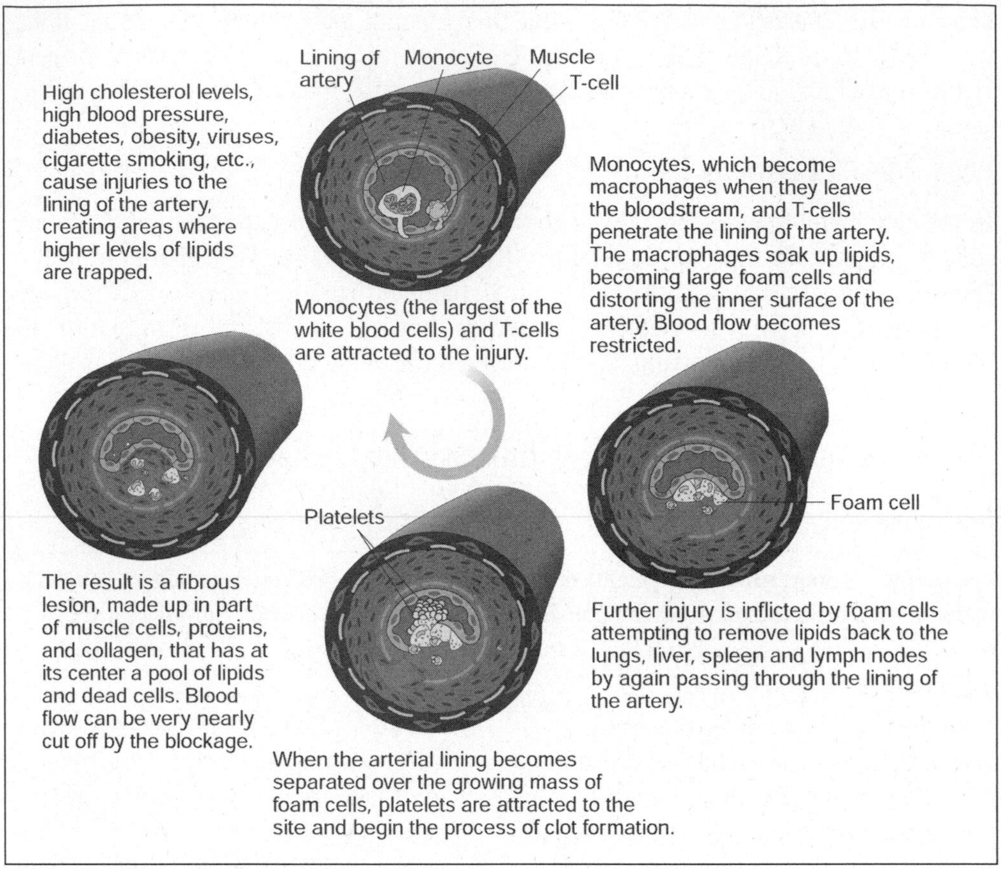

The progression of arteriosclerosis, which may in turn lead to a heart attack.

days after the attack; it is a leading cause of death in the United States. Also, almost half of sudden deaths due to myocardial infarction occur before hospitalization. However, the possibility of recovery improves if vigorous treatment begins immediately.

How are the forms of **cancer** classified?

The over 150 different types of cancer are classified into four major groups:

1. Carcinomas—Nine in 10 cancers are carcinomas, which involve the skin and skin-like membranes of the internal organs.
2. Sarcomas—Involve the bones, muscles, cartilage, fat, and linings of the lungs, abdomen, heart, central nervous system, and blood vessels.
3. Leukemias—Develop in blood, bone marrow, and the spleen.
4. Lymphomas—Involve the lymphatic system.

What are **HeLa cells**?

HeLa cells, used in many biomedical experiments, were obtained from a cervical carcinoma in a woman named Henriette Lacks. Epithelial tissue obtained by biopsy became the first continuously cultured human malignant cells.

If the sap of the **poison ivy** plant touches the skin, will a rash develop?

Studies show that 85 percent of the population will develop an allergic reaction if exposed to poison ivy, but this sensitivity varies with each individual according to circumstance, age, genetics, and previous exposure. The poison comes mainly from the leaves whose allergens touch the skin. A red rash with itching and burning will develop, and skin blisters will usually develop within six hours to several days after exposure. Washing the affected area thoroughly with mild soap within five minutes of exposure can be effective; sponging with alcohol and applying a soothing and drying lotion, such as calamine lotion, is the prescribed treatment for light cases. If the affected area is large, fever, headache, and generalized body weakness may develop. For severe reactions, a physician should be consulted to prescribe a corticosteroid drug. Clothing that touched the plants should also be washed.

A person with dyslexia may reverse the order of words or letters, as illustrated here.

What is **dyslexia** and what causes it?

Dyslexia covers a wide range of language difficulties. In general, a person with dyslexia cannot grasp the meaning of sequences of letters, words, or symbols or the concept of direction. The condition can affect people of otherwise normal intelligence. Dyslexic children may reverse letter and word order, make bizarre spelling errors, and may not be able to name colors or write from dictation. It may be caused by minor visual defects, emotional disturbance, or failure to train the brain. New evidence shows that a neurological disorder may be the underlying cause. Approximately 90 percent of dyslexics are male.

The term *dyslexia* (of Greek origin) was first suggested by Professor Rudolph Berlin of Stuttgart, Germany, in 1887. The earliest references to the condition date as far back as 30 C.E. when Valerius Maximus and Pliny described a man who lost his ability to read after being struck on the head by a stone.

What is **anorexia**?

Anorexia simply means a loss of appetite. Anorexia nervosa is a psychological disturbance that is characterized by an intense fear of being fat. It usually affects teenage or young adult women. This persistent "fat image," however untrue in reality, leads the patient to self-imposed starvation and emaciation (extreme thinness) to the point where one-third of the body weight is lost. There are many theories on the causes of this disease, which is difficult to treat and can be fatal. Between five and 10 percent of patients hospitalized for anorexia nervosa later die from starvation or suicide. Symptoms include a 25 percent or greater weight loss (for no organic reason) coupled with a morbid dread of being fat, an obsession with food, an avoidance of eating, compulsive exercising and restlessness, binge eating followed by induced vomiting, and/or use of laxatives or diuretics.

Why do deep-sea divers get **the bends**?

Bends is a painful condition in the limbs and abdomen. It is caused by the formation and enlargement of bubbles of nitrogen in blood and tissues as a result of rapid reduction of pressure. This condition can develop when a diver ascends too rapidly after being exposed to increased pressure. Severe pain will develop in the muscles and joints of the arms and legs. More severe symptoms include vertigo, nausea, vomiting, choking, shock, and sometimes death. Bends is also known as decompression sickness, caisson disease, tunnel disease, and diver's paralysis.

What is **progeria**?

Progeria is premature old age. There are two distinct forms of the condition, both of which are extremely rare. In Hutchinson-Gilford syndrome, aging starts around the age four, and by 10 or 12, the affected child has all the external features of old age, including gray hair, baldness, and loss of fat, resulting in thin limbs and sagging skin on the trunk and face. There are also internal degenerative changes, such as athero-

What is pica?

Pica refers to the craving for unnatural or non-nutritious substances. It is named after the magpie (*Pica pica*), which has a reputation for sticking its beak into all kinds of things to satisfy its hunger or curiosity. It can happen in both sexes, all races, and in all parts of the world, but is especially noted in pregnant women.

sclerosis (fatty deposits lining the artery walls). Death usually occurs at puberty. Werner's syndrome, or adult progeria, starts in early adult life and follows the same rapid progression as the juvenile form. The cause of progeria is unknown.

How many people in America are estimated to have **Alzheimer's disease**?

According to the Alzheimerís Association, as many as 5.2 million Americans are suffering from some degree of Alzheimerís disease. Alzheimer's disease is a progressive condition in which nerve cells in the brain degenerate and the brain substance shrinks. Although the cause is unknown, some theorize that it is toxic poisoning by a metal such as aluminum. Others believe it to be of genetic origin. There are three stages; in the first, the person becomes forgetful; in the second, the patient experiences severe memory loss and disorientation, lack of concentration, loss of ability to calculate and find the right word to use (dysphasia), anxiety, and sudden personality changes. In the third stage the patient is severely disoriented and confused, suffers from hallucinations and delusions, and has severe memory loss; the nervous system also declines, with regression into infantile behavior, violence, etc., often requiring hospital care.

What is **pelvic inflammatory disease**?

Pelvic inflammatory disease (PID) is a term used for a group of infections in the female organs, including inflammations of the Fallopian tubes, cervix, uterus, and ovaries. It is the most common cause of female infertility today. PID is most often found in sexually active women under the age of 25 and almost always results from gonorrhea or chlamydia, but women who use IUDs are also at risk. A variety of organisms have been shown to cause PID, including *Neisseria gonorrhoeae* and such common bacteria as staphylococci, chlamydiae, and coliforms (*Pseudomonas* and *Escherichia coli*). Signs and symptoms of PID vary with the site of the infection, but usually include profuse, purulent vaginal discharge, low-grade fever and malaise (especially with *N. gonorrhoeae* infections), and lower abdominal pain. PID is treated with antibiotics, and early diagnosis and treatment will prevent damage to the reproductive system. Severe, untreated PID can result in the development of a pelvic abscess that requires drainage. A ruptured pelvic abscess is a potentially fatal complication, and a patient who develops this complication may require a total hysterectomy.

What is the chemical composition of **kidney stones**?

About 80 percent are calcium, mainly calcium oxalate and/or phosphate; five percent are uric acid; two percent are amino acid cystine; the remainder are magnesium ammonium phosphate. About 20 percent of these stones are infective stones, linked to chronic urinary infections, and contain a combination of calcium, magnesium, and ammonium phosphate produced from the alkalinity of the urine and bacteria action on urea (a substance in urine).

How are **burns** classified?

Type	Causes and effects
First-degree	Sunburn; steam. Reddening and peeling. Affects epidermis (top layer of skin). Heals within a week.
Second-degree	Scalding; holding hot metal. Deeper burns causing blisters. Affects dermis (deep skin layer). Heals in two to three weeks.
Third-degree	Fire. A full layer of skin is destroyed. Requires a doctor's care and grafting.
Circumferential	Any burns (often electrical) that completely encircle a limb or body region (such as the chest), which can impair circulation or respiration; requires a doctor's care; fasciotomy (repair of connective tissues) is sometimes required.
Chemical	Acid, alkali. Can be neutralized with water (for up to half an hour). Doctor's evaluation recommended.
Electrical	Destruction of muscles, nerves, circulatory system, etc., below the skin. Doctor's evaluation and ECG monitoring required.

If more than 10 percent of body surface is affected in second-and third-degree burns, shock can develop when large quantities of fluid (and its protein) are lost. When skin is burned, it cannot protect the body from airborne bacteria.

What is the **phobia** of number 13 called?

Fear of the number 13 is known as tridecaphobia, tredecaphobia, or triskaidekaphobia. Persons may fear any situation involving this number, including a house number, the floor of a building, or the 13th day of the month. Many buildings omit labeling the 13th floor as such for this reason. A phobia can develop for a wide range of objects, situations, or organisms. The list below demonstrates the variety:

Phobia subject	Phobia term
Animals	Zoophobia
Beards	Pogonophobia
Books	Bibliophobia
Churches	Ecclesiaphobia
Dreams	Oneirophobia
Flowers	Anthophobia
Food	Sitophobia
Graves	Taphophobia
Infection	Nosemaphobia
Lakes	Limnophobia
Leaves	Phyllophobia
Lightning	Astraphobia
Men	Androphobia
Money	Chrometophobia
Music	Musicophobia
Sex	Genophobia
Shadows	Sciophobia
Spiders	Arachnophobia
Sun	Heliophobia
Touch	Haptophobia
Trees	Dendrophobia
Walking	Basiphobia
Water	Hydrophobia
Women	Gynophobia
Work	Ergophobia
Writing	Graphophobia

HEALTH CARE

What is the **Hippocratic Oath**?

The Hippocratic Oath is an oath demanded of physicians who are entering practice and can be traced back to the Greek physician and teacher Hippocrates (ca. 460-ca. 377 B.C.E.). The oath reads as follows:

"I swear by Apollo the physician, by Aesculapius, Hygeia, and Panacea, and I take to witness all the gods, all the goddesses, to keep according to my ability and my judgment the following Oath:

"To consider dear to me as my parents him who taught me this art; to live in common with him and if necessary to share my goods with him; to look upon his children as my own brothers, to teach them this art if they so desire without fee or written

Who is generally regarded as the father of medicine?

Hippocrates (ca. 460-ca. 377 B.C.E.), a Greek physician, holds this honor. Greek medicine, previous to Hippocrates, was a mixture of religion, mysticism, and necromancy. Hippocrates established the rational system of medicine as a science, separating it from religion and philosophy. Diseases had natural causes and natural laws: they were not the "wrath of the gods." Hippocrates believed that the four elements (earth, air, fire, and water) were represented in the body by four body fluids (blood, phlegm, black bile, and yellow bile) or "humors." When they existed in harmony within the body, the body was in good health. The duty of the physician was to help nature to restore the body's harmony. Diet, exercise, and moderation in all things kept the body well, and psychological healing (good attitude toward recovery), bed rest, and quiet were part of his therapy. Hippocrates was the first to recognize that different diseases had different symptoms; and he described them in such detail that the descriptions generally would hold today. His descriptions not only included diagnosis but prognosis.

promise; to impart to my sons and the sons of the master who taught me and the disciples who have enrolled themselves and have agreed to rules of the profession, but to these alone, the precepts and the instruction. I will prescribe regiment for the good of my patients according to my ability and my judgment and never to harm anyone. To please no one will I prescribe a deadly drug, nor give advice which may cause his death. Nor will I give a woman a pessary to procure abortion. But I will preserve the purity of my life and my art. I will not cut for stone, even for patients in whom the disease is manifest; I will leave this operation to be performed by practitioners (specialists in this art). In every house where I come I will enter only for the good of my patients, keeping myself far from all intentional ill-doing and all seduction, and especially from the pleasures of love with women or with men, be they free or slaves. All that may come to my knowledge in the exercise of my profession or outside of my profession or in daily commerce with men, which ought not to be spread abroad, I will keep secret and will never reveal. If I keep this oath faithfully, may I enjoy life and practice my art, respected by all men and in all times; but if I swerve from it or violate it, may the reverse be my lot."

The oath varies slightly in wording among different sources.

Who was the founder of **modern medicine**?

Thomas Sydenham (1624-1689), who was also called the English Hippocrates, reintroduced the Hippocratic method of accurate observation at the bedside, and recording of observations, to build up a general clinical description of individual diseases. He is also considered one of the founders of epidemiology and was among the first to describe scarlet fever and Sydenham's chorea.

What is the difference between **homeopathy**, **osteopathic medicine**, **naturopathy**, and **chiropractic** medicine?

Developed by a German physician, Christian F. S. Hahnemann (1755-1843), the therapy of homeopathy treats patients with small doses of 2,000 substances. Based on the principle that "like cures like," the medicine used is one that produces the same symptoms in a healthy person that the disease is producing in the sick person.

Chiropractic medicine is based on the belief that disease results from the lack of normal nerve function. Relying on physical manipulation and adjustment of the spine for therapy, rather than on drugs or surgery, this therapy, used by the ancient Egyptians, Chinese, and Hindus, was rediscovered in 1895 by American osteopath Daniel David Palmer (1845-1913).

Developed in the United States by Dr. Andrew Taylor Still (1828-1917), osteopathic medicine recognizes the role of the musculoskeletal system in healthy function of the human body. The physician is fully licensed and uses manipulation techniques as well as traditional diagnostic and therapeutic procedures. Osteopathy is practiced as part of standard Western medicine.

Naturopathy is based on the principle that disease is due to the accumulation of waste products and toxins in the body. Practitioners believe that health is maintained by avoiding anything artificial or unnatural in the diet or in the environment.

What is the difference between a **skilled nursing facility**, an **intermediate care facility**, and an **assisted living facility**?

A skilled nursing facility is required to provide twenty-four-hour nursing supervision by registered or licensed nurses. Residents of skilled nursing facilities need assistance with many aspects of day-to-day living and daily care. Skilled nursing facilities provide medical, nursing, dietary, pharmacy, and activity services.

An intermediate care facility is required to provide eight hours of nursing supervision per day. Residents of an intermediate care facility are usually ambulatory and require less assistance with day-to-day living.

An assisted living facility is a home-like environment that provides individualized health and personal care assistance. Assisted living facilities offer personal care assistance, health care monitoring, limited health care services, and/or the dispensing of medications. Assisted living facilities promote independence by meeting residents' supportive needs.

What is the difference between the degrees **doctor of dental surgery** (DDS) and **doctor of medical dentistry** (DMD)?

The title depends entirely on the school's preference in terminology. The degrees are equivalent.

How many people **visit a dentist** regularly?

Only about half the population visits a dentist as often as once a year. Children, ages two to 17, visit the dentist more frequently than adults.

Age	Percent who visited a dentist in the last year
2-17	72.6%
18-64	64.6%
65 and over	55.0%

What is the difference between an **ophthalmologist**, **optometrist**, and **optician**?

An ophthalmologist is a physician who specializes in care of the eyes. Ophthalmologists conduct examinations to determine the quality of vision and the need for corrective glasses or contact lenses. They also check for the presence of any disorders, such as glaucoma or cataracts. Ophthalmologists may perform surgery or prescribe glasses, contact lenses, or medication, as necessary.

An optometrist is a specialist trained to examine the eyes and to prescribe, supply, and adjust glasses or contact lenses. Because they are not physicians, optometrists may not prescribe drugs or perform surgery. An optometrist refers patients requiring these types of treatment to an ophthalmologist.

An optician is a person who fits, supplies, and adjusts glasses or contact lenses. Because their training is limited, opticians may not examine or test eyes or prescribe glasses or drugs.

DIAGNOSTIC EQUIPMENT, TESTS, ETC.

What is the meaning of the **medical abbreviation NYD**?

Not yet diagnosed.

How is **blood pressure** measured?

A sphygmomanometer is the device used to measure blood pressure. It was invented in 1881 by an Austrian named Von Bash. It consists of a cuff with an inflatable bladder that is wrapped around the upper arm, a rubber bulb to inflate the bladder, and a device that indicates the pressure of blood. Measuring arterial tension (blood pressure) of a person's circulation is achieved when the cuff is applied to the arm over the artery and pumped to a pressure that occludes or blocks it. This gives the systolic measure, or the maximum pressure of the blood, which occurs during contraction of the ventricles of the heart. Air is then released from the cuff until the blood is first heard passing through the opening artery (called Korotkoff sounds). This gives diastolic pressure, or the minimum value of blood pressure that occurs during the relaxation of the arterial-filling phase of the heart muscle.

What is the meaning of the numbers in a **blood pressure reading**?

When blood is forced into the aorta, it exerts a pressure against the walls; this is referred to as blood pressure. The upper number, the systolic, measures the pressure during the period of ventricular contraction. The lower number, the diastolic, measures the pressure when blood is entering the relaxed chambers of the heart. While these numbers can vary due to age, sex, weight, and other factors, the normal blood pressure is around 110/60 to 140/90 millimeters of mercury.

Is there a name for the **heart-monitoring machine** that people sometimes wear for a day or two while carrying on their normal activities?

A portable version of the electrocardiograph (ECG) designed by J. J. Holter is called a Holter monitor. Electrodes attached to the chest are linked to a small box containing a recording device. The device records the activity of the heart.

What is **nuclear magnetic resonance imaging**?

Magnetic resonance imaging (MRI), sometimes called nuclear magnetic resonance imaging (NMR), is a non-invasive, non-ionizing diagnostic technique. It is useful in detecting small tumors, blocked blood vessels, or damaged vertebral disks. Because it does not involve the use of radiation, it can often be used where X-rays are dangerous. Large magnets beam energy through the body causing hydrogen atoms in the body to resonate. This produces energy in the form of tiny electrical signals. A computer detects these signals, which vary in different parts of the body and according to whether an organ is healthy or not. The variation enables a picture to be produced on a screen and interpreted by a medical specialist.

What distinguishes MRI from computerized X-ray scanners is that most X-ray studies cannot distinguish between a living body and a cadaver, while MRI "sees" the difference between life and death in great detail. More specifically, it can discriminate between healthy and diseased tissues with more sensitivity than conventional radiographic instruments like X-rays or CAT scans. CAT (computerized axial tomography) scanners have been around since 1973 and are actually glorified X-ray machines. They offer three-dimensional viewing but are limited because the object imaged must remain still.

The concept of using MRI to detect tumors in patients was proposed by Raymond Damadian (1936-) in a 1972 patent application. The fundamental MRI imaging concept used in all present-day MRI instruments was proposed by Paul Lauterbar in an article published in *Nature* in 1973. The main advantages of MRI are that it not only gives superior images of soft tissues (like organs), but can also measure dynamic physiological changes in a non-invasive manner (without penetrating the body in any way). A disadvantage of MRI is that it cannot be used for every patient. For example, patients with implants, pacemakers, or cerebral aneurysm clips made of metal cannot be examined using MRI because the machine's magnet could potentially move these objects within the body, causing damage.

Ultrasound is another type of 3-D computerized imaging. Using brief pulses of ultrahigh frequency acoustic waves (lasting 0.01 second), it can produce a sonar map of the imaged object.

Who invented the **pacemaker**?

Paul Zoll (1911-1999) invented an electric stimulator device to deliver electrical impulses to the heart externally. In 1958, biomedical engineer Wilson Greatbatch (1919-), in cooperation with doctors William M. Chardack and Andres A. Gage, invented the first internal pacemaker. It was a small, flat, plastic disk powered by a battery. It was implanted into the body and connected by wires sewn directly onto the heart. The wires emitted rhythmic electric impulses to trigger the heart's action. Pacemaker batteries now last from six to ten years.

What are the normal **test ranges** for total **cholesterol**, low-density lipoproteins (**LDL**), and high-density lipoproteins (**HDL**)?

The National Cholesterol Education Program has drawn up these guidelines:

	Desirable	Borderline	High Risk
Total Blood Cholesterol	Less than 200 mg/dl	200-239 mg/dl	240 mg/dl or more
LDL	Less than 130 mg/dl	130-159 mg/dl	160 mg/dl or more
HDL	45-65 mg/dl	35-45 mg/dl	Below 35 mg/dl

mg/dl = milligrams per deciliter

When were **hearing aids** first invented?

Specially designed hearing aids were described as early as 1588 by Giovanni Battista Porta (1535-1615) in his book *Natural Magick*. These hearing aids were made out of wood in the shape of the ears of animals with a sharp sense of hearing. During the 1700s, speaking tubes and ear trumpets were developed. Bone conduction devices to transmit sound vibrations from outside to the bones of the ear, first suggested in 1550 by Gerolamo Cardano (1501-1576), were further developed during the 1800s. The first battery-powered hearing aid in the United States was made by the Dictagraph Company in 1898. Miller Reese Hutchison (1876-1944) filed the patent for the first electric hearing aid in 1901. Refinements were made to the hearing aids throughout the twentieth century. Miniaturization and microchips made it possible for hearing aids to become so small they now fit invisibly inside the ear.

What is the instrument a doctor uses to check **reflexes**?

A plessor or plexor or percussor is a small hammer, usually with a soft rubber head, used to tap the part directly. Also called a reflex hammer or a percussion hammer, it is used by a doctor to elicit reflexes by tapping on tendons. In the most common test, the patient sits on a surface high enough to allow his legs to dangle freely, and the physician lightly taps the patellar tendon, just below the kneecap. This stimulus briefly stretches the quadriceps muscle on top of the thigh. The stretch causes the muscle to contract, which makes the leg kick forward. The time interval between the tendon tap and the start of the leg extension is about 50 microseconds. That interval is too short for the involvement of the brain and is totally reflexive. This test indicates the status of an individual's reflex control of movement.

DRUGS, MEDICINES, ETC.

What is **pharmacognosy**?

It is the science of natural drugs and their physical, botanical, and chemical properties. Natural products derived from plant, vegetable, animal, and mineral sources have been a part of medical practice for thousands of years. Today about 25 percent of all prescriptions dispensed in pharmacies contain active ingredients that are extracted from higher plants, and many more are found in over-the-counter products.

Why do physicians use the symbol **Rx** when they write their prescriptions?

There are several explanations for the symbol Rx. One common explanation is that it comes from the Latin word *recipi* or *recipere*, which means "take" and is abbreviated as Rx. The symbol can also be traced to the sign of Jupiter, which was found on ancient prescriptions to appeal to the Roman god Jupiter. In ancient medical books the crossed R has been found wherever the letter R occurred.

Others believe that the origin of the Rx symbol can be found in the Egyptian myth about two brothers, Seth and Horus, who ruled over Upper and Lower Egypt as gods. Horus's eye was injured in a battle with Seth and healed by another god, Thoth. The eye of Horus consisted of the sun and the moon, and it was the moon eye that was damaged. This explained the phases of the moon—the waning of the moon was the eye being damaged and the waxing, the healing. The eye of Horus became a powerful symbol of healing in the eyes of the Egyptians. In Egyptian art, the eye of Horus strongly resembles the modern Rx of the physician.

What is a **double-blind study**?

In drug tests a double-blind study is a study in which neither the investigator administering the drug nor the subject taking it knows if the patient is receiving the experimental drug or a neutral substitute called a placebo. In this manner, bias, either on the part of the administrator or the subject, can be eliminated from the study.

What is the meaning of the **abbreviations** often used by a doctor when writing a **prescription**?

Latin phrase	Shortened form	Meaning
quaque hora	qh	every hour
quaque die	qd	every day
bis in die	bid	twice a day
ter in die	tid	three times a day
quarter in die	qid	four times a day
pro re nata	prn	as needed
ante cibum	a.c.	before meals
post cibum	p.c.	after meals
per os	p.o.	by mouth
nihil per os	n.p.o.	nothing by mouth
signetur	sig	let it be labeled
statim	stat	immediately
ad libitum	ad lib	at pleasure
hora somni	h.s.	at bedtime
cum	c	with
sine	s	without
guttae	gtt	drops
semis	ss	a half
et	et	and

What are the common **medication measures**?

Approximate equivalents of apothecary measures are given below.

Volume	Apothecary volume equivalent
1 minim	0.06 milliliters or 0.02 fluid drams or 0.002 fluid ounces
1½ minims	0.1 milliliters
15 minims	1 milliliter
480 minims	1 fluid ounce
1 dram	3.7 milliliters or 60 minims
1 t (teaspoon)	60 drops
3 t (teaspoons)	½ ounce
1 T (tablespoon)	½ ounce
2 T (tablespoons)	1 ounce
1 C (cup)	8 ounces or 30 milliliters

Apothecary weights

Weight	Equivalent
1 grain	60 milligrams or ½ dram
60 grains	1 dram or 3.75 grams
8 drams	1 ounce or 30 grams

How long does it take for a **new drug** to be **developed**?

Pharmaceutical research is a long process. Only about one out of every 10,000 investigated substance reaches the market in the form of a new drug. Drug development research can take eight to fifteen years. The cost to develop a new drug can amount to about $300-500 million for each new drug.

How many of the **medications** used today are **derived from plants**?

Of the more than 250,000 known plant species, less than one percent have been thoroughly tested for medical applications. Yet out of this tiny portion have come 25 percent of our prescription medicines. The United States National Cancer Institute has identified 3,000 plants from which anti-cancer drugs are or can be made. This includes ginseng (*Panax quinquefolius*), Asian mayapple (*Podophyllum hexandrum*), western yew (*Taxus brevifolia*), and rosy periwinkle. Seventy percent of these 3,000 come from rain-forests, which also are a source of countless other drugs for diseases and infections. Rainforest plants are rich in so-called secondary metabolites, particularly alkaloids, which biochemists believe the plants produce to protect them from disease and insect attack. However, with the current rate of rainforest destruction, raw materials for future medicines are certainly being lost. Also, as tribal groups disappear, their knowledge of the properties and uses of these plants species will be lost.

What are some **medications** that have been obtained from **rain forest** plants, animals, and microorganisms?

Drug	Medicinal Use	Source
Allantoin	Wound healer	Blowfly larva
Atropine	High blood pressure	Bee venom
Cocaine	Analgesic	Coca bush
Cortisone	Anti-inflammatory	Mexican yam
Cytarabine	Leukemia	Sponge
Diosgenin	Birth control	Mexican yam
Erythromycin	Antibiotic	Bacterium
Morphine	Analgesic	Opium poppy
Quinine	Malaria	Chincona tree bark
Reserpine	Hypertension	Rauwolfia plant
Tetracycline	Antibiotic	Bacterium
Vinblastine	Hodgkin's disease and leukemia	Rosy periwinkle plant

What is **herbal medicine**?

Herbal medicine treats disease and promotes health with plant material. For centuries herbal medicines were the primary methods to administer medicinally active compounds.

What are some of the most **common herbal remedies**?

Herb	Botanical name	Common use
Aloe	*Aloe vera*	Skin, gastritis
Black cohosh	*Cimicifuga racemosa*	Menstrual, menopause
Dong quai	*Angelica sinensis*	Menstrual, menopause
Echinacea	*Echinacea angustifolia*	Colds, immunity
Ephedra (ma huang)	*Ephedra sinica*	Asthma, energy, weight loss
Evening primrose oil	*Oenothera biennis*	Eczema, psoriasis, premenstrual syndrome, breast pain
Feverfew	*Tanacetum parthenium*	Migraine
Garlic	*Allium sativum*	Cholesterol, hypertension
Ginger	*Zingiber officinale*	Nausea, arthritis
Ginkgo biloba	*Ginkgo biloba*	Cerebrovascular insufficiency, memory

Herb	Botanical name	Common use
Ginseng	*Panax ginseng, Panax quinquifolius, Panax pseudoginseng, Eleutherococcus senticosus*	Energy, immunity, mentation, libido
Goldenseal	*Hydrastis candensis*	Immunity, colds
Hawthorne	*Crateaegus laeviagata*	Cardiac function
Kava kava	*Piper methysticum*	Anxiety
Milk thistle	*Silybum marianum*	Liver disease
Peppermint	*Mentha piperita*	Dyspepsia, irritable bowel syndrome
Saw palmetto	*Serona repens*	Prostate problems
St. John's Wort	*Hypericum perforatum*	Depression, anxiety, insomnia
Tea tree oil	*Melaleuca alternifolia*	Skin infections
Valerian	*Valeriana officinalis*	Anxiety, insomnia

What is a **dietary supplement**?

According to the Dietary Supplement Health and Education Act (DSHEA), a dietary supplement is a product taken by mouth that contains a "dietary ingredient" intended to supplement the diet. The dietary ingredient may include: vitamins, minerals, herbs or other botanicals, amino acids, a dietary substance to supplement the diet by increasing the total dietary intake or a concentrate, metabolite, constituent, or extract. They may be in any form—tablets, capsules, liquids, gelcaps, or powders. The DSHEA places dietary supplements in a special category under the general umbrella of "foods," not drugs, and requires that every supplement be labeled a dietary supplement.

How long is a **tetanus shot** effective?

In the United States, infants are vaccinated against tetanus at two months, four months, and six months. The vaccination is part of the DPT shot, which protects against diphtheria, tetanus, and pertussis (whooping cough). In order to insure immunity, booster doses are given every 10 years or at the time of a major injury if it occurs more than five years after a dose.

Who discovered **penicillin**?

British bacteriologist Sir Alexander Fleming (1881-1955) discovered the bacteria-killing property of penicillin in 1928. Fleming noticed that no bacteria grew around bits of the *Penicillium notatum* fungus that accidentally fell into a bacterial culture in his laboratory. However, although penicillin was clinically used, it was not until 1941 that Dr. Howard Florey (1898-1968) purified and tested it. The first large-scale plant to

Sir Alexander Fleming, the British bacteriologist who discovered the medicinal properties of penicillin in 1928.

produce penicillin was constructed under the direction of Dr. Ernest Chain (1906-1979). By 1945, penicillin was commercially available. In that year, Chain, Florey, and Fleming received a joint Nobel Prize for their work on penicillin.

Today penicillin is still used successfully in the treatment of many bacterial diseases, including pneumonia, strep throat, scarlet fever, gonorrhea, and impetigo. Its discovery also led to the development of other antibiotics that are useful in destroying a broad spectrum of pathogenic bacteria.

Who discovered the antibiotic **streptomycin**?

The Russian-born microbiologist Selman A. Waksman (1888-1973) coined the term "antibiotic" and subsequently discovered streptomycin in 1943. In 1944 Merck and Company agreed to produce it to be used against tuberculosis and tuberculosis meningitis.

Streptomycin ultimately proved to have some human toxicity and was supplanted by other antibiotics, but its discovery changed the course of modern medicine. In addition to its use in treating tuberculosis, it was also used to treat bacterial meningitis, endocarditis, pulmonary and urinary tract infections, leprosy, typhoid fever, bacillary dysentery, cholera, and bubonic plague. Streptomycin saved countless lives, and its development led scientists to search the microbial world for other antibiotics and medicines.

Who developed the **poliomyelitis vaccine** in America?

Immunologist Jonas E. Salk (1914-1995) developed the first vaccine (made from a killed virus) against poliomyelitis. In 1952 he prepared and tested the vaccine, and in 1954 massive field tests were successfully undertaken. Two years later immunologist Albert Sabin (1906-1993) developed an oral vaccine made from inactivated live viruses of three polio strains. Because of its easy administration and the fact that it requires fewer booster inoculations, Sabin's vaccine has replaced the Salk vaccine as the one to prevent polio. However, Salk remains known as the man who defeated polio.

Who was the first to use **chemotherapy**?

Chemotherapy is the use of chemical substances to treat diseases, specifically malignant diseases. The drug must interfere with the growth of bacterial, parasitic, or tumor cells, without significantly affecting host cells. Especially effective in types of cancer such as leukemia and lymphoma, chemotherapy was introduced in medicine by the German physician Paul Ehrlich (1854-1915).

What are **monoclonal antibodies**?

Monoclonal antibodies are artificially produced antibodies designed to neutralize a specific foreign protein (antigen). Cloned cells (genetically identical) are stimulated to produce antibodies to the target antigen. Most monoclonal antibody work so far has used cloned cells from mice infected with cancer. In some cases they are used to destroy cancer cells directly; in others they carry other drugs to combat the cancer cells.

How are **anabolic steroids** harmful to those who use them?

Anabolic (protein-building) steroids are drugs that mimic the effects of testosterone and other male sex hormones. They can build muscle tissue, strengthen bone, and speed muscle recovery following exercise or injury. They are sometimes prescribed to treat osteoporosis in postmenopausal women and some types of anemia. Some athletes use anabolic steroids to build muscle strength and bulk and to allow a more rigorous training schedule. Weightlifters, field event athletes, and body-builders are most likely to use anabolic steroids. The drugs are banned from most organized competitions because of the dangers they pose to health and to prevent an unfair advantage.

Adverse effects include hypertension, acne, edema, and damage to liver, heart, and adrenal glands. Psychiatric symptoms can include hallucinations, paranoid delusions, and manic episodes. In men, anabolic steroids can cause infertility, impotence, and premature balding. Women can develop masculine characteristics, such as excessive hair growth, male-pattern balding, disruption of menstruation, and deepening of the voice. Children and adolescents can develop problems in growing bones, leading to short stature.

How does **RU-486** cause an abortion?

A pill containing RU-486 (mifepristone) deprives a fertilized embryo of a compatible uterine environment, terminating a pregnancy within 49 days of fertilization. It was approved for use in the United States on September 28, 2000.

What were the **birth defects** caused by the drug **Thalidomide**?

In the early 1960s, Thalidomide was marketed as a sedative and anti-nausea drug. It was found to cause birth defects in babies whose mothers had taken the drug for morning sickness. Some babies were born without arms or legs. Others were born blind or deaf or with heart defects or intestinal abnormalities. Although some were

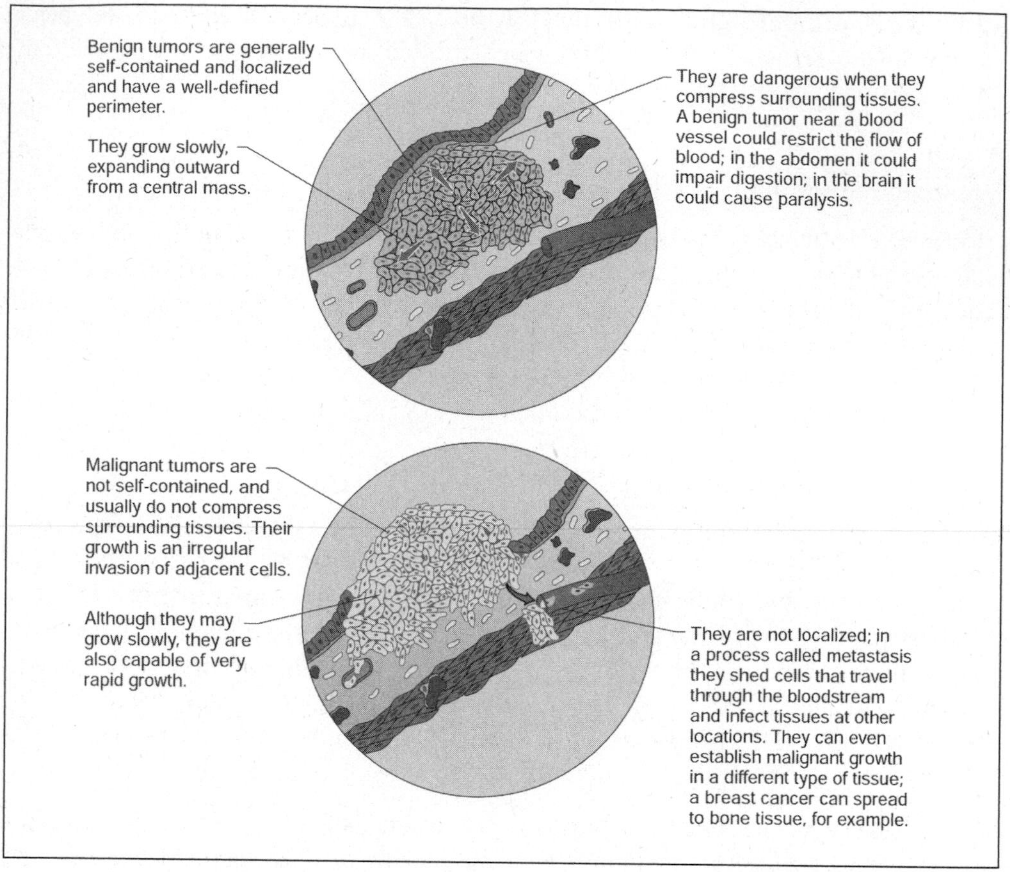

A comparison of benign and malignant tumor characteristics.

mentally retarded, most were of normal intelligence. This tragedy led to much stricter laws regulating the sale and testing of new drugs.

What are **designer drugs**, such as **China White**?

Designer drugs are synthesized chemicals that resemble such available narcotics as fentanyl and meperidine. China white (3-methyl-fentanyl) is one of these drugs and is an analogue of fentanyl. It is 3,000 times more potent than morphine. Even small amounts can be fatal, and it has been responsible for more than 100 overdose deaths in California.

What is a **controlled substance**?

The Comprehensive Drug Abuse Prevention and Control Act of 1971 was designed to control the distribution and use of all depressant and stimulant drugs and other drugs of abuse or potential abuse. Centrally acting drugs are divided into five classes called Schedule I through V.

	Includes	Examples
Schedule I	Experimental and illegal drugs. They are not prescribable and do not have an acceptable medical use.	Heroin, LSD, Peyote
Schedule II	Like Schedule I drugs, Schedule II drugs can be abused. However, they have acceptable medical uses. Prescriptions cannot be renewed.	Amphetamine, Cocaine, Codeine, Morphine
Schedule III	Less likely to be abused than Schedule II drugs. Prescriptions can be refilled up to 5 times in 6 months.	Aspirin with codeine, Methylprylon, Phendimetrazine
Schedule IV	Lower potential for abuse than Schedule I-III. Usually they fall under similar refill regulations as Schedule III drugs.	Chloral hydrate, Diazepam, Phenobarbital
Schedule V	Low potential for abuse. May contain small amounts of narcotics. Regulated in the same manner as non-scheduled prescription drugs.	Lomotil, Parapectolin, Cheracol, Robitussin

What is the difference between **cocaine, freebase**, and **crack**?

Cocaine comes in several different forms. Coca paste is widely used in South America and is usually added to and smoked in tobacco or marijuana cigarettes. Cocaine hydrochloride, the form most common in the United States, is a white powder. It is inhaled through the nose ("snorted") from tiny spoons, rolled-up dollar bills, or straws. It can also be mixed with water and injected.

Freebase is a purified form of cocaine that is smoked in a water pipe. It is prepared by applying ether, baking powder, or other solvent to cocaine powder and heating the mixture.

Crack is freebase that comes in ready-to-smoke chunks or "rocks." Crack is usually smoked in a water pipe. Some users apply it to tobacco or marijuana cigarettes.

Which tests detect **illegal drug use**?

Blood samples are rarely if ever used in routine screening of individuals for drug abuse. Blood samples provide little valuable information unless the drug was consumed a short time before the blood was drawn. Urine, on the other hand, is easily

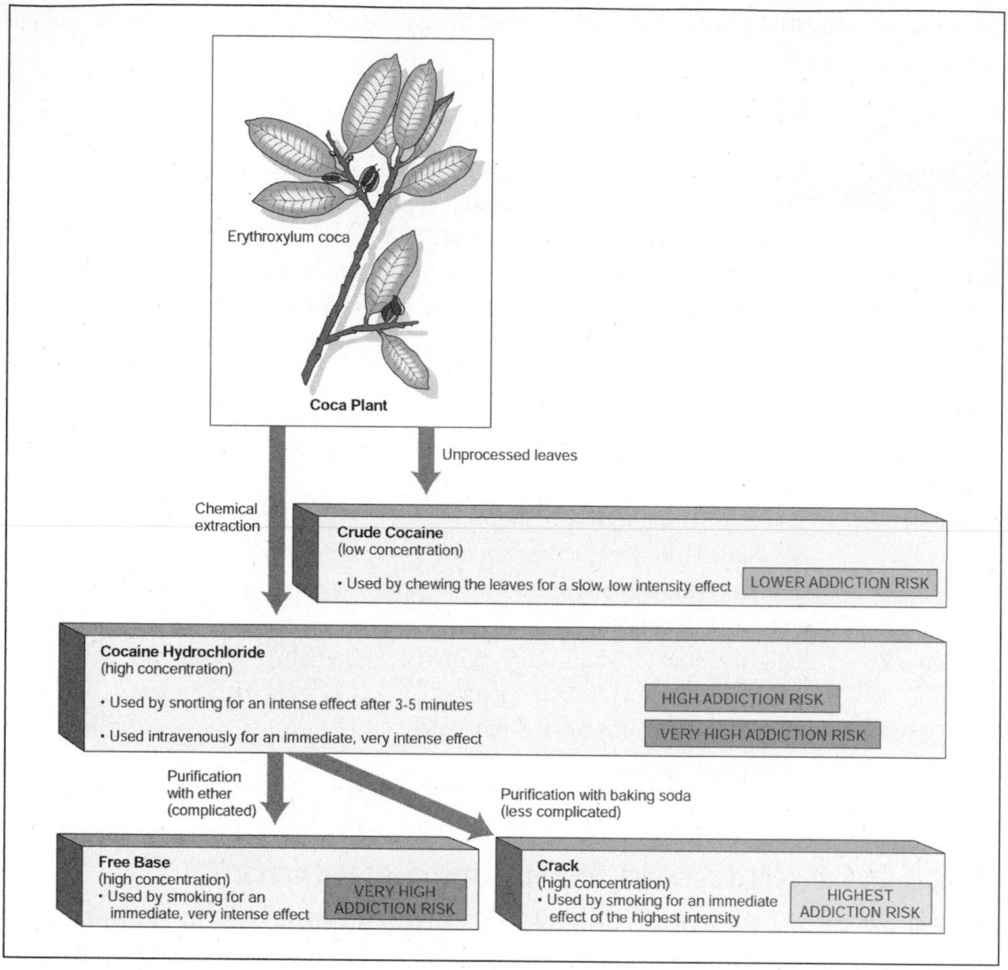

Various forms of cocaine and the addiction risks associated with them.

collected and can be analyzed and transported cheaply. Samples of skin, saliva, and hair can also be tested but with greater difficulty.

Urine tests detect cocaine used by a person within the past 24 to 36 hours. Hair analysis can detect cocaine used more than a year ago. Other drugs that can be detected by urine testing are:

PCP (phencylidine)—up to 7-8 days

Barbiturates—up to 72 hours

Morphine—1-2 days

Heroin—2-3 days or 4-5 days if larger doses are taken

Methaqualone (Quaalude)—up to 10 days

Cannabis (marijuana)—up to 5 days for infrequent users; up to 10 days for heavy smokers

How long do **chemicals from marijuana** stay in the body?

When marijuana is smoked, tetrahydrocannabinol (THC), its active ingredient, is absorbed primarily in the fat tissues. The body transforms the THC into metabolites, which can be detected by urine tests for up to a week. Tests involving radioactively labeled THC have traced the metabolites for up to a month. The retention of labeled THC in humans is about 40 percent at three days and 30 percent at one week.

SURGERY AND OTHER NON-DRUG TREATMENTS

How does **minimally invasive surgery** differ from traditional, major, open surgery?

Traditional, major, open surgery requires a major incision in the body, often several inches long, allowing surgeons to physically place their hands inside the body to work. In minimally invasive surgery the incision is very small and surgeons do not place their hands inside the body. Using a laparoscope, a narrow wand containing a video camera, surgeons are able to insert tools into tiny surgical openings to remove diseased tissue. Laparoscopy was introduced in the 1970s for gynecological treatment and gall bladder removal. At least half of all surgeries are now minimally invasive (laparoscopic or arthroscopic) with a wide range of applications—gall bladder removal, appendix removal, hernia repair, gynecological, colon removal, partial lung removal, spleen removal, and surgery for chronic heartburn or reflux disease.

The major advantages of minimally invasive surgery is that it is less traumatic to the patient. There is less scarring, and recovery time is much quicker. Hospital stays are shorter.

Who received the **first heart transplant**?

On December 3, 1967, in Capetown, South Africa, Dr. Christiaan Barnard (1922-2001) and a team of 30 associates performed the first heart transplant. In a five-hour operation the heart of Denise Ann Darval, age 25, an auto accident victim, was transplanted into the body of Louis Washansky, a 55-year-old wholesale grocer. Washansky lived for 18 days before dying from pneumonia.

Who was the first African American surgeon to perform heart surgery?

Dr. Daniel Hale Williams (1858-1931) was a pioneer in open heart surgery. In 1893, he was able to save a knifing victim by opening up the patient's chest with the help of a surgical team, exposing the beating heart. He sewed the knife wound a fraction of an inch from the heart without the aid of X-rays, blood transfusions, or anesthetics.

The first heart transplant performed in the United States was on a 2½-week-old baby boy at Maimonides Hospital, Brooklyn, New York, on December 6, 1967, by Dr. Adrian Kantrowitz (b. 1918). The baby boy lived 6½ hours. The first adult to receive a heart transplant in the United States was Mike Kasperak, age 54, at the Stanford Medical Center in Palo Alto, California, on January 6, 1968. Dr. Norman Shumway (b. 1923) performed the operation. Mr. Kasperak lived 14 days.

From December 1967 until March 31, 1993, 14,085 heart transplants have been performed. Interestingly, almost no transplants were done in the 1970s because of the problem of rejection of the new heart by the recipient's immune system. In 1969, Jean-François Borel discovered the anti-rejection drug cyclosporine, but it was not widely used until 1983 when the FDA granted approval. Today heart transplantation is an established medical procedure.

Is is possible to use **animal organs** as replacements for human organ transplantation?

In 1984, a 12-day-old infant, Baby Fae, received a baboon's heart. She lived for 20 days before her body rejected the transplanted heart. Since the supply of human organs is far less than the need for human organs, researchers continue to search for alternative sources of organs. In 1999, the Food and Drug Administration (FDA) prohibited the used of nonhuman primate organs for human transplantation unless researchers could assess the risk of disease. A major concern had been that viruses and other diseases that were harmful to the animals would be deadly to humans. Researchers continue to search for alternate sources of organs, including pigs.

When was the **first artificial heart** used?

On December 2, 1982, Dr. Barney B. Clark (1921-1983), a 61-year-old retired dentist, became the first human to receive a permanently implanted artificial heart. It was known as the Jarvik-7 after its inventor, Dr. Robert Jarvik (b. 1946). The 7.5-hour operation was performed by Dr. William DeVries (b. 1943), a surgeon at the University of Utah Medical Center. Dr. Clark died on March 23, 1983, 112 days later. In Louisville, Kentucky, William Schroeder (1923-1986) survived 620 days with an artificial heart (November 25, 1984 to August 7, 1986). On January 11, 1990, the United States Food and Drug Administration (FDA) recalled the Jarvik-7, which had been the only artificial heart approved by the FDA for use.

The Jarvik-7 artificial heart—invented by Dr. Robert Jarvik—was first implanted into a human being in 1982.

How much does the **cardiac pacemaker** weigh?

The modern pacemaker generator is a hermetically sealed titanium metal can weighing from one to 4.5 ounces (30 to 130 grams) and powered by a lithium battery that can last two to 15 years. Used to correct an insufficient or irregular heartbeat, the cardiac pacemaker corrects the low cardiac rhythm through electrical stimulation, which increases the contractions of the heart muscle. The contraction and expansion of the heart muscle produces a heartbeat, one of three billion in an average lifetime, which pumps blood throughout the body. A pacemaker has gold or platinum electrodes, conducting wires, and a pacing box (miniature generator). In both kinds of pacemakers—those implanted in the chest or externally—the electrode is attached to the heart's right ventricle (chamber), either directly through the chest or by being threaded through a vein.

Why are **eye transplants** not available?

It is because the eye's retina is part of the brain, and the retina's cells are derived from brain tissue. Retinal cells and the cells that connect them to the brain are the least amenable to being manipulated outside the body.

Who was the **first test-tube baby?**

Louise Brown, born on July 25, 1978, is the first baby produced from fertilization done in vitro—outside the mother's body. Patrick Steptoe (1913-1988) was the obstetrician and Robert Edwards (1939-) the biologist who designed the method for in-vitro fertilization and early embryo development.

In-vitro fertilization occurs in a glass dish, not a test tube, where eggs from the mother's ovary are combined with the father's sperm (in a salt solution). Fertilization should occur within 24 hours, and when cell division begins these fertilized eggs are placed in the mother's womb (or possibly another woman's womb).

What is **lithotripsy**?

Lithotripsy is the use of ultrasonic or shock waves to pulverize kidney stones (calculi), allowing the small particles to be excreted or removed from the body. There are two different methods: extracorporeal shock wave lithotripsy (ESWL) and percutaneous lithotripsy. The ESWL method, used on smaller stones, breaks up the stones with external shock waves from a machine called a lithotripter. This technique has eliminated the need for more invasive stone surgery in many cases. For larger stones, a type of endoscope, called a nephroscope, is inserted into the kidney through a small incision. The ultrasonic waves from the nephroscope shatter the stones, and the fragments are removed through the nephroscope.

What is **synthetic skin**?

The material consists of a very porous collagen fiber bonded to a sugar polymer (glycoaminoglycan) obtained from shark cartilage. It is covered by a sheet of silicon rubber. It was developed by Ioannis V. Yannas (1935-) and his colleagues at Massachusetts Institute of Technology around 1985. Soon after its introduction, synthetic skin was used to successfully treat more than 100 severely burned victims.

What is **reflexology**?

Reflexology is the application of specific pressures to reflex points in the hands and feet. The reflex points relate to every organ and every part of the body. Massaging of the reflex points is done to prevent or cure diseases. Believed to have been used in Asian cultures as long as 2,000 years ago, reflexology was introduced to the United States at the turn of the century by Dr. William Fitzgerald and Eunice D. Ingham. Today nearly 25,000 certified practitioners can be found throughout the world.

What is **iridology**?

Iridology is the study of the iris of the eye with the intent of diagnosing weaknesses in the body. Iridologists believe that areas of the iris correspond with different body parts. Among the conditions they monitor are color, clarity, texture, fibers, rings, and spots on the iris. Once the diagnosis is made, they recommend natural methods of healing and conditioning of weak areas.

Index

Note: (ill.) indicates photos and illustrations.

D

E

F

G

L

M

Q–R

S

T